NORTH CAROLINA
GEOLOGICAL AND ECONOMIC SURVEY

JOSEPH HYDE PRATT, STATE GEOLOGIST

VOLUME II

THE FISHES

OF

NORTH CAROLINA

By HUGH M. SMITH

Deputy U. S. Commissioner of Fisheries

RALEIGH
E. M. UZZELL & CO., STATE PRINTERS AND BINDERS
1907

GEOLOGICAL BOARD.

GOVERNOR R. B. GLENN, *ex officio Chairman*........................... Raleigh.

HENRY E. FRIES .... Winston-Salem.

FRANK R. HEWITT .... Asheville.

HUGH MacRAE.. Wilmington.

FRANK WOOD.. Edenton.

JOSEPH HYDE PRATT, State Geologist .... Chapel Hill.

LETTER OF TRANSMITTAL.

CHAPEL HILL, N. C., January 1, 1907.

To His Excellency, GOVERNOR R. B. GLENN.

SIR:—I have the honor to submit for publication, as Volume II of the reports of the North Carolina Geological and Economic Survey, the report of Dr. Hugh M. Smith, Deputy United States Commissioner of Fisheries, on The Fishes of North Carolina.

This publication is the second of the series of volumes which represent more elaborate reports on various subjects and embody, as far as practicable, the results of maturer investigations.

Yours obediently,

JOSEPH HYDE PRATT,

State Geologist.

PREFACE

The following report on The Fishes of North Carolina has been prepared to meet the numerous inquiries that are constantly being received by the Geological and Economic Survey concerning the fishes found in the different waters of the State. It has been the desire of the State Geologist to awaken an increased interest in the local fishes, and to give to the people of North Carolina and to others a more accurate knowledge of the abundance, distribution, habits, migrations, spawning, food value, etc., of the fishes, in the belief that such knowledge will lead to a fuller realization of the economic importance of the fishery resources of the State. It is desirable also that there be created a deeper interest in the welfare of both fishes and fishermen, and a better understanding of the condition and needs of the fishing industry, with a view to placing this important branch on a permanent basis and making it yield an increasing revenue to both State and people.

In this report there is an account of every fish that has been ascertained to inhabit the fresh, brackish, or salt waters of North Carolina. All local names by which the fishes are known are recorded, and diagnostic descriptions are given that are often based on local specimens. Colored plates or text cuts representing a very large number of the species have been provided. While the chief aim in preparing the report has been to make it of practical usefulness to the fishing interests, the scientific aspects of the subject have not been neglected, and the work will be found to have a value to ichthyologists and to zoölogists in general.

The report is particularly useful in that it affords a means of identifying any fish that may be taken in State waters. The artificial keys are based on external characters that commercial fishermen and anglers may readily appreciate; and the copious index of common names gives a further clue to all the species whose size makes them objects of capture.

In the preparation of this work the assistance and knowledge of many local people have been availed of, and to these Dr. Smith makes acknowledgment in his introduction and text.

It is hoped that this volume will be the means of creating such an interest in the fisheries that suitable laws for their protection may be enacted as needed, and that the State officers charged with the administration of the fisheries may have the sympathy and coöperation of all citizens.

Joseph Hyde Pratt,

State Geologist.

CONTENTS.

LIST OF ILLUSTRATIONS.

TRUNK-FISH, front view.

BIOLOGICAL LABORATORY OF THE U. S. BUREAU OF FISHERIES IN BEAUFORT HARBOR, ERECTED IN 1902.

BOATING A SHAD SEINE, ALBEMARLE SOUND.

THE FISHES OF NORTH CAROLINA

By HUGH M. SMITH,

Deputy U. S. Commissioner of Fisheries.

INTRODUCTION.

At the request of Professor J. A. Holmes, former director of the North Carolina Geological and Economic Survey, the writer several years ago undertook the preparation of a report which would serve as a popular guide to the fishes of North Carolina.

While it has been possible to devote to the preparation of this report only such time as the writer could utilize outside of his regular duties, the task has been made easier by the attitude of the Honorable George M. Bowers, U. S. Commissioner of Fisheries, who has not only given the work his entire approval but has provided many special facilities, in the belief that an increased knowledge of and interest in the fishery resources and fisheries on the part of the people of North Carolina, and a more intimate acquaintance with the habits, migrations, spawning, growth and distribution of the local fishes, would greatly inure to the benefit of the state, and at the same time promote the usefulness of the biological and hatching stations of the United States Bureau of Fisheries by creating an intelligent sympathy with the work. The writer therefore desires to express his special thanks to Commissioner Bowers for courtesies and assistance, which have likewise been extended indirectly but no less effectively to the State of North Carolina.

Professor Holmes showed a very liberal spirit in planning for the scope, illustration, and publication of this report, and has placed the writer under great obligations, as has also Dr. Joseph Hyde Pratt, the present state geologist.

It has been the special aim to make the report useful to all the fishing interests of the state. To this end, no essential technical considerations have been slighted, but scientific treatment has been adapted to the needs of fishermen and others who have had no opportunity to study ichthyology; and it is hoped and believed that laymen generally will be able to make use of the work in the identification of species.

While the very considerable amount of literature relating to the fishes and fisheries of North Carolina has been freely utilized in the preparation of this report, the latter is not without much new and original matter which has been supplied by the author and by many associates and correspondents.

In the preparation of this report, the author has had the generous assistance and advice of associates in the Bureau of Fisheries, particularly Dr. Barton W. Evermann, assistant in charge of scientific inquiry; Dr. W. C. Kendall, Mr. E. L. Goldsborough and Mr. T. E. B. Pope, scientific assistants; Mr. S. G. Worth, superintendent of the Edenton station; Dr. Caswell Grave, late director of the Beaufort laboratory; Dr. Robert E. Coker, late custodian of the laboratory; and Mr. H. D. Aller, present custodian.

The Bureau of Fisheries has permitted free access to the collections and records of the Beaufort laboratory; this material has been invaluable, and has contributed more than anything else to the knowledge of the salt-water fishes of the state. The Bureau has also permitted the copying of many of the cuts of fishes, the use of photographs illustrating the fisheries, and the compilation of special statistics of the North Carolina fishing industry.

Special acknowledgments are due to Dr. Coker for much detailed information regarding the abundance, habits, and commercial importance of the fishes of Beaufort and vicinity.

To Dr. Kendall the writer is under obligations for the use of his manuscript notes on fishes of various parts of the North Carolina coast, and for material assistance in studying several collections of small fishes received from the Beaufort laboratory and other sources.

The material for the historical and descriptive account of fish culture in North Carolina has been furnished by Mr. S. G. Worth, who, as former fish commissioner of North Carolina and present superintendent of the government fish-cultural work in the state, is better qualified to discuss the subject than any other person. Mr. Worth has also supplied many interesting notes and specimens from the region of Beaufort and vicinity.

The authorities of the National Museum have given access to the fish records and collections, and have permitted the making of many illustrations of fishes from cuts belonging to that institution. Mr. Barton A. Bean, of the department of fishes, has furnished every facility for the examination of the extensive series of fishes from North Carolina in the museum, and has also supplied data based on his own collections and observations.

Mr. William P. Seal, of Delair, N. J., has supplied very useful information concerning the fishes of the Wilmington region, and has forwarded a number of specimens therefrom which represented species not previously known from the state.

Dr. Theodore Gill, associate in zoölogy of the Smithsonian Institution, has given valuable advice and suggestions.

Useful information, valuable specimens, and various courtesies and assistance have been received from local fishermen, fish dealers, fishery operators, and others in the State, their service extending over many years and being shown either directly to the author or to his associates at the Beaufort laboratory.

Among those to whom acknowledgments are due the following may be specially mentioned:

Mr. William Arandel .... Morehead City.
Mr. C. S. Brimley .... Raleigh.
Mr. H. H. Brimley .... Raleigh.
Dr. W. R. Capehart .... Avoca.
Mr. Charles P. Dey .... Beaufort.
Mr. A. V. Evans .... Manteo.
Mr. Daniel G. Fowle .... Washington.
Mr. Mason B. Gowdy .... Beaufort.
Dr. E. W. Gudger .... Greensboro.
Mr. Charles Hatsel .... Beaufort.
Mr. George N. Ives .... New Bern.
Mr. Joseph Lewis .... Beaufort.
Mr. William A. Mace .... Beaufort.
Mr. J. H. Potter .... Beaufort.
Mr. A. B. Riggin .... Marshalburg.
Mr. W. A. Sanders .... Wilmington.
Mr. Allen Taylor .... Wit.
Mr. R. W. Taylor .... Morehead City.
Mr. C. S. Wallace .... Morehead City.
Mr. Alonzo Thomas .... Beaufort.
Prof. H. V. Wilson .... Chapel Hill.
Mr. Frank Wood .... Edenton.
Mr. W. N. Yopp .... Wilmington.

Mr. A. H. Baldwin, the well-known fish artist, has made especially for this work a series of water-color drawings of some of the more important and characteristic fishes of the state. These drawings were based on living specimens and faithfully represent their colors; and in the accompanying plates made therefrom by Messrs. Hoen & Company the colors have been accurately reproduced.

THE WATERS OF NORTH CAROLINA.

THE THREE PHYSIOGRAPHIC SECTIONS OF THE STATE.

The surface of North Carolina is naturally divisible into three great sections, or provinces, each with a peculiar character of waters and more or less sharply defined fish fauna. These sections are the coastal plain, the Piedmont plateau, and the Appalachian mountain regions.

The coastal plain region begins at the seashore and extends inland for 120 to 160 miles, embracing an area of about 25,000 square miles. A large part of the eastern portion of this region is very low, poorly drained, and hence covered with extensive swamps, the streams being sluggish and discolored by vegetable matter; the western part is more elevated, with a more irregular surface, is better drained, and the streams are more rapid. More than three-fifths of the region is wooded, the trees of the uplands being chiefly pines and those of the swamps deciduous.

The inner margin of the coastal plain region is determined by the so-called "fall-line", characterized by the occurrence of falls or rapids in the streams. The rivers are more or less tortuous and their banks are mostly sandy, clayey, or loamy, the unstable character of the banks resulting in undermining, washing away of trees, and the frequent formation of new channels.

The Piedmont plateau region extends from the "fall-line" to the mountains, and has an average width of 125 miles and an area of 20,000 square miles. The average elevation above the sea is 900 feet, the eastern half averaging about 750 feet and the western half 1,200 feet. Forests, consisting of deciduous trees interspersed with the short-leaved pine, cover upwards of fifty per cent of the region. The geological formations, consisting of upturned belts of slates, granites, gneisses, etc., running parallel with the mountains, have resulted in the development of cascades, rapids, and shoals, owing to the unequal erosion of the rocks of varying hardness.

The Appalachian mountain region, which reaches from New York to Alabama, attains its greatest height in North Carolina. Here the mountainous area is an exceedingly rugged and irregular timbered tableland of some 6,000 square miles, which lies between the Blue Ridge Mountains on the southeast and the Great Smoky Mountains on the northwest, the tableland being crossed by numerous ridges which are separated by narrow valleys and deep-worn gorges. The average elevation is about 2,700 feet above the sea; there are many peaks over 5,000 feet high and a number over 6,000 feet, the highest being Mount Mitchell. The Blue Ridge chain constitutes the divide between the waters of the Atlantic slope and those of the Mississippi basin. The mountain streams are cold, clear, and swift, and possess a rare beauty.

THE COASTAL REGION.

The peculiar, not to say remarkable, character of the coastal section of North Carolina has much influence on the variety and abundance of the fish life and has favored the development of most extensive fisheries. Nearly the entire coast of the state is skirted by low, narrow, sandy islands and peninsulas, locally known as "banks", between which and the mainland there are numerous sounds, some of large size. The sounds communicate with the ocean either directly through narrow inlets or through other sounds; and many receive the drainage of important streams. The sounds in geographic order are Currituck, Albemarle, Roanoke, Croatan, Pamlico, Core, Bogue, Stump, Topsail, Middle, Masonboro, and Myrtle, and they constitute a series such as exists in no other state.

Currituck Sound is the most northern. It is parallel with the coast, and extends from Virginia to the eastern end of Albemarle Sound, into which it discharges. Its length is 40 miles and its width 3 to 4 miles. The water is quite shallow, nowhere exceeding 9 or 10 feet, and is fresh except during periods of little rainfall. Up to 1800 it communicated with the ocean by means of Caffey

Inlet and contained marine fishes, but since that time it has had no direct connections with the sea and is now inhabited by anadromous and fresh-water species. Black bass and white perch are very abundant, and striped bass and alewives enter it in large numbers. The region is visited by enormous flocks of water fowl, and is one of the most noted hunting resorts on the Atlantic coast.

Albemarle Sound is said to be the largest coastal body of fresh water in the world. Its extreme length from east to west is 60 miles and its maximum breadth is 15 miles, the average being 6 to 8 miles; its area is about 450 square miles. The water is normally quite fresh, but in dry weather it may become brackish or salt, especially at its eastern end. Formerly there was direct communication with the sea. The bottom is level, the depth is quite uniform, and strong tides or currents do not exist. Eight rivers enter the sound, 4 on the north, 2 on the west, and 2 on the south. The Roanoke and Chowan, which flow into the extreme western end, are among the largest in the state; the others—the North, Pasquotank, Little, and Perquimans on the north, and the Scuppernong and Alligator on the south—are short, wide streams draining extensive low or swampy districts, the most important of these the celebrated Dismal Swamp, which lies partly in North Carolina and partly in Virginia. The sound, with its tributaries, is an exceedingly important spawning ground for shad, alewives, striped bass, and other migratory fishes, and also contains many other valuable species. Its fishery resources exceed those of any of the other sounds, and this fact, together with the facility with which all kinds of nets may be set and operated, makes its fisheries of great importance.

Roanoke and Croatan sounds extend from the southern part of the eastern end of Albemarle Sound to Pamlico Sound, are parallel with the coast, and are separated by Roanoke Island. Roanoke Sound lies next to the ocean, is 8 miles long and 1.5 to 2 miles wide, and is quite shallow except in a narrow channel skirting the island. Croatan Sound has the same length as Roanoke Sound, but is 2 to 4 miles wide and much deeper; most of the drainage from Albemarle Sound passes through it. The combined area of these two sounds is about 75 miles. These waters abound with anadromous and salt-water fishes, and support valuable fisheries; and they are of special interest because they are the routes by which all fish bound into and out of Albemarle Sound must pass.

Pamlico Sound is an imposing body of water, and, next to Long Island, is the largest sound on the Atlantic coast of the United States. Its length is 75 miles and its width from 10 to 30 miles, the area being about 1,860 square miles. The general depth is 15 to 20 feet. The waters of Currituck, Albemarle, Croatan, and Roanoke sounds discharge into it, and on the south Core Sound communicates with it. The long narrow strip of desolate sand with sparse vegetation which separates the sound from the sea is broken by Oregon, New, Loggerhead, Hatteras, and Ocracoke inlets. Two important rivers, the Pamlico and the Neuse, flow into the sound from the west, their mouths being broad estuaries; while several short, wide streams—the Pungo and Bay rivers—also enter the western part of the sound.

Pamlico Sound is bountifully provided with fishes and other water products, and supports very valuable fisheries, participated in by a large proportion of the male population. Besides being traversed by immense bodies of shad, alewives, striped bass, and other migratory fishes on their way to and from the fresh waters, Pamlico Sound is the resort of many important salt-water species, among which are the mullets, squeteagues, spot, croaker, drums, blue-fish, menhaden, sheepshead, and hog-fish. The anadromous fishes on their way to Albemarle Sound for the most part pass through New Inlet and to a less extent through Oregon and Hatteras inlets; while most of the fishes bound for the Neuse and Pamlico come from the ocean through Ocracoke and Hatteras inlets.

Core Sound begins at the extreme southern part of Pamlico Sound and extends southwesterly to the vicinity of Beaufort, while Bogue Sound begins at the latter place and stretches westerly These two bodies of water are upwards of 60 miles long and 1 to 6 miles wide, and, with their tributaries, have an area of about 200 square miles. The water is quite shoal, rarely exceeding 10 feet and averaging only 4 to 5. Two broad expansions, with numerous arms, known as North and Newport rivers, occur at the intersection of the two sounds, and discharge through Beaufort Inlet; while White Oak River enters the extreme western end of Bogue Sound and discharges through Bogue Inlet. The "banks" separating these sounds from the sea are very narrow and in places quite elevated, owing to the drifting of the sand. About midway a long narrow tongue projects southward, forming Cape Lookout, the "bight" of which, on its western side, affords a fine harbor for small craft and constitutes a great natural fish trap. The waters of this section abound with the characteristic salt-water fishes of the state, and are particularly noted for the immense quantities of mullet, squeteague, spot, croaker, whiting, drum, blue-fish, Spanish mackerel, menhaden, etc., which visit them; several of these species are here taken in greater numbers than anywhere else.

To the southward of Bogue Inlet, the coast is fringed with numerous small, shallow sounds into or through some of which streams of considerable volume discharge; the chief of these are Stump Sound, entered by New River and communicating with the ocean through New River Inlet; Topsail, Middle, Masonboro, and Myrtle sounds, all to northward of the Cape Fear River.

North Carolina is singularly deficient in lakes, and all those whose size entitles them to mention in this connection are in the coastal plain region and for the most part lie in groups. The most noteworthy group is in the broad peninsula lying between Albemarle Sound and Pamlico Sound and River, and includes Mattamuskeet, Phelps or Scuppernong, Alligator, and Pungo lakes.

Mattamuskeet, the largest North Carolina lake, occupies a considerable part of Hyde county; its length is 14 miles and its greatest width 7 miles. The water is very shallow, being only 2½ feet deep over a large part and having a maximum depth of 7 feet in the middle of the western end. In winter and early spring the lake is muddy and roily, owing to strong winds stirring the bottom and to the suspension of light soil and vegetable matter brought from the swamps and farm lands; but in summer the water is generally clear, with a brownish color, and is what is known as "juniper water". The bottom is mostly of fine sand mixed with mud, and is fairly hard. This section was at one time inhabited by a tribe of Indians, and the lake has received the tribal name of Mattamuskeet. The Indian tradition as to the origin of the lake—which is the popular one to-day—is that it was due to a fire which burned many months, affecting a far larger area than is now covered by the lake. In support of this theory the people point out blackened and water-worn cypress stumps everywhere abundant near the shores and argue that the surrounding territory, being swampy and peaty and covered with cypress trees, is even now liable to have just such another fire. Prof. Holmes, however, states that this tradition is untenable and that Mattamuskeet, like others with the same story of origin—Lake Drummond, in the Dismal Swamp, for instance—is a natural lake. The northern and western shores are swampy and marshy, while on the south and east there are extensive farms, generally dry and very fertile. Cypress and willow trees form an almost continuous border around the lake and grow out into it. The lake is fed by drainage from swamps and farms, and discharges into Alligator River and Yeosocking Bay through canals.

The lake supports but little sport fishing and no market fishing, although considerable quantities of fish are taken for local consumption with rod and line and gill net. While the variety of food-fishes found in the lake is rather small, it embraces a number of first-class species. The most highly prized and the most important from a local standpoint is the white perch, which is exceedingly abundant, reaches a large size, and occurs everywhere in the lake and drainage ditches. The yellow perch, locally called "redfin", is also abundant, but less so than formerly. The blue bream is very common and ranks next to the white perch in popular estimation. The large-mouth black bass, having the local names of "chub" and "welshman", is present in considerable numbers. The pike (*Esox reticulatus*) attains a large size and is numerous, and the pickerel (*Esox americanus*), called "jack", also occurs. Cat-fishes and eels are abundant. The latter are not much used, although at one time a religious sect called "The Sanctified" made a business of catching eels in the lake and shipping them north. Other fishes inhabiting this interesting lake are the pumpkin-seed and several other sun-fishes, the roach or dace, the carp, the dog-fish or grindle, the hog-choker, and various minnows.

The remaining lakes of this group have a combined area less than half of that of Lake Mattamuskeet. They are similar to the latter in their physical characters and, so far as known, in their fish life. Phelps, the largest, is the source of Scuppernong River.

On the peninsula south of Neuse River, in Craven and Jones counties, there is a compact group of 5 lakes known as Great, Long, Ellis, Catfish, and Little lakes. The first is largest, being 5 miles long and 3 miles wide, with a maximum depth of 10 to 12 feet. Ellis Lake is nearly 2 miles in diameter, but averages less than 2 feet in depth. These waters, which are connected with the Neuse and White Oak rivers, contain cat-fishes, minnows, pikes, perches, sun-fishes, and basses. The large-mouth black bass abounds, and reaches a weight of 7 to 8 pounds.

The only other lakes worthy of mention are Black and Bartrams, lying between South and Cape Fear rivers, in Bladen county; and Waccamaw, on one of the branches of Waccamaw River in Columbia County.

In addition to the admirable facilities for fishing afforded by the smooth, sandy outer beaches, there are important offshore fishing grounds along the entire coast of North Carolina. Among the species thus taken are blue-fish, especially north of Cape Hatteras in winter; menhaden, of which immense bodies occur and are sought by steam and sail vessels, some belonging in the state and some coming from points far to the north; and various bottom fishes, inhabiting the submerged banks and caught chiefly with lines, among which are cod, sea bass, grunts, and pig-fish. The most celebrated and most exploited of the off-shore grounds are the "black-fish" banks lying off the Cape Fear River.

THE RIVERS OF THE ATLANTIC COAST.*

The rivers of North Carolina which drain into the Atlantic include some of the finest streams on the eastern seaboard of the United States. The principal ones rise on the slopes of the Blue Ridge, flow across the Piedmont plateau region and then traverse the wide coastal plain region, where they discharge, mostly through wide estuaries, after pursuing a generally southeasterly course. The rivers that merit separate mention are the Chowan, the Roanoke, the Tar, the Neuse, the Cape Fear, the Yadkin, and the Catawba.

The Chowan River rises in southeastern Virginia, flows through a wooded swampy region, and enters the western end of Albemarle Sound. The chief tributary is the Blackwater, in Virginia. That part of the Chowan which is in North Carolina in about 50 miles long, and in the lower 20 miles of its course is very broad and shallow. The Chowan is one of the most important streams in the state for shad, alewives, and other migratory fishes, while black bass, crappy, sun-fishes, yellow perch, pike, suckers, and cat-fish are among the permanent inhabitants. The discoloration of the water by the decomposition of vegetable matter in the cypress swamps is quite marked and is generally regarded as affecting the run of shad and alewives, which are attracted thereby.

The Roanoke River is one of the longest streams of North Carolina. Its headwaters flow from the slopes of the Alleghany Mountains in southeastern Virginia, and it is formed by the union of the Dan and Staunton rivers in Mecklen-burg County, Virginia. The Dan rises in Virginia near Buffalo Knob in Patrick County, enters North Carolina, reenters Virginia, returns to North Carolina, and then enters Virginia again and joins the Staunton. After pursuing a very tortu-ous course in a southeasterly direction, the Roanoke debouches into the extreme

*For a very full account of the water courses of North Carolina, reference is made to Bulletin No. 8 of the North Carolina Geological Survey, comprising "Papers on the Water Power of North Carolina," by George F. Swain, J. A. Holmes and E. W. Myers. Raleigh, 1899.

PLATE 2

STURGEON (ACIPENSER OXYRHYNCHUS)

western end of Albemarle Sound by several narrow mouths adjacent to the mouth of the Chowan. The Dan is upwards of 400 miles long, and the area drained by the two streams is about 5,600 square miles. The "fall-line" occurs between Weldon and Gaston, the falls extending for about ten miles with a descent of 84 feet. Above Weldon, which is about 130 miles above the mouth, the bed of the river is usually composed of solid rock, but sometimes of gravel and sand, and sometimes of clay, with banks of variable height and structure; the width of the stream is considerable, and islands and exposed rocks are numerous. Below Weldon the river's bed is generally sandy, with a few ledges, and is comparatively narrow. The stream is subject to violent freshets, and has risen as much as 50 feet at Weldon. For about half the distance from Weldon to the mouth the ordinary rise is 10 to 30 feet, gradually diminishing toward the mouth, where it is only about 2 or 3 feet.

The Roanoke carries out into the southern half of Albemarle Sound an immense volume of muddy water of a yellowish color, which is often seen 40 miles from its mouth, contrasting very strongly with the clear dark water brought down by the Chowan. It appears that striped bass, white perch, and sturgeon prefer this kind of water and can always be taken there in greater numbers than on the northern side of the sound, where shad and alewives always occur more abundantly. The fishermen have learned by experience that the larger run of striped bass is in the Roanoke and the larger run of shad is in the Chowan. The river is, in fact, one of the chief resorts of the striped bass and contains perhaps the most important spawning grounds for the species. Other species of which there is a numerous run in the lower Roanoke besides sturgeon, white perch, shad, and alewives, are suckers, hickory shad, and gizzard shad. The non-migratory species of greatest importance are cat-fishes, pikes, black bass, crappy and various other sun-fishes, yellow perch, and wall-eyed pike. The common flounder (*Paralichthys*) often ascends the river for several miles. The principal fishes of the upper waters are suckers, minnows, sun-fishes, and darters.

The Tar River rises in Granville and Person counties, North Carolina, near the Virginia line, and, flowing in a generally southeasterly direction, terminates in a long arm of Pamlico Sound known as Pamlico River. The largest tributaries are Fishing Creek and Swift Creek. The river has an approximate length of 175 miles, and drains an area of nearly 3,000 square miles. The fall-line occurs at Rocky Mount, about 73 miles above the mouth. The stream is quite similar to the Roanoke; the bed is composed of sand, gravel, clay, mud, or rock, and the banks in the upper part of its course are comparatively high. At Rocky Mount a dam extends across the river from bank to bank, and constitutes a barrier impassable to fish. The Pamlico River, which is about 37 miles long, is entered by the common migratory fishes of the state, and supports important net fishing; the same fishes continue up the Tar River until stopped by the dam mentioned. The resident fishes of the Tar River are similar to those of the Roanoke on one side and the Neuse on the other, and comprise an abundance of cat-fishes, suckers, minnows, pike, sun-fishes, and darters, although the number of species is rather small.

The Neuse River begins in Wake County, North Carolina, and is formed by the junction of the Flat, Eno, and Little rivers, which rise in Orange and Person counties. After pursuing a winding but generally southeasterly course of more than 300 miles, it enters the extreme southwestern end of Pamlico Sound, the lower forty miles being a very broad and fine estuary. The important tributaries of the Neuse are Trent River, joining the main stream at New Bern and being altogether the largest branch; Contentnea Creek, which joins the river 30 miles above Trent and is about 140 miles long; and Little River, which is about 100 miles long and enters the Neuse from the north near Goldsboro. The drainage area of the Neuse and its tributaries is 5,300 square miles, and the stream, its bed, and its banks, resemble the Roanoke. The fall-line crosses the river near Smithfield, 190 miles above its mouth, but the first considerable falls met with in ascending the stream is at Millburnie, or Neuse Mills, 25 miles above Smithfield, where the descent is about 12 feet; the Falls of the Neuse, having a descent of 18 feet, occur 13 miles north of Raleigh.

The run of shad in the Neuse is larger than in any other North Carolina stream, and the fisheries are correspondingly important. The resident fishes are also numerous as to both species and individuals. The basin of the Neuse has been more systematically explored by ichthyologists and more kinds of fishes are recorded from it than any other river in the state. Among those who have collected and written on the fishes of the Neuse are Professors Cope, Jordan, Evermann, Meek, and Jenkins. About 60 species of permanent residents have been listed, and half a dozen species now regarded as valid were based on examples from this river; of the latter several have not as yet been met with elsewhere.

The Cape Fear River is one of the longest of the streams wholly within the limits of the state. It rises in the uplands to the northward of Greensboro only a short distance from the headwaters of the Roanoke, and enters the ocean at the cape which has the same name, after a course of over 200 miles. Its principal components are the Deep and the Haw rivers; near Wilmington it is joined by the North East Cape Fear and the South rivers. The upper waters of the Cape Fear for the most part flow through a soil of red clay, and are during most of the year discolored by a clayey sediment. The fall-line crosses the river about 27 miles above Fayetteville, and Smileys Falls is the result. From Wilmington to the sea, a distance of 30 miles, this stream is quite wide, in places over a mile; and at its mouth it is 3 miles across.

The area drained by the Cape Fear comprises upwards of 8,000 square miles. The annual rainfall in the basin, amounting to about 50 inches, is nearly equally divided between the four seasons, but notwithstanding this the flow is quite variable owing to peculiar conditions of the soil. Violent freshets sometimes occur, and in the vicinity of Fayetteville the rise has amounted to 58 feet.

The lower Cape Fear basin is annually visited by the common migratory fishes of the region, but the run of shad, alewives, and striped bass is smaller than in some of the other streams of the state. The resident fishes are more closely related to those of the adjacent South Carolina rivers than to those of the Neuse, and include a number not known from more eastern waters of the state. Among these are the flat-headed cat-fish, *Ameiurus platycephalus*, which is very abundant, and several minnows. The smaller tributaries of the lower course of the Cape Fear and extensive swampy tracts adjacent thereto now constitute the most promising field for the collector and will doubtless be found to contain a considerable number of species which there reach their northernmost limit. Quite recently this region has yielded half a dozen species not before known from the state, including *Elassoma, Copelandellus, Heterandria, Chologaster*, and *Dormitator*.

The Yadkin, or Great Pedee, is a very large and important stream whose upper waters are in North Carolina and whose lower course is in South Carolina, Winyah Bay being its place of discharge. Its entire length is more than 400 miles, and the area which it drains is about 17,000 square miles, of which more than half is in North Carolina. The headwaters come from the slopes of the Blue Ridge in Wilkes, Caldwell, and Watauga counties. After flowing nearly due east and receiving as tributaries from the north numerous rapid mountain streams, among which are Reddies, Fishers, Ararat, Roaring, and Mulberry rivers, Rock and Elk creeks, and Lewis and Stony forks, the Yadkin bends abruptly and pursues a generally southward course. The principal North Carolina tributaries below the bend are the South Yadkin, Uharie, Rocky, and Little rivers, and the Little Pedee, Lumber, and Waccamaw rivers, which rise in North Carolina but join the main stream in South Carolina. The Great Pedee crosses the fall-line near Cheraw, South Carolina. The upper waters resemble the Roanoke and Cape Fear; the slopes are steep, but the presence of heavy timber makes the flow quite regular and reduces the violence of freshets. The river and its tributaries are for the most part discolored almost all the time by the red clays of the Piedmont region; and fish life is not abundant in that part of the stream within the state of North Carolina. While additional collecting will doubtless increase the number of species known from the Yadkin, at this time only about a score of fishes have been recorded, by Professor Cope in 1870 and by Professor Jordan in 1889. Perhaps the most characteristic feature of the fish fauna is the occurrence of a number of species of coarse-scaled suckers (*Moxostoma*), which are of large size and exist in considerable abundance, running in spring from the main rivers into the tributaries to spawn.

The Catawba and Broad rivers are the North Carolina tributaries of the Santee. The Catawba, known in South Carolina as the Wateree, rises in McDowell County, on the eastern slope of the Blue Ridge near Swannanoa Gap, and first flows eastward and then southward into South Carolina, where it unites with the Congaree to form the Santee. The Broad rises near the headwaters of the Catawba, and flows southeasterly into South Carolina, there joining the Saluda to form the Congaree. The Catawba is the largest and clearest of the branches of the Santee. Its course in North Carolina is 180 miles long; the headwaters are nearly 2,700 feet above the tide, and the descent within the state is about 2,150 feet, or an average of 12 feet per mile. The upper part of the river is enclosed between parallel mountain ranges which are heavily timbered; the lower part is in a fertile and populous valley 15 to 20 miles wide. The only tributary of importance is South Fork, which flows from the northwest and enters the river near the state line. The drainage basin of the Catawba in North Carolina is upward of 3,000 square miles.

The Broad River lies entirely above the fall-line, and is quite similar to the upper Catawba, but with less descent. Its important tributaries in North Caro lina are the Green, First Broad, and Second Broad rivers, which, with the main stream, have a drainage of 1,400 square miles in the state.

The various branches of the Santee have essentially the same fish life. The number of species known from the Catawba is relatively large, the principal groups being the suckers, minnows, and darters, all of which are abundant. Brook trout abound in the headwaters.

THE RIVERS OF THE MISSISSIPPI DRAINAGE BASIN.

The streams on the western slope of the Blue Ridge in North Carolina belong to two systems—the Kanawha and the Tennessee—which are respectively tributary to the Ohio and the Mississippi. While representing a comparatively small part of the fresh waters of North Carolina, these streams, have special inter est because of their beauty, the picturesque mountain regions through which they flow, and the nature of their fish life.

That part of the Kanawha River within the state of North Carolina is the headwaters, under the name of New River, which rises in Watauga, Ashe, and Alleghany counties, and soon passes out of the state into Grayson County, Vir ginia. The principal branches are North and South forks and Little River, whose drainage area is between 700 and 800 square miles. The tributaries of the New River within North Carolina are rapid mountain streams running mostly through deep rocky gorges.

The upper waters of the Tennessee River within the borders of North Carolina are the tributaries of the Holston River, the Hiawassee River, and the head waters of the Tennessee proper.

The branches of the Holston River are the Watauga, the Toe or Doe, and the French Broad, the last sometimes considered an independent tributary of the Tennessee. The Watauga River takes its rise on the northern side of Grand father Mountain and has a course of 30 miles within the state, cutting through a deep mountain gorge at the Tennessee state line; it drains about 160 square miles of mountain and cultivated lands in North Carolina, and is throughout a swift stream. The Toe River is formed by several branches arising in Mitchell and Yancey counties; the length of the main stream, until it breaks through the mountains and enters Tennessee, is about 75 miles, and it drains 640 square miles, mostly virgin forest. In Tennessee and also in the adjoining part of North Carolina, this stream is called the Nolechucky. The French Broad River rises in numerous mountain springs in Transylvania, Henderson, Buncombe, and Madison counties, and has a length of 70 miles and a drainage area of 4,745 square miles before it enters Tennessee. Its principal tributaries are Laurel, Ivy, Swannanoa, and Pigeon rivers, the last the most important; these and various creeks are nearly always cold and clear, and are among the most beautiful streams in North Carolina. The Pigeon River drains practically the whole of Haywood County, having a length of 60 miles and a drainage basin of 570 square miles. In the last 40 miles of its course in North Carolina it has a fall of 1,300 feet; it breaks through the Great Smoky Mountains in a deep, wild, rocky gorge, and 25 miles further on joins the French Broad.

The most extensive of the river basins west of the mountains in North Carolina is that of the Little Tennessee, which embraces all of the counties of Macon, Jackson, Graham, and Swain, an area of more than 1,800 square miles, of which nearly nine-tenths is forest-clad. The length of the main stream within the state is about 80 miles. The principal tributaries are the Cheowah, Tuckaseegee, and Nantahala rivers, all mountain streams with rapids and falls, some of the latter being high and beautiful. The Little Tennessee enters the main river.

Flowing through Clay and Cherokee counties toward the northwest is the Hiawassee River, the most western of the important streams of North Carolina. This river, whose two most important tributaries are the Nottely and Valley rivers, has a drainage basin of more than 1,000 square miles before it leaves the state to join the main Tennessee River in Tennessee. This is a rapid mountain stream, at least 60 miles of which are within the limits of North Carolina; in places the river is 300 feet wide, but for the most part it is narrowly confined within steep, rocky banks.

The fishes of these waters belong to a very different fauna from those inhabiting the streams which drain into the Atlantic, and in fact are very dissimilar as to species. The anadromous fishes, which constitute the most characteristic feature of the streams east of the mountains, are entirely absent from these waters, while minnows and darters attain a great development. Of the fishes of the upper waters of New River nothing definite is known, as no collections have been made in that part of the basin within the state. The headwaters of the Watauga abound in trout and darters. The upper tributaries of the French Broad are among the finest and most beautiful trout streams in the entire Alleghany region, and are also well supplied with other food and game fishes, including pike, pike perch, rock bass, small-mouth black bass, spotted cat-fish, green cat-fish, and suckers, together with a host of minnows and darters. The streams west of the French Broad have been only very superficially examined with reference to their fish life; while the fishes are doubtless quite similar to those of other tributaries of the Tennessee, it is quite possible that some undescribed species remain to be discovered and it is certain that a number of minor species will eventually be added to the state's fauna from those waters.

THE FISH FAUNA OF NORTH CAROLINA.

SOURCES OF INFORMATION.

The information regarding the fish life of North Carolina in the form of printed reports, manuscripts, and collections which has been available to the author has been entirely adequate for the preparation of a complete annotated catalogue of the fishes of all parts of the state; and it may safely be assumed that but few species regularly inhabiting the state are unknown. North Carolina has received an exceptional amount of attention from ichthyologists, and both its fresh and its salt waters have been quite thoroughly examined with reference to their fish life. There remain only a few waters where further collecting would be likely to yield interesting results, and perhaps add to the number of species known from the state; these are the Hiawassee, Little Tennessee, Pigeon, New, and Dan rivers; the coastal region adjacent to the mouth of the Cape Fear; and the extensive lowlands stretching from the Cape Fear to the South Carolina border.

Some of the best-known American zoölogists and ichthyologists have studied the fishes of the state in the field, and have made reports based on their collections and observations. Associated with our knowledge of the fish life of the state are the names of such prominent biologists as Spencer F. Baird, Edward D. Cope, Elliott Coues, G. Brown Goode, William Stimpson, Theodore Gill, David S. Jordan, Charles H. Gilbert, Tarleton H. Bean, Barton W. Evermann, W. K. Brooks, Henry V. Wilson, Oliver P. Jenkins, and Seth E. Meek. Many other persons well-known in fish culture, or in scientific or economic work connected with the fisheries, have also made North Carolina the scene of their operations or North Carolina fishes and fisheries the objects of their attention; among such have been Charles Hallock, Henry C. Yarrow, Marshall McDonald, R. Edward Earll, James W. Milner, Pierre L. Jouy, W. de C. Ravenel, Stephen G. Worth, Caswell Grave, Barton A. Bean, William C. Kendall, and Charles H. Bollman.

The fresh-water fishes of North Carolina have been the subject of many investigations and reports, the most important of which are here mentioned. Various other reports which were of minor scope or in which North Carolina fishes are considered only incidentally are noted in the bibliography (page 419).

During the fall of 1869, Professor Cope visited the basins of the Tennessee, Catawba, Yadkin, and Neuse, and in 1870 published a report, based on his observations and collections, entitled "A partial list of the fishes of the fresh waters of North Carolina", which appeared in the Proceedings of the American Philosophical Society, 1870.

The streams of the Alleghany region of North Carolina were investigated in the summer of 1888 by Dr. Jordan, assisted by Professors Jenkins, Evermann, Meek, and Mr. Bollman, under the auspices of the U. S. Bureau of Fisheries, and extensive collections, comprising many new species, were made. The results of this work were embodied in a "Report of explorations made during 1888 in the Alleghany region of Virginia, North Carolina, and Tennessee, and in Western Indiana, with an account of the fishes found in each of the river basins of those regions" appearing in the Bulletin of the U. S. Fish Commission for 1888, the new forms having previously been described in the Proceedings of the U. S. National Museum for the same year. The North Carolina streams visited in the course of these explorations were the headwaters of the Pamlico, Neuse, Cape Fear, Great Pedee, Santee, and French Broad rivers.

The fishes of the Albemarle Sound section were considered in a paper by the present writer, "Notes on a collection of fishes from the Albemarle region of North Carolina", in the Bulletin of the U. S. Fish Commission for 1891.

A paper dealing with "The fishes of the Neuse River basin", by Evermann and Cox, was published in the Bulletin of the U. S. Fish Commission for 1895; this paper, while based on a small collection made by the Messrs. Brimley near Raleigh, gives a complete list of the fishes recorded from the Neuse and cites all the published references to the fishes of that stream.

The fishes of Lake Mattamuskeet were collected for the U. S. Bureau of Fisheries by Dr. John D. Milligan, of the steamer Fish-Hawk, in the winter of 1899–1900, and a brief account thereof was published by the author in the Report of the U. S. Fish Commissioner for 1900.

In 1903 Mr. Barton A. Bean published a "Notice of a collection of fishes made by H. H. Brimley in Cane River and Bollings Creek, North Carolina, with a description of a new species of *Notropis* (*N. brimleyi*)", this section being one whose fishes were but little known.

Various collections from the fresh waters of North Carolina have from time to time reached the U. S. National Museum and the U. S. Bureau of Fisheries, and have been duly considered in the present connection. Collections of the National Museum on which no special reports have been published were made by J. W. Milner on Albemarle Sound, Neuse and Tar rivers in 1878; Spencer F. Baird at Wilmington in 1877; W. R. Capehart on Albemarle Sound in 1877 to 1881; Marshall McDonald on the Neuse and Cape Fear rivers in 1880; S. G. Worth on the Swannanoa River in 1880; P. L. Jouy on Richland Creek, tributary of the Big Pigeon River, in 1890; and W. P. Seal at Wilmington in 1899. Fresh-water fishes received by the Bureau of Fisheries have included small collections by W. C. Kendall in Albemarle Sound in 1897; by W. P. Seal in the vicinity of Wilmington in 1906; and by D. P. Cabe from Middle Creek, tributary of the Little Tennessee River in Macon County, in 1904, these being the only avaliable specimens from that part of the state. Still further information concerning the fresh-water fishes has been obtained from detailed manuscript notes of Dr. W. C. Kendall on the Albemarle region in April and May, 1897, and from numerous visits of the writer to various parts of the state, including the Dismal Swamp, Albemarle Sound, and Pasquotank, Chowan, Roanoke, Tar, and Neuse rivers.

A good idea of the fish life of Lake Ellis and the adjacent lakes in Craven and Jones counties has been communicated by Mr. C. S. Brimley, who made observations and collections in 1905 and 1906, the specimens being deposited in the State Museum.

The salt-water fishes of North Carolina are well known, chiefly as a result of observations and collections made at and in the vicinity of Beaufort. Beaufort has long been a favorite place of resort for persons interested in ichthyology and other branches of zoölogy. Here, in the spring of 1860, Dr. Theodore Gill, in company with Dr. Wm. Stimpson, spent several weeks making collections of fishes and other marine animals; among the fishes then obtained were a labroid described as new under the name *Halichœres grandisquamis* but now regarded as identical with *Halichœres bivittatus*, and *Branchiostoma*, not previously known from the United States coast. Here, in 1871–2, while stationed at Fort Macon, at the entrance to Beaufort Harbor, Drs. Coues and Yarrow gave attention to the fish life, their observations being recorded by Yarrow in a paper, "Notes on the natural history of Fort Macon, N. C. and vicinity—No. 3, Fishes", published in the Proceedings of the Academy of Natural Sciences of Philadelphia for 1877. Here, in 1878, came Drs. Jordan and Gilbert, with assistants, to make collections of fishes, which were described in "Notes on the fishes of Beaufort Harbor", in the Proceedings of the U. S. National Museum for 1878, in which paper are included also the species listed by Yarrow. Here again, in the summer of 1885, Dr. Jenkins collected fishes of which a partial list was published in Johns Hopkins University Circular for October, 1885, and a full account, under the title "A list of the fishes of Beaufort harbor, N. C.", in Studies from the Biological Laboratory, Johns Hopkins University, vol. iv, 1887. Jenkins' collection was made the basis of a short paper by Dr. Jordan, "Notes on fishes collected at Beaufort, N. C., with a revised list of the species known from that locality", in the Proceedings of the U. S. National Museum for 1886.

By far the most complete collections and observations on the fishes of the Beaufort region have been made by assistants of the U. S. Bureau of Fisheries since the establishment at Beaufort of the government biological laboratory in 1899. The collections and records of the laboratory have been freely drawn on for information regarding numerous species, and the data furnished by Prof. H. V. Wilson, Dr. Caswell Grave, Dr. R. E. Coker, and Mr. H. D. Aller while connected with the laboratory have been especially valuable. Prof. Wilson, in his paper on "Marine biology at Beaufort," published in The American Naturalist in 1900, gave a running list of the commoner fishes and made the following general statement in regard to the fish life of this section:

The variety of fishes that may be taken in a short time in Beaufort harbor and the adjoining waters is so great as to make it evident that the number recorded for the region will be greatly increased when systematic collecting has been carried on for a few years. Some nine miles from Beaufort inlet the coast line makes a sharp, right-angled bend, with Cape Lookout at the angle. From the end of the cape a narrow line of shoals extends much farther out. The cape and its submerged continuation form a wall, as it were, reaching seaward for fifteen miles. Cape Lookout itself is so shaped as to embrace a bay, a quiet and beautiful sheet of water, Lookout Bight. The coast configuration thus forms a remarkable natural trap into which fish, migrating northwards, fall. It is doubtful whether a better place can be found anywhere on our coast for the carrying out of observations on oceanic species and on bay and river species during the oceanic period of their life. The seining that has been carried on at Cape Lookout has been extremely interesting and successful, both as regards the variety of forms and the number of individuals taken.

The steamer Fish-Hawk, while attached to the Beaufort laboratory in 1902, made collections on some of the off-shore grounds and surveyed an important outlying fishing bank. A number of fishes not previously recorded from North Carolina were found during this vessel's operations.

The fishermen and fish dealers of Beaufort and Morehead have supplied interesting specimens and useful information which have contributed to the completeness of our knowledge of the salt-water fishes of the state.

In 1904, Mr. Barton A. Bean, of the department of fishes of the U. S. National Museum, made an extensive collection of fishes at Beaufort. This collection, together with numerous specimens of North Carolina fishes which have been accumulating in the museum for many years, has been taken into consideration.

A fish collection of special interest is that in the State Museum at Raleigh. The specimens have been drawn chiefly from the Beaufort and Cape Fear sections, and have been brought together by Mr. H. H. Brimley, to whom the writer is under obligations for information in regard to this collection.

Other salt-water collections and observations of importance were made by the late R. Edward Earll in the Wilmington region in 1880; and by Dr. W. C. Kendall, while attached to the steamer Fish-Hawk in the winter and spring of 1890–91, who has furnished the writer with interesting notes on the fishes of the Cape Fear, Beaufort, Cape Lookout, and Hatteras sections. In 1905, Mr. W. H. Yopp, of Wilmington, supplied interesting data concerning the salt-water fishes of the Wilmington market.

Reference should be made to the studies of the parasites and food of the fishes of the Beaufort region by Prof. Edwin Linton in 1901 and 1902. His report, "Parasites of fishes of Beaufort, North Carolina" (1905), contains much information not obtainable elsewhere regarding the food of the numerous fishes taken at that locality in summer.

A number of papers dealing with individual species of fishes studied or collected in the state have been published from time to time, and will be found in the list of literature cited. Among these may be mentioned three papers by E. W. Gudger which appeared in 1905, namely, "The breeding habits and the segmentation of the egg of the pipe-fish, *Siphostoma floridæ*", "A note on the habits of *Rissola marginata*", and "A note on the egg and egg-laying of *Pterophyrne histrio*, the gulfweed-fish"; "The devil-fish and some other fishes in North Carolina", by Theodore Gill (1903) and "Notes on the habits of an opidiid (cusk eel)", by the same writer (1905); and "Notes on a rare flying-fish (*Cypselurus lutkeni*)", by Hugh M. Smith (1905).

One of the most voluminous writers on the fishes of the state is Mr. Stephen G. Worth, former superintendent of fish and fisheries of North Carolina and for many years superintendent of the Edenton station and various local substations of the U. S. Bureau of Fisheries. Mr. Worth's papers, which pertain more particularly to the artificial propagation of fishes, appear in the state agricultural reports and the Bulletins of the U. S. Fish Commission, and constitute an invaluable record.

Among the sources of information should be mentioned a number of early general works on North Carolina in which the fishes receive more or less attention; these works are chiefly valuable for the historical insight they afford as to the knowledge of the fish fauna in the latter part of the seventeenth century and the first half of the eighteenth century. "Carolina; or a description of the present state of that country", by Thomas Ash, published in London in 1682, makes brief mention of the fishes (including salmon, trouts, and bass). The best of the early works was that of John Lawson, surveyor-general of North Carolina, entitled "A new voyage to Carolina; containing the exact description and natural history of that country", etc., published in London in 1709. It contains many quaint and interesting notes, and has been hereinafter quoted in the accounts of a number of species. This was followed by "The natural history of North Carolina" of John Brickell, M. D., printed in Dublin in 1737, which is chiefly remarkable for its free plagiarism of Lawson's work. John Edward Holbrook's excellent "Ichthyology of South Carolina" contains a number of references to North Carolina.

Among the general works on American fishes and fisheries in which North Carolina receives due consideration are "The Fisheries and Fishery Industries of the United States", by George Brown Goode and associates, 7 volumes (1884–1887); "American Game Fishes", by Goode (1887), with revised edition edited by Dr. Theodore Gill (1903); "Statistics of the Fisheries of the South Atlantic States", by Hugh M. Smith (1893), with illustrations and local names of all the important food fishes of the region; various other statistical papers published by the U. S. Bureau of Fisheries; "The Fishes and Fish-like Vertebrates of North and Middle America", by Jordan and Evermann, 4 volumes (1896–1900); and "American Food and Game Fishes", by Jordan and Evermann (1902).

GENERAL CHARACTER OF THE FAUNA.

While the fish life of North Carolina is not of a peculiar or distinctive type, and bears a close resemblance to that of the adjoining states, it nevertheless has some features of exceptional interest.

The great variety in the topography of the state; the number, length, and volume of the streams; the remarkable coast-wise fringe of large, shallow sounds; and the long coast-line, have contributed to the development of a fish fauna rich in both species and individuals. Many species of fishes were first made known from North Carolina waters, and a considerable number of these have not been found elsewhere and will probably prove to be peculiar to this state. Other species here exist in greater abundance than in other states. Among the prominent features of the fish fauna are:

(a) The abundance of certain anadromous fishes, whose numbers are scarcely surpassed in any other waters, the chief of these being the shad, the alewives, and the striped bass.

(b) The variety and abundance of suckers, minnows, and sun-fishes in the fresh waters generally and of darters in the headwaters of the streams on both sides of the Alleghanies.

(c) The occurrence in the sounds and along the outer shores of immense schools of mullet, squeteague, menhaden, blue-fish, croaker, spot, pig-fish, pin-fish, and other food fishes.

(d) The extension to the North Carolina coast of many species which are characteristic of the West Indies or Florida.

(e) A few species of the Atlantic coast reach their southern limit in North Carolina (such as the cod and tautog) or do not occur in noteworthy numbers further south (such as the white perch and striped bass).

The number of species of fishes known from North Carolina waters and herein described is 345, excluding several introduced species which have become more or less established. The native fishes belong in 99 families and 215 genera, giving an average of 3.5 species per family and 1.6 species per genus. The twelve largest families, which contain 184 species and 89 genera, are as follows:

Cat-fishes	12	species in	4	genera.	
Suckers	18	"	"	5	"
Minnows	36	"	"	9	"
Killi-fishes	9	"	"	5	"
Mackerels	8	"	"	6	"
Carangids	17	"	"	8	"
Sun-fishes	17	"	"	10	"
Perches	24	"	"	12	"
Sea basses	11	"	"	7	"
Sparids	7	"	"	6	"
Drums	14	"	"	10	"
Flounders	11	"	"	7	"

Among the genera containing a noteworthy number of species are *Moxostoma* (suckers) with 13 species, *Notropis* (minnows) with 22 species, *Hybopsis* (minnows) with 6 species, and *Etheostoma* (darters) with 7 species.

Classifying the fishes of the state according to whether they are (1) marine or brackish water species, (2) fresh-water species, or (3) anadromous or catadromous species, it appears that 209 belong in the first class, 125 in the second, and 11 in the third.

Of the fresh-water fishes, the largest number inhabit the waters of the Atlantic slope; a comparatively small percentage are confined to the western slope of the Alleghanies; while a few inhabit both regions. The distribution of the fresh-water fishes (including the migratory ones) may be thus summarized:

Species peculiar to waters of Atlantic slope 85
Species peculiar to waters of Mississippi basin 36
Species found in both regions...15

FISHES FIRST DESCRIBED FROM NORTH CAROLINA WATERS.

Twenty-nine species of fishes have been based on specimens collected in North Carolina, in addition to a large number described by Linnæus and other early ichthyologists from "Carolina", which in most cases, however, meant South Carolina. On the following page are given the species first described from the state and now recognized as valid.

FISHES FIRST DESCRIBED FROM NORTH CAROLINA WATERS.

PRESENT IDENTIFICATION.	ORIGINAL NAME.	TYPE LOCALITY.	DESCRIBER AND YEAR.
SILURIDÆ:			
Schilbeodes furiosus	Noturus furiosus	Neuse River	Jordan & Meek, 1889
CATOSTOMIDÆ:			
Moxostoma papillosum	Ptychostomus papillosus	Catawba and Yadkin rivers	Cope, 1870
Moxostoma collapsum	Ptychostomus collapsus	Neuse, Yadkin and Catawba rivers	Cope, 1870
Moxostoma pidiense	Ptychostomus pidiensis	Yadkin River	Cope, 1870
Moxostoma coregonus	Ptychostomus coregonus	Catawba and Yadkin rivers	Cope, 1870
Moxostoma album	Ptychostomus albus	Catawba River	Cope, 1870
Moxostoma thalassinum	Ptychostomus thalassinus	Yadkin River	Cope, 1870
Moxostoma robustum	Ptychostomus robustus	Yadkin River	Cope, 1870
Moxostoma crassilabre	Ptychostomus crassilabris	Yadkin River	Cope, 1870
Moxostoma conus	Ptychostomus conus	Yadkin River	Cope, 1870
Moxostoma rupiscartes	Moxostoma rupiscartes	Catawba River	Jordan & Jenkins, 1889
CYPRINIDÆ:			
Notropis pyrrhomelas	Photogenis pyrrhomelas	Catawba River	Cope, 1870
Notropis niveus	Hybopsis niveus	Catawba River	Cope, 1870
Notropis chlorocephalus	Hybopsis chlorocephalus	Catawba River	Cope, 1870
Notropis brimleyi	Notropis brimleyi	Cane River	Bean, 1903
Notropis chiliticus	Hybopsis chiliticus	Yadkin River	Cope, 1870
Notropis altipinnis	Alburnellus altipinnis	Yadkin River	Cope, 1870
Notropis umbratilis matutinus	Alburnellus matutinus	Neuse River	Cope, 1870
Hybopsis labrosus	Ceratichthys labrosus	Catawba River	Cope, 1870
Hybopsis hysinotus	Ceratichthys hysinotus	Catawba River	Cope, 1870
PŒCILIIDÆ:			
Fundulus rathbuni	Fundulus rathbuni	Cape Fear River	Jordan & Meek, 1889
EXOCŒTIDÆ:			
Cypselurus lutkeni	Exocœtus lutkeni	Beaufort	Jordan & Evermann, 1896
PERCIDÆ:			
Boleosoma maculaticeps	Boleosoma maculaticeps	Catawba River	Cope, 1870
Etheostoma rufilineatum	Pœcilichthys rufilineatum	French Broad River	Cope, 1870
Etheostoma swannanoa	Etheostoma swannanoa	Swannanoa River	Jordan & Evermann, 1889
Etheostoma vulneratum	Pœlichthys vulneratus	French Broad River	Cope, 1870
Ioa vitrea	Pœcilichthys vitreus	Neuse River	Cope, 1870
TRIGLIDÆ:			
Prionotus scitulus	Prionotus scitulus	Beaufort	Jordan & Gilbert, 1882
GOBIIDÆ:			
Microgobius holmesi	Microgobius holmesi	Beaufort	Smith, 1907

In the foregoing table the species are arranged systematically under the names herein used; there are also shown the name under which each species was first described, the type locality, the person by whom named, and the date when the species was established.

Of the species here listed, 21 were described by Professor Cope, the pioneer ichthyologist of North Carolina and the most voluminous writer on North Carolina fishes; many of Cope's species have not been met with by other collectors and are therefore known only from Cope's descriptions and types.

FISHES FOUND ONLY IN NORTH CAROLINA.

Of the fishes originally described from North Carolina, the following 18 have as yet been found in no other state, although it is likely that in time some of both the fresh-water and salt-water species will be noted in other states.

Schilbeodes furiosus (Jordan & Meek).	Notropis brimleyi Bean.
Moxostoma collapsum (Cope).	Notropis chiliticus (Cope).
Moxostoma pidiense (Cope).	Notropis altipinnis (Cope).
Moxostoma coregonus (Cope).	Notropis umbratilis matutinus (Cope).
Moxostoma album (Cope).	Fundulus rathbuni Jordan & Meek.
Moxostoma thalassinum (Cope).	Cypselurus lutkeni (Jordan & Evermann).
Moxostoma robustum (Cope).	Boleosoma maculaticeps Cope.
Moxostoma crassilabre (Cope).	Etheostoma swannanoa Jordan & Evermann.
Moxostoma conus (Cope).	Microgobius holmesi Smith.

FISHES NOT PREVIOUSLY RECORDED FROM NORTH CAROLINA WATERS.

In the inquiries and investigations on which the present work is based, there have been obtained records of numerous species of fishes which have not hitherto been noted as occurring in North Carolina in the very considerable ichthyologic literature of the state. Most of these species are marine, and most of them have been added to the local fauna as a result of the collections at Beaufort by the United States Bureau of Fisheries. The list, which includes 59 salt-water species and 10 fresh-water and anadromous species, is as follows:

Salt-water Fishes:

Hexanchus griseus	Scomberomorus cavalla
Catulus uter	Istiophorus nigricans
Squatina squatina	Tetrapturus albidus
Rhinobatus lentiginosus	Oligoplites saurus
Raia eglanteria	Caranx ruber
Bascanichthys scuticaris	Trachinotus glaucus
Lycodontis ocellatus	Trachinotus goodei
Anchovia mitchilli	Psenes maculatus
Chlorophthalmus chalybeius	Epinephelus striatus
Hemirhamphus brasiliensis	Mycteroperca venenosa
Auxis thazard	Mycteroperca bonaci
Gymnosarda alleterata	Diplectrum formosum
Sarda sarda	Lobotes surinamensis

Salt-water Fishes—Continued:

Pseudopriacanthus altus
Lutianus blackfordi
Lutianus griseus
Lutianus apodes
Lutianus analis
Otrynter caprinus
Calamus leucosteus
Eucinostomus pseudogula
Cynoscion nothus
Larimus fasciatus
Stellifer lanceolatus
Eques acuminatus
Lachnolaimus maximus
Doratonotus megalepis
Xyrichthys psittacus
Sparisoma niphobles
Chætodon ocellatus

Hepatus hepatus
Hepatus bahianus
Balistes carolinensis
Ceratacanthus punctatus
Lactophrys triqueter
Spheroides spengleri
Diodon hystrix
Chilomycterus antillarum
Mola mola
Scorpæna plumieri
Scorpæna brasiliensis
Microgobius holmesi
Microgobius eulepis
Gobiesox virgatulus
Syacium papillosum
Citharichthys spilopterus
Ogcocephalus vespertilio

Fresh-water and Anadromous Fishes:

Petromyzon marinus
Hiodon selenops
Fundulus nottii
Heterandria formosa
Chologaster cornutus

Copelandellus quiescens
Elassoma evergladei
Elassoma zonatum
Mesogonistius chætodon
Dormitator maculatus

THE LOCAL NAMES OF THE FISHES.

In the following systematic list, every name known to be applied by North Carolinians to the fishes of the state is given, along with other common names which the fishes bear in other parts of the country, the local names being distinguished by quotation marks. From the index of common names (page 425) it will be possible to find the detailed account of any species.

A knowledge of the local names of the fishes of the state is not without value, and it is a matter of some historical as well as ichthyological interest to record the early names applied to the various species and to compare them with the present designations. With the advent of fishermen from other states and with the extension of knowledge of the fishes the original local names will in time be supplemented or supplanted.

One of the most entertaining lists of the vernacular names of North Carolina fishes is that embodied in Lawson's "A new voyage to Carolina". It is interesting to note that nearly all of the fishes named are easily recognizable, that most of them still bear the same names, and that certain names now in use are perhaps there recorded for the first time. Among the salt-water fishes of the state he mentions "thrashers" (thrasher sharks), two sorts of sharks, "paracooda-noses" and "shovel-noses", "dog-fish" (the small shark so called), "divel-fish" (the giant ray), "scate or stingray", "sword-fish" (saw-fish), "Spanish mackerel", "cavallies", "boneto's", "blue-fish", "red drum", "black drum-fish", "angel-fish" (spade-fish), "bass, or rock-fish", "sheeps-heads", "plaice", "flounders", "soles", "mullets", "shad", "fat-backs" (menhaden), "white guard" (fresh-water gar), "green guard" (marine gar), "congar eels", "lamprey-eels", "eels", "sun-fish" (perhaps the common pompano, by which name the fish is still known at Beaufort), "toad-fish", "sea-tench" (identified by Dr. Theodore Gill as the tautog*), "trouts of the salt-water" (squeteagues), "crocus", "smelts" (silversides?), "bream", and "taylors" (young blue-fish). The fresh-water species enumerated are "sturgeon", "jack, pike or pickerel", "trouts" (brook trout), "gudgeon", "English pearch" (yellow perch, now called "Englishman"), "brown pearch, or Welchmen" (black bass, still so called), "flat, mottled pearch, or Irishman" (crappy), "round-robins" (sun-fish), "carp", "roach", "dace", "loaches" (killi-fishes?), "sucking-fish" (a name still used in the Albemarle section for suckers), "cat-fish", "grindals", "old-wives" (alewives), "fountain-fish", and "white-fish".

The author has published (1893) a table of common names applied to certain fishes of the Albemarle region, where some very inappropriate and singular names are in use, including some mentioned by Lawson. The wall-eyed pike or pike perch (*Stizostedion vitreum*) is sometimes called "salmon" or "California salmon"; the yellow perch is known as "red-fin", "raccoon perch", and "Englishman"; the large-mouth black bass is called "chub" and "Welshman"; the strawberry bass is the "speckled perch" on all parts of the sound; the gizzard shad (*Dorosoma cepedianum*) is generally known as "nanny shad", which designation, togther with "nancy shad", is also employed in other sections of the state; and various small minnows (*Notropis, Hybognathus*) are generally known as "chobies" (doubtless a corruption of anchovies).

Among the vernacular fish names which appear to be restricted to North Carolina may be mentioned "black-fish" (grindle), "shad" (menhaden), "nanny shad" or "nancy shad" (mud shad), "gourd-fish" (butter-fish), "oyster-fish" (tautog), "cabio" (crab-eater; called "cabby-yew" in Bermuda; the name cobia usually given this fish is not known to American fishermen, and may have originally been a misprint for cabio), "jimmy" (spot), "sea-mink" (king-fish), "Englishman" (yellow perch), "Welshman" (black bass), "robin" and "robin perch" (sun-fishes), and "steamboat" (triple-tail).

*Forest and Stream, May 30, 1903.

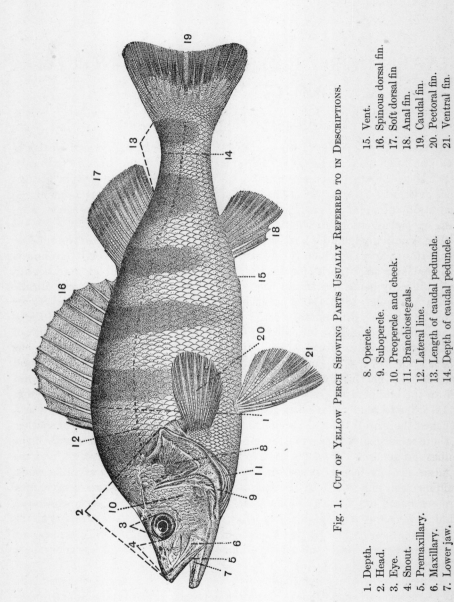

Fig. 1. Cut of Yellow Perch Showing Parts Usually Referred to in Descriptions.

1. Depth.
2. Head.
3. Eye.
4. Snout.
5. Premaxillary.
6. Maxillary.
7. Lower jaw.

8. Opercle.
9. Suboperele.
10. Preopercle and cheek.
11. Branchiostegals.
12. Lateral line.
13. Length of caudal peduncle.
14. Depth of caudal peduncle.

15. Vent.
16. Spinous dorsal fin.
17. Soft dorsal fin
18. Anal fin.
19. Caudal fin.
20. Pectoral fin.
21. Ventral fin.

SYSTEMATIC CATALOGUE OF NORTH CAROLINA FISHES.

EXPLANATORY NOTES.

A full list of all species of fishes known to inhabit the fresh or salt waters of North Carolina is here presented. The plan which has been followed is to give for each species its technical name and original describer, and its popular names; a brief synonymy; a diagnostic description; and then a general account of the distribution, abundance, size, habits, food value, economic importance, etc., having special reference to North Carolina.

The synonymy includes a reference to the original description of the species, all important papers in which the occurrence of the species in North Carolina is mentioned, and an authority for the terminology which has been adopted herein, this last usually being Jordan and Evermann's "The fishes of North and Middle America", 4 vols., 1896–1900, published as Bulletin 47 of the United States National Museum. Citations of works pertaining wholly or partly to North Carolina are condensed and are intended to be taken in conjunction with the index of North Carolina fish literature which appears on page 419; thus, "*Ptychostomus robustus* Cope, 1870, 473", means that the species so called by Cope will be found described on page 473 of the work published by him in 1870. Other works, not given in the bibliography, are referred to with greater fullness in the synonymy.

In order to render the catalogue useful in the identification of North Carolina fishes, there are introduced artificial keys* to the families, genera, and species; and there are also given, as a matter of general information, brief accounts of the families and genera. The keys have in most cases been adapted from, and the diagnoses also are largely based on, Jordan and Evermann's invaluable work, which has been followed in the arrangement of the families. Numerous original diagnoses based on North Carolina specimens have, however, been introduced. Technical terms used in descriptions are explained in the glossary on page 403.

The common names applied to fishes by the people of North Carolina are given in quotation marks; and other vernacular names in more or less general use are also shown.

A special object in view has been to clothe the technical descriptions in simple language, so that fishermen and the general public may be able to make

---

*In using the keys for the identification of specimens of North Carolina fishes, first determine which of the major groups the species is in and then take up in regular order the letters under each group; if the characters of the specimens do not agree with those given for the single letters, then look under the same double letters, ignoring all intervening matter.

use of the work in identifying the species; the diagnoses have likewise been made as brief as is consistent with this purpose and have been based almost exclusively on external characters.   A free translation of the meaning of all the generic and specific names has been given.*

THE CLASSES OF FISHES AND FISH-LIKE ANIMALS.

The creatures popularly called fishes belong in three great classes, which may be distinguished by the following characters.   The first two classes are quite unimportant in the present connection, each having only a single representative in the state; and only the last class contains the fishes properly speaking.

Key to the classes of fishes and fish-like animals.

i. Animals with cartilaginous skeleton and without brain or skull; fins rudimentary and only on median line of body; mouth a slit surrounded by bristles; heart a tubular vessel without separate chambers; blood colorless; gill-slits numerous, the respiratory cavity opening into the abdomen; inspired water discharged through a special abdominal pore.

LEPTOCARDII (lancelets).

ii. Animals with cartilaginous or bony skeleton; skull and brain present; heart developed as a cavity with at least two chambers; blood red.

  a. Eel-shaped; skeleton cartilaginous; skull imperfect; mouth circular, suctorial; no jaws or paired fins; a single median nostril; gills pouch-shaped and numerous; skin naked; alimentary canal straight, without cœca; pancreas and spleen absent.

MARSIPOBRANCHII (lampreys, etc.).

  aa. Skull well-developed; jaws distinct; fins usually highly-developed, some of them paired; skin usually scaly; nostrils at least two, not median; gill-openings a single slit on each side in most fishes (numerous in a few families); alimentary canal more or less convoluted; pancreas and spleen present .... PISCES (fishes).

---

*Following is an explanation of some of the arbitrary features adopted in describing the species:

In the statement of the general shape of a species the relation of the depth and the length of head to the length is given.   By depth is understood the greatest vertical diameter of the body, while length or total length means the distance in a straight line from the end of snout to end of the backbone, or, what usually amounts to practically the same thing, to the base of the caudal fin; the length of head is the distance in a straight line from the end of snout to the most posterior part of the gill-cover.   The relative size of parts may vary with the size, age, sex, and spawning condition of the individual; and the figures given in the diagnoses must be regarded as simply averages for adult fishes.   In the young, the head and eye are usually larger, the depth less and the mouth smaller than in mature examples.

In noting the fin formulæ, spinous rays are always recorded with Roman numerals and soft rays with Arabic figures.   Thus, "dorsal rays 10" means that a fish has a single dorsal fin with 10 soft rays; "dorsal rays IV, 10" means that a fish has a continuous dorsal fin composed of 4 spines and 10 soft rays; "dorsal rays IV + 10" means that a fish has two separate dorsal fins, the anterior with 4 spines and the posterior with 10 soft rays; and "dorsal rays III + 1, 10" means that a fish has two separate dorsal fins, the anterior with 3 spines and the posterior with 10 rays preceded by a single spine.

The number of scales in lateral series is usually computed along the lateral line, and often corresponds with the number of pores or tubes in the lateral line: when the lateral line is absent or incomplete, the count is made from the gill-opening to the base of the caudal fin.   The number of scales in crosswise series is determined by counting an oblique row from the base of dorsal fin to the lateral line and from the lateral line to the base of anal fin or to the vent

Class LEPTOCARDII. The Leptocardians.

Order AMPHIOXI. The Cirristomes.

Family BRANCHIOSTOMIDÆ. The Lancelets.

Very small, elongated, compressed, translucent marine creatures, having no scales, rudimentary fins and eyes, the mouth a longitudinal slit surrounded by a fringe of cirri, and various other characters shown in the foregoing key. There are two or three genera and about eight species, distinguishable chiefly by the number of muscular bands with which the body is marked; only one genus is represented in United States waters.

Genus BRANCHIOSTOMA Costa. Lancelets.

Small, lance-shaped animals living buried in sand in comparatively shallow water, with gonads on both sides of the median line, an anal fin containing traces of rays, and no caudal fin. Represented on the United States coasts by two or three species, of which one is found in North Carolina. (*Branchiostoma*, gill-like mouth, the cirri having been mistaken for gills.)

1. BRANCHIOSTOMA CARIBÆUM Sundevall.
Lancelet; Amphioxus.

Branchiostoma caribœum Sundevall, Kongliga Vetenskaps-Förhandlingar, 12, 1853; St. Thomas and Rio Janeiro.
  Yarrow, 1877, 218; Beaufort. Jordan & Evermann, 1896, 3, pl. i, fig.1; Beaufort, N. C., to South America.
Amphioxus, Baird, Smithsonian Report, 1860, 71; Beaufort. Wilson, 1900, 354; Beaufort.
Amphioxus caribœus, Jordan & Gilbert, 1879, 388; Beaufort.
Branchiostoma lanceolatum, Jordan, 1886, 26; Beaufort. Jenkins, 1887, 83; Beaufort.

DIAGNOSIS.—Depth about .11 total length; number of muscular bands (myocommata) about 58, of which 7 to 10 are posterior to vent; gonads on each side 22 to 26; length under 2 inches. (Named from the Caribbean Sea.)

Fig. 2. LANCELET. *Branchiostoma caribœum.*

This curious and interesting species, which is probably only a variety of *Branchiostoma lanceolatum* of Europe and Chesapeake Bay, is found coastwise from North Carolina to Argentina. The presence of the amphioxus in United States waters was first determined by Dr. Theodore Gill, from specimens collected at Beaufort in 1860. Yarrow found a number of specimens on Bird Shoal, and others have obtained the species there. Wilson states that it is not common at Beaufort and that the pelagic larvæ are taken there in the tow in July. In 1902 the Fish-Hawk dredged many specimens at various points off Cape Lookout (stations 7312, 7320, 7338,7341) in depths of 8, 10, 13.5 and 29 fathoms.

Class MARSIPOBRANCHII. The Pouch-gilled Animals.

Order HYPEROARTII. The Hyperoartians.

Family PETROMYZONTIDÆ. The Lampreys.

Oviparous, eel-like vertebrates, with circular, toothed mouth adapted for sucking, nostril on top of head in front of eyes, 7 gill-openings on each side of the body anteriorly, no scales, dorsal fin notched or divided and continuous with anal fin around the tail. The young differ considerably from the adults, having rudimentary eyes, and being usually toothless; they were for a long time regarded as belonging to different genera. Some of the American species are marine, some are strictly fresh-water, and some are anadromous. They attach themselves to fishes, make ulcers or holes in their sides, and suck their blood. One species is found in North Carolina.

Genus PETROMYZON Linnæus. Sea Lampreys.

Large anadromous lampreys, distinguished by tooth-like processes on what corresponds to the upper and lower jaws of fishes, the superior teeth 2 or 3 in number, pointed, and close together; the large sucking disk with numerous teeth in concentric lines; parts of dorsal fin separated. (*Petromyzon*, stone-sucker.)

2. PETROMYZON MARINUS Linnæus.

"Lamprus Eel"; "Lamprey Eel"; "Lamprey"; Sea Lamprey.

Petromyzon marinus Linnæus, Systema Naturæ, ed. x, 230, 1758; European seas. Jordan & Evermann, 1896, 10, pl. i, fig. 3.

DIAGNOSIS.—Head long, its length greater than distance between first and last gill-openings; eye nearer to first gill-opening than to anterior end of head; mouth large, with numerous conical teeth in oblique rows; lips fringed; dorsal fins low and well separated. Color: back and sides slaty brown, sharply mottled with black; below white or pale yellow. (*marinus*, marine.)

Fig. 3. SEA LAMPREY. *Petromyzon marinus.*

Inhabits the coasts of the North Atlantic Ocean, ranging as far south as North Carolina, going from the sea to the rivers to spawn. The species ascends some of the North Carolina streams in spring along with shad and alewives, but is less abundant than in more northern waters. It has been observed by the writer in Albemarle Sound at Avoca, where larval lampreys (*Ammocœtes*) 6 or 8 inches long and adults 2 to 3 feet long are caught in shad seines. It is also known from the Neuse at Kinston, and at Raleigh, where Mr. C. S. Brimley reports it as rare, the adults being observed in April and the young in June. The species is thus referred to by Lawson in "A New Voyage to Carolina", published in 1709:

Lampreys are not common; I never saw but one, which was large, and caught by the Indians in a ware. They would not eat him, but gave him to me.

Lampreys attach themselves to shad, cat-fish, sturgeon, and various other fishes, making ulcerous sores and sometimes producing death by perforating the abdominal walls. The rapidity of their respiratory movements is quite remarkable; in a healthy 2-foot specimen observed by the writer the respirations averaged 124 per minute.

Outside of a few localities in New England, the lamprey has no recognized food value in the United States, although in Europe it has been more or less celebrated from early times.

Class PISCES.   The Fishes.

The North Carolina representatives of this class fall into 2 easily recognized groups or sub-classes, (1) the sharks, skates, and rays, and (2) the true fishes, which are distinguished anatomically as follows:

i. Skeleton cartilaginous; skull without sutures and without membranous bones; gill-openings numerous (5 to 7) and slit like, the gills attached to the skin; tail heterocercal; skin tough, naked or covered with small rough scales, spines, or tubercles; air-bladder absent; jaws separable from skull; species viviparous or ovoviviparous, the eggs large and few in number; embryo with deciduous external gills.
SELACHII or ELASMOBRANCHII (sharks, skates, rays, etc.).
ii. Skeleton bony in all but a few families; skull with sutures and membranous bones (opercula, etc.); gill-openings a single slit on each side, the gills attached to bony arches; tail heterocercal or homocercal; body usually covered with numerous flat scales; air-bladder present or absent; jaws not distinct from the skull; species oviparous (exceptionally viviparous), the ova small and numerous .... TELEOSTOMI (true fishes).

Sub-Class SELACHII. The Sharks, Skates, and Rays.

Key to the orders of selachians represented in North Carolina waters.

i. Form typically fish-like; one or two well-developed dorsal fins; anal fin present; caudal fin large; pectoral fins distinct; gill-openings lateral.
  a. Gill-openings 6 or 7 in number; dorsal fin single.... DIPLOSPONDYLI (notidanoid sharks).
  aa. Gill-openings 5 in number; two dorsal fins.......... ASTEROSPONDYLI (typical sharks).
ii. Form not fish-like, much depresssed and expanded laterally; dorsal fins wanting, or small and inserted on tail; anal fin absent; caudal fin small or wanting.
  b. Pectoral fins expanded laterally, but not confluent with body, separated from neck by a deep notch in which are the gill-openings; gill-openings lateral, partly inferior; ventral fins large...... CYCLOSPONDYLI (suborder TECTOSPONDYLI, the angel-fishes).
  bb. Pectoral fins expanded laterally and confluent with body; gill-openings ventral; ventral fins small. .... BATOIDEA (the skates and rays).

Order DIPLOSPONDYLI. The Notidanoid Sharks.

These sharks are distinguished by having 6 or 7 gill-openings on each side, a single dorsal fin, and 2 vertebræ and 2 neural arches arising from each segment of the backbone, together with other skeletal characters. Numerous species of fossil sharks are allied to the few living members of the order. One American family.

Family HEXANCHIDÆ.   The Cow Sharks.

A small family of viviparous sharks, some of them of large size, characterized by 6 or 7 wide gill-slits and a single dorsal fin, together with a more or less
elongate body, depressed head, large and subinferior mouth without labial fold,
and teeth in upper jaw unlike those in lower.   Two American genera, with 6 and 7
gill-openings respectively.

Genus HEXANCHUS Rafinesque.   Cow Sharks.

In having 6 gill-openings, this genus differs from all other known sharks
with the exception of a deep-water form (*Chlamydoselachus*) from Japan and
Madeira.   The teeth in the upper jaw consist of about 4 pointed ones in front,
3 on each side of these with 1 or many cusps, and lateral ones with numerous
cusps; the teeth in the lower jaw are a small median one with or without cusp
and lateral serrated ones with numerous cusps.   Two species, one in the Atlantic,
the other in the Pacific.   (*Hexanchus*, six-slitted.)

3. HEXANCHUS GRISEUS (Gmelin).
Cow Shark.

Squalus griseus Gmelin, Systema Naturæ, 1495, 1788; Mediterranean.
Hexanchus griseus, Jordan & Evermann, 1896, 19, pl. ii, fig. 8.

DIAGNOSIS.—Body deepest over pectorals, tapering gradually to base of caudal, greatest
depth less than length of head and about .16 total length to tip of caudal; head large, blunt;
mouth large, posterior angle extending nearly to first gill-opening; 2 teeth on each side of upper
jaw in front and curved outward, other teeth with 6 or more cusps; lateral teeth in lower jaw
with 7 to 9 cusps; eye small, placed far forward; snout short, nostrils near its tip; gill-slits
rather wide, anterior widest, others progressively reduced; dorsal placed far backward, its
origin opposite posterior end of base of ventrals; anal similar to dorsal but more posterior;
caudal stout, its length 1.5 times head; length of pectorals about equal to head to anterior gill-
slit. Color: dark gray. (*griseus*, gray.)

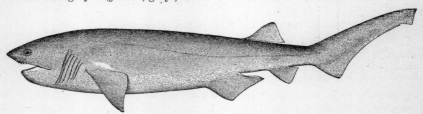

Fig. 4. COW SHARK.   *Hexanchus griseus*.

The cow shark frequents the Mediterranean Sea and the west coast of
Europe, and is reported by Poey to be often taken about Cuba.   There appears
to be only a single record of its occurrence on the coast of the United States.   In
March, 1886, a specimen 10 feet 2 inches long was secured at the Currituck Inlet
life-saving station, North Carolina, and forwarded to the U. S. National Museum
by D. M. Etheridge; a plaster cast of the fish is now on exhibition. This shark
attains a length of 26 feet, and may always be readily distinguished from all
other species inhabiting our coast by the single dorsal fin and the 6 gill-openings.

Order ASTEROSPONDYLI. The Typical Sharks.

All but one of the sharks as yet known from the state are placed in this order, characterized by five gill-openings, two dorsal fins without spines, an anal fin, and internal calcareous layers of each vertebra radiating from the central ring. Besides the families given in the following key, there are others which will doubtless in time be represented in the local fauna by species* of wide distribution.

Key to the families and genera of North Carolina typical sharks.
i. First dorsal fin over or behind the ventrals; no membrance for closing the eye.
SCYLLIORHINIDÆ (genus CATULUS).
ii. First dorsal fin more or less in advance of the ventrals.
   a. Last gill aperture above base of pectoral fin; membrane for closing eye present.
     b. Head typically shark-like.
GALEIDÆ (genera MUSTELUS, SCOLIODON, and CARCHARHINUS).
     bb. Head atypical, being greatly prolonged laterally. . . . SPHYRNIDÆ (genus SPHYRNA).
  aa. Last gill slit in front of pectoral fin; no membrane for closing eye.
CARCHARIIDÆ (genus CARCHARIAS).

Family SCYLLIORHINIDÆ. The Cat Sharks.

Ovoviviparous sharks with large quadrate egg-cases, the four corners produced into long tubes for attaching the cases to submerged objects; gill-openings small, the most posterior one above base of pectorals; mouth broad, with small teeth in several rows, each tooth with a median cusp and 1 or more cusps on each side; nostrils near to or confluent with mouth; dorsal fins small; anal fin usually anterior to second dorsal; caudal rather long, without median keel. Two American genera.

Genus CATULUS A. Smith. Cat Sharks.

Very small sharks with nostrils widely separated and near the wide mouth, inhabiting rather deep water in the Atlantic and Pacific oceans. Of the five North American species, only one is found on the Atlantic coast. (*Catulus*, little cat.)

4. CATULUS RETIFER (Garman).
Cat Shark.

Scyllium retiferum Garman, Bulletin Museum Comparative Zoölogy, viii, 233, 1881; 80 miles east of Virginia coast in 89 fathoms.
Catulus retifer, Jordan & Evermann, 1896, 25.

DIAGNOSIS.—Body moderately elongate, head much depressed, mouth broad; teeth small, each with a central cusp and 2 small cusps on each side; first dorsal fin near middle of body; pectorals short and broad; vent anterior to middle of body. Color: light brown, with groups of black lines making an irregular meshwork; yellow beneath. (*retifer*, net-bearing, in allusion to the markings.)

Several specimens of this rare shark have been obtained off the South Atlantic States and in the West Indies. In August, 1902, the Fish-Hawk collected 10 specimens 6 inches long with a 7-foot beam trawl 37 to 40 miles southeast of Cape Lookout in 141 and 172 fathoms of water. Maximum length about 1 foot.

---

* Among these are (1) the mackerel shark (*Isurus dekayi*), ranging from the West Indies to Cape Cod; (2) the porbeagle, or mackerel shark (*Lamna cornubica*), a very large pelagic form occasionally taken on the Atlantic coast; (3) the man-eater shark or great white shark (*Carcharodon carcharias*), which is found in all temperate and tropical seas and reaches a length of 30 feet.

Family GALEIDÆ.   The Requiem Sharks.

Ovoviviparous sharks, with the first dorsal fin short and high, entirely in advance of ventrals; the second dorsal small and opposite anal; gill-openings of moderate size; the last slit above base of pectorals; spiracles small or obsolete; no keel on side of caudal peduncle; nictitating membrane present; no dorsal spines. A very large family, found in all seas, with numerous genera, of which the following are represented in South Atlantic fauna and several others may be looked for*:

i. Teeth blunt, flat, paved, without cusps or ridges; spiracles present; embryos not attached by a placenta..MUSTELUS.
ii. Teeth compressed, with entire or serrate edges; spiracles obsolete; embryos attached by a placenta.
  a. Angle of mouth without a groove which extends along either jaw; all teeth more or less serrate; first dorsal nearer to pectorals than to ventrals.......CARCHARHINUS.
  aa. Angle of mouth with a groove which extends along either jaw; teeth entire; first dorsal midway between pectorals and ventrals...........................SCOLIODON.

Genus MUSTELUS Cuvier.   Dog-fishes.

Small sharks, usually swimming in droves; body elongate, slender; mouth small, crescent-shaped, with conspicuous labial folds; snout long and flat; teeth small, many-rowed, pavement-like, those in two jaws similar; eye large, oval; spiracles small; pectorals large; caudal nearly straight, the basal lobe very small. Two American species, one on Pacific coast of Mexico, and one on Alantic coasts of America and Europe.   (*Mustelus*, weasel or marten.)

5. MUSTELUS CANIS (Mitchill).
"Dog-fish"; Smooth Dog-fish.

Squalus canis Mitchill, Transactions of Literary and Philosophical Society of New York, i, 486, 1815; New York.
Mustelus lævis, Goode, History of the American Menhaden, 41, 1879; Cape Hatteras.
Mustelus canis, Jordan & Evermann, 1896, 29.

DIAGNOSIS.—Body cylindrical, slender, peduncle long; head .25 total length without caudal, twice greatest depth of body; snout .33 length of head; eye .4 length of snout; teeth in about 10 rows in each jaw; caudal fin as long as head, its lower lobe .33 length of upper.   Color: uniform ashy gray, sometimes with pale spots; beneath white.   (*canis*, dog.)

The dog-fish is one of the most abundant of the sharks on the Atlantic coast of the United States.   Its maximum length is 5 feet and the average 2.5 to 3 feet. It feeds largely on crabs, lobsters, and other bottom invertebrates.   The flesh is very palatable, and in Bermuda is highly esteemed, but in the United States the fish has no economic value at present, but, on the contrary, is very destructive in the New England fisheries, chiefly because it eats the food fish that have been caught with lines and gill nets.

The dog-fish is abundant at times off the North Carolina coast, and is often caught in the beach seines in winter, although it usually keeps offshore.   It is

* Other sharks of this family that may eventually be recorded from North Carolina are: (1) The leopard, tiger or spotted shark (*Galeocerdo tigrinus*), not uncommon on the east coast as far north as Massachusetts; a large species, attaining a length of 30 feet.   (2) The great blue shark (*Prionace glauca*), rare on the Atlantic coast (two Massachusetts records).   (3) The tiburon (*Aprionodon isodon*), known from New York, Virginia and Cuba.

very common at Cape Lookout from fall to April or May, when it departs, going north as the fishermen believe. Many are caught there in the sink nets; and they are often quite annoying and destructive, eating the fish in the nets and chewing the twine. Commander Robert Platt, U. S. N., states that the fish is at times abundant off Cape Fear. Lawson's account of the fishes of North Carolina contains this reference:

> The dog-fish are a small sort of the shark kind; and are caught with hook and line, fishing for drums. They say, they are good meat; but we have so many other sorts of delicate fish, that I shall hardly ever make tryal what they are.

The eggs of the dog-fish are fertilized internally, and the young are about 1 foot long when born. From 4 to 12 fish are produced at one time.

The abundance of this species, the facility with which it may be caught, and the quality of its flesh warrant the belief that before long it will become the object of a special fishery in North Carolina as in other states. Its non-utilization in America up to this time depends on ignorance of its value and prejudice because of its name and relationship.

Genus CARCHARHINUS Blainville. Flat-headed Sharks.

This genus includes numerous species of medium and large sized sharks, of voracious habits, found in all oceans. First dorsal fin placed anteriorly, nearer to pectorals than to ventrals; no spiracles; all teeth in adults with serrate edges; no groove from angles of mouth along jaws. Two species are known from North Carolina, but several others undoubtedly occur, judging from their general range and from incomplete descriptions of examples caught by anglers at Beaufort; the recorded species (with others that may be looked for) are thus distinguished:

i. Teeth in upper jaw broad, in lower jaw narrower.
  a. Pectoral fins very long and falcate, reaching beyond base of first dorsal; snout obtuse.
      obscurus.
  aa. Pectoral fins shorter, not reaching to base of first dorsal.
    b. Length of snout anterior to mouth equal to width of mouth; fins not dark-tipped.
      milberti.
    bb. Length of snout anterior to mouth equal .66 width of mouth; fins dark-tipped.
      platyodon.
ii. Teeth in both jaws narrow and constricted at base; length of snout equal to width of mouth; pectoral fins falcate, extending beyond base of first dorsal; all fins black-tipped.
      limbatus.

(*Carcharhinus*, jagged shark.)

6. CARCHARHINUS OBSCURUS (LeSueur).
Dusky Shark.

Squalus obscurus LeSueur, Journal Academy Natural Sciences, Philadelphia, 1818, 223; New York.
Carcharhinus obscurus, Jordan & Evermann, 1896, 35. Linton, 1905, 339; Beaufort.

DIAGNOSIS.—Head broad, flat; snout broad and rounded; teeth in upper jaw with a deep notch on outer edge; second dorsal fin smaller than anal and considerably produced posteriorly; pectorals long and falcate, their length 3 times breadth. Color: dusky blue above, white below. (*obscurus*, dusky.)

Along the east coast of the United States this shark is common and well known. It reaches a length of 14 feet. Prof. Edwin Linton examined a number taken at Beaufort, North Carolina, in July and August 1901 and 1902; the largest specimen was 7.5 feet long and weighed 203 pounds. These are the only records for the state, but the species is probably a regular member of the local fauna.

7. CARCHARHINUS MILBERTI (Müller & Henle).
Blue Shark.

Carcharias milberti Müller & Henle, Plagiostomen, 38, 1838; New York.
Carcharhinus milberti, Jordan & Evermann, 1896, 37.   Linton, 1905, 341; Beaufort.

DIAGNOSIS.—Body stout; head broad, depressed; mouth very broad, its width equal to length of snout; upper teeth broad, triangular, coarsely serrate, lower teeth narrower, finely serrate; pectoral fins small, not falcate, their length contained 6.5 times in total body length. Color: intense blue above, white below.   (Named in honor of a French naturalist, M. Milbert.)

Inhabits the Atlantic coast from Massachusetts southward, and is not rare. Specimens have recently been brought to the Beaufort laboratory from the harbor and adjacent waters.   The largest example was caught with rod-and-line by Mr. Russell J. Coles in Newport Channel near the Morehead railroad pier July 25, 1902; it was 9 feet 2 inches long and 5 feet 2 inches in circumference at thickest part of body; the head was 3 feet 11 inches in circumference at gape; the mouth was 15.5 inches wide; the largest teeth were 0.9 inch along the cutting surface and nearly as wide as base; the specimen contained 4 small embryos.

Genus SCOLIODON Müller & Henle.   Oblique-toothed Sharks.

Small sharks, with obsolete spiracles, a groove extending from angles of mouth along both jaws, and teeth flat, pointing toward sides of mouth, each tooth with a deep notch on outer margin near the sharp point.   Two North American species, one on each coast.   (*Scoliodon*, oblique-toothed.)

8. SCOLIODON TERRÆ-NOVÆ (Richardson).
"Sharp-nosed Shark".

Squalus terræ-novæ Richardson, Fauna Boreali-Americana, iii, 289, 1836; Newfoundland? (probably Carolina).
Scoliodon terræ-novæ, Jordan & Gilbert, 1879, 388; Beaufort harbor.   Jordan & Evermann, 1896, 43.
Carcharhinus terræ-novæ, Jordan, 1886, 26; Beaufort   Jenkins, 1887, 84; Beaufort.   Wilson, 1900, 355; Beaufort.   Linton, 1905, 342; Beaufort.

DIAGNOSIS.—Body slender; snout flattened; mouth U-shaped; first dorsal fin midway between pectorals and ventrals; second dorsal very small, smaller than anal; pectorals large, extending to middle of first dorsal. Color: gray; caudal fin margined with black. (*terræ-novæ*, Newfoundland.)

Ranges from Massachusetts to Brazil, and is numerous on the South Atlantic coast.   It is one of the commonest sharks at Beaufort, and is frequently caught from the wharf of the government laboratory.   In the winter of 1891 Dr. Kendall saw many taken in the beach seines at Cape Lookout.   The usual length is about 3 feet, but Jenkins records the capture of a 7-foot specimen at Beaufort.

The food is quite varied; while fish probably constitute the principal food at Beaufort, blue crabs, hermit crabs, fiddler crabs, shrimp, annelids, sea lettuce, and mud have there been found in their stomachs.   The young are born in summer.

Family SPHYRNIDÆ.   The Hammer-headed Sharks.

This family resembles the Galeidæ, but has the head peculiarly modified into a hammer shaped organ, with the eyes widely separated; teeth small, oblique, similar in the two jaws; spiracles absent; caudal with a notch toward its top and with a well developed lower lobe.   One genus, represented in warm seas in most parts of the world.   The young numerous and born alive.

Genus SPHYRNA Rafinesque.   Hammer-headed Sharks.

These sharks are readily distinguishable by their peculiarly shaped heads, which by lateral extension have become hammer-shaped or kidney-shaped, the eyes being at the ends of the lateral processes.   Teeth small, notched on outer edge, obliquely set in jaws; first dorsal and pectoral fins large, second dorsal and anal fins small.   The two species which are found on the Atlantic coast and are taken in North Carolina waters may be distinguished as follows:

i. Head kidney-shaped, the anterior and lateral margins confluent; groove from nostril to front of head obsolete.. *tiburo.*
ii. Head hammer-shaped, the anterior and posterior margins nearly parallel; nasal groove conspicuous.. *zygæna.*

(*Sphyrna,* hammer.)

9. SPHYRNA TIBURO (Linnæus).
"Bonnet-nosed Shark"; "Shovel-headed Shark";   Bonnet-headed Shark.

Squalus tiburo Linnæus, Systema Naturæ, ed. x, 234, 1758; America
Reniceps tiburo, Yarrow, 1877, 217; Beaufort.
Sphyrna tiburo, Jordan & Gilbert, 1879, 387; Beaufort. Jordan. 1886, 26; Beaufort. Jenkins, 1887, 84; Beaufort. Jordan & Evermann, 1896, 44, pl. v, fig. 19. Wilson, 1900, 355; Beaufort. Linton, 1905, 344; Beaufort.

DIAGNOSIS.—Body slender, slightly compressed; head flattened, .16 total length to end of tail, semi-circular in front, its width slightly less than length; mouth small, crescentic; first dorsal very high, second dorsal smaller, produced behind; anal larger than second dorsal; pectorals large; ventrals moderate; upper caudal lobe long.   Color: light gray above, whitish beneath.   (*tiburo,* a Spanish name for shark.)

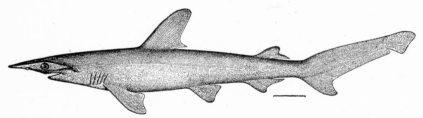

Fig. 5.   BONNET-HEADED SHARK.   *Sphyrna tiburo.*

The bonnet-headed shark is abundant on the Atlantic coast of the United States, and is common in the Beaufort region.   It is much smaller than the hammer-headed shark, rarely exceeding 5 feet.   Specimens examined at Beaufort in summer had been feeding on crabs, shrimp, and other crustaceans.   One brought to the laboratory July 25, 1902, contained 8 young.

10. SPHYRNA ZYGÆNA (Linnæus).
"Hammer-head"; "Hammer-headed Shark".

Squalus zygæna Linnæus, Systema Naturæ, ed. x, 234, 1758; Europe, America.
Sphyrna zygæna, Yarrow, 1877, 217; Beaufort. Jordan & Gilbert, 1879, 387; Beaufort. Jordan, 1887, 26;
  Beaufort. Jordan & Evermann, 1896, 45. Wilson, 1900, 355; Beaufort.

DIAGNOSIS.—Body slender, head about twice as wide as long; nostril near eye, prolonged
into a groove; first dorsal large, second dorsal small, anal small but larger than second dorsal;
pectorals large. Color: gray above, white beneath. (*zygæna*, an ancient Greek name for this
fish.)

Fig. 6 (*a* and *b*). HAMMER-HEADED SHARK. *Sphyrna zygæna*. Dorsal and
dorso-lateral views.

This singular species, at home in the warm seas, occurs as a straggler on our
Atlantic and Pacific coasts. Dr. Yarrow records a single specimen from Beaufort. Another was taken near Morehead in 1902. Professor Wilson states that
some years the young are very abundant at Beaufort in early summer. This is
a voracious species, attaining a length of over 15 feet; it often swims with its
dorsal and caudal fins exposed.

Family CARCHARIIDÆ. The Sand Sharks.

Voracious, moderate-sized sharks, belonging to a single genus. Body
elongate; snout sharp; mouth crescentic; teeth long, narrow and sharp, mostly
with 1 or 2 cusps at base; gill-slits large, all anterior to pectorals; both dorsal fins
and anal fin of similar size, first dorsal posterior to pectorals; pectorals short; no
keel on peduncle; upper caudal lobe about twice length of lower, with a well-
marked notch below; nictitating membrane absent; spiracles reduced to mere
pores.

Genus CARCHARIAS Rafinesque.   Sand Sharks.

This genus, whose characters are given above, contains several species of which only one is American.   (*Carcharias*, old name for the cub shark, or requiem, of Europe and tropical America.)

11. CARCHARIAS LITTORALIS (Mitchill).

"Sand-bar Shark"; "Sand Shark"; Shovel-nose.

Squalus littoralis Mitchill, American Monthly Magazine, ii, 328, 1818; New York.
Eugomphodus littoralis, Yarrow, 1877, 217; Beaufort.
Carcharias americanus, Jordan & Gilbert, 1879, 387; Beaufort.
Carcharias littoralis, Jordan, 1886, 26; Beaufort.   Jordan & Evermann, 1896, 46; 1898, 2748; (Beaufort).

DIAGNOSIS.—Body elongate, its depth .16 its length; head small, pointed, its length about .14 total length; all fins small, first dorsal about same size as second and anal.   Color: dark gray above, white below.   (*littoralis*, pertaining to the shore.)

This is a well known shark of the Atlantic coast, inhabiting sandy shores and feeding chiefly on fishes.   It is one of the most vicious of sharks, and is able to inflict serious injury to the careless fisherman.   The usual length is under 5 feet, but a length of 10 or 12 feet is sometimes reached.   Two specimens 9 feet long were obtained at Beaufort by Mr. H. H. Brimley in 1900; one of these, a female, skinned and mounted, is now in the State Museum at Raleigh.

This appears to be the species known at Cape Lookout as the "sand-bar shark"; a specimen caught there April 21, 1904, was between 8 and 10 feet long and was said by the fishermen to contain a "bushel of eggs".

Order CYCLOSPONDYLI.   The Cyclospondylous Sharks.

This order is thus far represented in North Carolina by a single species*, which is intermediate between the sharks and the rays.   The anal fin is absent, the dorsal fins are small, and the internal calcareous layers of each vertebra are arranged concentrically about the central ring.

Family SQUATINIDÆ.   The Angel Sharks.

Ray-like sharks, with broad, flattened body; obtuse snout; terminal mouth; large, expanded pectoral fins, separated from neck by a deep notch; large ventral fins; two small dorsal fins on the tail, behind the ventrals; no anal fin; wide lateral gill-slits, partly inferior; wide, crescentic spiracles; nostrils on anterior margin of snout.   One genus.

Genus SQUATINA Duméril.   Angel-fishes.

This genus, which is sufficiently characterized above, includes a single widely distributed species.   (*Squatina*, the ancient Latin name for this fish.)

*The spiny dog-fish (*Squalus acanthias*), which ranges along our east coast from Cuba northward and is common in Maine and Massachusetts, belongs in this order.

12. SQUATINA SQUATINA (Linnæus).

"Nurse-fish"; "Jakie"; Angel-fish; Monk-fish.

Squalus squatina Linnæus, Systema Naturæ, ed. x, 233, 1758; Europe.
Squatina squatina, Jordan & Evermann, 1896, 58.

DIAGNOSIS.—Body broad, flat, the length about 2.5 times width; snout small, sharp, separated; eyes small; skin with small prickles, most evident on middle line of back; caudal fin triangular; dorsal fins short and high.   Color: above ashy gray, with brownish blotches; beneath white.

This ray-like shark is found in all warm seas.   On our east coast it ranges from Florida to Cape Cod, but is not common.   It has not heretofore been recorded from North Carolina, although apparently to be met with regularly. On April 22, 1904, the writer observed an example 2.5 feet long at Cape Lookout, where it had been caught in a deep-water gill net the day before; the local fishermen, who call the fish "nurse-fish" and "jakie", state that they catch a number every season, some of them 4 to 5 feet long.   The species is often troublesome, getting snarled in the nets or eating other fish caught therein; it also bites the fishermen if they are not wary.   The example seen by the writer contained fragments of fish and bivalve shells.

Order BATOÏDEA.   The Skates and Rays.

These fishes inhabit salt water, and are of moderate or large size.   They are chiefly bottom-loving, and some are found at considerable depths.   Reproduction is by means of large, encapsuled eggs, few in number, which are fertilized internally and may undergo considerable development before being laid. These fishes are of little direct economic value, being rarely eaten or otherwise utilized in America, although of some importance in Europe and Asia.   All of the 7 families found in North America are represented in the state; they fall into 2 divisions, based on the character of the tail.

Key to the families of skates and rays found in North Carolina waters.

i. Tail comparatively thick, without a serrated erectile spine; 2 dorsal fins and usually a caudal fin.
   a. Snout flat, produced, with a series of long teeth on each side....PRISTIDÆ (saw-fishes).
  aa. Snout not saw-like.
    b. Electric organs present; skin smooth...............NARCOBATIDÆ (electric rays).
   bb. Electric organs absent; skin not smooth.
     c. Disc-like pectoral fins extending to snout, abruptly contracted behind; tail distinct .... RAJIDÆ (skates).
    cc. Disc-like pectoral fins not extending as far as snout, not abruptly contracted. behind but passing gradually into the tail ...... RHINOBATIDÆ (guitar-fishes)
ii. Tail comparatively slender, usually with a serrated spine on its upper surface; dorsal fin single or absent.
   d. Pectoral fins united around the snout .... DASYATIDÆ (sting rays).
  dd. Pectoral fins forming detached horn-like processes ("cephalic fins") anteriorly.
    e. Teeth few and large ....MYLIOBATIDÆ (eagle rays).
   ee. Teeth numerous, very small, wanting in upper jaw.......MANTIDÆ (devil-fishes).

Family PRISTIDÆ.   The Saw-fishes.

Huge, powerful, shark-like rays characterized by a long, broad, depressed body; a snout consisting of a long, hard, thin process, beset with numerous strong teeth along each lateral edge; minute jaw teeth; inferior gill-slits and nostrils; wide spiracles, situated behind eyes; large dorsal fins, pectoral fins with front margin free and not extending to head; and well developed caudal.   One genus, viviparous.

Genus PRISTIS Latham.   Saw-fishes.

This genus, the characters of which are indicated above, contains two American species, one of which occurs on our South Atlantic and Gulf coasts.   Species usually marine, but sometimes entering fresh water; found chiefly in shallow sounds and rivers with sandy bottom.   (*Pristis*, one who saws.)

13. PRISTIS PECTINATUS Latham.
"Saw-fish"

Pristis pectinatus Latham, Transactions Linnæan Society, ii, 278, 1794; ocean.   Jenkins, 1885, 11; Beaufort. Jordan, 1886, 26; Beaufort. Jenkins, 1887, 84; Beaufort. Jordan & Evermann, 1896, 60, pl. viii, fig. 27; 1898, 2749 (Beaufort). Wilson, 1900, 355; Beaufort.
Pristis antiquorum, Yarrow, 1877, 217; Bogue Sound, Core Sound, and New River.

DIAGNOSIS.—"Saw" with 24 to 32 teeth on each side; first dorsal fin opposite ventrals; second dorsal about as large as first; caudal fin without lower lobe.   Color: dark brown above, pale yellow below.   (*pectinatus*, comb-toothed.)

Fig. 7.   SAW-FISH.   *Pristis pectinatus.*

This curious fish inhabits the Caribbean Sea, Gulf of Mexico, and east coast of the United States as far north as Chesapeake Bay.   Its maximum length is about 20 feet, the saw representing rather less than .33 the total length.   The flesh is coarse and rarely eaten; the skin may be made into a kind of leather.   The species is very destructive to fishermen's nets.   The young are born in summer, and number at least 20; they are able to swim at birth, although the saw and teeth are at first soft like leather.

This fish is not rare in the sounds and brackish rivers of North Carolina, and large specimens (16 or more feet long) have been taken there.   In the Beaufort region and at Cape Lookout the species is observed almost every year, and some seasons is common.   The fishermen avoid it and endeavor to keep it out of their nets.   A "saw" in the Beaufort laboratory bears 28 pairs of teeth and is 3 feet 1 inch long from tip to the posterior pair of teeth.

Lawson (1709), when he mentioned the "sword-fish" among the fishes of North Carolina, probably had the saw-fish in mind.   Brickell (1737), who usually copied from Lawson without credit or discrimination, listed the "sword-fish or saw-fish", gave a figure of the sword-fish (Xiphias), and noted that the fish attacked whales, a habit ascribed to the sword-fish but a hardly conceivable one of the saw-fish.   Yarrow (1877) reported the saw-fish as hostile to porpoises in North Carolina, an observation which needs verification.

Family RHINOBATIDÆ.   The Shark-like Rays.

Rays resembling sharks, with body long, flat, moderately broad, and gradually merging into the long tail; skin nearly smooth, with no conspicuous spines; 2 well developed dorsal fins without spine; rayed part of pectoral fins not connected with snout; caudal fin with a prominent fold of skin on each side. Viviparous fishes of the warm seas, about 5 genera represented on the Atlantic coast.

Genus RHINOBATUS Bloch & Schneider.   Guitar-fishes.

Body depressed, broad anteriorly, tapering posteriorly into tail; snout long, formed by an extension of cartilage, space between snout and pectoral fins covered with membrane; 2 dorsal fins, both posterior to ventral fins; caudal fin with no lower lobe; spiracles wide; nostrils wide, oblique; skin covered with rough scales, with a few spines on various parts of upper surface. Seven or eight American species, one occurring on South Atlantic coast. (*Rhinobatus*, shark-skate.)

14. RHINOBATUS LENTIGINOSUS Garman.
"Ray"; "Clear-nose"; Guitar-fish.

Rhinobatus lentiginosus Garman, Bulletin Museum Comparative Zoölogy, vi, 168, 1880; Florida. Jordan & Evermann, 1896, 62, pl. viii, fig. 28; pl. ix, figs. 28a and 28b.

DIAGNOSIS.—Disk sub-triangular, its width .33 total length; tail .5 length; snout slender; pointed; mouth straight, its width somewhat less than interorbital space; teeth small, obtuse; eyes twice as large as spiracles; spines on back and anterior to eyes small; spines on shoulders and between eyes obsolete; 5 larger spines on tip of snout. Color: above brown, with numerous small, round, light spots; below pale. (*lentiginosus*, freckled.)

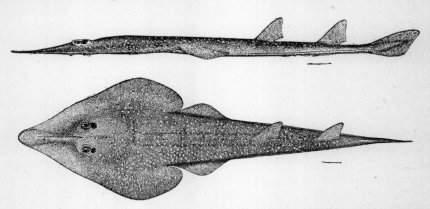

Fig. 8 (*a* and *b*).   GUITAR-FISH. *Rhinobatus lentiginosus*. Lateral and dorsal views.

This species, heretofore known only from Charleston southward, occurs on the North Carolina coast at Beaufort and doubtless elsewhere. A 2-foot specimen was taken in a drag-net near Middle Marsh, in Beaufort harbor, July 6, 1899; this is the only example recorded at the laboratory, but it appears from informa-ation furnished by the local fishermen that it is not rare in that region. Dr. Coker states that the name "ray" as used by the Beaufort fishermen is restricted to this species, which is also known as "clear-nose". The usual length is 2 feet.

Family RAJIDÆ. The Skates.

A numerous family of typical rays, having a broad, rhomboidal body; stout tail distinct from the trunk; 2 dorsal fins on tail; pectoral fins extending to but not around snout; no spine on tail; teeth small and paved. One American genus.

Genus RAJA Linnæus. Skates.

In this genus the caudal fin is absent or very small, the ventrals are deeply divided, the teeth are in numerous series in each jaw and differ somewhat in the two sexes, and the male usually has a special patch of spines on each pectoral flap.

Most of the skates inhabit shoal water, living on the bottom and feeding on bottom animals (fish, crabs, mollusks, etc.). All the species are oviparous, the eggs being in large oblong leathery cases which are attached to stones or marine plants by a long horn at each of the four corners; the dried egg-cases are often found washed up on the seashores. Valuable for food, and caught incidentally in large numbers in seines and traps, and also taken with lines, but only sparingly consumed in the United States; the large fleshy pectoral fins are the parts which are eaten. Most common northward, only sparingly represented on the South Atlantic coast. Only one species has heretofore been recorded from North Carolina, but the brier ray (*Raja eglanteria*) has recently been collected by the writer at Cape Lookout. These two species may be distinguished as follows:

a. Teeth in 30 rows; spines few and small, mostly on snout, on anterior border of pectoral fins, about eyes, and on median line of back and tail; color, brown with pale spots.
   lævis.
aa. Teeth in 50 rows; spines numerous, small, and sharp, on all parts of upper surface; color, light brown, with dark markings ....*eglanteria.*

(*Raja*, ray or skate.)

15. RAJA LÆVIS Mitchill.
Barndoor Skate; Winter Skate; Smooth Skate.

Raja lævis Mitchill, American Monthly Magazine, ii, 327, 1817; New York. Yarrow, 1877, 217; Beaufort. Jordan & Evermann, 1896, 71. Linton, 1905, 346; Beaufort.

DIAGNOSIS.—Disc very wide, 1.5 times length of body to base of tail; tail less than width of disc, 1.15 times length of body; snout long, sharp, its sides concave, its tip rough; lateral angles of disc acute; spines comparatively few and small, a median row on tail and back, a patch on each wing, another about eye and spiracle, and a zone on anterior border of pectorals; teeth in about 30 rows. Color: brownish, with pale spots; white below. (*lævis*, smooth.)

This, the largest of the Atlantic skates, is found from Maine to Florida, and is not uncommon in North Carolina. It reaches a length of 4 feet. Small specimens were collected by the steamer Fish-Hawk off Cape Lookout on August 14, 1902, at station 7310, in 18 fathoms; they had shrimp and bivalve mollusks in their stomachs.

16. RAJA EGLANTERIA Bosc.

"Clear-nose"; Brier Ray.

Raja eglanteria Bosc, in Lacépède, Histoire Naturelle des Poissons, ii, 103, 1800; Charleston, S. C.
Raja eglanteria, Jordan & Evermann, 1896, 71.

DIAGNOSIS.—Snout long, acute, translucent; lateral angles of disc acute; body covered with sharp prickles, with larger spines about eyes, on snout, and on back and tail; teeth in 50 rows. Color: light brown, with numerous dark brown elongated spots. (eglanteria, from eglantere, the brier rose.)

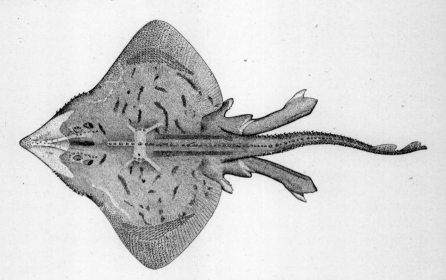

Fig. 9.   BRIER RAY.   *Raja eglanteria.*   Male.

This skate, which reaches a length of about 2 feet, ranges along the Atlantic coast between Massachusetts and Florida. It has not previously been recorded from North Carolina, although it doubtless occurs along the entire coast of that state. At Cape Lookout, on April 22, 1904, the author observed numerous specimens on the beach, and was informed that many are caught in the deep-water gill nets set in that region. In allusion to their pointed, translucent snout, they are called "clear-noses" by the local fishermen. No use is made of them.

Family NARCOBATIDÆ.   The Electric Rays.

Moderate or large-sized rays, inhabiting chiefly warm waters, having a peculiar electric organ capable of giving a powerful shock to man or other animals. Body broad and thick, skin smooth, tail short and thick with a fold on each side, caudal fin with rays, 2-rayed dorsal fins, nasal valves confluent into a quadrangular lobe. Of the 7 genera, 2 are represented on the Atlantic coast of the United States, only one, however, north of Florida.

Genus TETRONARCE Gill. Torpedoes.

Large fishes with pectoral fins rounded, so that outline anterior to ventrals is almost circular; tail thick, abruptly tapering from pectorals to caudal; spiracles large, immediately behind eyes, their edges entire; mouth small, teeth pointed; caudal fin large; ventrals large, separated from pectorals by a deep notch. Two American species, one Californian and the following. (*Tetronarce*, four-cornered torpedo).

17. TETRONARCE OCCIDENTALIS (Storer.)
"Shock-fish"; Torpedo; Cramp-fish; Electric Ray.

Torpedo occidentalis Storer, American Journal of Science and Arts, 1843, 165; Massachusetts. Yarrow,1877 216; Beaufort. Jenkins, 1887, 84; Beaufort.
Tetronarce occidentalis, Jordan & Evermann, 1896, 77, pl. xi, fig. 33.

DIAGNOSIS.—Breadth of disk .75 length of body and equal to distance from front of disk to origin of first dorsal fin; space between eyes and anterior margin of disk about 3 times diameter of eye; first dorsal about twice size of second, its origin a little in advance of posterior edge of ventrals; caudal fin triangular, slightly emarginate posteriorly. Color: dark purplish brown above, with darker spots; white below. (*occidentalis*, western.)

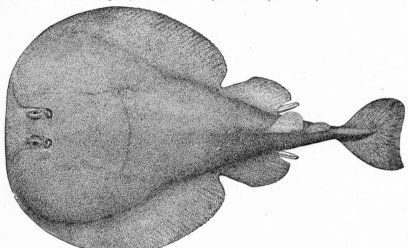

Fig. 10. TORPEDO. *Tetronarce occidentalis*.

The torpedo inhabits coastal waters from Cuba northward, and is common in some localities, such as southern Massachusetts. It attains a weight of 100 pounds, but specimens weighing more than 75 pounds are rare, and the average is probably under 30 pounds. The fish is able to emit a very strong electric discharge, from a large organ situated on either side just back of the head; the shock from a large fish can knock a man down.

No collector seems to have actually observed this species in North Carolina waters. Yarrow (1877) reported it at Beaufort, where "the fishermen state they are rarely seen." Jenkins (1887) says: "A fisherman described to me the catching and experimenting with a torpedo". The inquiries of Dr. Coker failed to elicit any positive information as to the occurrence of this fish at Beaufort in recent years.   At Cape Lookout, however, where this species is known as "shock-fish", it is at times not uncommon and has often been taken in nets.

Family DASYATIDÆ.   The Sting-rays.

Rays, usually of large size, characterized by the union of pectoral fins around the snout; body very depressed, skull flat (not elevated as in Myliobatidae, etc.); tail either very long and slender or short and stout, with or without a barbed spine; spiracles large, near eyes.   Viviparous or ovoviviparous.   Numerous genera and species; the two following genera represented on Atlantic coast.

i. Tail long and slender; caudal spine strong; body roundish....................DASYATIS.
ii. Tail short; caudal spine weak or absent; body much broader than long ...PTEROPLATEA.

Genus DASYATIS Rafinesque.   Sting-rays.

Body rounded, very flat; snout more or less prominent; whip-like tail with a strong, barbed spine near its base, without fins but with one or two vertical folds; skin usually spiny; teeth small, paved.   Species of large size, and said to be ovoviviparous.   Used for food in Gulf States.   Four or five species on Atlantic coast; 2 are known to occur in North Carolina, and another (*Dasyatis hastata*) may be looked for.

i. Tail with a small keel only on under side; back and tail with stout spines in adult.. *centrura*.
ii. Tail with a keel on both upper and under surface; skin nearly smooth, medium line of
      back with only 1 spine...*say*.

(*Dasyatis*, rough skate.)

19. DASYATIS CENTRURA (Mitchill).
Sting-ray; Stingaree; Clam-cracker.

Raja centrura Mitchill, Transactions Literary Society of New York, i, 479, 1815; New York.
Dasyatis centrura, Jordan & Evermann, 1896, 83.

DIAGNOSIS.—Body quadrangular, .25 wider than long; snout slightly projecting; tail more than twice the length of body, spiny, a keel below, one or more barbed spines near base; skin smooth in young, tuberculate on head, back and tail in adults; teeth blunt, smooth, in groups of 5.   Color: dark brown above, white below.   (*centrura*, spine-tailed.)

A large northern species, ranging southward to Cape Hatteras.   Maximum, length, including tail, 12 feet.   Feeds exclusively on invertebrates (crabs, clams, squids, etc).   The species called *Trygon centrura* by Yarrow in his Beaufort list is doubtless *Dasyatis say*.

18. DASYATIS SAY (LeSueur).
"Sting-ray"; "Stingaree"; Whip-ray.

Raja say LeSueur, Journal Academy of Natural Sciences of Philadelphia, i, 421, 1817; New Jersey.
Trygon centrura, Yarrow, 1877, 216; Beaufort.
Dasybatis centrurus, Jordan and Gilbert, 1879, 386; Beaufort.
Trygon sayi, Jenkins, 1887, 84; Beaufort.   Wilson, 1900, 355; Beaufort.
Dasybatis sayi, Jordan, 1886, 26; Beaufort
Dasyatis say, Jordan & Evermann, 1896, 86.   Linton, 1905, 346; Beaufort.

DIAGNOSIS.—Body quadrangular, .16 wider than long, outer and posterior angles rounded; snout not prominent; ventrals rounded; tail .5 longer than body, with a keel above and below, and a barbed spine in front of upper keel; teeth smooth in young and in female, sharp in male: 3 papillæ at bottom of mouth and 1 on either side; skin on body and tail smooth.   Color; dark brown above, white below.   (Named after Thomas Say.)

This species is common from North Carolina southward, occasionally straying to New York. It feeds largely on shellfish. The tail is used as a whip, and
the barbed spine is sometimes driven into the hands or feet of fishermen, inflicting a very painful and troublesome wound, from septic infection. A leather
shoe or rubber boot is readily pierced by the spine. At Beaufort this ray is
abundant in summer. Dr. Yarrow noted there a southward migration in the
latter part of October. Dr. Kendall observed many caught in beach seines at
Cape Lookout in 1891.

Genus PTEROPLATEA Müller & Henle. Butterfly Rays.

Body wider than long, flat, the anterior angle obtuse, the lateral angles acute;
tail slender, shorter than body, with or without a small barbed spine and without
any fin. Fish of rather large size, viviparous. One species on the Atlantic
coast, two on the Pacific. (*Pteroplatea*, broad-finned.)

20. PTEROPLATEA MACLURA (LeSueur).
"Skate"; Butterfly Ray; Sand Skate.

Raja maclura LeSueur, Journal Academy of Natural Sciences of Philadelphia, i, 14, 1817; Rhode Island.
Pteroplatea maclura, Yarrow, 1877, 216; Beaufort. Jordan & Gilbert, 1879, 386; Beaufort. Jordan, 1886, 26;
Beaufort. Jenkins, 1887, 84; Beaufort. Jordan & Evermann, 1896, 86. Wilson, 1900, 355; Beaufort.
Linton, 1905, 348; Beaufort.

DIAGNOSIS.—Body about twice as wide as long; anterior edge of pectorals slightly concave; snout slightly projecting; tail only .33 length of body, spine usually (always?) lacking;
skin smooth. Color: above olive brown, marbled and speckled, a row of light spots on front
of body, tail with 4 dark blotches. (Named after William Maclure, founder of the Philadelphia Academy of Sciences.)

This common fish of the North Carolina coast ranges from New York to
South America. It is numerous at Beaufort. The great width of its wing-like
pectoral fins has given it the name "butterfly ray". The body reaches a length
of 4 feet.

The species is viviparous, and the normal number of young produced
appears to be two. On July 29, 1902, a specimen 14.5 inches long and 26.5 inches
wide was delivered of two young at the Beaufort laboratory, and on August 11,
1903, another specimen gave birth to two young; the young in both cases were 6
inches wide.

Numerous specimens examined at Beaufort by Professor Linton in July and
August contained fish, shrimp, or razor clams.

Family MYLIOBATIDÆ. The Eagle Rays.

Large, viviparous sting-rays easily recognizable by the very broad body,
long, whip-like tail, and pectoral fins which extend forward only to sides of head
and reappear in a greatly modified form on the snout. The ventral fins are
short and rounded. The teeth are large, paired, and adapted for crushing. The
tail bears a single dorsal fin at its base and a large serrated spine capable of

inflicting a serious wound. The skin is smooth. Three American genera, all represented on the North Carolina coast.

Key to genera of eagle rays.

i. Snout produced, rounded; teeth broad, in single series.....................AËTOBATUS.
ii. Snout short; teeth in several series.
    a. Snout entire...MYLIOBATIS.
    aa. Snout concave..RHINOPTERA.

Genus AËTOBATUS Blainville. Eagle Rays.

Body very wide, the wings pointed; cephalic fin forming a rounded projection on the snout; teeth plate-like, in a single row; eyes on side of head. One Atlantic coast species. (*Aëtobatus*, eagle ray.)

21. AËTOBATUS NARINARI (Euphrasen).
"Devil-fish"; "Sting-ray"; "Lady-ray"; Spotted Sting-ray.

Raia narinari Euphrasen, Svenska Vetenskaps Akademien, nya handlingar, xi, 217, 1790; Brazil.
Aëtobatus narinari, Yarrow, 1877, 216; Beaufort. Jordan & Gilbert, 1879, 386; Beaufort. Jordan & Ever-
    mann, 1896, 88, pls. xv, xvi, figs. 37, 37*a*.
Stoasodon narinari, Jordan, 1886, 26; Beaufort.

DIAGNOSIS.—Disk twice as wide as long; outer angle of wings acute; posterior angle rounded; cephalic fin .33 broader than long; ventrals rounded; tail 2.5 to 4 times as long as body, with a large barbed spine at its base. Color: above brown, with numerous small, round, pale spots and transverse parallel dark lines; below white. (*narinari*, a Brazilian name.)

The range of this tropical species extends northward on the Atlantic coast to Virginia. Under the names "sting-ray" and "lady-ray" it is recorded by Dr. Yarrow from Beaufort as very common and reaching a large size. A specimen caught by fishermen in a seine on Shark Shoal, Beaufort harbor, in September, 1901, was 4 feet wide and 2 feet 2 inches long, the length of the tail being 4 feet 8 inches.

Genus MYLIOBATIS Duméril. Eagle Rays.

Body as in *Aëtobatus*; cephalic fin a convex fleshy appendage in front of snout; a median row of very broad teeth, flanked by several rows of smaller, narrow teeth; dorsal fin small; one or two serrated caudal spines. One species on Atlantic coast. (*Myliobatis*, grinder ray.)

22. MYLIOBATIS FREMINVILLEI LeSueur.
Eagle Ray.

Myliobatis freminvillei LeSueur, Journal Academy Natural Sciences Philadelphia, iv, 111, 1824; Rhode Island.
    Jordan & Gilbert, 1879, 386; Beaufort. Jordan, 1886, 26; Beaufort. Jordan & Evermann, 1896, 89.

DIAGNOSIS.—Body much broader than long, its width equal to tail; central row of teeth 4 to 6 times broader than long; 3 rows of teeth on each side of main row; a whitish swelling over each eye; skin smooth. Color: above reddish brown; tail black; below white. (Named for the French naturalist, Fréminville.)

The range of this species is from Massachusetts to Brazil. It is recorded from Beaufort, but is apparently not common in North Carolina. It does not attain a very large size.

Genus RHINOPTERA Kuhl. Cow-nosed Rays.

Body broader than long, but not so broad as in other genera; cephalic fin emarginate and below level of pectorals, the snout thus appearing four-lobed; teeth in 5 to 20 rows; dorsal fin small, immediately in front of a long serrated spine. Viviparous. One species on Atlantic coast. (*Rhinoptera*, snout-finned.)

23. RHINOPTERA BONASUS (Mitchill).
"Devil-fish"; Cow-nosed Ray; Corn-cracker; Whip-ray; Whipparee.

Raja bonasus Mitchill, Transactions Literary and Philosophical Society of New York, 1815, 479: New York.
Rhinoptera bonasus, Jordan & Evermann, 1896, 90.
Rhinoptera quadriloba, Wilson, 1900, 355; Beaufort.

DIAGNOSIS.—Body about .33 broader than long; anterior border of pectorals straight, the outer angles acute; tail very slender, rather longer than body; teeth in 7 rows in each jaw, the median teeth very broad; skin smooth. Color: brown above, pale below. (*bonasus*, buffalo.)

This is a common species from Massachusetts to Florida. In North Carolina it is found at all times of the year, but is usually most abundant in spring; in September, 1903, however, it was very numerous in Beaufort Harbor. The species reaches a large size, some examples observed in Florida being 7 feet wide. It feeds largely on mollusks, which it crushes with its powerful paired jaws; the razor-clam and the oyster are favorite foods. The young, numbering two or three, are born in spring or summer, and are very active from birth. The stout barbed spine is usually covered with mucous, and the wounds which it inflicts are painful and often dangerous.

Family MANTIDÆ. The Sea-devils.

Immense ovoviviparous rays of the tropical seas, with broad body; lateral eyes; wide mouth, numerous teeth; widely separated nostrils whose valves form a wide flap; pectoral fins developed anteriorly as horn-like appendages; long, whip-like tail, with a dorsal fin at base and with or without a spine; skin rough. Two genera, of which the following is represented on the United States coast.

Genus MANTA Bancroft. Sea-devils.

Body broader than long; anterior margin of pectorals convex, posterior concave, the outer angles sharp; cephalic fins long, curved inward; mouth terminal, teeth very small and numerous, in lower jaw only; skin rough, having small tubercles. Two species, one American. (*Manta*, blanket.)

24. MANTA BIROSTRIS (Walbaum.)
"Devil-fish"; Sea-devil.

Raia birostris Walbaum, Genera Piscium, 535, 1792.
Ceratoptera vampirus, Yarrow, 1877, 216; Beaufort. Jordan & Gilbert, 1879, 386; Beaufort.
Manta birostris, Jordan, 1886, 26; Beaufort. Jenkins, 1887, 85; Cape Lookout. Jordan & Evermann, 1896, 92, pl. xviii, fig. 39. Wilson, 1900, 355; Cape Lookout. Gill, 1903; North Carolina.

DIAGNOSIS.—Body twice as broad as long; head square in front; teeth in about 100 series; tail very slender, about length of body, a barbed spine near its base; body and tail covered with small tubercles; the horn-line processes capable of being folded across mouth. Color: dark brown above, white below. (*birostris*, two-beaked.)

This huge ray, which inhabits the tropical waters of America, strays northward to New Jersey and has been observed a number of times on the North Carolina coast. It is the largest of the rays, and one of the largest of water animals, reported to attain a width of more than 25 feet and a weight of over 10,000 pounds. It is said to feed on shellfish, and in the Gulf of Mexico is reputed to do considerable damage to oyster beds, but the character of its teeth would seem to preclude any such feeding habits, and the fish has undoubtedly been confounded with other large rays.

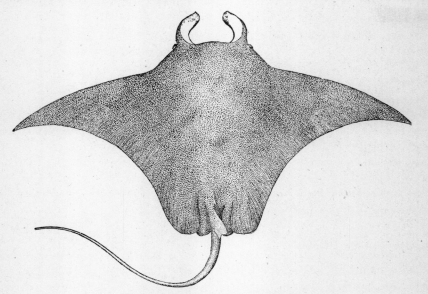

Fig. 11. SEA-DEVIL. *Manta birostris.*

This fish is reported by the fishermen of Cape Lookout as occasionally seen and is called by them the "devil-fish", a name which in North Carolina is shared by most of the large rays. Judging, however, from the size of some of the examples observed, there can be no doubt that the *Manta* sometimes occurs. Lawson (1709) has this to say of the giant ray in North Carolina:

The divel-fish lies at some of our inlets, and, as near as I can describe him, is shaped like a scate, or stingray; only he has on his head a pair of very thick strong horns; and is of a monstrous size; for this fish has been known to weigh a sloop's anchor, and run with the vessel a league or two, and bring her back, against tide, to almost the same place.

The horn-like appendages which give this creature its name of sea-devil or devil-fish are freely movable and serve the purpose of carrying food to the mouth. Mr. Hector von Bayer, of the U. S. Bureau of Fisheries, who has observed the animal in the Gulf of California, states that each of these appendages may be curved on itself like an elephant's trunk, and can firmly grasp objects within reach.

Sub-class TELEOSTOMI. The True Fishes.

The true fishes herein considered fall into 2 groups or series, the ganoids (p. 54) and the bony fishes, or teleosts (p. 61), the leading features of which are noted under the respective captions. The numerous families represented in the local fauna and differentiated in the following key may be divided into 4 groups based on the character of the ventral and dorsal fins, as follows: I. Ventral fins attached to abdomen, 1 dorsal fin; II. Ventral fins attached to abdomen far posterior to pectoral fins, 2 dorsal fins, the anterior composed of spiny rays; III. Ventral fins attached to thorax or throat, under, anterior to, or slightly behind pectorals; IV. Ventral fins absent.

I. Ventral fins attached to abdomen; 1 dorsal fin.
  a. An adipose fin behind the dorsal fin.
    b. Barbels (4 to 8 in number) on upper and lower jaws; a stout spine in dorsal and pectoral fins; body not scaled.....................................SILURIDÆ (cat-fishes).
    bb. Barbels wanting; no spine in dorsal or pectoral fins; body scaled.
      c. Margin of upper jaw formed by maxillary bone, which has a supplemental bone; air-bladder large; pyloric cœca numerous; species chiefly fresh water.
        SALMONIDÆ (trouts and salmons).
      cc. Margin of upper jaw formed by a long and slender premaxillary; air-bladder small or absent; pyloric cœca few; species marine......SYNODONTIDÆ (lizard-fishes).
  aa. No adipose fin behind the dorsal fin.
    d. Tail heterocercal. (Ganoid fishes.)
      e. Body without true scales; mouth inferior.
        f. Skin naked; barbels absent; snout paddle-shaped.
          POLYODONTIDÆ (paddle-fishes).
        ff. Skin with 5 rows of bony shields; 4 barbels present; snout elongate.
          ACIPENSERIDÆ (sturgeons).
      ee. Body scaled; mouth terminal.
        g. Scales cycloid; snout short; dorsal fin very long.
          AMIATIDÆ (fresh-water dog-fishes).
        gg. Scales ganoid; snout greatly elongated; dorsal fin very short.
          LEPISOSTEIDÆ (fresh-water gars)
    dd. Tail homocercal. (Non-ganoid fishes.)
      h. Pectoral fins inserted relatively high on sides, on or near the axis of body; lateral line low, on side of belly; lower pharyngeal bones united; form very elongate.
        i. One or both jaws produced into a long slender beak; pectoral fins small.
          j. Both jaws greatly produced; jaw teeth both long and short.
            TYLOSURIDÆ (marine gars).
          jj. Only lower jaw greatly produced; jaw teeth small.
            HEMIRHAMPHIDÆ (half-beaks).
        ii. Neither jaw produced into a long, slender beak; pectoral fins very large, used as organs of flight ....EXOCŒTIDÆ (flying-fishes).
      hh. Pectoral fins inserted relatively low on sides, below axis of body; lower pharyngeal bones separate.
        k. Gill-membranes united to isthmus; head scaleless; jaws without teeth; dorsal fin inserted near middle of back.
          l. Gill-membranes more or less completely united to isthmus; vent close behind gill-openings; small fishes, mostly without external eyes (the local representative of family with small eyes and no ventral fins).
            AMBLYOPSIDÆ (blind- or cave-fishes).
          ll. Gill-membranes broadly united to isthmus; vent posterior; eyes normal.
            m. Margin of upper jaw formed by premaxillary in middle and maxillary on side; pharyngeal teeth numerous and in a single row.
              CATOSTOMIDÆ (suckers).
            mm. Margin of upper jaw formed exclusively by premaxillaries; pharyngeal teeth few (less than 8) and in 1 to 3 rows..............CYPRINIDÆ (minnows).
        kk. Gill-membranes not united to isthmus.
          n. Head scaly; jaws with teeth; upper jaw protractile or not; color not silvery.

o. Upper jaw not protractile, its margin formed by maxillary; dorsal fin always inserted near caudal.

 p. Jaws prolonged and depressed; teeth cardiform; lateral line present; size large. . . . . Esocidæ (pikes).

 pp. Jaws not prolonged nor depressed; teeth villiform; lateral line absent; size very small. . . . . Umbridæ (mud-fishes).

oo. Upper jaw protractile, its margin formed by premaxillary; lateral line absent; dorsal fin inserted at or near middle of back; size small.
                  Pœciliidæ (killi-fishes).

nn. Head naked; jaws with or without teeth; upper jaw not protractile; color bright silvery.

 q. An external bony plate between branches of lower jaw; mouth large, with bands of small teeth on jaw, vomer, palatines, and tongue; lateral line present. Elopidæ (big-eyed herrings).

 qq No external bony plate on lower jaw; mouth large or small, with teeth present or absent; lateral line present or absent.

  r. Lateral line and teeth present.

   s. Mouth small, inferior; bands of villiform teeth on jaws, vomer, and palatines, and patches of paved teeth on back of tongue and roof of mouth; snout very long. . . . . Albulidæ (lady-fishes)

   ss. Mouth moderate, terminal; pointed teeth on jaws, vomer, palatines, tongue, and roof of mouth, no paved teeth; snout very short. Hiodontidæ (moon-eyes)

  rr. Lateral line and teeth absent.

   t. Mouth small, inferior; snout short, blunt; stomach gizzard-like. Dorosomidæ (mud-shads).

   tt. Mouth small, terminal, snout pointed; stomach not gizzard-like. Clupeidæ (shads and herrings).

   ttt. Mouth very large, inferior; maxillary very long; snout overhanging, pig-like. . . . . Engraulidæ (anchovies).

aaa. Dorsal fin followed by a series of detached finlets; anal similar; jaws elongated to form a slender beak. . . . . Scombresocidæ (sauries).

II. Ventral fins attached to abdomen, far posterior to pectoral fins; 2 dorsal fins, the anterior composed only of spiny rays.

 a. Head long, mouth large, teeth strong and of unequal length; body elongate; lateral lines present . . . . Sphyrænidæ (barracudas).

 aa. Head short, mouth small, teeth weak or absent, lateral line absent or rudimentary.

  b. Anal spines 3; body stout; size large. Mugilidæ (mullets).

  bb. Anal spine single; body slender; size small. . . . . Atherinidæ (silversides).

III. Ventral fins attached at thorax or throat, under, anterior to, or slightly behind pectorals.

 a. Ventral rays always 1,5.

  b. Gill-openings anterior to pectoral fins.

   c. Body scaly or with bony plates.

    d. Ventral fins united; gill-membranes joined to isthmus; lateral line absent. Gobiidæ, in part (gobies).

   dd. Ventral fins separate.

    e. A bony stay extending from below eye across cheek toward preopercle.

     f. Body scaly; head with rough, spinous bones externally; 3 lower pectoral rays separated from remainder of fin and having form of slenderfingers. Triglidæ (sea-robins).

     ff. Body scaly; head without rough spinous bones externally; pectoral fins without lower rays separated.

      g. Dorsal spines 4; eyes small, directed upward. Uranoscopidæ (star-gazers).

      gg. Dorsal spines 8 to 17; eyes large or moderate, directed laterally. Scorpænidæ (scorpion-fishes).

    ee. No bony stay extending from below eye across cheek toward preopercle.

     h. Anterior dorsal fin represented by a large sucking disk extending on top of head. . . . . Echeneididæ (remoras).

    hh. Anterior dorsal fin normal (not converted into a sucking apparatus).

     i. Dorsal and anal fins followed by detached finlets. . . . Scombridæ (mackerels).

     ii. Dorsal and anal fins not followed by detached finlets.

      j. Form elongate, spindle shaped; dorsal spines not connected by membrane. . . . . Rachycentridæ (cabios).

      jj. Form not elongate and spindle-shaped.

k. Esophagus with dilated sacs containing hooked teeth; dorsal fins divided, the spines 7 to 11.....STROMATEIDÆ, in part (butter-fishes).

kk. Esophagus without dilated sacs containing hooked teeth.

  l. Form oblong or ovate, compressed; caudal peduncle very slender; anal fin preceded by 2 free spines; posterior part of lateral line with or without a series of keeled plates; gill-membranes free from isthmus; preopercle not serrate.

                           CARANGIDÆ (crevalles, pompanoes, etc.).

  ll. Form compressed, anal fin preceded by 2 obsolete spines; lateral line without keeled plates; gill-membranes not attached to isthmus; preopercle serrate....................POMATOMIDÆ (blue-fishes).

  lll. Form very deep and compressed; caudal peduncle wide: anal spines connected with remainder of fin; no series of keeled plates on lateral line; gill-membranes broadly joined to isthmus; preopercle not serrate.

                           EPHIPPIDÆ (spade-fishes).

  llll. Form compressed, shape various; no free anal spines; no series of keeled plates on lateral line.

    m. A concealed, erectile, lancet-like spine on each of caudal peduncle; gill-membranes united to isthmus; preopercle not serrate; body ovate..........................HEPATIDÆ (surgeon-fishes).

    mm. No spine on side of caudal peduncle.

      n. Chin with 2 long barbels; 2 dorsal fins well separated.

                      MULLIDÆ (goat-fishes).

      nn. Chin without barbels.

        o. Lateral line extending to posterior margin of caudal fin.

          p. Anal spines 3; dorsal fins continuous.

                    HÆMULIDÆ (grunts).

          pp. Anal spines 1 or 2; dorsal fins distinct.

                    SCIÆNIDÆ (drums).

        oo. Lateral line extending only to base of caudal fin.

          q. Gill-arches 3.5, a small cleft or no cleft behind last

            r. Teeth on each side of each jaw united, forming a kind of beak.....................SCARIDÆ (parrot-fishes).

            rr. Teeth more or less distinct and separated.

                  LABRIDÆ (lipped-fishes).

         qq. Gill-arches 4, a long cleft behind last.

           s. Teeth setiform: body very deep, nearly as deep as long; soft fins scaly; lateral line present; gill-membranes united to isthmus; dorsal fins continuous.

                  CHÆTODONTIDÆ (butterfly-fishes).

           ss. Teeth not setiform; body much longer than deep; dorsal fins either continuous or separate.

             t. Gill-membranes broadly united to isthmus; lateral line absent...................GOBIIDÆ, in part (gobies).

             tt. Gill-membranes free from isthmus; lateral line present.

               u. Premaxillaries excessively protractile, with long basal processes............GERRIDÆ (moharras).

               uu. Premaxillary not protractile or only moderately so.

                 v. Pseudobranchiæ absent or undeveloped.

                  w. Dorsal fin composed of soft rays only, beginning on head; caudal fin very deeply forked; large pelagic fishes.......CORYPHÆNIDÆ (dolphins).

                  ww. Dorsal fin with strong spinous rays anteriorly, not beginning on head; caudal fin not very deeply if at all forked; fresh-water fishes.

                    x. Anal spines 3 to 10; dorsal spines 4 to 13.

                    CENTRARCHIDÆ. (fresh-water basses).

                   xx. Anal spines 1 or 2; dorsal spines 6 to 15.

                    PERCIDÆ (perches).

                vv. Pseudobranchiæ developed.

                  y. Maxillary not sheathed by the preorbital, or only partly covered by the latter; no accessory scale in axil of pectoral; accessory ventral scale small or wanting; a spine on posterior margin of opercle.

z. Anal spines 2; dorsal fins separated, vomer toothed..CHEILODIPTERIDÆ (cardinal-fishes).
zz. Anal spines 3; dorsal fins continuous or divided.
  a′. Vomer toothed.
    b′. Body and head much compressed, and covered with small, very rough scales; eye very large. PRIACANTHIDÆ (big-eyes).
    bb′. Body and head not greatly compressed, and not covered with rough scales; eye moderate......SERRANIDÆ (sea basses).
  aa′. Vomer toothless; dorsal fins continuous; body compressed, back elevated.
    LOBOTIDÆ (thrashers).
yy. Maxillary sheathed by the preorbital and slipping under it for most of its length; an accessory scale in axil of ventral; no spine on posterior margin of opercle.
  c′. Vomer and palatines toothed; preopercle finely or obsoletely serrate.
    d′. Jaw teeth never incisors or molars, all acute. LUTIANIDÆ (snappers).
    dd′. Jaw teeth mostly incisors, no molars or canines.......KYPHOSIDÆ (rudder-fishes).
  cc′. Vomer and palatines toothless; preopercle entire; jaw teeth incisors or conical in front, molars on sides.
    SPARIDÆ (scup, breams, etc.).
cc. Body scaleless, the skin smooth, prickly, tuberculate, or with scattered bony plates.
  e′. A sucking-disk on breast.
    f′. Sucking-disk between ventral fins; no spinous dorsal fin; gill-membranes not united to isthmus.............................GOBIESOCIDÆ (cling-fishes).
    ff′. Sucking-disk formed from ventral fins; dorsal spines present; gill-membranes united to isthmus...............................LIPARIDIDÆ (sea-snails).
  ee′. No sucking-disk on breast.
    g′. Gill-membranes broadly united to isthmus; ventral fins united.
    GOBIIDÆ, in part (gobies).
    gg′. Gill-membranes nearly or entirely separate from isthmus; ventral fins not united...COTTIDÆ (sculpins).
bb. Gill-openings behind, above, or below pectoral fins.
  h′. Mouth small; gill-openings in or behind upper axil of pectorals.
    OGCOCEPHALIDÆ (bat-fishes).
  hh′. Mouth moderate or large; gill-openings in or behind lower axil of pectorals.
    i′. Mouth moderate, oblique or nearly vertical; pseudobranchiæ absent; body somewhat compressed; size small.................ANTENNARIIDÆ (frog-fishes).
    ii′. Mouth exceedingly large, horizontal; pseudobranchiæ present; body greatly depressed; size large...............................LOPHIIDÆ (goose-fishes).
aa. Ventral rays not always 1,5.
  j′. Form unsymmetrical, the eyes and color being on one side, leaving other side blind and colorless.
    k′. Eyes large, usually well separated; mouth moderate or large; teeth well developed; margin of preopercle not concealed by skin and scales. PLEURONECTIDÆ (flounders).
    kk′. Eyes small, close together; mouth very small, more or less twisted; teeth rudimentary or absent; margin of preopercle concealed by skin and scales.
    SOLEIDÆ (soles).
  jj′. Form symmetrical, the eyes and color not confined to one side.
    l′. All fins without spinous rays; a barbel on chin; ventral rays 2 to 7. GADIDÆ (cods).
    ll′. Some fins with spinous rays.
    m′. Ventral opening far forward (under head in adult); ventral rays 7; dorsal fin single, with 3 or 4 anterior rays spinous; size small; fresh-water species.
    APHREDODERIDÆ (pirate perches).
    mm′. Ventral opening in normal position; ventral soft rays fewer than 5.
    n′. Dorsal fins with some spines.
      o′. Upper jaw not produced in the form of a sword; fishes of moderate or small size.

p'. Dorsal fin with soft rays anteriorly and spines posteriorly; ventral fins very small; gill-membranes broadly joined to isthmus; form elongate.

ZOARCIDÆ (eel-pouts).

pp'. Dorsal fin with spines anteriorly and soft rays posteriorly.

q'. Cheeks covered with bony armor; pectoral fins divided, the lower part very large like the "wing" of a flying-fish.

CEPHALACANTHIDÆ (flying-gurnards).

qq'. Cheeks not covered with bony armor; pectoral fins not divided.

r'. Dorsal fins 2, the spines 3; gills 3; mouth very large and fringed; size moderate......................... BATRACHOIDIDÆ (toad-fishes).

rr'. Dorsal fin single, the spines numerous (at least 11); gills 4; mouth small not fringed; size small.................... BLENNIIDÆ (blennies).

oo'. Upper jaw produced in the form of a powerful sword; fishes of very large size .... ISTIOPHORIDÆ (sail-fishes).

nn'. Dorsal fins without spines; a large sucking-disk between ventral fins.

GOBIESOCIDÆ, in part (cling-fishes).

IV. Ventral fins absent.

a. Body eel-shaped; maxillary and premaxillary bones absent or fused with palatines.

b. Gill-openings vertical, usually well developed; skin with or without scales; a tongue present; pectoral fins present or absent.

c. Skin covered by rudimentary linear scales; pectoral fins well developed.

ANGUILLIDÆ (common eels).

cc. Skin scaleless.

d. Tip of tail with a distinct fin, confluent with the dorsal and anal; pectoral fins well developed; dorsal fin beginning posterior to gill-openings; mouth large.

LEPTOCEPHALIDÆ (conger eels).

dd. Tip of tail without a fin and projecting beyond dorsal and anal fins; pectoral fins rudimentary (in local representative); dorsal fin beginning on head; mouth small.

OPHICHTHYIDÆ (snake eels).

bb. Gill-openings small, roundish; skin scaleless; tongue absent; pectoral fins absent.

MURÆNIDÆ (morays).

aa. Body not eel-shaped; maxillary and premaxillary bones present.

e. Gill-membranes broadly joined to isthmus.

f. Snout tubular, with a small, toothless mouth at end; body more or less encased in bony rings .... SYNGNATHIDÆ (pipe-fishes and sea-horses).

ff. Snout not tubular; body not encased in bony rings.

g. Two dorsal fins, anterior with spinous rays, posterior with soft rays; body deep and greatly compressed.

h. Dorsal spines 2 or 3 in number; skin covered with small, rough scales.

BALISTIDÆ (trigger-fishes).

hh. Dorsal spine single; skin covered with minute, rough scales,

MONACANTHIDÆ (file-fishes).

gg. One dorsal fin, composed of soft rays only.

i. Teeth in each jaw fused into 1.

j. Body compressed; dorsal and anal fins very high and pointed; skin without spines; size very large .... MOLIDÆ (head-fishes).

jj. Body not compressed; dorsal and anal fins small; skin thickly covered with long spines; size moderate.................. DIODONTIDÆ (porcupine-fishes).

ii. Teeth in each jaw fused into 2; skin more or less prickly.

TETRAODONTIDÆ (puffers).

iii. Teeth in each jaw not fused; body encased in a bony armor.

OSTRACIIDÆ (trunk-fishes).

ee. Gill-membranes not joined to isthmus.

k. Ventral opening at throat; body elongate; dorsal fin single, short, of soft rays only; size very small....................... AMBLYOPSIDÆ (swamp and cave fishes).

kk. Ventral opening situated posteriorly.

l. Mouth large; body elongate, without scales; size large.

m. Jaws nearly equal, and armed with large teeth; body very long, compressed; dorsal fin low and extending entire length of body; caudal fin absent.

TRICHIURIDÆ (cutlass-fishes).

mm. Upper jaw produced to form a long, powerful sword; mouth toothless; body moderately elongate, not compressed; caudal fin large and forked.

XIPHIIDÆ (sword-fishes).

ll. Mouth small; body compressed and deep, and covered with small scales; dorsal and anal fins elongate, with interior rays produced; caudal deeply forked; size small....................................... STROMATEIDÆ (butter-fishes).

Series GANOIDEA. The Ganoid Fishes.

The ganoids are primitive fishes, mostly fossils, with only a few living representatives. The group is not sharply defined, but is chiefly characterized by a more or less complete armor covering the body, by numerous valves in the arterial bulb which forms a part of the heart, and by a spiral valve in the lower part of the intestine. The American species are few in number, and fall into four families which are easily distinguished. The salient characters of each are given in the following key in greater detail than in the preceding general key to the true fishes:

Key to the families of ganoid fishes.

i. Skeleton chiefly cartilaginous; skin either armed with bony plates or naked; branchiostogals single or absent; spiracles present.

    a. Snout prolonged into a long, paddle-shaped blade; no barbels; sides of tail with small bony plates; mouth broad, terminal; air-bladder cellular...............POLYODONTIDÆ.

    aa. Snout prolonged, but not flat and paddle-like; barbels present on under side of snout; body imperfectly covered with large bony plates; mouth circular, inferior; air-bladder a simple sac...ACIPENSERIDÆ.

ii. Skeleton bony; body completely covered with small bony scales; branchiostegals few or numerous; spiracles absent; air-bladder cellular.

    b. Both jaws more or less prolonged, toothed, the upper jaw projecting; nostrils near end of upper jaw; no barbels; dorsal fin short, high, placed posteriorly, opposite anal; branchiostegals 3. ....LEPISOSTEIDÆ.

    bb. Jaws not produced; nostrils widely separated; a barbel at anterior nostril; dorsal fin very long, low, beginning nearly opposite pectorals; branchiostegals 10 to 12.

                                            AMIATIDÆ.

Order SELACHOSTOMI. The Shark-mouthed Ganoids.

Family POLYODONTIDÆ. The Paddle-fishes.

Body elongate, slightly compressed; snout a greatly prolonged flattened blade, widest toward the rounded tip; skin nearly smooth, with rhombic bony plates on side of tail; mouth wide, tongue absent, teeth in jaws and on palatines numerous, small, and disappearing with age; operculum rudimentary, pseudobranchiæ absent; a single branchiostegal; lateral line present, continuous; spiracles present; nostrils double, located at base of blade; air-bladder cellular; intestine with a spiral valve; dorsal and anal fins soft-rayed, placed far backward; pectorals thoracic, ventrals abdominal. Only two genera known, one Chinese, the other American.

Genus POLYODON Lacépède. Paddle-fishes.

This genus, which includes a single species, has numerous very long, slender gill-rakers, in a double series on each gill-arch; and caudal fin forked, its bent portion with 12 to 20 fulcral plates, in addition to the foregoing family characters. (*Polyodon*, many-toothed.)

25. POLYODON SPATHULA (Walbaum).

Paddle-fish; Spoon-billed Cat-fish.

Squalus spathula Walbaum, Artedi Genera Piscium, 522, 1792.
Polyodon folium, Cope, 1870*b*, 492; French Broad River near Asheville.
Polyodon spathula, Jordan & Evermann, 1896, 101, pl. 20, figs. 43, 43*a*.

DIAGNOSIS.—Head, with snout, more than .5 total length of body; snout or spatula reticulated, .25 to .4 total length, longest in young; opercular flap very long, extending nearly to ventrals; prexamillary bone reaching behind the eye; eye very small, above tip of lower jaw; a minute barbel on spiracle; skin scaleless, and smooth except on side of tail; dorsal fin behind ventrals, the rays 50 to 60; anal arising under middle of dorsal, the rays 50 to 65; caudal large, forked, asymmetrical. Color: pale green above, white below. (*spathula*, spatula.)

The claim of this species to a place in the North Carolina fauna rests on Professor Cope's statement that it ascends the French Broad River to near Asheville. It inhabits the Mississippi and tributaries. The length reaches 6 feet, of which the paddle is about one-third. It was formerly supposed that the paddle was used to stir up the mud, which was eaten for the minute animals it contained, the interlacing gill-rakers serving as a strainer to intercept the food articles, while the silt passed through; but recent investigation has shown that the species feeds near the surface. Nothing is known of its spawning habits. Within a comparatively few years the fish, formerly regarded as of little value, has come into use on account of its eggs, which are made into caviar, and also on account of its flesh, which is now highly regarded and brings a good price.

Order CHONDROSTEI. The Cartilaginous Ganoids.

Family ACIPENSERIDÆ. The Sturgeons.

Large fishes of elongate, cylindrical form; cartilaginous skeleton; body imperfectly covered with 5 longitudinal rows of large bony plates or shields, between which are small irregular plates; head covered with similar large plates; snout produced, with 4 flexible barbels hanging from its lower surface; mouth on under side of head, small, without teeth, capable of being protracted for feeding; eyes small; tail heterocercal; air-bladder large, simple, connected with the esophagus by a duct. The largest fishes found in fresh waters of northern parts of America, Europe and Asia; some migratory, some found only in fresh water; very valuable as food. Three genera, including seven American species.

Genus ACIPENSER Linnæus. Sturgeons.

Bony plates not confluent; one series on back and a lateral and abdominal series on each side, ventral plates often deciduous; snout more or less conical, depressed; spiracle over eye; gill-rakers small, pointed. Two Atlantic coast species, both found in North Carolina, differing greatly in length of snout and in other respects. (*Acipenser*, sturgeon.)

26. ACIPENSER OXYRHYNCHUS Mitchill.

"Sturgeon"; Sharp-nosed Sturgeon.

Acipenser oxyrhynchus Mitchill, Transactions Literary and Philosophical Society of New York, i, 462, 1814
    New York. Yarrow, 1877, 216; North, New, and Neuse rivers.
Acipenser sturio oxyrhynchus, Smith, 1893a, 190, 193, 198; Pasquotank River, Edenton Bay, Roanoke River
    Jordan & Evermann, 1896, 105, pl. xx, fig. 45.

DIAGNOSIS.—Body elongate, its greatest depth about .16 total length; head long, about .33 total length of body; snout long and sharp, its length about equal to remaining part of head, becoming shorter with age; the smaller bony plates between the dorsal and lateral series are stellate, rather large, and in 5 to 10 series; dorsal plates 10 to 14, lateral 27 to 29, ventral 8 to 11; dorsal rays 38 to 40, anal rays 23 to 27.   Color: gray or brown above, creamy, whitish, or light gray below.   (*oxyrhynchus*, sharp-snouted.)

This, the common sturgeon of northwestern Europe and the Atlantic coast of the United States as far southward as South Carolina, is found in the eastern rivers of North Carolina, which it ascends in spring to spawn.   It attains a large size, examples having been taken that were 12 feet long and weighed over 500 pounds; the average length, however, does not exceed 5 feet.   Two fish caught at Hatteras in the spring of 1906 were 9 and 11 feet long, according to Dr. E. W. Gudger, who examined their skins.

In the Roanoke River near Plymouth, young sturgeon, about a foot in length, begin to run as early as February and are caught in seines hauled for striped bass, but the adult fish do not appear until the latter part of April, after the main run of shad is over.   Young sturgeon are also taken at sea; on April 22, 1904, the author observed 3 examples 15 inches long caught in a gill net at Cape Lookout.

Fig. 12.   STURGEON.   *Acipenser oxyrhynchus.*

The sturgeon is a bottom feeder, and subsists on a great variety of animal and vegetable food which it takes up with its protractile, sucker-like mouth.

The mature ovaries of this species may constitute 25 per cent of the total weight of the fish, and may yield from 1,000,000 to 2,500,000 eggs.   The eggs are about .11 inch in diameter, and when deposited become agglutinated and attached to brush, weeds, stones, etc.   The young come from the eggs in about 1 week in water having a temperature of 64° F.

Writing of the North Carolina sturgeon in 1709, John Lawson said:

Of the sturgeon we have plenty, all the fresh parts of our rivers being well stored therewith. The Indians upon and towards the heads and falls of our rivers, strike a great many of these, and eat them; yet the Indians near the salt-waters will not eat them.   I have seen an Indian strike one of these fish, seven foot long, and leave him on the sands to be eaten by the gulls.   In May, they run up towards the heads of the rivers, where you see several hundreds of them in one day. The Indians have another way to take them, which is by nets at the end of a pole.   The bones of these fish make good nutmeg-graters.

The available statistics of the sturgeon fishery of North Carolina show a very irregular production, owing to changing conditions, such as non-appreciation, over-fishing and increasing demand.   The catch in 1880 was 436,900 pounds, worth $18,094. In 1889 the total yield was 227,797 pounds, valued at $5,754. The next year the catch fell to 175,210 pounds, worth $4,467. Seven years later it rose to 371,625 pounds, for which the fishermen received $13,525. In 1902, although the catch was only 134,125 pounds, the value of the fish was $15,347, including caviar. Dare County now produces the great bulk of the sturgeon placed on the market, the fish being caught in gill nets.

This species is now much less abundant than formerly, and in North Carolina has undergone the same diminution seen in other states. Whereas it was formerly regarded as a nuisance, and ruthlessly destroyed and thrown away whenever caught, it is now one of the most valuable of the east coast fishes; the principal fishery is in Delaware Bay and River. It is caught in gill nets, pound nets, seines, and other appliances, and may also be taken on set lines baited with fish. Besides its flesh, which is marketable in a fresh or smoked condition, its eggs are very valuable for use in making caviar, its swim-bladder is convertible into a high-grade isinglass, and its skin is also utilized.

In some of the large shad seines in Albemarle Sound it has sometimes happened during the past 7 or 8 years that not a single adult sturgeon has been caught during an entire season, whereas, 20 years ago sturgeon were abundant here and each season the shores were covered with dead fish for which there was no sale. When the fishermen finally realized the value of the fish, they pursued the fishery so actively that the species was almost wiped out in a short time and has never been able to reëstablish itself. According to Mr. Frank Wood, of Edenton, in one season $50,000 worth of sturgeon caviar was prepared in the Albemarle region.

The sturgeon is by far the most valuable fish, individually considered, inhabiting the waters of North Carolina or, in fact, the Atlantic coast of the United States. A full-sized female with roe will now often bring the fisherman $80; and it is a matter of record that in 1906 a North Carolina fisherman who caught 47 large sturgeon in salt water received for them over $2,500 after deducting all expenses of shipment.

It is incumbent on the state to take prompt and radical measures to prevent the further diminution in the supply of this excellent fish, and to restore it to something like its original abundance, if this is now possible. Besides prohibiting absolutely the killing of any examples under 3 feet long, it will probably be desirable to stop the destruction of large fish for a term of years. Supplementary to these restrictive aids, the state or the general government should undertake the artificial propagation of the sturgeon on several of the rivers where the fish is still found.

27. ACIPENSER BREVIROSTRUM LeSueur.

"Sturgeon"; Short-nosed Sturgeon.

Acipenser brevirostrum LeSueur, Transactions American Philosophical Society, i, 130, 1818. Yarrow, 1877
216; North, New and Neuse Rivers. Jordan, 1887, 26; Beaufort region. Jordan & Evermann, 1896,
106, pl. xxi, fig. 46.

DIAGNOSIS.—Head short, about .25 total body length; snout short and blunt, only .25 to .33 length of head; dorsal plates 8 to 11, lateral plates 22 to 33, ventral plates 6 to 9; dorsal rays 33, anal rays 19 to 22. Color: brown above, white below; peritoneum dark, viscera black. (*brevirostrum*, short-beaked.)

Fig. 13. SHORT–NOSED STURGEON. *Acipenser brevirostrum.*

This is a comparatively rare species, not usually recognized by fishermen, ranging from Massachusetts to Florida. Its maximum length is under 3 feet, and it is mature when under 2 feet. Its habits are similar to those of the long-nosed sturgeon. While it doubtless ascends all suitable streams in North Carolina, actual records of its occurrence are rare.

Order RHOMBOGANOIDEA.   The Rhomboid Ganoids.

Family LEPISOSTEIDÆ.   The Gar Pikes.

Large fresh-water fishes, of little economic value, with very elongate, more or less cylindrical body, covered with small, hard plates in regular rows; elongate jaws, both armed with sharp teeth; external skull bones rough and hard; small eyes; an accessory gill on the under side of opercle; short gill rakers; and other features shown in the key. Very destructive to other fishes and comparatively free from enemies owing to their strong armor. One genus and five American species, one of which, the alligator gar of the South Central States, attains a length of 10 feet.

Genus LEPISOSTEUS Lacépède.   Gar Pikes.

Characters of the genus are shown above. One species inhabits North Carolina waters. (*Lepisosteus*, bony-scaled.)

28. LEPISOSTEUS OSSEUS (Linnæus).
"Gar Pike"; Long-nosed Gar; Bill-fish.

Esox osseus Linnæus, Systema Naturæ, ed. x, 313, 1758; Virginia.
Lepidosteus osseus, Cope, 1870b, 492; Yadkin and other rivers of eastern North Carolina. Jordan, 1886, 26; Beaufort. Earll, 1887, 484, 485; Neuse River. Jenkins, 1887, 85; Beaufort.
Lepidosteus huronensis, Cope, 1870b, 492, 495; French Broad River.
Lepisosteus osseus, Jordan, 1889b, 125; Pamlico River. Evermann & Cox, 1896, 304; Neuse River (Raleigh), Jordan & Evermann, 1896, 109.

DIAGNOSIS.—Body elongate, cylindrical, depth .08 of total length; head .33 total length; snout very long, .66 total length of head and 15 to 20 times as long as wide; upper jaw the longer, with a single row of large teeth on each side; lower jaw with several series of teeth; dorsal rays 7 or 8; anal rays 9; scales in lateral line, 62 to 65. Color: green above, silvery on sides, white beneath; body and fins with numerous round black spots. (*osseus*, bony.)

The long-nosed gar inhabits the Great Lakes, the Mississippi Valley, and the seaboard states from New Hampshire to Texas. It attains a length of 5 or 6 feet, and is a very hardy, destructive species, preying on almost every other kind of fish. It spawns in spring, in shallow water.

In North Carolina it is found in the lowland streams and sluggish coastal waters generally, sometimes entering salt water. In Albemarle Sound the species is not rare, and is taken in shad seines and other apparatus. At the Avoca shad fishery in April, 1899, the author saw two 4-foot gars skinned, boiled, and eaten with gusto by negro fishermen. Dr. Capehart states that before the days of steel plows his grandfather used to cover his plow-shares with the skin of the gar pike.

Mr. Earll, in 1880, noted a fishery for gars in Neuse River near New Bern, and said of the fish trade of that city:

The coarsest species are not only seen in the markets, but they make up the bulk of the sales. The gar (*L. osseus*), not seen by us in any other market in the country, is one of the principal food-fishes here, where it is highly prized by negroes.

At the present time the gar can not be said to be one of the principal food fishes of the New Bern market; but the fish is still regularly sold there, and one of the common sights on the water front is a negro skinning a gar.

The expression "common as gar broth" is proverbial. The meat of this fish, however, is well-flavored and wholesome, and its consumption should become more general. There is a limited demand for the skin, which may be used in covering boxes, sword hilts, etc.

It is now nearly 200 years since Lawson wrote the following account of the "white guard-fish", in contradistinction to the "green guard-fish" (*Tylosurus*):

The white guard-fish is shaped almost like a pike, but slenderer; his mouth has a long small bill set with teeth, in which he catches small fish; his scales are knit together like armour. When they dress him, they strip him, taking off scales and skin together. His meat is very white, and rather looks like flesh than fish. The English account them no good fish; but the Indians do. The gall of this fish is green, and a violent cathartick, if taken inwardly.

Order CYCLOGANOIDEA. The Cylindrical Ganoids.

Family AMIATIDÆ. The Bow-fins.

This family includes only one living species, widely distributed in the United States. Features by which the family may be distinguished are given in the foregoing key. Body long and stout; head blunt; jaws toothed, the lower jaw with a bony plate between the rami; teeth also on vomer, palatal, and pterygoid bones; tongue thick; nostrils well separated; cheeks and top of head with bony plates; a broad flat skin on the edge of the opercle; no pseudobranchiæ; gill-rakers short and stout; scales hard, cycloid, with a soft border; lateral line present; tail heterocercal; air-bladder bifid anteriorly, serving as a lung.

Genus AMIATUS Rafinesque. Bow-fins.

Characters of the genus are sufficiently indicated in the family diagnosis. The generic name *Amia*, which has heretofore been used in this connection, appears to be no longer applicable, as it was originally given by Gronow to a genus of cardinal-fishes until recently called *Apogon*. (*Amiatus*, from *amia*, an ancient Greek fish name.)

29. AMIATUS CALVA (Linnæus).
"Black-fish"; "Grindle"; "Brindle-fish"; Dog-fish; Mud-fish; Bow-fin.

Amia calva Linnæus, Systema Naturæ, ed. x, 500, 1766; Charleston, South Carolina. Cope, 1870*b*, 492; Neuse River. Jordan, 1889*b*, 127; Neuse River. Smith, 1893*a*, 190, 193, 198; Pasquotank River, Edenton Bay, Roanoke River. Jordan & Evermann, 1896, 113, pl. 22, figs. 51, 51*a*. Smith, 1900, 134; Lake Mattamuskeet.

DIAGNOSIS.—Body long but robust, the depth about .2 total length; head conical, its length about .25 total length of body; mouth large, jaws nearly equal, upper jaw extending beyond eye; jaws with strong conical teeth, with a band of finer teeth in lower jaw; a small barbel near anterior nostril; scales hard, cycloid, 62 to 70 in lateral series and 18 to 20 in transverse series; dorsal rays 42 to 53; anal rays 10 to 12. Color: dark olive above, greenish reticulations on sides, whitish below; round dark spots on lower jaw; dorsal and caudal fins mottled; in male a round black spot with orange border at base of tail, this spot very faint in female. (*calva*, bald.)

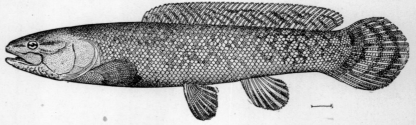

Fig. 14.   MUD–FISH; BOW–FIN.   *Amiatus calva.*

The bow-fin is one of the most interesting of American fishes, being the only living representative of an order and family of which various fossil members have been found.   It ranges from the Great Lakes to Virginia, Florida, and Texas, and is abundant throughout most of its habitat.   Sluggish waters are its favorite haunts.

It occurs along the entire length of the coastal plain region of North Carolina, and is well known to fishermen and others under the local name of "black-fish", "grindle" or "grindal", and "brindle-fish".

As early as 1709 we find the name "grindle" given to this species by Lawson, who wrote:

Grindals are a long scaled fish with small eyes; and frequent ponds, lakes, and slow-flowing creeks and swamps.   They are a soft sorry fish, and good for nothing; though some eat them for good fish.

The female attains a length of 2 to 3 feet, while the male is considerably smaller.   The largest recorded specimen weighed 12 pounds.   The species is noted for its voracity, all kinds of fishes falling an easy prey.   This habit, together with its hardiness and its comparative immunity from attack by other fishes, makes it a very undesirable inhabitant of our waters. It is able to live out of water for many hours, even when exposed to direct sun rays; and the young will exist for months in small aquaria without change of water.

Spawning occurs in spring, the eggs being deposited in sluggish or stagnant waters. The eggs and young are guarded by the parent fish, after the manner of the sun-fishes.

The bow-fin is particularly common in Albemarle Sound, and it also ascends all the rivers tributary to the sound but is less common therein. It is often caught in nets employed for shad and alewives, but it has no commercial value, although sometimes eaten by negroes; the flesh is described as "cottony."

Series TELEOSTEI.   The Bony Fishes.

The teleosts constitute the most numerous group of fishes, and are distinguished by a perfectly ossified skeleton and the absence of the characters found in the ganoids; that is, the body is not covered with ganoid scales or bony plates, the arterial bulb of the heart is thin-walled and has a pair of opposite valves, there is no spiral valve in the intestine, and the optic nerves do not form a solid chiasm. There are numerous orders, which, in most cases, are not here referred to at length, as they contain but a single family whose description will suffice for an understanding of the ordinal characters; but other orders, with many local species representing two or more families, have been considered in some detail.

Order NEMATOGNATHI.   The Whiskered Fishes.

Family SILURIDÆ.   The Cat-fishes.

The cat-fishes are readily distinguished by smooth scaleless bodies, adipose dorsal fin, stout spines in dorsal and pectoral fins, and barbels or whiskers on upper and lower jaws (whence the name cat-fishes). They inhabit both fresh and salt waters, and are very hardy. Some attain a large size, and are important food fishes. Many of them guard their eggs and young like the basses; some of the species are ovoviviparous. The North Carolina cat-fishes represent 12 species, and fall in the following genera:

Key to the North Carolina genera of cat-fishes.

i. Anterior and posterior nostrils close together, neither with a barbel; barbels 4 or 6; marine species.
    a. Lower jaw with 2 barbels, dorsal and pectoral spines ending in a long filament.
                                               FELICHTHYS.
    aa. Lower jaw with 4 barbels, dorsal and pectoral spines without filaments.
                                               GALEICHTHYS.
ii. Anterior and posterior nostrils well separated, the posterior nostril with a barbel; barbels 8; fresh-water species.
    b. Adipose fin with its posterior margin free.
        c. Band of teeth in upper jaw terminating abruptly behind, not extending backward at outer angles.
            d. A continuous bony ridge (under skin) from snout to dorsal fin, the supraoccipital bone being extended backward to dorsal spine; caudal fin always forked.
                                               ICTALURUS

 dd. No continuous bony ridge from snout to dorsal fin; caudal typically short and
   square...Ameiurus.
 cc. Band of teeth in upper jaw extending backward at its outer posterior angles.
                             Leptops.
 bb. Adipose fin ridge-like, its posterior edge attached to back or continuous with caudal; a
   poison gland at base of pectoral fins..............................Schilbeodes.

While not the objects of special fisheries, the cat-fishes are caught in large
quantities in various parts of the state, and are of increasing economic importance. From 55,220 pounds, worth $1,248, in 1889, the catch rose to 404,600
pounds, worth $11,971, in 1902. The counties which lead in cat-fish production
are Currituck, Pasquotank, Chowan, Dare, Beaufort, and New Hanover, more
than 25 per cent of the output in the last named year being from Dare. The
flesh of the cat-fishes is fine, white, and well-flavored; and the demand for them
both locally and for shipment outside the state seems to be growing, especially
as regards the fresh-water species.

Genus FELICHTHYS Swainson. Sea Cat-fishes.

This genus, represented by a number of salt-water species on both coasts of
tropical America, has one member inhabiting the Atlantic coast of the United
States. The mouth is large; the lower jaw projects; the teeth on vomer and
palatines form a crescent-shaped band; the nape has a granulated bony buckler;
the caudal is deeply forked. (*Felichthys*, cat-fish.)

Fig. 15. Sea Cat–fish. *Felichthys felis.*

30. FELICHTHYS FELIS (Linnæus).

"Silver Cat-fish"; "Sea Cat-fish"; Gaff-topsail Cat (Ga.);
Large-mouthed Cat (S. C.).

Silurus felis Linnæus, Systema Naturæ, ed. xii, 503, 1766; Charleston, S. C.
Ælurichthys marinus, Yarrow, 1877, 216; Beaufort. Jordan & Gilbert, 1879, 385; Beaufort. Jordan, 1886,
  26; Beaufort. Smith, 1893*a*, 188, 194; Edenton Bay. Smith, 1893*b*, pl. xliv.
Felichthys marinus, Jordan & Evermann, 1896, 118, pl. xxxiii, fig. 52.
Ælurichthys felis, Günther, Proceedings Linnæan Society of London, 1899, 30.
Felichthys felis, Jordan & Evermann, 1900, 3196.

Diagnosis.—Body elongate, depth more than .2 total length; head short, broad, rather
less than .25 total length, maxillary barbels very long, extending beyond base of dorsal fin;

eye placed low on side of head; dorsal rays 1,7, situated far forward, the spine terminating in a long filament; pectoral spine ending similarly; anal rays 23. Color: dusky above, silvery below. (*felis*, cat.)

This sea cat-fish ranges from Massachusetts to Texas, being common in the South Atlantic and Gulf States in salt and brackish water; it also enters fresh water, such as the western end of Albemarle Sound, where it is recognized by the fishermen as a straggler from salt water and called "silver cat-fish". It is probably ovoviviparous. The food value of the species is slight.

Genus GALEICHTHYS Cuvier & Valenciennes. Sea Cat-fishes.

A numerous genus of marine cat-fishes, only one species inhabiting United States waters. Mouth comparatively small, the lower jaw shorter; teeth in patches on vomer and palatines; dorsal fin short and high; anal fin short; caudal deeply forked. (*Galeichthys*, weasel-fish.)

31. GALEICHTHYS MILBERTI (Cuvier & Valenciennes).
"Cat-fish"; "Sea Cat-fish"; Small-mouthed Cat (S. C.).

Arius milberti Cuvier & Valenciennes, xv, 74, 1840; New York; Charleston.
Ariopsis milberti, Yarrow, 1877, 216; Beaufort.
Ariopsis felis, Jordan & Gilbert, 1879, 385; Beaufort.
Galeichthys felis, Jordan, 1886, 26; Beaufort. Jenkins, 1887, 85; Beaufort.
Hexanematichthys felis, Jordan & Evermann, 1896, 128, pl. xxiii, fig. 53.
Galeichthys milberti, Jordan & Evermann, 1900, 3196. Linton, 1905, 349; Beaufort.

DIAGNOSIS.—Body elongate, depth .2 total length; head small, depressed, rather more than .25 total length; mouth small, maxillary barbel nearly as long as head; dorsal rays 1,7; anal rays 16; caudal deeply forked. Color: steel blue above, silvery sides and belly. (Named after the French naturalist, Milbert.)

Fig. 16. SEA CAT-FISH. *Galeichthys milberti.*

This species is found along the entire coast of the United States south of Cape Cod, but is not common northward. It frequents the North Carolina beaches, sounds and bays, and is the most abundant of the salt-water cat-fishes. It attains a length of 2 feet and a weight of 12 pounds, but averages much smaller.

It is a bottom-loving fish, feeding chiefly on worms and small crustaceans but readily eating fish, flesh, or fowl, dead or alive. At Beaufort, its food comprises fish, crustaceans, and mollusks, as well as sea-cucumbers, worms, and algæ.

Spawning occurs in summer, the large eggs being first deposited in a sandy depression and subsequently taken into the mouth of one of the parents (male?) where they remain until hatching ensues; the young are retained in the parent's mouth for some time after hatching. From the mouth of a fish 10 inches long, 11 young 1-inch long have been taken; and in another of the same size 8 or 9 eggs as large as marbles were found.

The sea cat-fish is often caught with a hook, but it is not an important commercial species, although the flesh is quite palatable.

Genus ICTALURUS Rafinesque.   Channel Cat-fishes; Fork-tailed Cat-fishes.

Large North American cat-fishes, with widely-forked tails, preferring channels of larger streams. Form more graceful than that of other cat-fishes; head slender, conical, mouth small, upper jaw longer; dorsal fin short and high; anal fin long. (*Ictalurus*, cat-fish.)

32. ICTALURUS PUNCTATUS (Rafinesque).

"Blue Cat-fish"; Spotted Cat-fish; Channel Cat-fish (S. C., Fla.); Eel Cat-fish; Mississippi Cat-fish.

Silurus punctatus Rafinesque, American Monthly Magazine, 359, 1818; Ohio River.
Ictalurus cærulescens Cope, 1870b, 489; French Broad and other North Carolina tributaries of Tennessee.
Ictalurus punctatus, Jordan, 1889b, 151; French Broad River. Smith, 1893b, pl. xliv. Jordan & Evermann, 1896, 134, pl. xxv, fig. 58.

DIAGNOSIS.—Body long and slender, depth .2 total length; head small, comparatively narrow, .25 total length; mouth small, maxillary barbels reaching beyond gill-opening; dorsal rays 1,6; anal large, with 25 to 30 rays. Color: above light grayish-green; below silvery; back and sides with small, round, irregularly placed dark spots; the body color sometimes a very dark velvety green, obscuring the spots. (*punctatus*, spotted.)

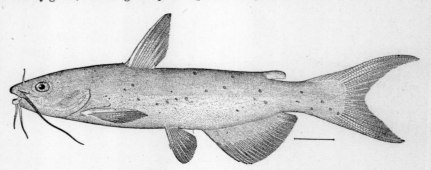

Fig. 17.   SPOTTED CAT-FISH.   *Ictalurus punctatus*.

The spotted cat-fish inhabits the Mississippi basin, streams of the Great Lakes region, and streams tributary to the Gulf of Mexico; and has been very successfully introduced into the Potomac. The only records of the occurrence of this species in North Carolina waters are those of Cope and Jordan before cited. Cope stated that the species abounded in the French Broad, and was much used as food. Jordan reported the young as abundant in channels of the French

Broad near Hot Springs, the species being recognized as a food fish and known as "blue cat".

The species attains a weight of 25 pounds, and is regarded as probably the best of the cat-fishes in food value and gaminess. It takes the hook readily, and affords fine sport.

Genus AMEIURUS Rafinesque. Horned Pouts; Bullheads; Mud Cat-fishes, etc.

Well known and abundant fishes, found in almost every pond and stream. Some species have forked or lunate tails and are very similar to *Ictalurus*; the typical species with square tails. The 5 species recorded from North Carolina may be distinguished as follows:

i. Caudal fin strongly forked...*catus*.
ii. Caudal fin square or slightly emarginate.
  a. Anal fin long, 22–27 rays, its base more than .25 total length.
  aa. Anal fin shorter, 15–22 rays, its base less than .25 total length.
    b. Form elongate, back elevated, pectoral and dorsal spines very long.....*erebennus*.
    bb. Form robust, back low, pectoral and dorsal spines moderate.............*natalis*.
    c. Body stout, rather short or moderately elongate, depth contained 3.5 to 4.5 times in total length, head not markedly flat ....*nebulosus*.
    cc. Body very long and slender, depth .12 to .20 total length, head broad and very flat. ....*platycephalus*

(*Ameiurus*, not curtailed, in allusion to unnotched caudal fin.)

33. AMEIURUS CATUS (Linnæus).

"White Cat-fish"; "Black Cat-fish"; "Bullhead"; "Creek Cat-fish"; "River Catfish"; "Forktailed Cat-fish"; Channel Cat-fish.

Silurus catus Linnæus, Systema Naturæ, ed. x, 305, 1758; northern part of America.
Ameiurus niveiventris Cope, 1870b, 488; Neuse River. Jordan, 1889b, 128: Neuse River.
Ameiurus albidus, Jordan, 1889b, 134; Yadkin River. Smith, 1893a, 190, 193, 198; Albemarle Sound and tributaries.
Ameiurus catus, Jordan & Evermann, 1896, 138. Evermann & Cox, 1896, 304; Neuse River.

DIAGNOSIS.—Form robust, the depth contained 3.5 to 3.75 times in total length; head rather greater than depth, in adults the head larger and wider and the mouth wider than in any other species; maxillary and mandibular barbels long; humeral process very rough; dorsal rays 1,6; anal rays 19 to 22; caudal forked, upper lobe longer. Color: variable; back whitish, gray, bluish, or black; below white or silvery. (*catus*, cat.)

This species, whose form and color vary with age and environment, inhabits coastwise fresh waters from New Jersey to Texas. In North Carolina it is recorded from Albemarle Sound and tributaries, the Neuse, and the Yadkin, being especially abundant in the first-named region. The maximum length is 2 feet.

In Pasquotank River, under the name of "white cat", the fishermen recognize fish having a milky or dusky color, dull red fins with dark edges, and white iris, which are most common in the lower part of the river, where they seem partial to the sandy shoals, whence, probably, their bleached appearance. Between these light-colored fish and the very dark ones of the upper river called "black cats", there is a complete gradation. The main run of alewives in this river is always followed by a noticeable increase in the abundance of this cat-fish, and the fishermen have a saying that when the cat-fish come the herring season is over.   An instance of this was observed by the writer in April, 1892, when, during a period of four days a seine caught 118,000 herring, while on the fifth day no herring were taken but an enormous haul of cat-fish was made.

In Roanoke River, cat-fish 5 to 6 inches long are exceedingly abundant in spring, and are caught in seines and weirs.   The fishermen call the large pale examples of the lower river "sound cats" and "bullheads", and call the small dark ones "river cats" and "creek cats".

During the spring fishing season, many are caught in seines hauled for shad and alewives, especially in the night hauls on the flats.   The species resorts to the shad spawning-grounds to feed on the eggs, and must be enormously destructive in this way.   On April 24, 1899, at Capehart's shad fishery at Avoca, not less than 5,000 white cat-fish, from 6 to 24 inches long, were caught at one evening haul, and these were without exception absolutely gorged with shad spawn, so that their white bellies were distended like balloons.   Schools of alewives are followed to their spawning-grounds by droves of cat-fish, which feed on the eggs. The spawn of white perch, yellow perch, and other species is also entensively consumed by this cat-fish.

Spawning occurs in summer, and the spawning habits appear to be quite similar to those of the bullhead (*Ameiurus nebulosus*) of which an account is herein given.

As food, this is one of the best of the cat-fishes, although its commercial importance in North Carolina is comparatively slight, owing in part to the abundance of other desirable fishes and in part to the fact that most of the cat-fish are caught when shad, alewives, and striped bass are receiving special attention.

34. AMEIURUS EREBENNUS Jordan.
Goode's Cat-fish; Black Cat-fish.

Ameiurus erebennus Jordan, Bulletin U. S. National Museum, x, 85, 1877; St. Johns River, Fla.   Jordan, 1889*b*,
125, 127; Tar and Neuse rivers.   Jordan & Evermann, 1896, 139.

DIAGNOSIS.—Body long, compressed, its depth somewhat less than .25 total length; head large, .25 length of body, greatest width less than its length; jaws about equal; pectoral spine .5 length of head; anal fin deep, .3 total length, 22 to 24 rays; adipose fin large; caudal short, posterior margin straight.   Color: black above, pale below, fins and barbels black.   (*erebennus*, very black.)

Inhabits coastwise waters from New Jersey to Florida.   Length 1 foot. Apparently rare in North Carolina, and as yet known only from Tar River near Rocky Mount and Moccasin Swamp of the Neuse River near Goldsboro.

35. AMEIURUS NATALIS (LeSueur).
Yellow Cat-fish.

Pimelodus natalis LeSueur, Memoirs du Musée d'Histoire Naturelle, v, 154, 1819; North America.
Ameiurus natalis, Jordan, 1889*b*, 127; tributaries of Neuse River near Goldsboro.   Evermann & Cox, 1896;
Neuse River near Raleigh.   Jordan & Evermann, 1896, 139.

DIAGNOSIS.—A variable species; body usually short and stout, sometimes very obese; head short and broad; dorsal and pectoral spines comparatively short; anal rays 24 to 27; adipose fin long. Color: yellow, yellow-brown, green, or black, pale below. (*natalis*, having large buttock.)

This species ranges from the Great Lakes region to Virginia and Texas, and is abundant in many places, but in North Carolina was until recently known only from the upper waters of the Neuse. In June, 1905, and May, 1906, it was found to be common by Mr. C. S. Brimley in a canal connected with Lake Ellis in Craven county; and it doubtless occurs in various other localities in the state.

36. AMEIURUS NEBULOSUS (LeSueur).
"Yellow Cat-fish"; Bullhead; Horned Pout.

Pimelodus nebulosus LeSueur, Memoirs du Musée d'Historie Naturelle, v, 149, 1819; Lake Ontario.
Ameiurus nebulosus. Jordan, 1889*b*, 125; Tar River near Rocky Mount. Smith, 1893*a*, 190, 194, 198; tributaries of Albemarle Sound. Jordan & Evermann. 1896, 140.

DIAGNOSIS.—Form variable, color ranging from yellowish to black. Example 12.5 inches long from Pasquotank River: Head .28 total length; depth .25 total length; anal base .25 total length, anal rays 22; pectoral spine .4 length of head; above dark green, sides golden yellow, obscurely mottled with green, beneath pale yellow or white. (*nebulosus*, clouded.)

The common bullhead is widely distributed and is one of the most abundant and best known of the cat-fishes. From Maine and the Great Lakes it ranges to Florida and Texas, inhabiting streams, ponds, and lakes. It is doubtless more common in North Carolina than the published records of its capture would indicate, for besides the Albemarle region, it is reported only from Tar River. In the western end of Albemarle Sound and in Pasquotank and Roanoke rivers, it is common, but much less numerous than *Ameiurus catus*. It attains a length of 18 inches, but averages much less.

The species is omnivorous, although probably preferring fish food. It is fond of the eggs and young of various fishes, and is generally regarded as very destructive in this respect. It often frequents the vicinity of wharves and drains, and feeds on refuse.

The breeding habits of the bullhead are probably better known than those of any other cat-fish herein listed. The writer published the following brief account in *Science* (February 13, 1903), a more detailed description appearing later:*

A pair of fish from the Potomac River in the Fish Commission aquarium at Washington made a nest on July 3, 1902, by removing in their mouths upwards of a gallon of gravel from one end of the tank, leaving the slate bottom bare. On July 5 about 2,000 eggs, in four separate agglutinated clusters, were deposited between 10 and 11 a. m. on the scrupulously clean bottom. Ninety-nine per cent hatched in five days in a mean water temperature of 77° F. The young remained on the bottom in dense masses until 6 days old, when they began to swim, at first rising vertically a few inches and immediately falling back. By the end of the seventh day they were swimming actively, and most of them collected in a school just beneath the surface, where they remained for two days, afterwards scattering. They first ate finely ground

*Breeding habits of the yellow cat-fish. By Hugh M. Smith and L. G. Harron Bulletin U. S. Fish Commission 1902, p. 151-154.

liver on the sixth, and fed ravenously after the eighth day. The fish were 4mm. long when hatched, and grew rapidly, some being 18mm. long on the eleventh day, and at the end of two months their average length was 50mm. Both parents were very zealous in caring for the eggs, keeping them agitated constantly by a gentle fanning motion of the lower fins. The most striking act in the care of the eggs was the sucking of the egg masses into the mouth and the blowing of them out with some force. The fanning and mouthing operations were continued with the fry until they swam freely, when the care of the young may be said to have ceased. During the first few days after hatching, the fry, banked in the corners of the tank, were at irregular intervals actively stirred by the barbels of the parents, usually the male. The predaceous feeding habits of the old fish gradually overcame the parental instinct; the tendency to suck the fry into their mouths continued, and the inclination to spit the mout diminished, so that the numbers of young dwindled daily, and the 500 that had been left with their parents had completely disappeared in six weeks, although other food was liberally supplied.

The yellow cat-fish is frequently eaten, but its food value is decidedly inferior; and in North Carolina it is not regarded with favor and has little commercial importance.

37. AMEIURUS PLATYCEPHALUS (Girard).
Mud Cat-fish; Brown Cat-fish.

Pimelodus platycephalus Girard, Proceedings Academy of Natural Sciences of Philadelphia, 1859, 161; Anderson, S. C.
Ameiurus platycephalus, Cope, 1870b, 486; Catawba and Yadkin rivers. Jordan, 1889b, 131, 134, 136; Cape Fear (Haw), Yadkin, and Catawba rivers. Jordan & Evermann, 1896, 142, pl. xxvii, fig. 61.

DIAGNOSIS.—Form very elongate, the depth .12 to .20 total length; head low, flat, broad, .28 total length; upper jaw longer; dorsal fin high, .66 length of head, rays 1,6; anal base .16 total length, rays 16 to 20; caudal fin emarginate. Color: olive brown, yellowish or greenish above; a dark horizontal bar or shade at dorsal base; pale below. (*platycephalus*, broad-headed.)

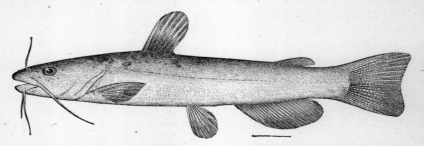

Fig. 18. BROWN CAT-FISH. *Ameiurus platycephalus*.

The range of this species is restricted, embracing only the streams from the Cape Fear to the Chattahoochee. In the streams of the western part of North Carolina, the species is well represented. Dr. Jordan found it excessively abundant in branches of Haw River, a tributary of Cape Fear River, in Guilford County; also in Little Yadkin River near Salisbury, in Catawba River near Marion, and in St. Johns River near Morgantown. The maximum length is somewhat over a foot.

An interesting and peculiar fact about this fish is that it is largely, if not almost exclusively, a vegetable feeder, its intestine being long and usually filled with remains of water plants. Both Cope and Jordan note that it is largely used for food.

Genus LEPTOPS Rafinesque. Mud Cat-fishes.

This genus contains a single large species, and, in addition to the features given in the key, is characterized by a slender body much depressed anteriorly, very thick skin, long adipose fin, short anal fin, and broad pectoral spine serrated on both edges. (*Leptops*, slender-faced.)

38. LEPTOPS OLIVARIS (Rafinesque).
"Yellow Cat-fish"; Mud Cat-fish; Bashaw; Goujon.

Silurus olivaris Rafinesque, American Monthly Magazine, 1818, 355; Ohio River.
Leptops olivaris, Jordan, 1889b, 151; French Broad and Swannanoa rivers. Jordan & Evermann, 1896, 143, pl. xxvii, fig. 62.

DIAGNOSIS.—Depth .16 total length; head very flat, .28 total length; lower jaw projecting; eye very small; dorsal spine weak, short, more or less covered by skin; dorsal rays i,6; anal short, .16 total body length, rays 12 to 15; adipose fin nearly as long and half as high as anal; caudal nearly straight behind. Color: yellow above with green or brown markings, white below. (*olivaris*, olive-colored.)

Fig. 19. YELLOW CAT-FISH. *Leptops olivaris*.

While this is an abundant species in parts of the Mississippi basin and in the Gulf States, its range barely extends into North Carolina, in the headwaters of the Tennessee. Dr. Jordan found the young not uncommon in channels of French Broad River at Hot Springs and South Fork of Swannanoa River near Black Mountain. The fish is there called "yellow cat", and is a food fish of some importance. The species attains a weight of 100 pounds and a length of 5 feet, and has an ugly, coarse appearance. Its flesh, however, is fine and well-flavored, and in Louisiana and other southern states the fish is of considerable economic importance.

Genus SCHILBEODES Bleeker. Mad-toms.

Small cat-fishes inhabiting creeks and brooks of the eastern states. The pectoral spine, which is often serrated, can inflict a very painful wound; and in the axil of the fin a poison gland discharges through a small orifice. The fish

are of no economic value.   The characters of the genus have been indicated in
the foregoing key.   The three species known from North Carolina may be distinguished as follows:

i. Pectoral spines about half length of head, with posterior serræ short, their length not .5
    width of spines; vertical fins with broad black edges ....*insignis.*
ii. Pectoral spines more than .5 length of head, with recurved posterior serræ nearly as long
    as spines are wide.
    a. Color nearly plain brownish, with faint blotches; dorsal black at tip; maxillary barbels
        not reaching gill-opening .... *eleutherus.*
    aa. Color light brown, with distinct black saddle-like blotches; fins mottled with black; maxil-
        lary barbels reaching to gill-opening..................................*furiosus.*

(*Schilbeodes*, like *Schilbe*, a genus of African cat-fishes.)

39. SCHILBEODES INSIGNIS (Richardson).
Mad-tom.

Pimelodus insigne Richardson, Fauna Boreali-Americana, iii, 32, 1836; (type locality not known).
Noturus marginatus, Cope, 1870b, 484; Catawba and Yadkin rivers.
Noturus insignis, Jordan, 1889b, 125, 127, 131, 134, 136; Tar, Neuse, Cape Fear, Yadkin, Catawba rivers.   Ever-
    mann & Cox, 1896, 304; Neuse River.
Schilbeodes insignis, Jordan & Evermann, 1896, 147, pl. xxviii, fig. 66.

DIAGNOSIS.—Form elongate, depth .16 total length; head broad, flat, contained 4.25 times
in length; upper jaw projecting; humeral process sharp; dorsal fin .25 higher than long, nearer
anal than snout; anal rays 14 to 16; pectoral spine .5 length of head, with retrorse teeth
on external surface and simple, weak teeth on internal surface.   Color: dark mottled brown,
fins with broad dark margins.   (*insignis*, distinguished.)

This species inhabits streams on the eastern slope of the Alleghany mountains from Pennsylvania to South Carolina, and is abundant and widely distributed in North Carolina, having been recorded from the Tar, Neuse, Yadkin,
Catawba, and Cape Fear rivers.   It is the largest mad-tom, reaching a length of
1 foot.

40. SCHILBEODES ELEUTHERUS (Jordan.)
Mad-tom.

Noturus eleutherus Jordan, Annals New York Lyceum Natural History 1877, 371; Big Pigeon River, Tennessee,
    tributary of French Broad River.   Jordan, 1889b, 151; French Broad River at Hot Springs, N. C.
Schilbeodes eleutherus, Jordan & Evermann, 1896, 148; French Broad River.

DIAGNOSIS.—Head broad, depressed, a little more than .25 total length; lower jaw included; eye contained 5.5 times in length of head; anal rays 13; pectoral spine stout, .5 length
of head or longer, the outer margin with retrorse teeth, the inner edge with 6 to 8 curved hooks
Color: brown, with fine dark dots and black blotches on back; dorsal fin black at tip.   (*eleutherus*, free.)

Peculiar to the Mississippi basin, and recorded from North Carolina only in
the French Broad River at Hot Springs, where Dr. Jordan obtained one young
specimen in 1888.   Length, 4 inches.

41. SCHILBEODES FURIOSUS (Jordan & Meek).
"Mad-tom"; "Tabby-cat".

Noturus furiosus Jordan & Meek, in Jordan, 1889a, 351, pl. xliii; Neuse River near Raleigh.   Jordan, 1889b, 125,
127; Tar and Neuse rivers.
Noturus eleutherus, Jordan & Brayton, 1878; Tar River (not *N. eleutherus* of Jordan).   Jordan & Gilbert, 1879,
368; Neuse River at Goldsboro.
Schilbeodes furiosus, Jordan & Evermann, 1896, 149, pl. xxix, figs. 69, 69a, 69b; eastern North Carolina.

DIAGNOSIS.—Depth contained 5.5 times in total length; head contained 3.75 times in
length; lower jaw included; dorsal spine less than .5 length of head; pectoral spine very broad
and long, contained 1.25 times in length of head, anterior (outer) margin finely serrate, posterior margin with 6 to 8 strong recurved hooks; adipose fin large; anal rays 14; caudal fin long
and rounded.   Color: light brown, with black saddle-like blotches on back and head, and black
bars or streaks on dorsal, adipose, caudal, anal, and ventral fins.   (*furiosus*, furious.)

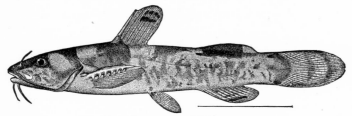

Fig. 20.   MAD-TOM.   *Schilbeodes furiosus.*

Found only in Tar, Neuse, and Little rivers.   Length 4 inches.   The pectoral spines are more strongly developed than in any other species of American
cat-fish, and the secretion of the axillary gland is said to be more poisonous than
in any other mad-tom.

Order PLECTOSPONDYLI.   The Carp-like Fishes.

This order includes a majority of the fresh-water fishes of the world, and is
numerously represented in the local fauna.   The 4 anterior vertebræ are united
and peculiarly modified, giving rise to a series of small bones (Webberian ossi-
cles) which connect the air-bladder with the ear; the opercular bones are well
developed; the branchiostegals are few in number; the body is scaled; the dorsal
fin is single, and it and the other fins are without true spines.   Most of the American species belong in a suborder (Eventognathi) in which the jaws are toothless,
the inferior pharyngeal bones are falicform, and the upper pharyngeals are 2 in
number; the gill-slits are restricted; and the gill-membranes are joined to the
isthmus.   The 2 families having species in North Carolina are typified by the
suckers and minnows, and may be thus distinguished:

i. Maxillaries forming part of the margin of the jaw; pharyngeal teeth numerous and comb-
like. . . . . .CATOSTOMIDÆ.
ii. Premaxillaries alone forming margin of upper jaw; pharyngeal teeth few. . . .CYPRINIDÆ.

Family CATOSTOMIDÆ.   The Suckers.

Suckers are well represented in North Carolina streams, and are among the
best known and most easily recognized of the fresh-water fishes.   The body is

elongate, sometimes much compressed, sometimes nearly cylindrical. The head is usually conical, with mouth inferior, protractile, fleshy-lipped, and without teeth in the jaws. The margin of the upper jaw is formed in part by the maxillary bones and in part by the premaxillaries. There are 4 gill-arches; the gill-membranes are joined to the isthmus; the branchiostegals number 3; and pseudo-branchiæ are present. The lower pharyngeal bones are sickle-shaped and surmounted by a single row of coarse teeth. The cycloid scales are either large or small; no scales appear on the head. All the fins are well developed; the dorsal is comparatively long, the anal short, the caudal large and usually forked. The large air-bladder is divided by transverse constrictions. The suckers are medium-sized fishes, normally found only in fresh water, ascending streams and brooks in spring to spawn. Their feeding habits are determined by their peculiar mouth, the pharyngeal teeth acting as grinders. Their food consists of animals (insects and other small aquatic forms) and also mud, which is doubtless ingested for the animal matter it contains; food articles are taken into the mouth by suction. In some species the males in spring acquire red or black pigment on body or fins, and develop tubercles on head, body, and fins.

North Carolina has more species of suckers than any other state, and more species described from and peculiar to it than any other state. Most of the suckers peculiar to the state were described by Professor Cope in 1870 from the Allegheny region, and some of them have not been met with since that time. While some of those now recognized as valid will doubtless be excluded when further information regarding them is obtained, in the present state of our knowledge they must be retained as distinct species.

While abundant and caught in large numbers in North Carolina, the suckers are of less value commercially than they are for home consumption, especially in the upper courses of the streams, where they furnish a not insignificant part of the food of the people at times, being the principal food fishes of the upland streams. The quantity of suckers marketed and the price received therefor by the fishermen are here given for three years: 1890—60,550 pounds, $1,779; 1897—135,230 pounds, $3,037; 1902—169,350 pounds, $7,874.

Key to the North Carolina genera of suckers.

i. Air-bladder constricted into 2 parts.
   a. Lateral line complete and continuous; scales small....................CATOSTOMUS.
  aa. Lateral line interrupted or wanting; scales large.
     b. Lateral line entirely wanting; fish small ....ERIMYZON.
    bb. Lateral line more or less developed; fish larger...................MINYTREMA.
ii. Air-bladder constricted into 3 parts.
   c. Pharyngeal teeth flattened; mouth moderate or small; lips usually folded..MOXOSTOMA.
  cc. Pharyngeal teeth enlarged, cylindrical; mouth large; lips thick ......PLACOPHARYNX.

Genus CATOSTOMUS LeSueur. Fine-scaled Suckers.

Common fishes peculiar to the United States, with the exception of one species found in Siberia. The mouth, on the under side of head, has a thick upper lip covered with papillæ, and a very large lower lip with a broad margin; the small eye is placed rather high on the side of the head; the dorsal fin begins in the center of the body, the ventrals are under the dorsal, the anal is short and deep, and the caudal is evenly forked; lateral line distinct, more or less straight. The two species inhabiting North Carolina may be readily distinguished by the number of scales. (*Catostomus*, inferior-mouthed.)

42. CATOSTOMUS COMMERSONII (Lacépède).

"Sand Sucker"; Common Sucker; White Sucker.

Cyprinus commersonii Lacépède, Histoire Naturelle des Poissons, v, 502, 1803; locality not known.
Catostomus teres, Cope, 1870b, 468, 495; "in all the rivers of the state and on both sides of the Allegheny watershed". Jordan, 1889b, 136, 151; Catawba and French Broad rivers.
Catostomus commersonii, Jordan & Evermann, 1896, 178, pl. xxxiv, fig. 83. Bean, 1903, 914; Cane River, tributary of French Broad.

DIAGNOSIS.—Form rather stout, but little compressed, depth .22 to .25 of total length; head large, conical, about .25 total length in adults; snout projecting but little beyond mouth; mouth large, lips papillose, the papillæ of upper lip in 2 or 3 rows; scales 64 to 70 in lateral series, 10 above lateral line and 9 below, crowded anteriorly, larger on side than below; dorsal rays 12, second and third rays longest; anal rays 7, third and fourth rays longest. Color: olivaceous above, whitish below; males in spring have a rosy band or stripe along sides; young brownish, mottled, with dark lateral band or blotches. (Named after M. Commerson, an early French traveler.)

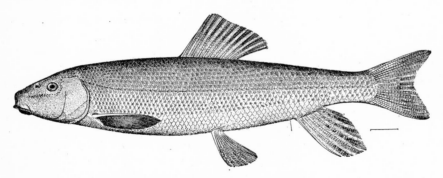

Fig. 21. WHITE SUCKER. *Catostomus commersonii.*

This very abundant and well known sucker occurs from New England throughout the Great Lakes to Montana and thence southward to Georgia and Kansas. Dr. Jordan found it common in Catawba River near Marion, and in French Broad and Swannanoa rivers near Asheville. In the French Broad it is known as "sand sucker" and is a food fish of some importance. Cope lists the species from French Broad, Catawba, Yadkin, and Neuse rivers. Its maximum length is 2 feet and its maximum weight 5 pounds. Insects, small mollusks, worms, and other animals are eaten. Spawning occurs in spring in the headwaters of small streams. It is not infrequently caught on the hook baited with angleworm.

43. CATOSTOMUS NIGRICANS LeSueur.
"Hog Sucker"; Black Sucker; Stone-roller.

Catostomus nigricans LeSueur, Journal Academy Natural Sciences of Philadelphia, 1817, 102; Lake Erie. Cope, 1870b, 468; French Broad River. Jordan, 1889b, 125, 128, 151; Pamlico, Neuse, and tributaries of French Broad River. Jordan & Evermann, 1896, 181. Bean, 1903, 914; Cane River, tributary of French Broad.

DIAGNOSIS.—Form elongate, not compressed, the depth contained 4.5 to 5 times in total length; head about equal to depth of body, flattened above, concave between eyes; eye small, about .33 length of snout and .2 length of head; mouth large, lips well developed and covered with numerous small papillæ; fins large; dorsal base .66 length of head, its rays 10 or 11; anal rays 7; pectoral longer than dorsal; caudal moderately forked; scales 48 to 55 in lateral series, 12 to 15 in transverse series. Color: brownish above, with blackish blotches (becoming obsolete with age), sides golden or brassy, below white; lower fins dull red; young irregularly blotched. (*nigricans*, blackish.)

The black sucker has a range almost as wide as the white sucker; it extends from New York to Minnesota, and thence to South Carolina, Arkansas, and Kansas. In North Carolina it is common on both sides of the Alleghanies. In size and habits it resembles the white sucker, although it is more partial to clear, cold water. Its food value is slight.

Genus ERIMYZON Jordan. Chub Suckers.

Small fish of streams and lakes with a wide distribution east of Rocky Mountains. Body rather short, compressed; lower lip large, v-shaped, with many folds; gill-rakers long; pharyngeal teeth small, slender, compressed; scales rather large, crowded anteriorly; dorsal and anal fins short and high, caudal slightly forked or merely concave. One species, variable. (*Erimyzon*, sucker.)

44. ERIMYZON SUCETTA (Lacépède).
"Mullet"; Chub Sucker.

Cyprinus sucetta Lacépède, Histoire Naturelle des Poissons, v, 606, 1803; South Carolina.
Moxostoma oblongum, Cope, 1870b, 468; Neuse River.
Erimyzon sucetta, Jordan, 1889b, 128, 132; Neuse and Cape Fear rivers. Smith, 1893a, 194; Edenton Bay. Evermann & Cox, 1896, 304; Neuse River. Jordan & Evermann, 1896, 185, pl. xxxvi, fig. 89.

DIAGNOSIS.—Body oblong, compressed, back elevated, depth .33 total length; head rather short, its length .25 total body length; space between eyes broad; mouth small, protractile; eye .20 to .25 length of head; dorsal fin short, high, the rays 12 to 15 in number; anal rays 7; caudal slightly forked; scales closely overlapping, rather large, 35 to 40 in lateral series, 13 to 15 in transverse series. Color: variable with age and environment; adults light brown above, pale below, usually with pale longitudinal streaks along scales, a bronze or coppery sheen over all; young with black lateral band, becoming broken into blotches and forming transverse bands, these disappearing with age; males in spring with several large tubercles on each side of snout. (*sucetta*, from the French *sucet*, sucker.)

This handsome and well marked species is abundant in the Great Lakes, the Mississippi Valley, and seaboard streams from Virginia to Texas; a northern variety (*oblongus*) ranges from Virginia to Maine. The species probably inhabits all the North Carolina streams flowing into the Atlantic, and is known from Albemarle Sound, the Neuse River, and Cape Fear River. It is common in the

Neuse from Goldsboro upward, and has also been found in the lower Neuse at Kinston, where in 1875 and 1883 J. W. Milner collected specimens now in the National Museum. In June, 1905, Mr. C. S. Brimley obtained several specimens in Lake Ellis, Craven County; these are now in the State Museum at Raleigh. It has no distinctive name in North Carolina, and is called simply "mullet". The maximum length is about 10 inches.

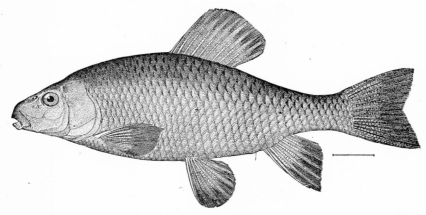

Fig. 22. CHUB SUCKER. *Erimyzon sucetta.*

Genus MINYTREMA Jordan. Spotted Suckers.

Intermediate between *Erimyzon* and *Moxostoma*; form elongate; mouth inferior, horizontal, upper lip large, lower lip small, v- shaped, with folds; gill-rakers long; scales large; lateral line absent in young, interrupted in adult; dorsal and anal fins short and high, caudal slightly forked. One species, of moderate size. (*Minytrema*, reduced aperture, in allusion to imperfect lateral line.)

45. MINYTREMA MELANOPS (Rafinesque).
"Black Winter Sucker"; Spotted Sucker; Winter Sucker.

Catostomus melanops Rafinesque, Ichthyologia Ohiensis, 57, 1820; Ohio River.
Minytrema melanops, Jordan, 1889b, 132; Haw River, tributary of Cape Fear River. Jordan & Evermann, 1896, 187, pl. xxxvi, fig 90.

DIAGNOSIS.—Depth about .25 length, greater in adults than in young; head rather less than .33 total length; eye small, .16 to .20 length of head; dorsal rays 12, anal rays 7; scales large, 44 to 48 in lengthwise series, 12 to 14 in crosswise series. Color: dusky above, pale below with brassy luster; a black spot at base of each scale along sides of body forming distinct lines; a black spot on back behind dorsal fin; old males in spring with tubercles on head. (*melanops*, having a black appearance.)

While this sucker has a wide range, extending from the Great Lakes to Texas, it is a rare species in North Carolina. It is known from Reedy Fork of Haw River, a tributary of Cape Fear River, at a point 11 miles northeast of Greensboro, where two specimens were obtained by Dr. Jordan in 1888 and where the fish is called "black winter sucker". The U. S. National Museum has four specimens from Neuse River at Kinston, collected by J. W. Milner in 1875, and another from Cape Fear River collected by Marshall McDonald in 1880. The fish reaches a length of 18 inches.

Fig. 23. SPOTTED SUCKER. *Minytrema melanops.*

Genus MOXOSTOMA Rafinesque. Red-horses.

A numerous genus of large-sized suckers found all over the United States east of Rocky Mountains. The elongate body is more or less compressed and the back elevated; size of head, mouth, and eye variable; lips well developed, with transverse folds; gill-rakers long and weak; scales large; dorsal fin rather long and high, in about middle of body; anal fin short and high; caudal large and well forked. The genus is more numerously represented in North Carolina than in any other state, and some of the nominal species are difficult to distinguish and are perhaps not distinct. Following are some of the characters by which the species may be separated, according to Cope and Jordan & Evermann:

Key to the North Carolina species of red-horses.

i. Labial folds broken up into conspicuous papillæ; mouth very small; snout projecting; dorsal
  rays 12 to 14 . . . .*papillosum.*
ii. Labial folds not broken up into distinct papillæ.
  a. Dorsal fin long, with 15 to 18 rays; lower lip v-shaped; mouth quite small. . .*collapsum.*
  aa. Dorsal fin shorter, with 10 to 14 or 15 rays.
    b. Lower lip narrow, infolded, v-shaped, with distinct median crease in which the halves
      meet at an acute angle.
      c. Body elongate, subcylindrical, little compressed; snout truncate . . . . . .*pidiense.*
      cc. Body compressed, back elevated, muzzle projecting beyond very small mouth.
                                                                        coreaonus.
    bb. Lower lip thin, forming a narrow, crescent-shaped border around mandible.
      d. Head small, .20 total length; snout prominent; dorsal rays 12 to 14 . . . .*album.*
      dd. Head larger, .25 total length; snout not projecting; dorsal rays 14 or 15.
                                                                        thalassinum.
  bbb. Lower lip full, truncate behind, not distinctly v-shaped or u-shaped.
    e. Dorsal fin moderate, rays usually 13 (12 to 14); body more or less compressed.
      f. Lobes of caudal fin approximately the same length.
        g. Dorsal fin with free margin nearly straight; lower fins always red in life.
          h. Body elongate, back little elevated . . . .*aureolum.*
          hh. Body stout, back much elevated . . . .*robustum.*
        gg. Dorsal fin with free margin concave; lower fins pale.

   i. Head moderate; back not elevated ....*macrolepidotum.*
   ii. Head very short and blunt; back elevated ....*crassilabre.*
  ff. Upper lobe of caudal fin more or less produced and falcate; head short; snout much
    projecting; mouth small; first dorsal rays produced ....*conus.*
 ee. Dorsal fin short, rays 10 to 12; body elongate, subcylindrical or slightly compressed.
  j. Scales 50 in lateral series, 18 before dorsal fin; color plain brownish, tips of dorsal
    and caudal fins dusky. ....*rupiscartes.*
  jj. Scales 43 in lateral series, 15 before dorsal fin; series of streaks along sides, tips of
    dorsal and caudal fins black.....................................*cervinum.*

(*Moxostoma,* sucking-mouth.)

46. MOXOSTOMA PAPILLOSUM (Cope).
"Red-horse"; "Shiner"; White Mullet.

Ptychostomus papillosus Cope, 1870*b*, 470; Catawba and Yadkin rivers. Jordan, 1878, 134; North Carolina.
Moxostoma papillosum, Jordan, 1889*b*, 125, 128, 131, 136; Tar, Neuse, Cape Fear, and Catawba rivers. Evermann & Cox, 1896, 305; Neuse River near Raleigh. Jordan & Evermann, 1896, 189.

DIAGNOSIS.—Body deeper than thick, dorsal outline not elevated, depth contained 4 to
4.5 times in total length; head elongate, not more than .25 total length; muzzle truncate in
profile, the upper lip hanging free, the lower deeply incised behind so as to be v-shaped; both
lips finely granular, not plicate; top of head flat; scales large, 42 in lengthwise series, 6 + 5 in
crosswise series; dorsal rays 12. Color: silvery white, except some blackish shades at the
bases of the scales of the dorsal region; fins in life pure white. (*papillosum,* full of papillæ.)

  This sucker, which is one of the commonest species found in North Carolina,
ranges from the Dismal Swamp tò Cape Fear River, and thence to Georgia. Dr.
Jordan reported it as common in Tar River near Rocky Mount; in Neuse River near
Raleigh; in Little River near Goldsboro; in Haw River near Greensboro; and in
Catawba River at Morgantown. Specimens from Neuse River at Kinston,
collected by J. W. Milner, are in the U. S. National Museum.

  According to Cope, in 1869 this species was quite abundant in the Catawba
and Yadkin rivers, and was highly valued by the inhabitants as an article of food,
being regarded as the best of the suckers. It was less frequently caught on a
hook than some other species, but in autumn it ran into the weirs in considerable
numbers. The fishermen of that section called it "shiner". The largest specimens Cope found were only 1 foot long and weighed a pound; Jordan, however,
collected examples 18 inches long and weighing upwards of 3 pounds.

47. MOXOSTOMA COLLAPSUM (Cope).
"Sucking Mullet"; Small-mouthed Red-horse.

Ptychostomus collapsus Cope, 1870*b*, 471; Neuse, Yadkin and Catawba rivers.
?Catostomus anisurus Rafinesque, Ichthyologia Ohiensis, 54, 1820; Ohio River.
Myxostoma velatum, Jordan, 1878, 132; Neuse, Yadkin, and Catawba rivers (after Cope).
Moxostoma anisurum, Smith, 1893*a*, 198; Roanoke River.
Moxostoma collapsum, Jordan & Evermann, 1896, 190.

DIAGNOSIS.—Body rather stout, compressed, back elevated, the depth contained 3.33
times in total length; head short, small, conic, broad and flat above, its length .25 of total
length; mouth small, lips plicate, muzzle truncate and overhanging the mouth; eye in middle
of side of head, .25 length of head, twice length of snout, and .66 width of interorbital space;
dorsal fin long, free edge straight, its base .83 length of head, rays 15: caudal lobes subequal;

scales 42 in longitudinal series, 11 in transverse series. Color: silvery, dusky above, whitish below; dorsal and caudal membranes blackish, other fins pale; "inferior fins all orange" (Cope). (*collapsum*, flattened sidewise.)

This species is found only in the lowland streams in North Carolina. Cope's type specimens were only a foot long, but he saw specimens from Catawba River of 3 and 4 pounds weight. He reported it as immensely numerous, and as caught in weir traps in spring and autumn; as a food fish it is inferior to *Moxostoma papillosum*, "but it is not at all to be rejected".

This appears to be the species of which numerous specimens were observed by the writer at the seining beaches in Roanoke River near Plymouth in April, 1892. The largest examples seen were 10 inches long. From *Moxostoma crassilabre*, which was abundant at the same time and place, it was easily distinguishable by the absence of dark spots at the bases of scales, by the straight margin of the dorsal fin, etc. This fish is possibly identical with *Moxostoma anisurum* (Rafinesque) from the Ohio valley and Great Lakes.

48. MOXOSTOMA PIDIENSE (Cope).
Sucker.

Ptychostomus pidiensis Cope, 1870b, 471; Yadkin River.
Moxostoma pidiense, Jordan & Evermann, 1896, 191.

DIAGNOSIS.—Form cylindric, little compressed; head long, contained 4.5 times in total length; muzzle truncate; eye small; dorsal rays 12. Color: light brownish yellow, fins light red. (*pidiense*, inhabiting the Pedee.)

This species is named after the Pedee River, of which the Yadkin is a tributary, and is known only from that stream. It is a small, rare species (10 inches long), and is known only from Cope's description of a few specimens he obtained from traps.

49. MOXOSTOMA COREGONUS (Cope).
"Blue Mullet".

Ptychostomus coregonus Cope, 1870b, 472; Catawba and Yadkin rivers.
Moxostoma coregonus, Jordan & Evermann, 1896, 191.

DIAGNOSIS.—Body fusiform, back arched; head very small, .20 total length; muzzle regularly conic, projecting far beyond mouth; mouth very small, but little protractile; eye large, .25 to .33 length of head; dorsal rays 14. Color: silvery, scales shaded with leaden above and with black pigment at their bases, giving a dusky hue to whole; belly and inferior fins pure white. (*coregonus*, the white-fish, in allusion to the shape.)

Cope found this fish very abundant in Catawba and Yadkin rivers, never exceeding a foot in length; it was caught with *Moxostoma collapsum* and *pidiense* and used for food, but it was the least valued of all the species. At Morganton it was known as the "blue mullet". The species does not appear to have been recorded since Cope's time, although it is a strongly marked fish, "easily distinguishable by its very small head, with conic muzzle, elevated arched back, minute inferior mouth, combined with small size".

50. MOXOSTOMA ALBUM (Cope).
"White Mullet".

Ptychostomus albus Cope, 1870b, 472; Catawba River.
Myxostoma album, Jordan, 1878, 130; Kinston (Neuse River).
Moxostoma album, Jordan & Evermann, 1896, 191.

DIAGNOSIS.—Form elliptical, somewhat compressed, back slightly elevated, depth contained about 3.3 times in total length; head small, short, broad, .20 length; muzzle prominent but less so than in *M. collapsum;* mouth moderate, lower lip a narrow crescent following the edge of the mandible, not folding in median line; dorsal fin high, rays 12 to 14; caudal deeply forked. Color: very pale, lower fins white. (*album,* white.)

Cope's note regarding this fish is: "In size this species is one of the largest, reaching 4 pounds and over. It is much valued by the people living in the neighborhood of the Catawba River, North Carolina, as an article of food. They call it the 'white mullet'. I have not seen it in the Yadkin or any other river". The U. S. National Museum has specimens from the Neuse River at Kinston collected by J. W. Milner and from unknown localities in North Carolina obtained by Dr. G. B. Goode in the Washington (D. C.) market. This may be the species called "white-fish" by Lawson (1709) and thus referred to by him:

The white-fish are very large; some being two foot and a half long and more. They are found a great way up in the freshes of the rivers; and are firm meat, and an extraordinary well-relish'd fish.

51. MOXOSTOMA THALASSINUM (Cope).
Sucker.

Ptychostomus thalassinus Cope, 1870b, 472; Yadkin River.
Moxostoma thalassinum, Jordan & Evermann, 1896, 191.

DIAGNOSIS.—Similar to *Moxostoma collapsum,* but differing in shape of lower lip, which is narrowly crescentric; fusiform, back elevated; head elongate, flat above, .25 total length; muzzle not very prominent, mouth small; dorsal rays 14 or 15. Color: sea green above, white below: fins white. (*thalassinum,* sea green.)

This is one of the largest suckers, exceeding 5 pounds in weight, according to Cope. It was reported to be abundant in the Yadkin and used for food, but nothing further is known about it.

52. MOXOSTOMA AUREOLUM (LeSueur).
"Red-horse"; "White Sucker".

Catostomus aureolus LeSueur, Journal Academy of Natural Sciences of Philadelphia, i, 95, 1817; Lake Erie.
Ptychostomus erythurus, Cope, 1870b, 474; French Broad River (Tennessee).
Moxostoma duquesnei, Jordan, 1889b, 150, 151; French Broad River.
Moxostoma aureolum, Jordan & Evermann, 1896, 192.

DIAGNOSIS.—Form stout or moderately elongate; head long, blunt, broad and flat above, .20 to .25 total length; mouth large, lips full; snout blunt, projecting; eye large; dorsal rays 12 to 14, free edge nearly straight, longest ray shorter than head; scales large, 45 in lateral series. Color: gray, greenish or rosy above, sides silvery, fins orange in adults. (*aureolum,* golden.)

An abundant species, ranging from Lake Ontario and Lake Michigan south to Arkansas, Georgia, and North Carolina. In North Carolina this sucker occurs

only in those streams tributary to the Ohio.   Jordan found the young not rare in
French Broad River and Spring Creek at Hot Springs.   It is a food fish of that
section, under the name of "white sucker".   Cope noticed it in French Broad
River in Tennessee, where examples weighing 12 pounds were reported.

53. MOXOSTOMA ROBUSTUM (Cope).
"Red-horse".

Ptychostomus robustus Cope, 1870b, 473; Yadkin River.
Moxostoma robustum, Jordan & Evermann, 1896, 193.

DIAGNOSIS.—Form very short and stout, compressed, the back elevated; head short, deep,
contained 4 or 4.5 times in total length; muzzle not prominent, truncate; lower lip very large
and full, entirely covering space between rami of jaw; eye .20 to .25 length of head; dorsal fin
short, free margin straight, rays 12.   Color: smoky or clouded above, mingled with golden
reflections, sides similar; yellowish below; dorsal, caudal and anal fins dark crimson.   (*robustum*, robust.)

No one seems to have recorded the capture of this species except Cope.
He found it only in the Yadkin, and reported it to be highly valued for the table
by people living along the river.   It was taken in spring-nets and weirs.   The
weight attained is 6 pounds or more.   This species is perhaps identical with
Moxostoma aureolum.

54. MOXOSTOMA MACROLEPIDOTUM (LeSueur).
Red-horse.

Catostomus macrolepidotus LeSueur, Journal Academy of Natural Sciences of Philadelphia, i, 94, 1817; Delaware
    River.
Ptychostomus lachrymalis, Cope, 1870b, 474; Neuse River at New Bern.
Moxostoma macrolepidotum, Jordan & Evermann, 1896, 193.

DIAGNOSIS.—Body compressed, back gently arched, the depth more than .25 length;
head stout, of moderate length; mouth large, lips large and thick, inferior lip with concave
posterior margin; eye about .5 width of interorbital space and .6 length of snout; dorsal margin
slightly concave, the rays 12 or 13; 44 to 46 scales in lateral series.   Color: dull reddish-brown,
scales dusky at base, fins pale.   (*macrolepidotum*, large-scaled.)

Inhabits lowland streams from New Jersey to North Carolina.   Jordan &
Evermann regard Cope's *Ptychostomus lachrymalis* from the Neuse at New Bern
as being the same as this species.   It grows to a length of 18 inches.

55. MOXOSTOMA CRASSILABRE (Cope).
"Red-horse"; "Red-horse Mullet"; "Sucker Mullet"; "Trout Sucker";
"Golden Mullet"; "Golden-finned Mullet"; "Horse-fish"; "Redfin"; "Mullet".

Ptychostomus crassilabris Cope, 1870b, 477; Neuse River near Raleigh.
Moxostoma crassilabre, Jordan, 1889b, 128; Little River at Goldsboro. Smith, 1893a, 194, 198; Edenton Bay
    and Roanoke River at Plymouth and Weldon.   Jordan & Evermann, 1896, 194.

DIAGNOSIS.—Body compressed, back elevated, depth contained 3.5 times in length;
head very small, broad above, .20 total length; snout blunt, overhanging the mouth; mouth
of moderate size, the lower lip truncate behind and finely papillose; eye contained 4.5 times in
length of head, 2.33 times in interorbital space and 1.5 times in snout; dorsal fin with free

border deeply incised, rays 12 or 13, longest ray longer than head and base of fin; caudal lobes equal; scales 45 in lateral series, 10 or 11 in transverse series. Color: generally pale yellowish-red, dusky above, lighter beneath, with silvery reflections; each scale above the lateral line with a black spot at base of exposed part; lower fins pale orange or red, dorsal membrane black. (Description of 15-inch specimen from Edenton Bay, April, 1902.) (*crassilabre*, thick-lipped.)

Since Cope described this species from Neuse River near Raleigh, it had not been met with until 1888, when Jordan found one specimen in Little River, a tributary of the Neuse, at Goldsboro. In 1892 the writer observed it in Edenton Bay and Roanoke River. It is abundant in the Albemarle region, and the larger fish have considerable market value. It is caught in spring, in seines and pound nets, with shad and alewives, and appears to be ascending the rivers with those species. Fish from 8 to 20 inches long were observed.

All of the common names before given were heard by the writer. "Golden mullet" and "golden-finned mullet" are trade names in use at Edenton, Elizabeth City, and other places on the sound. The smaller fish, with plain colors, are called "sucking mullet" and "trout sucker". At Plymouth the name "red-horse" is applied to the largest fish. The names "mullet", "redfin", and "horse-fish", heard at Weldon, are doubtless given also to other suckers.

56. MOXOSTOMA CONUS (Cope).
Sucker.

Ptychostomus conus Cope, 1870b, 478; Yadkin River.
Moxostoma conus, Jordan, 1889b, 128; Little River at Goldsboro. Jordan & Evermann, 1896, 196.

DIAGNOSIS.—Body much compressed, the back elevated; head small, conic; eye large; mouth exceedingly small, lower lip truncate behind; snout conic, much produced; dorsal rays 14. Color: smoky above, the scales with black bases; below white; dorsal fin dusky, inferior fins white. (*conus*, cone, in allusion to shape of snout.)

Cope found this species numerous in Yadkin River, where it was taken in large numbers with other suckers. Jordan took a single young specimen in Little River.

57. MOXOSTOMA RUPISCARTES Jordan & Jenkins.
"Jumping Mullet"; Jump-rocks.

Ptychostomus cervinus Cope, 1870b, 478 (in part); Catawba River.
Moxostoma rupiscartes Jordan & Jenkins, in Jordan, 1889a, 353; Catawba River and Bucks Creek, North Carolina; also various rivers in South Carolina and Georgia. Jordan, 1889b, 137; Catawba River near Marion, Johns River near Morgantown, and Bucks Creek at Pleasant Garden. Jordan & Evermann, 1896, 196, pl. xxxvii, fig. 93.

DIAGNOSIS.—Body long and low, depth contained 5.5 to 6 times in length; head very short, broad, flat above, a little more than .2 length; snout blunt, projecting beyond mouth; lips full, the folds somewhat broken into papillæ; scales rather small, 50 in lateral series; dorsal fin low and small, free margin concave, rays 11, first ray .66 length of head; caudal short, lunate, lobes blunt; pectorals long; anal rays 8. Color: dark olive brown, becoming paler below; young with pale lateral streaks; a faint dark spot above pectoral; tips of dorsal and caudal dusky. (*rupiscartes*, rock-jumper.)

This species is abundant in the large tributaries of the Santee and extends its range as far as the Chattahoochee. It attains a large size, and is most common about rocks and in rapids. It appears to have been confounded with *Moxostoma cervinum*. Under the latter name Cope refers to this fish in the Catawba, stating that it does not exceed a foot in length, is but little valued as food, and is called by the fisherman "jumping mullet" because of its peculiar habit of leaping from the water. Jordan heard the name "jump-rocks" in Georgia.

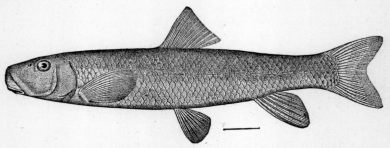

Fig. 24.　Sucker; Jump–rocks.　*Moxostoma rupiscartes.*

58. MOXOSTOMA CERVINUM (Cope).
Red-horse.

Teretulus cervinus Cope, Journal Academy of Natural Sciences of Philadelphia, 1868, 236, pl. 24, fig. 3; Roanoke and James rivers, Virginia.
Ptychostomus cervinus, Cope, 1870b, 478; Roanoke River, North Carolina and Virginia.
Moxostoma cervinum, Jordan, 1889b, 125, 129; Tar and Neuse rivers. Evermann & Cox, 1896, 305; Neuse River. Jordan & Evermann, 1896, 197.

Diagnosis.—Form elongate, cylindrical; head very short, .2 total length; mouth large, lips thick, strongly plicate; eye small; fins very small, dorsal rays 10 to 12, free margin straight, longest ray less than head; scales, 43 in lengthwise series, 11 in crosswise series. Color: yellowish brown or greenish brown above ("emerald green after death", Cope), a pale blotch on each scale forming lengthwise streaks; back often marked by dark transverse shades or blotches; fins brownish or slightly reddish, dorsal and caudal with inky black tips. (*cervinum*, fawn-colored.)

This species is known only from Roanoke, Tar, and Neuse rivers. Cope attributed the species to Catawba River, but according to Jordan the Catawba fish is *Moxostoma rupiscartes*. The species is reported as common in Tar and Neuse rivers. Its size is small, probably never more than a foot in length and often not exceeding 4 to 6 inches.

Genus PLACOPHARYNX Cope.　Big-jawed Suckers.

Similar to Moxostoma but with the pharyngeal bones much larger and stouter and with teeth less numerous and larger, those on lower part of bones from 6 to 10 in number, cylindrical, and with a broad grinding surface. Mouth large, oblique; lips thick. One species, of large size. (*Placopharynx*, broad-throated.)

59. PLACOPHARYNX DUQUESNII (LeSueur).
"Red-horse".

Catostomus duquesnii LeSueur, Journal Academy Natural Sciences Philadelphia, i, 105, 1817; Ohio River.
Placopharynx carinatus, Jordan, 1878, 108; French Broad River. Jordan, 1889*b*, 151; French Broad River.
Placopharynx duquesnii, Jordan & Everman, 1896, 198, pl. xxxiii, fig. 82.

DIAGNOSIS.—Form rather short, somewhat compressed, the depth of body more than .25 total length; head large, broad, flat, .25 total length; eye small, posterior to middle of side of head; mouth large, upper jaw oblique, the plicated lips protractile forward and downward; dorsal rays 12 or 13, the free edge concave; upper caudal lobe longer and narrower than lower; scales 45 in lengthwise series, 12 in crosswise series. Color: dark green above, sides brassy; lower fins and caudal orange red. (Named after Ft. Duquesne, now Pittsburg.)

This sucker ranges from the Great Lakes region to Arkansas and North Carolina. In the latter state it inhabits only the French Broad and tributaries. Jordan (1878) states that he collected numerous large specimens in the French Broad River, at Wolf Creek and other localities in North Carolina, where it is the most abundant member of the family, known to all fishermen as the "red-horse". He also records (1889*b*) that "large numbers run in the French Broad in June". The fish reaches a length of 2.5 feet.

Family CYPRINIDÆ.   The Minnows and Carps.

This very numerous and important family contains many well known fresh-water fishes, although only a few are of sufficient size to make them of economic value. In North Carolina, as in most other parts of the country, these fishes are almost invariably represented in the catch of youthful anglers. They are for the most part defenceless, harmless species, and their principal value is as food for other fishes. Following are the leading anatomical characters of the family as represented in North America: Body more or less elongate, compressed or rounded; margin of the upper jaw formed only by the premaxillary bones; lower pharyngeal bones supporting 1 to 3 series of teeth, which are few in number and may differ in number on the two sides; body scaly, head naked; barbels usually absent, but if present small and 2 or 4 in number; gills 4 in number, gill-membranes joined to the isthmus; pseudobranchiæ present; branchiostegals 3 in number; dorsal fin short; ventral fins abdominal; air-bladder comparatively large; stomach a simple dilatation of intestine, without appendages; coloration mostly plain. In breeding season the males of some species develop peculiarities, such as tubercles on head and body and pigmentation of fins and body, the pigment usually red but sometimes glistening white, yellow, or black. All of our species are oviparous. Some forms subsist on vegetable matter, some on animal matter, and a few are predaceous.

This family includes a number of foreign fishes (the carp, the gold-fish, the tench, and the golden ide or orf) which have been introduced into American waters; some have become wild, while others are as yet found chiefly in aquaria, fountains, and private ponds.

Many of the genera and species of minnows are very similar, so that their identification is frequently difficult; this is especially the case with the small forms belonging in the genus Notropis. The number of scales and the number and arrangement of the pharyngeal teeth are important diagnostic characters.

The pharyngeal bones in the smaller species can be removed by inserting a pin (or, better, a small hook) though the gill opening under the shoulder girdle. The teeth should be carefully cleaned with a tooth-brush, or, better, a jet of water, and when dry may be examined by any small lens. In most cases a principal row of 4 or 5 larger teeth will be found, in front of which is a set of 1 or 2 smaller ones. The two sides are usually, but not always, symmetrical. Thus, "teeth 2,4—5,1" indicates two rows of teeth on each side, on the one side 4 in the principal row and 2 in the lesser; on the other side 5 in the main row and 1 in the other. "Teeth 4—4" indicates a single row of 4 on each pharyngeal bone, and so on. (Jordan & Evermann.)

This family is represented in North Carolina by 9 genera and 36 species, having more members in this state than any other family. The following key to the genera must be used in conjunction with the full generic descriptions, which come in their proper order.

*Key to the North Carolina genera of minnows and carps.**

i. Intestine very long, convoluted, and surrounding the air-bladder; peritoneum black; teeth
      4—4 or 1,4—4,0...CAMPOSTOMA.
ii. Air-bladder not wrapped in folds of intestine.
    a. Alimentary canal long, 3 to 10 times length of body; peritoneum black; teeth 4—4 with
          well-developed grinding surface...............................HYBOGNATHUS.
   aa. Alimentary canal short, less than twice length of body; peritoneum pale; teeth in 1 or 2
          rows, slender, hooked.
      b. Teeth in main row 5—5 or 4—5.
         c. Median line of abdomen behind ventral fins rounded, scales passing over it; anal
               base short.
            d. A small barbel on maxillary ....SEMOTILUS.
           dd. No barbel on maxillary ....LEUCISCUS.
        cc. Median line of abdomen behind ventral fins compressed to a sharp edge over
               which scales do not extend; anal base elongate.
      bb. Teeth in main row 4—4, lesser row often lacking.
         e. Maxillary without barbels.
            f. Teeth 4—4, 1,4—4,1, 1,4—4,0, or 2,4—4,2; lower jaw with lip thin.
                                                                         NOTROPIS.
           ff. Teeth 4—4, lower jaw with lip developed as a fleshy lobe on each side.
                                                                         PHENACOBIUS.
        ee. Maxillary with 1 or 2 small barbels near extremity.
            g. Premaxillary bones not protractile, joined to forehead by a broad frenum;
                  teeth 2,4—4,2; scales small; dorsal fin posterior.
                                                                         RHINICHTHYS.
           gg. Premaxillaries protractile; teeth 4—4, or 1,4—4,1, or 1,4—4,0; scales large;
                  dorsal fin medium.......................................HYBOPSIS.

Genus CAMPOSTOMA Agassiz. Stone-rollers.

Small American fishes, vegetable feeders, unique in having the very long intestine coiled many times around the suspended air-bladder. Teeth 4—4 or 1,4—4,0, with a grinding surface, 1 or 2 teeth having a slight hook; fins small, dorsal inserted over ventrals, anal short. The common name is in allusion to the habit of turning and rolling small stones, probably to feed on the attached algæ. Several species, of which one is common over a large part of eastern and central sections. (*Campostoma*, curve-mouthed.)

* The introduced carp has become so generally distributed and firmly established that it may properly be listed among fishes of the state, and it will be considered on page 105, after the native species of this family. The genus (Cyprinus) is characterized by a long dorsal fin, a strong serrated spine at the beginning of the dorsal and anal fins, 4 long barbels, and molar pharyngeal teeth of the formula 1, 1, 3 on each side.

60. CAMPOSTOMA ANOMALUM (Rafinesque).
Stone-roller, Stone-lugger.

Rutilus anomalus Rafinesque, Ichthyologia Ohiensis, 52, 1820; Licking River, Kentucky.
Campostoma anomalum, Cope, 1870*b*, 466; French Broad and Catawba rivers. Jordan, 1889*b*, 137, 152; Catawba River and tributaries, and French Broad River and tributaries. Bean, 1903, 914; Cane River, tributary of French Broad River. Jordan & Evermann, 1896, 205, pl. xxxix, fig. 95.

DIAGNOSIS.—Body rather stout, somewhat compressed, the greatest depth contained 4 to 4.5 times in total length; length of head rather less than .25 total length; snout obtuse, twice length of eye; maxilla does not extend as far as eye; dorsal rays 8; anal rays 7 or 8; scales 49 to 55 in lateral series, 15 or 16 in transverse series; teeth 4—4 or 1,4—4,0. Color: brown above with brassy luster, pale below, scales mottled with black; a dark vertical bar behind opercle; a dusky median crossbar on dorsal and anal fins, these fins olivaceous in female; the male in spring develops large rounded tubercles on head and sometimes over whole body, and the dorsal and anal take on a fiery red color. (*anomalum*, extraordinary.)

This interesting species ranges from New York to Wyoming and Texas, and in North Carolina occurs on both sides of the Alleghenies, in French Broad and Santee valleys. It has been found to be common in Catawba River near Marion, in Bucks Creek at Pleasant Garden, and in Johns River near Morgantown. In the basin of French Broad River, it has been reported as common in Spring Creek at Hot Springs, in Swannanoa River near Asheville, and in south fork of Swannanoa at Black Mountain station.

The stone-roller does not exceed 8 inches in length, and has no value as food for man. It feeds on plants, chiefly algæ, for which its extremely long intestine is adapted.

Genus HYBOGNATHUS Agassiz. Shiners; Gudgeons.

Small herbivorous fishes of silvery color, abundant in fresh water in eastern and central states and Mexico; species numerous. Form elongate, compressed; mouth nearly horizontal; teeth 4—4, with oblique grinding surface; intestine long, 3 to 10 times length of body; scales large, deciduous; lateral line complete; fins small. One species found in North Carolina. (*Hybognathus*, swell-jawed.)

61. HYBOGNATHUS NUCHALIS Agassiz.
"Choby"; "Shiner"; "Gudgeon"; "Roach"; Silvery Minnow; Smelt.

Hybognathus nuchalis Agassiz, American Journal of Sciences and Arts, 1855, 224; Quincy, Illinois. Jordan & Gilbert, 1879, 368; Neuse River at Goldsboro. Jordan, 1889*b*, 125, 127, 132, 134, 137; Tar, Neuse, Cape Fear, Yadkin, and Catawba rivers. Smith, 1893*a*, 190, 194, 199; Albemarle Sound and tributaries. Evermann & Cox, 1896, 305; Neuse River at Raleigh. Jordan & Evermann, 1896, 213.
?Hybognathus argyritis, Cope, 1870*b*, 466; Catawba River.

DIAGNOSIS.—Form rather slender, compressed, width only half depth, depth contained 4 to 4.3 times in total length; head rather short, tapering, its length rather less than .25 total length; upper jaw heavy, lower jaw thin and shorter than upper, mouth small, angles not extending as far back as eyes; eye rather longer than snout; lateral line anteriorly decurved; scales large, 37 to 45 in lateral series, 9 in transverse series, 13 to 15 before dorsal fin; teeth 4—4, comparatively long, scarcely hooked; dorsal fin over ventrals, rays 7 or 8 (+ 2 rudiments); anal fin with 7 or 8 rays (+ 2 rudiments); caudal deeply forked; intestine 7 to 10 times length of body. Color: olivaceous, translucent, sides silvery, fins plain. (*nuchalis*, relating to nape.)

This minnow inhabits clear streams from New Jersey to Missouri and Texas, and is abundant in most localities. In Pasquotank River in April, 1902, the present writer found this species numerous, probably surpassing in abundance any other fish of the family; it was also common in Albemarle Sound near Edenton and in Roanoke River near Plymouth. The maximum length is 6 to 7 inches, but the average is only 4 inches. The fish feeds largely on minute water plants and the intestine is often enormously distended with vegetable matter. It freely takes the hook baited with angle-worm and is often caught for food. It is important as food for other fishes, and is a desirable bait for black bass and perch.

Genus SEMOTILUS Rafinesque. Horned Dace; Fall-fishes.

Large minnows with rather robust form, large head, wide terminal mouth, protractile upper jaw, a small barbel at posterior extremity of each maxillary, short alimentary canal, complete lateral line, teeth 2,4—5,2, without grinding surface. Two species, one of which inhabits North Carolina waters. (*Semotilus*, spotted banner or fin.)

62. SEMOTILUS ATROMACULATUS (Mitchill).
Horned Dace; Dace; Chub.

Cyprinus atromaculatus Mitchill, American Monthly Magazine, ii, 1818, 324; Wallkill River.
Semotilus corporalis, Cope, 1870b, 457; French Broad, Catawba, Yadkin, Deep, and Neuse rivers.
Semotilus atromaculatus, Jordan 1889b, 125, 131; Tar and Cape Fear rivers. Smith, 1893a, 199; Roanoke River at Weldon. Evermann & Cox, 1896, 305; Neuse River near Raleigh. Jordan & Evermann, 1896, 222, pl. xl, fig. 100.

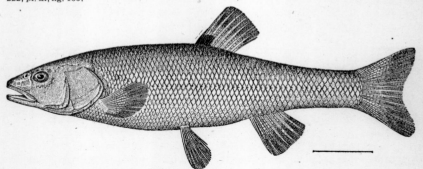

Fig. 25. HORNED DACE. *Semotilus atromaculatus.*

DIAGNOSIS.—Body rather elongate, back slightly elevated, the highest point being in front of dorsal fin; depth .25 length; head very large, broad, more than .25 length; snout broad, mouth wide, oblique, maxillary extending to pupil; barbel small, hardly visible in young fish; teeth 2,5—4,2; eye small, .2 length of head; scales 48 to 55 in lengthwise series, about 15 in crosswise series; lateral line abruptly decurved over pectorals, thence straight to tail; dorsal rays 7, anal rays 8. Color: dull bluish above, white or creamy on sides and belly; a black or dusky lateral band, most distinct in young and disappearing in large fish; a black spot always at anterior lower angle of dorsal fin, this spot edged with red in males; fins plain, the anal, ventral, and pectoral bases sometimes pinkish, and caudal yellowish; males in spring with rosy sides and coarse tubercles on snout (whence the common name of horned dace.) (*atromaculatus*, black-spotted.)

The typical form of this species is found from Maine to Wyoming and from Canada to Missouri. Some North Carolina specimens are referable to the variety *thoreauianus* of Jordan, which ranges from North Carolina to Alabama and is distinguished by a rather stouter body, larger scales, less distinct spot on dorsal fin, etc.; other examples are intermediate. The fish is widely distributed in the state, being known from the Roanoke to the Cape Fear, chiefly in brooks. It is the largest of the native cyprinoids in the state, and is often the largest fish in a creek or brook; the usual length is under a foot, but it attains a considerably larger size, and specimens have been taken weighing 4 pounds. It is a fair food fish, although very bony, and is often caught with hook and line. It feeds on worms, mollusks, small fish, and other animal food.

Genus LEUCISCUS Cuvier. Dace.

An old-world genus with numerous American representatives, small freshwater species found in all parts of the country. Form oblong, compressed or rounded; mouth large, terminal; teeth 2,5—4,2, 1,5—4,2, or 1,4—4,1, hooked, with or without a narrow grinding surface; lateral line decurved, more or less complete; scales of small or medium size; dorsal fin placed posteriorly; anal short or long; intestinal canal short; color varying, males often brilliant. One species found in North Carolina. (*Leuciscus*, ancient name for the European dace, from *leucus*, white.)

63. LEUCISCUS VANDOISULUS Cuvier & Valenciennes.
Dace.

Leuciscus vandoisulus Cuvier & Valenciennes, Histoire Naturelle des Poissons, xvii, 317, 1844; South Carolina. Jordan & Evermann, 1896, 239.
Clinostomus carolinus Girard, Proceedings Academy of Natural Sciences of Philadelphia, 1856, 212; Yadkin River, Salem, N. C.
Clinostomus affinis, Cope, 1870b, 494; Catawba and Yadkin rivers.
Squalius vandoisulus, Jordan, 1889b, 138; Bucks Creek, tributary of Catawba River.

DIAGNOSIS.—Body elongate, deep, compressed, depth contained 4.33 times in length; head large, more than .25 total length; mouth large, oblique, lower jaw projecting, maxillary extending as far back as pupil; eye contained 3.5 times in length of head; teeth 2,5—5,2 or 2,5—4,2; lateral line complete; scales 48 to 55 in lateral series; dorsal rays 9, anal rays 8. Color: bluish green above, some scales darker; a dark lateral band, above which is a pale streak; males in spring with body bright rose-red. Length, 5 inches. (*vandoisulus*, from *vandoise*, French name for a dace.)

Ranges from Maryland to Georgia in clear brooks on both sides of the Alleghany Mountains. It is abundant in the Catawba (Bucks Creek at Pleasant Garden), and is accredited by Cope to the Yadkin as well as the Catawba. Recently (1904) the species has been recorded from Middle Creek, a tributary of the Little Tennessee River in Macon County, North Carolina, examples having been forwarded therefrom to the Bureau of Fisheries by Mr. D. P. Cabe, of Otto.

Genus NOTEMIGONUS Rafinesque.   Roaches.

A strongly marked genus, with body greatly compressed and very deep, the dorsal and ventral outlines being much curved; mouth small; teeth 5—5, hooked, having grinding surface with a fluted edge; scales large; lateral line very markedly curved; dorsal fin small, placed behind ventrals; anal base long, its rays rather numerous; intestine short.   One species, with several varieties. (*Notemigonus*, sharp-backed.)

64. NOTEMIGONUS CRYSOLEUCAS (Mitchill).
"Roach"; "Shiner"; "Shiner Sun-fish"; "Shad Roach"; Golden Shiner; Bream; Dace; Chub.

Cyprinus crysoleucas Mitchill, Report Fishes New York, 23, 1814; New York.
Stilbe americana, Cope, 1870b, 465; Catawba, Yadkin, and Neuse basins.
Notemigonus chrysoleucus, Jordan, 1889b, 126, 129, and 133; Tar, Neuse, and Cape Fear rivers.   Smith, 1893a, 191, 195, 199; Pasquotank River, Edenton Bay, Roanoke River at Plymouth and Weldon.
Notemigonus crysoleucas, Evermann & Cox, 1896, 305; Neuse River near Raleigh.
Abramis chrysoleucas, Smith, 1901, 134; Lake Mattamuskeet.
Abramis crysoleucas, Jordan & Evermann, 1896, 250, pl. xlv, fig. 111

DIAGNOSIS.—Body somewhat elongate, depth equal to .33 length; head small, compressed, conic, rather less than .25 length; eye .25 length of head; mouth oblique, small, upper jaw not extending to front of eye; dorsal fin short, high, rays 7 or 8; anal rays 13 to 16 in North Carolina specimens; scales 45 to 50 in lateral series, 10 above and 3 below lateral line.   Color: pale green, with uniform golden luster; fins yellowish, lower fins red or orange in breeding males (and sometimes in females).   (*crysoleucas*, golden-white.)

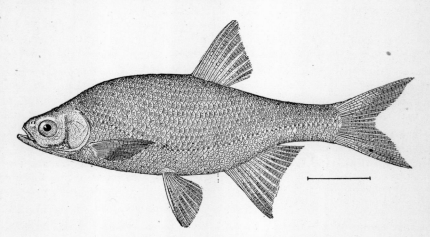

Fig. 26.   ROACH.   *Notemigonus crysoleucas.*

This minnow is abundant in all parts of North Carolina east of the mountains.   It is one of the best known of the family, and may be readily distinguished by the greatly decurved lateral line and the golden or brassy color. Cope reports it as common in still and sluggish waters in the basins of the Catawba, Yadkin, and Neuse; Jordan lists it from the Tar, Neuse, and Cape

Fear; Evermann & Cox report it as excessively abundant in the vicinity of Raleigh, especially in meadow ditches and isolated ponds and pools. It is everywhere abundant in the Albemarle region, being caught in large numbers in pound nets and seines during the shad season. Jordan's specimens are referred to the southern variety *bosci*, characterized by larger scales and more numerous anal rays, but some of the Albemarle Sound fish represent the typical form. The largest example obtained by the writer in Pasquotank River in April, 1902, was 7.75 inches long in spawning condition, with ventral fins crimson in color, anal dull orange at base with a black margin; in other specimens the lower fins were yellow; dorsal rays 7 or 8, anal rays 14 or 15, scales 45 to 50 in lateral line, 13 in crosswise series. Fish from Roanoke River had 13 or 14 anal rays and 50 scales in lateral series.

The roach has a number of common names in North Carolina; all of those shown above are in use in the Albemarle region except "shad roach", which is employed at Raleigh. The fish reaches a fair size for a minnow, the maximum length being 1 foot; it is often caught by anglers, and is used for home consumption, but has no commercial importance.

Genus NOTROPIS Rafinesque. Minnows and Shiners.

A very numerous genus or group of small fishes, abundant in fresh waters all over the eastern and central sections of the United States, some species found also in Canada and Mexico. The species are very similar, variable, and difficult to distinguish. For identification, reliance must be placed chiefly on the teeth and scales, but even these are variable parts. Body elongate, subcylindrical or compressed, abdomen always rounded; mouth usually terminal, sometimes slightly inferior; scales comparatively large; lateral line present, usually continuous; fins short, dorsal located over or posterior to ventrals; pharyngeal teeth in 1 or 2 rows, the larger row always containing four teeth on each side, hooked and with a narrow surface for grinding or with sharp cutting edge; colors usually plain, males in spring becoming gaily pigmented in some species.

These fish are usually regarded as the young of other fishes, and are so small and inconspicuous that they have rarely received any distinctive common names, all being known as minnows or shiners. They have no value as human food, but are enormously important as food for game fishes.

Represented in North Carolina by 22 known species, 3 of which are peculiar to the state; the key applies to typical specimens and must be used with caution and discrimination.

Key to the North Carolina species of Notropis.

i. Teeth 4—4, 1,4—4,0, or 1,4—4,1 (rarely 2 teeth in minor rows).
  a. Scales not closely overlapped and not especially deeper than long; dorsal fin over ventrals; anal rays 7 to 9; no black spot on dorsal fin; scales large, less than 40 in lateral series; 12 to 15 before dorsal; depth not more than .25 length.
    b. Teeth 4—4, well hooked; species very small.
      c. Base of caudal without black spot (except in very young)............*procne.*
      cc. Base of caudal with a distinct black spot......................*spectrunculus.*

bb. Teeth two-rowed, with grinding surface; a distinct black spot at base of caudal fin; species large . . . .*hudsonius.*
aa. Scales deeper than long, closely overlapped on sides of body; teeth 1,4—4,1; dorsal fin with large black blotch posteriorly; no conspicuous black spot at base of caudal.
   d. Anal rays 7 to 9; fins of breeding males with white pigment.
      e. Body fusiform, depth 5.5; dorsal outline more curved than ventral; a distinct bluish band on caudal peduncle; size small . . . .*niveus.*
      ee. Body compressed, depth 3.5; dorsal and ventral outlines similar; edges of teeth serrate; size medium . . . .*analostanus.*
      eee. Body fusiform, depth 4.33; edges of teeth entire; caudal base creamy yellow; size large . . . .*galacturus.*
   dd. Anal rays 10 or 11; breeding males with much red pigment on fins and body. *pyrrhomelas.*
ii. Teeth 2,4—4,2.
   f. Anal fin short, rays 7 to 9.
      g. Teeth with grinding surface.
         h. Lower jaw included; scales on sides very closely overlapped, so that exposed part is narrow; dorsal fin over ventrals; no dorsal or caudal spot; size large, coloration plain. . . . .*albeolus.*
         hh. Dorsal fin inserted more or less posterior to ventrals; no black spot at base of dorsal fin; coloration generally brilliant in spring males.
            i. Lower jaw projecting; depth 4.5 . . . .*coccogenis.*
            ii. Jaws about equal.
               j. Base of caudal without distinct black spot.
                  k. All fins more or less red in male; scales before dorsal fin 19; depth 4.5 *rubricroceus.*
                  kk. Dorsal and caudal red at base in male; scales before dorsal fin 16; depth 5 . . . .*chlorocephalus.*
                  kkk. Dorsal and caudal plain anteriorly, black posteriorly; scales before dorsal fin 18; depth 5.5 . . . .*brimleyi.*
               jj. Base of caudal with a dark spot.
                  l. Body elongate, depth 5.5; dorsal fin small . . . .*chiliticus.*
                  ll. Body rather short, depth 3.5; dorsal fin very high. . . . .*altipinnis.*
                  lll. Body moderately elongate, depth 5; dorsal fin high . . . . . .*chalybæus.*
      gg. Teeth without grinding surface; scales not closely overlapped; no black spot at anterior base of dorsal fin, but a jet black spot at base of caudal; dorsal fin placed behind ventrals . . . .*leuciodus.*
   ff. Anal fin long, rays 11 or 12.
      m. Scales not crowded on sides, those above lateral line large and few (in 5 to 7 series); eye longer than snout; no black spot at base of dorsal.
         n. Scales before dorsal fin large, 13 to 15; eye large.
            o. Lateral line straight or nearly so.
               p. Body elongate, little compressed, depth 4.75 to 5.5 times in length. *telescopus.*
               pp. Body very elongate, depth 6 times in length . . . .*arge.*
            oo. Lateral line decurved.
               q. Body short, compressed, back elevated, depth 4.5 times in length. .*scepticus.*
               qq. Body long and slender, compressed, back not elevated, depth 5.5 times in length . . . .*atherinoides.*
         nn. Scales before dorsal fin small, 22 to 25; eye smaller. . . . .*amœnus.*
      mm. Scales very closely imbricated on sides, those above lateral line in 7 to 10 series; eye scarcely longer than snout; a dark spot at base of dorsal fin anteriorly and a similar spot at base of caudal . . . .*umbratilis.*

(*Notropis*, keel-backed, a name of no significance for these fishes, being based on a mutilated specimen.)

65. NOTROPIS PROCNE (Cope).

"Choby"; Shiner.

Hybognathus procne Cope, Proceedings Academy of Natural Sciences of Philadelphia, 1864, 279; Delaware River and other streams in Pennsylvania.
Notropis procne, Jordan, 1889*b*, 125, 129, 132, 137; Tar, Neuse, Cape Fear, and Catawba rivers. Jordan & Evermann, 1896, 264.

DIAGNOSIS.—Body short, slender, compressed, the depth contained 5.25 times in total length; caudal peduncle long and slender; head small, contained 4.75 times in total length; snout obtuse, mouth small, jaws equal; eye large, .4 length of head; 32 to 34 scales in lateral series, 8 in transverse series, 13 before dorsal fin; dorsal fin high, its first ray as long as head, rays 8; anal rays 7, the longest .8 length of head; caudal long and forked. Color: olivaceous above, white or silvery below; a narrow black lateral band extending to nose, this overlaid by a plumbeous shade; a dark stripe along middle of back; fins slightly yellowish. Length, 2.5 inches. (*procne*, a swallow.)

Inhabits coastwise streams from New York to South Carolina. In North Carolina it has been found to be common in Tar River near Rocky Mount, in Neuse River at Milburnie, in Little River at Goldsboro, in tributaries of Haw River (tributary of Cape Fear) in Guilford County, and in Catawba River near Marion. Numerous specimens have been collected in Pembroke Creek, near the Edenton hatchery, by Mr. S. G. Worth, who states that the local name for this fish (and doubtless other similar species) is "chovy" or "choby"—obviously a corruption of anchovy.

66. NOTROPIS SPECTRUNCULUS (Cope).
Shiner.

Hybopsis spectrunculus Cope, Journal Academy of Natural Sciences of Philadelphia, 1868, 231; Holston River (Virginia?). Cope, 1870b, 460; tributaries of French Broad River.
Notropis spectrunculus, Jordan, 1889b, 152; north and south forks of Swannanoa River, and Spring Creek, tributaries of French Broad River. Jordan & Evermann, 1896, 265.

DIAGNOSIS.—Body long, depth less than .2 total length; head large, broad, flat, .25 total length; eye large, .33 length of head; mouth somewhat oblique, the upper jaw extending as far as eye; scales in lateral series 37, scales before dorsal 15; dorsal rays 8, anal rays 9. Color: pale green above, white below, a dull bluish band or stripe along sides; a distinct black spot at base of caudal fin; scales of back edged with black; dorsal and anal fins black at base; all fins tinged with orange or red in male. Length, 3 inches. (*spectrunculus*, diminutive of spectrum.)

This minnow is restricted to the headwaters of the Tennessee basin, and is common in mountain streams and springs. It is exceedingly abundant in the upper waters of the Swannanoa, but is scarce in other tributaries of the French Broad.

67. NOTROPIS HUDSONIUS (Clinton), var. SALUDANUS Jordan & Brayton.
Spawn-eater; Shiner; Silver-fin.

Alburnops saludanus Jordan & Brayton, 1878, 16; Saluda River, South Carolina.
Notropis saludanus, Jordan, 1889b, 132, 134, 137; Cape Fear, Yadkin, and Catawba rivers.
Notropis hudsonius, Jordan, 1889b, 129; Neuse River. Smith, 1893a, 190, 194; Pasquotank River and Albemarle Sound.
Notropis hudsonius saludanus, Jordan & Evermann, 1896, 270, pl. xlviii, fig. 120.

DIAGNOSIS (based on specimens from Albemarle region, 2.5 inches long).—Body elongate, somewhat compressed, depth contained 4.5 to 5 times in total length; head large, its length contained 4 to 4.5 times in length; mouth on level with lower edge of orbit, small, somewhat oblique, maxillary not reaching half way to eye from end of snout; snout round, rugose; eye large, longer than snout, contained about 2.75 times in length of head; teeth slightly hooked, some with a grinding surface, number variable, either 2,4—4,2 or 0,4—4,0; scales 36 in lateral series, 8 or 9 in transverse series; lateral line complete, nearly straight except at origin;

dorsal fin rather nearer snout than base of caudal, over ventrals, rays 8; anal rays 8; caudal deeply forked.   Color: pale green above, the scales with dark edges; a silvery lateral band, with black punctulations ending in a distinct roundish black spot at base of caudal.   (*hudsonius*, pertaining to Hudson River; *saludanus*, pertaining to Saluda River.)

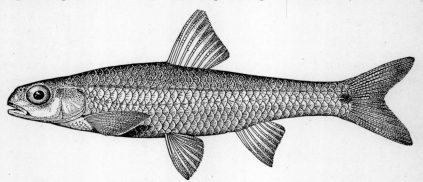

Fig. 27.   SPAWN–EATER; SHINER.   *Notropis hudsonius saludanus*.

Notropis hudsonius is a widely distributed and highly variable minnow.   It ranges from New York through the Great Lakes, to the Dakotas, and thence to Georgia and the Carolinas.   The southern form, variety *saludanus*, embraces most of the North Carolina specimens.   The fish has been found in Cape Fear, Yadkin, Catawba, Neuse, and Pasquotank rivers, but is not common in any of them; specimens have recently been examined from a tributary of Little Tennessee River in Macon County which were forwarded for identification by Mr. D. P. Cabe, of Otto.   The variety attains a length of 4 inches.

68. NOTROPIS NIVEUS (Cope).
"Shiner"; Snowy Minnow.

Hybopsis niveus Cope, 1870b, 460; upper Catawba River, North Carolina.
Notropis niveus, Jordan, 1889b, 125, 129, 132, 134, 138; Tar, Neuse, Cape Fear, Yadkin, and Catawba rivers.
    Smith, 1893a, 194; Albemarle Sound.   Evermann & Cox, 1896, 305; Neuse River near Raleigh.   Jordan
    & Evermann, 1896, 277.

DIAGNOSIS.—Body regularly fusiform, dorsal region more arched than ventral, depth .2 total length without caudal; head conic, its length contained 4.5 times in total body length; muzzle obtuse, mouth nearly terminal, slightly oblique, lower jaw included, maxilla extending to opposite anterior rim of orbit; eye equal to snout, contained 3 to 3.5 times in length of head; scales, 35 to 40 in lengthwise series, 9 in crosswise series, 15 or 16 before dorsal fin; lateral line decurved; dorsal rays 8, anal rays 8 or 9; teeth 1,4—4,1 (or 1,4—4,0), slightly hooked, with grinding surface.   Color: pale, a narrow bluish lateral band ending in a faint spot on caudal base; a large dark spot on upper posterior part of dorsal fin; dorsal and caudal yellow or creamy; tips of caudal and dorsal fins and whole of anal fin charged with milky white pigment. Length, 2.5 inches.   (*niveus*, snowy.)

This very small minnow, which is found from Virginia to South Carolina east of the mountains. inhabits most of the streams of North Carolina and is reported as abundant in the Tar, Neuse, and Catawba, and common in the Cape Fear and Yadkin.   It is also very abundant in the western end of Albemarle Sound.

69. NOTROPIS ANALOSTANUS (Girard).
Silver-fin; Satin-fin; Lace-fin.

Cyprinella analostana Girard, Proceedings Academy of Natural Sciences of Philadelphia, 1859, 59; Potomac River at Washington, D. C.
Hypsilepis analostanus, Cope, 1870b, 459; Catawba and Neuse rivers.
Notropis analostanus, Evermann & Cox, 1896, 309; Neuse River (after Cope). Jordan & Evermann, 1896, 279.

DIAGNOSIS.—Body somewhat compressed, the depth contained 3.5 times in total length; head rather short and deep; mouth small, oblique, lower jaw included within the upper when mouth is closed; scales in lateral series 34 or 35; edges of teeth serrate; dorsal rays 8, anal rays 8. Color: silvery blue on back, scales with dusky edges; a large black spot on upper posterior part of dorsal fin; in breeding males all fins more or less filled with satiny white pigment. Length, 4 inches. (*analostanus*, pertaining to Analostan Island.)

Cope states that this species is abundant in Catawba River and is also found in Neuse River; no one else, however, has reported it from North Carolina. The species is common in the Chesapeake and Delaware basins.

70. NOTROPIS GALACTURUS (Cope).
Milky-tailed Minnow.

Hypsilepis galacturus Cope, Proceedings Academy of Natural Sciences of Philadelphia, 1867, 160; Holston River, Virginia. Cope, 1870b, 459; French Broad River.
Notropis galacturus, Jordan, 1889b, 152; Swannanoa River and Spring Creek at Hot Springs, N. C. Jordan & Evermann, 1896, 279, pl. xlviii, fig. 122.

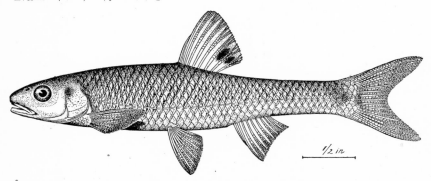

Fig. 28. MILKY–TAILED MINNOW. *Notropis galacturus.*

DIAGNOSIS.—Body elongate, fusiform, slightly compressed, the depth a little less than .25 total length; length of head equal to depth of body; mouth large, horizontal, lower jaw included within the upper; eye small; lateral line somewhat decurved; scales in lateral series 41, in cross series 9; dorsal rays 8, anal rays 8. Color: males steel blue (females olivaceous) above, silvery below; a black blotch on posterior dorsal rays; caudal fin creamy yellow at base, dusky distally; males in spring with abdomen, paired fins, and tips of dorsal, anal, and caudal fins charged with milk-white pigment, anal and caudal fins sometimes reddish. Length, 6 inches. (*galacturus*, milky-tailed.)

This minnow inhabits mountain streams from Missouri to Virginia, west of the Allegheny mountains. In North Carolina, it is common in the upper tributaries of the French Broad River (Swannanoa, south fork of Swannanoa, and Spring Creek).

71. NOTROPIS PYRRHOMELAS (Cope).
Fiery-black Minnow.

Photogenis pyrrhomelas Cope, 1870b, 363; Catawba River.
Notropis pyrrhomelas, Jordan, 1889b, 134, 138; Yadkin and Catawba rivers.   Jordan & Evermann, 1896, 280.

DIAGNOSIS.—Body rather deep, compressed, the depth contained 3.75 to 4 times in total length; head short, blunt, .25 total length of body; mouth oblique, jaws equal, maxillary extending as far as anterior margin of orbit; eye large, its length contained 3 to 3.6 times in length of head and 1.25 times in interorbital space; teeth sharp, hooked, without grinding surface; scales 34 to 36 in lengthwise series, 9 in crosswise series; dorsal fin high, its height in males equal to head, rays 8; anal fin large, rays 10 or 11; pectoral fins reaching about to ventrals and the latter to anal; caudal fin broad and long, the peduncle stout and compressed. Color: males steel blue above, the scales darker edged, belly abruptly milky white; head pale reddish, muzzle, upper lip and iris vermillion; dorsal fin vermillion anteriorly, a black spot posteriorly, with a milk-white tip; caudal with a broad black posterior margin, next to which is a wide vermillion crescent, base of tail pale; anal and ventral fins with white pigment; females duller. Length, 3.5 inches. (*pyrrhomelas*, fiery-black.)

This minnow, described by Cope from tributaries of the upper Catawba, is known only from the Catawba and Yadkin basins. In 1869 Cope found it to be the most abundant fish in the upper Catawba region; and in 1888 the same statement applied to it. In the Yadkin, in the vicinity of Salisbury, it is common. It is probably the most beautiful of the minnows, the brilliant red, black, and white making a sharp contrast. The males retain their colors until autumn and possibly throughout the year.

72. NOTROPIS ALBEOLUS Jordan & Meek.
"Shiner".

Notropis megalops albeolus Jordan & Meek, in Jordan, 1889b, 123, 125, 129; Roanoke River, Va., Tar and Neuse
     rivers.
Hypsilepis cornutus, var. *cornutus*, Cope, 1870b, 459; Neuse River.
Notropis megalops, Evermann & Cox, 1896, 309; Neuse River (= *H. cornutus cornutus*, Cope, supra).
Notropis albeolus, Evermann & Cox, 1896, 305; Neuse River near Raleigh.   Jordan & Evermann, 1896, 283.

DIAGNOSIS.—A large species, with depth equal to .25 total length; head heavy, compressed, about .25 total length; mouth of moderate size, horizontal, lower jaw somewhat shorter than upper; eye rather large, contained 3.5 times in length of head; about 38 scales in lateral line, 14 scales between dorsal fin and nape; lateral line decurved; dorsal fin high, the free margin concave, rays 8; anal high, concave, rays 9; caudal fin and peduncle long. Color: olive green above, silvery white on sides; fins white; snout pink in males. (*albeolus*, whitish.)

Inhabits the channels and lower courses of Tar and Neuse rivers, and appears to be rather uncommon. It is one of the largest of the genus, attaining a length of 7 inches.

73. NOTROPIS COCCOGENIS (Cope).
Red-cheeked Minnow.

Hypsilepis coccogenis Cope, Proceedings Academy of Natural Sciences of Philadelphia, 1867, 160, pl. 27, fig.
     5; Holston River, Va.   Cope, 1870b, 459; French Broad River.
Notropis coccogenis, Jordan, 1889b, 152; French Broad, Swannanoa and tributaries.   Jordan & Evermann,
     1896, 284, pl. xlix. fig. 124.

DIAGNOSIS.—Body long, compressed, the depth a little less than .25 total length; head pointed, .25 total length; mouth large, oblique, lower jaw projecting, end of upper jaw extending beyond anterior margin of orbit; eye large, contained 3.5 times in length of head; 42 rows of scales between head and tail, 10 rows between dorsal fin and medium line of abdomen, 20 scales between dorsal fin and head; dorsal rays 7; anal rays 8. Color: light green on back, the scales with dark edges, a faint lateral stripe and dusky band on shoulders; a scarlet vertical bar between eye and gill opening; upper lip and muzzle red; sides and belly rosy in spring males, otherwise silvery; a red spot on body near base of pectoral; dorsal fin with lower half yellow and outer half black; lower fins white; females silvery, with only traces of red. Length, 5 inches. (*coccogenis*, red-cheeked.)

This beautiful minnow is very abundant in the mountain streams forming the headwaters of Tennessee River in North Carolina; in addition to the streams noted in the synonymy, it is known from Middle Creek, a tributary of the Little Tennessee River in Macon County. It inhabits also the basins of the Cumberland and Savannah rivers.

74. NOTROPIS RUBRICROCEUS (Cope).

Saffron-colored Minnow.

Hybopsis rubricroceus Cope, Journal Academy of Natural Sciences of Philadelphia, 1868, 231, pl. 38, fig. 4; Holston River, Va.
Notropis rubricroceus, Jordan, 1889b, 152; north and south forks of Swannanoa River. Jordan & Evermann, 1896, 286.

DIAGNOSIS.—Form elongated, compressed, the depth contained 4.5 times in total length of body; head long and pointed, .25 total length; mouth large, oblique, posterior angle of upper jaw extending beyond anterior margin of orbit; eye contained 3.3 times in length of head, equal to length of snout; teeth with grinding surface, the edges sometimes fluted; 38 scales in lengthwise series, 10 in crosswise series, 19 in front of dorsal fin; lateral line decurved; dorsal rays 8; anal rays 9. Color: males dark steel blue or green, with a black or blue lateral band and a yellowish-green lateral streak, the black band often passing through eye and around snout; silvery beneath; fins sometimes yellow but usually of various shades of red, from pink to scarlet; head and lower jaw red; males in highest coloration with entire body red; females dark green, tinged with red. Length, 4 inches. (*rubricroceus*, reddish-saffron.)

An exceedingly beautiful little fish, peculiar to the upper waters of the Savannah and Tennessee rivers, abounding in mountain streams and frequently found in pools below falls. In North Carolina it has been reported from both forks of the Swannanoa, where it is exceedingly abundant.

75. NOTROPIS CHLOROCEPHALUS (Cope).

Green-headed Minnow.

Hybopsis chlorocephalus Cope, 1870b, 461; Catawba River.
Notropis chlorocephalus, Jordan 1889b, 137; Catawba River. Jordan & Evermann, 1896, 286.

DIAGNOSIS.—Form rather stout, caudal peduncle deep, body depth .2 total length; head broad, .25 total length; orbit large, more than .33 length of head; interorbital region wide, exceeding length of snout; mouth oblique, end of maxilla extending beyond margin of orbit; lateral line slightly decurved; scales in lateral series 39, in transverse series 8 or 9, before dorsal fin 16; dorsal rays 8; anal rays 8. Color: green, everywhere dusted with black, except on belly and below eyes, the spots gathered into a lateral band which terminates in a basal caudal spot; fins unspotted; in life a metallic green line on back, and one from upper angle of operculum to caudal; below the latter line, dark crimson; dorsal and caudal fins, operculum and cheek, with end of nose, all crimson; part of operculum, preoperculum, postfrontal region, and top of head metallic green (Cope).   Length, 2. 5 inches.   (*chlorocephalus*, green-headed.)

Peculiar to the Santee basin.   Cope, in his original description, said: "This surpassingly beautiful fish is abundant in the clear waters which it inhabits—viz., the tributaries of the Catawba River".   Jordan found it abundant in the clear swift waters of Bucks Creek, tributary of the Catawba, at Pleasant Garden.

76. NOTROPIS BRIMLEYI B. A. Bean.
Brimley's Minnow.

Notropis brimleyi Bean, 1903, 913; Cane River, N. C.

DIAGNOSIS.—Body elongate, rounded, depth contained 5.3 times in total length; head .25 total length; mouth somewhat oblique, large, maxilla extending as far as pupil; eye contained 3.3 times in length of head, its diameter greater than length of snout, less than interorbital space; 43 scales in lateral line, 8 in transverse line, 18 before dorsal; dorsal rays 9; anal rays 9. Color: above light green, with dark punctulations, scales with dark edges; below s'lvery white; a dark stripe along middle of back from head to tail; a plumbeous band from upper angle of gill cover to caudal, where it broadens and extends to top of caudal peduncle; a dark shoulder band; posterior parts of dorsal and caudal black; fins otherwise pale.   Length, 3.75 inches. (Named for H. H. Brimley, of Raleigh.)

This recently described species is as yet known only from Cane River, a tributary of the French Broad, in Yancey County.

77. NOTROPIS CHILITICUS (Cope).
Red-lipped Minnow.

Hybopsis chiliticus Cope, 1870b, 462; Yadkin River.
Notropis chiliticus, Jordan, 1889b, 134; Yadkin River.   Jordan & Evermann, 1896, 287; basin of Great Pedee in N. C.

DIAGNOSIS.—Body elongate, the depth contained 5.5 times in total length; head broad behind, its length .25 total length; eye large, .33 length of head and longer than snout; maxillary extending beyond anterior rim of orbit; lateral line strongly decurved; 34 to 37 scales in lateral series; dorsal fin small, rays 8; anal rays 8.   Color: light green above, the scales brown-edged; a silvery lateral band; usually a black caudal spot; a vermillion band through anal fin, another through dorsal fin; lips and snout vermillion; in breeding males, whole body flushed with red.   Length, 2 inches.   (*chiliticus*, relating to lip.)

Peculiar to the Yadkin and tributaries.   The types were from Roane County, Cope remarking that the species is as beautiful as *Notropis chlorocephalus*, its tints being much more transparent.   The fish is not rare in the vicinity of Salisbury.

78. NOTROPIS ALTIPINNIS (Cope).
High-finned Minnow.

Alburnellus altipinnis Cope, 1870b, 464; Yadkin River.
Notropis altipinnis, Jordan, 1889b, 132; tributary of Cape Fear River.   Jordan & Evermann, 1896, 287.

DIAGNOSIS.—Body rather short and deep, depth contained 3.5 times in total length; head short, not wide, contained 4.3 times in total length; orbit very large, diameter exceeding length of snout and entering head 2.75 times; scales, 36 in lateral series, 5 or 6 rows above and 2 rows below lateral line, which is much decurved; dorsal unusually high, the longest ray equal to half distance from fin to end of snout, rays 8; anal rays 8 or 9; ventrals extending to anal fin, beyond dorsal. Color: pale green, a broad lateral silvery band with sharp black dots from snout to base of caudal; dorsal, anal, and caudal fins faintly reddish; snout yellowish; lower jaw always blackish; a black spot at base of caudal in young. Length, 2.25 inches. (*altipinnis*, high-finned.)

Described from Yadkin River in Roane County. Common in clear tributaries of Cape Fear River near Greensboro. Similar to *Notropis chalybæus*.

79. NOTROPIS CHALYBÆUS (Cope).
Iron-colored Minnow.

Hybopsis chalybæus Cope, Cyprinidæ of Pennsylvania, 383, 1866; Schuylkill River, Pa.
Notropis chalybæus, Jordan & Evermann, 1896, 288 (coastwise streams, Delaware to Ogeechee).

DIAGNOSIS.—Body moderately elongate, back slightly elevated, depth .2 total length; head flat above, its length contained 3.8 times in total length; muzzle rather pointed, mouth very oblique, lower jaw somewhat longer; eye large, .33 length of head; caudal peduncle slender; lateral line decurved; scales, 33 rows in lengthwise series, 6 rows above and 3 rows below lateral line, 16 to 18 scales anterior to dorsal; dorsal and anal fins short and high, rays 8 in each. Color: dark above, pale yellow below; a broad, lustrous black lateral band from snout to caudal base; a light band above dark one on snout; fins plain; a dark streak along anal base; abdomen bright orange in spring males. Length, 2 inches. (*chalybæus*, iron-colored.)

This species inhabits the lowland streams and swamps from Pennsylvania to Georgia, and doubtless occurs in North Carolina, although not yet collected there.

80. NOTROPIS LUCIODUS (Cope).
Minnow.

Photogenis luciodus Cope, Proceedings Academy of Natural Sciences of Philadelphia, 1867, 165; Holston River, Va. Cope, 1870*b*, 463; French Broad River.
Notropis luciodus, Jordan, 1889*b*, 152; French Broad and Swannanoa rivers. Jordan & Evermann, 1896, 291

DIAGNOSIS.—Body slender, depth .2 length; head contained 4.5 times in length; muzzle rounded, mouth oblique, lower jaw not projecting; lateral line straight; 39 scales in lateral series, 8 in crosswise series, 13 before dorsal fin; dorsal rays 8; anal fin short and high, rays 8. Color: dark green above, scales with dark edges; sides silvery; a purple lateral band; a black spot at base of caudal, always present; males with red snout and red dorsal base. Length, 3 inches. (*luciodus*, having a whitish appearance.)

Found only in the upper waters of the Tennessee basin. It is abundant in the tributaries of the French Broad in North Carolina, but does not ascend mountain streams.

81. NOTROPIS TELESCOPUS (Cope).
Minnow.

Photogenis telescopus Cope, Proceedings Academy of Natural Sciences of Philadelphia, 1867, 165; Holston River, Va. Cope, 1870*b*, 463; French Broad River.
Notropis telescopus, Jordan, 1889*b*, 152; French Broad River and tributaries. Jordan & Evermann, 1896, 292, pl. l, fig. 126.

DIAGNOSIS.—Body long, not greatly compressed, depth contained 4.75 to 5.5 times in total length; head rather less than .25 total length; mouth oblique, snout short and sharp, lower jaw not projecting; eye very large, longer than snout and more than .33 length of head; scales, 38 in lateral line, 8 in transverse series, 13 before dorsal; dorsal rays 8, anal rays 10. Color: pale green above, the scales dark-edged.   Length, 4 inches.   (*telescopus*, far-sighted.)

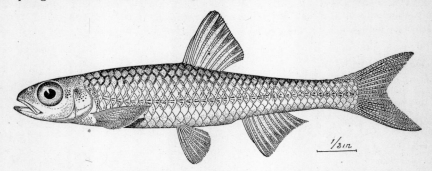

Fig. 29.   MINNOW.   *Notropis telescopus.*

Confined to the upper waters of the Tennessee; very abundant in tributaries of the French Broad in North Carolina.

82. NOTROPIS ARGE (Cope).
Minnow.

Alburnellus arge Cope, Cyprinidæ of Pennsylvania, 388, 1866; Detroit (or St. Joseph) River, Michigan.
Notropis arge, Bean, 1903, 914; Cane River, tributary of French Broad.

DIAGNOSIS.—Body very elongate, the depth .16 total length; head large, contained 4.25 times in length; mouth large, chin projecting; eye longer than snout, contained 2.75 to 3 times in length of head; scales, 39 in lateral line, 8 in transverse line; dorsal rays 8, anal rays 11. Color: pale green above, with a silvery band and a black line along sides; a dark streak on middle of back.   Length, 4 inches.   (*arge*, lustrous white.)

Inhabits southern Michigan and Ohio valley; recently recorded from North Carolina by Mr. B. A. Bean, who received 11 specimens, 2 to 4 inches long, from Cane River, in Yancey County.

83. NOTROPIS SCEPTICUS (Jordan & Gilbert).
Minnow.

Minnilus scepticus Jordan & Gilbert, Synopsis of the Fishes of North America, Bulletin No. 16 U. S. National Museum, 1883, 200; Saluda River, S. C.
Photogenis leucops, Cope, 1870b, 463; Catawba and Neuse rivers (in part).
Notropis scepticus, Jordan, 1889b, 132, 138; Haw River (tributary of Cape Fear), Catawba River, and Johns River (tributary of Catawba).   Jordan & Evermann, 1896, 296.

DIAGNOSIS.—Body short, compressed and elevated, depth contained 4.5 times in length; head large, deep, more than .25 total length; snout blunt, less than diameter of eye; mouth terminal, oblique, lower jaw shorter, maxilla extending to front of orbit; eye large, .33 length of head; lateral line much decurved; scales, 38 in lateral series, 9 in transverse series, 13 to 16 before dorsal; dorsal fin inserted well behind ventrals, rays 8; tips of ventrals extending to last dorsal rays; anal rays 10.   Color: pale green, scales with dark edges; a silvery lateral band; a dark line at base of dorsal fin.   Length, 3 inches.   (*scepticus*, observant.)

This species is known from the Cape Fear and Santee basins. It was found by Jordan to be very rare in Haw River, tributary of the Cape Fear, but not uncommon in Catawba River near Marion and in Johns River near Morgantown. This appears to be the fish which Cope assigns to the headwaters of the Catawba and to the Neuse near Raleigh under the name of *Photogenis leucops*.

84. NOTROPIS ATHERINOIDES Rafinesque.
Minnow.

Notropis atherinoides Rafinesque, American Monthly Magazine and Critical Review, 1818, 204; Lake Erie. Jordan, 1889b, 152; French Broad and Swannanoa rivers. Jordan & Evermann, 1896, 293.

DIAGNOSIS.—Body long and slender, compressed, not elevated, the depth contained 5.5 to 6 times in length; head blunt, conic, relatively short, contained 4.66 times in length; mouth of moderate size, oblique, maxillary reaching to margin of orbit; eye large, contained 3 to 3.25 times in length of head, longer than snout; lateral line decurved; scales, 38 in lateral series, 8 in transverse series, 15 anterior to dorsal fin; fins low, the dorsal well behind ventrals, rays 8; anal rays 11; ventrals reaching beyond middle of dorsal. Color: above translucent green, sides bright silvery. Length, 6 inches. (*atherinoides*, resembling a silverside.)

Inhabits Ohio and Mississippi valleys and Great Lakes region, entering North Carolina through Tennessee River, in the headwaters of which it is common (French Broad at Hot Springs, Swannanoa near Asheville).

85. NOTROPIS AMŒNUS (Abbott).
Minnow.

Alburnellus amœnus Abbott, American Naturalist, 1874, 334; Raritan River, N. J.
Notropis amœnus, Jordan, 1889b, 129; Neuse River. Jordan & Evermann, 1896, 296.

DIAGNOSIS.—Body long, compressed, the depth contained 4.75 to 5.5 times in total length; head .25 length; mouth large, oblique, jaws equal, maxillary extending to margin of orbit; eye large, longer than snout, contained 3.33 times in length of head; lateral line decurved; scales, 39 in lateral series, 9 in crosswise series (6 above lateral line), 22 to 25 before dorsal; dorsal fin high, rays 8; anal rays 10. Color: translucent green, sides silvery, a faint plumbeous lateral band. Length, 4 inches. (*amœnus*, comely.)

Found from the Raritan to the Neuse in clear streams on the eastern slope of Alleghenies. It is common in the Neuse at Millburnie and in Little River at Goldsboro.

86. NOTROPIS UMBRATILIS (Girard), var. MATUTINUS Cope.
Minnow.

Alburnellus matutinus Cope, 1870b, 465; Neuse River, Wake County, N. C.
Notropis matutinus, Jordan, 1889b, 125, 129; Tar and Neuse rivers.
Notropis umbratilis matutinus, Jordan & Evermann, 1896, 301.

DIAGNOSIS.—A compact slender species, depth .16 total length; head contained 4.25 times in length; orbit large, contained 3.5 times in head and once in interorbital space; dorsal rays 8, longest equal to .33 distance from fin to end of snout; anal rays 11; scales 44 in lateral line, 10 in transverse line, 20 to 25 before dorsal fin. Color: above olivaceous, scales edged with brown; a plumbeous lateral band; sides and below silvery; a dark spot at caudal base;

snout, chin, and upper part of dorsal bright rufous; a small black spot at anterior base of dorsal. Length, 2.5 inches. (*umbratilis*, shaded; *matutinus*, relating to the morning, i. e., rosy.)

This form is found in the Neuse and Pamlico basins, in which it prefers sandy brooks. It is common in Tar River at Rocky Mount and rather scarce in Neuse River near Raleigh.

Genus PHENACOBIUS Cope. Sucker-like Minnows.

Small minnows resembling suckers, inhabiting the region between Alleghany and Rocky mountains. Body long, slightly compressed; mouth inferior, lower lip enlarged into a fleshy lobe on each side; upper jaw protractile; teeth with no grinding surface; lateral line continuous; scales small; dorsal fin inserted anterior to ventrals; intestine short. One North Carolina species. (*Phenacobius*, deceptive-lived.)

87. PHENACOBIUS URANOPS Cope.
Minnow.

Phenacobius uranops Cope, Proceedings Academy of Natural Sciences of Philadelphia, 1867, 96; Holston River, Va. Jordan, 1889b, 152; Swannanoa River near Asheville and Spring Creek at Hot Springs. Jordan & Evermann, 1896, 304, pl. li., fig. 130.

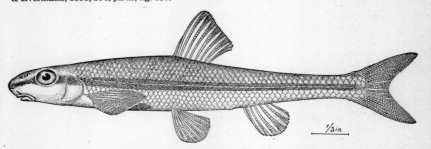

Fig. 30. MINNOW. *Phenacobius uranops.*

DIAGNOSIS.—Body very slender, little compressed, back not elevated; depth .16 length; head long, slender, flat above, snout broad, blunt, projecting, length of head contained 4.75 times in total length; mouth entirely inferior, lips conspicuous; eye large, high on side of head, its diameter contained 3.5 times in length of head; lateral line straight; scales, 60 in lateral series, 13 in transverse series, 24 before dorsal; breast and median line of belly without scales; isthmus broad, half length of head; dorsal rays 8, anal rays 7; all fins small. Color: olive green with black spot at caudal base. Length, 3.5 inches. (*uranops*, star-gazer.)

This minnow inhabits the upper part of the Tennessee basin, and is not rare at the points indicated in the synonymy. It prefers the channels of the rivers, and does not ascend brooks.

Genus RHINICHTHYS Agassiz. Black-nosed Dace.

Small fishes, living in clear cold streams. Body long; mouth small, inferior; a small barbel at end of maxillary; teeth 2,4—4, 2 (or 1), hooked, with no grinding surface; intestine short; scales small; lateral line complete; dorsal fin placed behind ventrals; pectoral fins enlarged in males. Represented in North Carolina by two species, found only in the Tennessee basin; these may be distinguished as follows:

i. Snout very long and prominent, twice length of eye, projecting much beyond mouth; no distinct black lateral band...*cataractæ.*
ii. Snout shorter and less prominent, not twice length of eye, projecting but little beyond mouth; a distinct lateral band ....*atronasus.*

(*Rhinichthys,* snout-fish.)

88. RHINICHTHYS CATARACTÆ (Cuvier & Valenciennes).
Long-nosed Dace.

Gobio cataractæ Cuvier & Valenciennes, Histoire Naturelle des Poissons, xvi, 315, 1842; Niagara Falls, N. Y.
Rhinichthys cataractæ, Bean, 1903, 914; Bollings Creek, tributary of French Broad River. Jordan & Evermann, 1896, 306.

DIAGNOSIS.—Body long, not elevated, rounded, depth .2 total length; head long, .25 total length; snout flat, narrow, and prominent, mouth inferior; eye .2 length of head and .5 length of snout; scales 62 to 68 in lateral series, 22 in transverse series; dorsal rays 8, anal rays 7. Color: back olive or black, usually mottled, below pale; no sharply defined lateral band; a black spot on opercle; spring males with lips, cheeks, and lower fins crimson. Length, 5 inches. (*cataractæ,* of the cataract, i.e., Niagara Falls.)

This species is found from New England to the basins of the Columbia and the Rio Grande. Its existence in North Carolina waters has recently been determined by the collection of specimens in Bollings Creek, a tributary of the French Broad, by Mr. H. H. Brimley, and in Middle Creek, a tributary of the Little Tennessee, by Mr. D. P. Cabe.

89. RHINICHTHYS ATRONASUS (Mitchill).
Black-nosed Dace.

Cyprinus atronasus Mitchill, Transactions Literary and Philosophical Society of New York, i, 1815, 460; Walkill River, N. Y.
Argyreus lunatus, Cope, 1870b, 459; French Broad River.
Rhinichthys obtusus, Jordan, 1889b, 152; north and south forks of Swannanoa River.
Rhinichthys atronasus croceus, Jordan & Evermann, 1896, 308.

DIAGNOSIS.—Body little compressed, depth contained 4.5 times in total length; head broad, .25 total length; upper jaw projecting, mouth small; eye small, .2 length of head; scales, 70 in lateral series; dorsal rays 7, anal rays 6. Color: back olive with dark mottlings, under parts silvery; a black lateral band margined with creamy yellow; a dusky blotch on base of dorsal fin; males with lateral band and lower fins red. Length, 3 inches. (*atronasus,* black-nosed.)

The black-nosed dace inhabits clear cold streams and brooks, from New England to Minnesota and thence to Alabama and Virginia. In North Carolina it has a very limited distribution, being recorded from that state only in tributaries of the French Broad. Cope reports it, under the name of *Argyreus lunatus,* as common, and Jordan found it in the north and south forks of Swannanoa River near Black Mountain. The form represented in the Tennessee basin is the variety *croceus* of Storer.

Genus HYBOPSIS Agassiz.   Horny-heads.

A numerous group of small fishes of the fresh waters of the United States and Mexico; related to Notropis, but distinguished by the presence of one or two barbels on each side of the upper jaw.   Shape of body various; mouth terminal or inferior; upper jaw protractile; teeth 4—4, 1,4—4,1 or 1,4—4,0, hooked, with or without narrow grinding surface; lateral line continuous; dorsal fin inserted in front of, over, or behind ventrals; head in breeding males covered wth tubercles. Six species have been recorded from North Carolina waters and another (*Hybopsis watauga*) may be looked for, as it exists in the headwaters of Tennessee River in Tennessee and Virginia.   (*Hybopsis*, swell-faced.)

Key to the North Carolina species of Hybopsis.

i. Size small (4 inches or less); mouth inferior, horizontal; coloration silvery.
   a. Teeth 1-rowed (4—4).
      b. Teeth without grinding surface; eye moderate or small (contained 3.5 to 5.5 times in head); no series of dark blotches on sides; a large black blotch on posterior part of dorsal fin; a dark spot at base of caudal.............................*monacus.*
      bb. Teeth with slight grinding surface; eye large (contained 2.75 times in head); series of dark blotches on sides, these being expansions of a dark lateral band; no black spot on dorsal or caudal fins ....*dissimilis.*
   aa. Teeth 2-rowed (1,4—4,1 or 1,4—4,0).
      c. Barbel very long; eye contained 3.3 times in head; a large dark spot on upper posterior part of dorsal fin ....*labrosus.*
      cc. No spot on dorsal fin.
         d. Eye moderate (3.25 to 3.5 times in head); a dark lateral band ending in spot at caudal base; depth .25 total length ....*hypsinotus.*
         dd. Eye large (2.75 to 3 in head); no dark caudal spot; depth .2 total length. . .*amblops.*
ii. Size large (10 inches or less); mouth large, nearly terminal; coloration not silvery; teeth 1-rowed or 2-rowed (4—4 or 1,4—4,1); top of head swollen ....*kentuckiensis.*

90. HYBOPSIS MONACUS (Cope).
Minnow.

Ceratichthys monacus Cope, Journal Academy of Natural Sciences of Philadelphia, 1867, 227; Holston River, Va.
Hybopsis monacus, Jordan, 1889b, 152; tributaries of the French Broad River, N. C.   Jordan & Evermann, 1896, 318.

Diagnosis.—Form slender, little compressed, depth contained 5.25 times in total length; head long, slender, flat above, .25 total length; snout projecting, mouth small, inferior, horizontal, maxillary not extending as far as orbit; eye small, less than .25 length of head; teeth 4—4; scales, 56 in lateral line, 12 in transverse line, 24 before dorsal fin; dorsal rays 8; anal rays 8. Color: light green above, silvery on sides and belly; black spot at caudal base; dorsal fin posteriorly black at base; a metallic band on middle of back.   Length, 4 inches.   (*monacus*, solitary.)

An uncommon species, peculiar to the upper waters of the Tennessee basin in North Carolina, known from Swannanoa River at Asheville and Spring Creek at Hot Springs.

91. HYBOPSIS DISSIMILIS (Kirtland).
Spotted Shiner.

Luxilus dissimilis Kirtland, Boston Journal of Natural History, iii, 1840, 341, pl. iv, fig. 2; Mahoning River, Ohio, and Lake Erie near Cleveland, Ohio.
Hybopsis dissimilis, Jordan, 1889b, 152; Swannanoa River and Spring Creek.   Jordan & Evermann, 1896, 318.

Diagnosis.—Form long and slender, slightly compressed; depth .2 total length; head long, flat above, contained 4.5 times in total length; snout slightly projecting beyond mouth, abruptly decurved; mouth small, horizontal, lower jaw included, upper jaw not extending to orbit; barbel shorter than pupil; eye large, .33 length of head, placed high on side of head; teeth, 4—4; lateral line straight; scales, 40 to 47 in lateral series, 11 in crosswise series, 16 to 18 before dorsal fin; dorsal large, 8 rays; anal small, 7 rays; caudal well forked. Color: back mottled green, sides silvery with bluish lateral band widened into dusky spots; dusky band through eyes and snout; fins unmarked. Length, 4 inches. (*dissimilis*, dissimilar.)

Ranges from Lake Erie to Iowa and Arkansas, southward to the headwaters of the Tennessee in North Carolina. Not rare in Swannanoa River at Asheville and in Spring Creek at Hot Springs, where highly colored specimens, with very distinct blue-black spots on back and sides, were collected by Jordan in 1888.

92. HYBOPSIS LABROSUS (Cope).
Thick-lipped Minnow.

Ceratichthys labrosus Cope, 1870b, 458; Catawba River, in Macdowell and Burke counties, N. C.
Hybopsis labrosus, Jordan, 1889b, 134, 138; Yadkin River and Pacollet River, S. C., tributary of Santee. Jordan & Evermann, 1896, 319.

DIAGNOSIS.—Body slender, depth less than head and contained 5.5 times in total length; head contained 4 to 4.5 times in total length, top gently decurved to snout; mouth horizontal, slightly inferior, lips thick, maxillary extending as far as margin of orbit; eye contained 3.33 to 3.75 times in head and slightly less than interorbital space; teeth 1,4—4,1; barbels longer than in any other species, more than half diameter of eye; scales closely imbricated, 34 to 40 in lateral line, 8 to 10 in transverse line, 16 in front of dorsal; fins small; dorsal rays 8, length of first ray equal to half distance from fin to anterior edge of pupil, dorsal inserted over ventrals; anal rays 7 or 8; caudal deeply forked, peduncle long and slender. Color: males dark blue above, with black markings on back; a dark lateral streak, and a small round black spot on caudal base; in large examples, a dark patch on posterior rays of dorsal; females silvery, with pale blue streak along sides of peduncle; males in spring with fins red and head and neck covered with tubercles, Length, 3 inches. (*labrosus*, thick-lipped.)

Cope, in his original account of this species, said it was not uncommon on the bottom in clear and rapid creeks which flow into the upper waters of Catawba River, in the counties of Macdowell and Burke. Jordan found the species common in Yadkin River near Salisbury. The fish resembles *Phenacobius* in having thick lips, and may be further recognized by the long barbels.

93. HYBOPSIS HYPSINOTUS (Cope).
High-backed Minnow.

Ceratichthys hypsinotus Cope, 1870b, 458; Catawba and Yadkin rivers.
Hybopsis hypsinotus, Jordan, 1889b, 138; Pacollet River, S. C., tributary of the Santee. Jordan & Evermann 1896. 320.

DIAGNOSIS.—Form stout, robust, compressed, depth contained 3.75 times in total length; head short, broad, flat, its length equal to body depth; muzzle not prominent, mouth inferior, horizontal; maxillary extending to margin of orbit; lips thin; barbels small; eye contained 3.5 times in length of head and once in interorbital space; line of back rises gradually to first dorsal ray, then descends abruptly, so that base of fin is oblique, the fin margin vertical, the posterior ray less than half length of anterior; dorsal fin placed in advance of ventrals, its rays 8; anal rays 8; teeth 1,4—4,1; scales, 38 to 41 in lateral line, 4 or 5 above lateral line and 3 below. Color: silvery, with a double series of black specks along lateral line and a blackish lateral band; a dark line around snout between eyes; in breeding males, fins bright red, body with violet luster. Length, 3 inches. (*hypsinotus*, high-backed.)

Inhabits only the headwaters of the Santee and Great Pedee basins. "Common in creeks heading the Catawba River in Macdowell County, N. C., or tributary to the Yadkin River in Roane County" (Cope).

94. HYBOPSIS AMBLOPS (Rafinesque).
Silver Chub.

Rutilus amblops Rafinesque, Ichthyologia Ohiensis, 51, 1820; Ohio River.
Ceratichthys hyalinus Cope, Journal Academy of Natural Sciences of Philadelphia, 1868, 226; Holston River,
　　Va.　Cope, 1870b, 459; French Broad River, N. C.
Hybopsis amblops, Jordan, 1889b, 152; Swannanoa River and Spring Creek

DIAGNOSIS.—Body rather slender, not greatly compressed, stout anteriorly, depth .2 total length; head large, flat, broad, .25 total length; eye .33 length of head, longer than snout and longer than interorbital space; mouth small, somewhat inferior, horizontal, maxillary not reaching anterior margin of orbit; snout blunt; teeth 1,4—4,1; scales, 38 in lateral series, 9 in transverse series, 16 in front of dorsal; lateral line decurved. Color: green above, scales dark-edged; a silvery lateral band, this usually superimposed on a plumbeous or blackish band; a dark stripe through eye to snout. Length, 3 inches. (*amblops*, blunt-faced.)

This species, which ranges from New York to Iowa and Alabama, is perhaps most numerous in the Ohio and Tennessee valleys. It is common in Swannanoa River near Asheville and in Spring Creek at Hot Springs.

95. HYBOPSIS KENTUCKIENSIS (Rafinesque).
"Knotty-head"; "Horny-head"; River Chub.

Luxilus kentuckiensis Rafinesque, Ichthyologia Ohiensis, 48, 1820; Ohio River.
Ceratichthys leptocephalus Girard, Proceedings Academy of Natural Sciences of Philadelphia, 1856, 213; Yadkin
　　River, at Salem, N. C.
Ceratichthys biguttatus, Cope, 1870b, 459, 494; Neuse, Yadkin, Catawba, and French Broad rivers.
Hybopsis kentuckiensis, Jordan, 1889b, 126, 129, 134, 139, 152; Tar, Neuse, Yadkin, Catawba, and French Broad
　　rivers. Evermann & Cox, 1896, 305; Neuse River near Raleigh. Bean, 1903, 914; Cane River.
　　Jordan & Evermann, 1896, 322.

DIAGNOSIS.—Body stout, slightly compressed, little elevated, depth contained 4.25 times in length; head large, broad, .25 total length; snout conical, blunt; mouth large, nearly terminal, lower jaw slightly shorter, upper jaw not extending to margin of orbit; barbel well developed; eye placed rather high in the side of head; teeth variable, 4—4, 1,4—4,1, or 1,4—4,0; scales large, 40 in lateral series, 10 in transverse series, 18 before dorsal; lateral line decurved; dorsal fins placed slightly posterior to ventrals, rays 8; anal rays 7. Color: bluish-green above, scales dark-edged, coppery and green reflections on sides, white below; fins pale orange; spring males with a red spot on each side of head and lower parts rosy; top of head in adults swollen into a high crest, which is covered with tubercles; a dark caudal spot in young. (*kentuckiensis*, inhabiting Kentucky.)

This is the commonest and most widely distributed of the species of Hybopsis in North Carolina. It exists in most of the rivers which flow into the Atlantic and also in tributaries of the French Broad, preferring the larger streams and seldom entering small brooks. In 1904 specimens from a tributary of the Little Tennessee River in Macon County, North Carolina, were sent to the Bureau of Fisheries by Mr. D. P. Cabe, who reported that the fish was known in that section as "knotty-head" or "horny-head". It reaches a length of 9 or 10 inches and is sometimes eaten.

Specimens of this fish appearing as no. 12 on the fish register of the U. S. National Museum were collected at Salem, in Forsyth County, by J. T. Lineback, in 1856, and were described by Dr. Girard as a new species under the name *Ceratichthys leptocephalus.*

Genus CYPRINUS Linnæus. Carps.

Large fresh-water fishes of Asia, with rather stout compressed body; moderate sized mouth, with thick, fleshy lips; broad molar pharyngeal teeth in several series; 2 barbels on each side of the maxillary; large cycloid scales; complete lateral line; large, thick-walled air-bladder; long dorsal fin, with a stout spinous anterior ray; short anal fin, the first ray spinous; and large, bilobed caudal fin. One species introduced into various parts of the world, and extensively cultivated. (*Cyprinus*, ancient name for the carp.)

96. CYPRINUS CARPIO Linnæus.

"Carp"; "German Carp"; Asiatic Carp.

Cyprinus carpio Linnæus, Systema Naturæ, ed. x, 1758b, 320. Smith, 1893b, pl. xlvii, 2 figs. Smith,1893a, 190, 199; Pasquotank and Roanoke rivers. Jordan & Evermann, 1896, 201.

DIAGNOSIS.—Depth contained about 3.5 times in length; head .25 length; snout blunt, .33 length of head; eye small, .15 length of head; mouth horizontal, the angle extending .5 distance between end of snout and anterior margin of eye; a short barbel at corner of mouth and a shorter one about middle of maxillary; lips full, sucker-like; teeth 1,1,3—3,1,1, with broad grinding surface; scales in lengthwise series 35 to 40, in transverse series 10 to 12, the nearly straight lateral line running about midway between dorsal and ventral profiles; alimentary canal long, pyloric appendages absent; air-bladder large, thick, with transverse constriction; dorsal fin beginning over ventrals, elevated anteriorly, the base .5 length of trunk, the rays 19 to 23 exclusive of rudiments, the first major ray being a stout spine with its posterior surface serrated; anal rays 6 or 7 besides rudiments, the anterior a serrated spine; caudal fin broad, deeply notched. Color: variable but usually dull, dark green, darker above and lighter below; under parts sometimes yellow, as are also cheeks, lips, lower side of head, and iris; fins in general like adjacent parts of body. (*carpio*, carp.)

Although the introduction of the carp into the United States from Europe was as recent as 1877, the species quickly became firmly established and is now the most generally distributed fish in this country.* The imported specimens whose progeny now exist in probably every state and territory (except Alaska) were brought over by the United States Fish Commission from Germany, where, as in other parts of Central Europe, the carp had been cultivated since the thirteenth century.

Long domestication and cultivation have resulted in the production of a number of races or varieties differing more or less strikingly from the typical form. Among those which are met with in the United States are (1) the scale carp, which differs the least from the original Asiatic type and is characterized by being uniformly covered with regularly arranged scales; (2) the mirror carp, with

*An admirable review of the carp and the various questions connected with its acclimatization appears in the Report of the Bureau of Fisheries for 1904 under the title "The German Carp in the United States," by Leon J. Cole.

greatly enlarged scales of irregular shape and arrangement, a part of the body being bare; and (3) the leather carp, so-called from its thick, smooth, velvety skin, which is either entirely destitute of scales or has only a few along the back or belly.

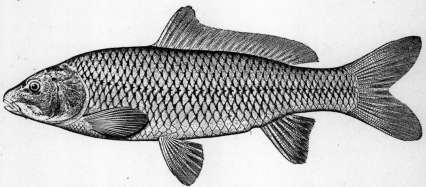

Fig. 31.   SCALE CARP; ASIATIC CARP.   *Cyprinus carpio.*

The carp attains a relatively large size—examples weighing upwards of 60 pounds being known in Europe and of fully 40 pounds in the United States, although full sexual maturity is attained by the second or third year when the fish weigh only 3 or 4 pounds.

Spawning occurs from April to June, according to latitude, the very small eggs being adhesive and becoming attached to any submerged objects, such as stones, sticks, and aquatic plants generally.   Prior to and during the egg-laying each female may be attended by from 2 to 6 males.   The carp is extraordinarily prolific, the number of eggs laid ranging from several hundred thousand in a fish

Fig. 32.   LEATHER CARP.   *Cyprinus carpio.*

of 4 or 5 pounds to upwards of 2 million in one weighing 15 or 20 pounds.   The eggs hatch in 2 to 20 days, depending on the temperature of the water.   By winter the young may exceed 7 inches in length and probably average 4 or 5 inches if food is sufficiently abundant.

The introduction of the carp into North Carolina waters began in 1879 and was very successful, the fish soon becoming widely distributed and abundant. It is now well-known in all parts of the state, but is most plentiful in the warmer, more sluggish lowland waters. It can not be said to have attained any great value as a market fish, although it is an item in the commercial fisheries of a dozen countries. In 1902, the quantity sold was 46,500 pounds, worth $2,100, the largest catch being credited to Washington, Martin, and Currituck counties. Here, as in many other states, the carp is of most importance for home consumption and as a food for other fishes. It is preëminently adapted for small, warm ponds, and it was brought to America primarily for stocking such waters, which often can not support any other fish life. By comparison with numerous native fishes, the carp is an inferior food; and in a state so well supplied with most desirable food fishes as North Carolina, there is no reason to believe the carp will ever become popular.

Order APODES. The Eels.

The eels, or apodal fishes, constitute a large and interesting order with representatives in tropical and temperate waters of all parts of the world. Some of the species are very small, others are so large as to deserve the popular name of "sea-serpents". The characters which distinguish them are, in addition to the elongate body, atrophied or absent premaxillary bones; absence of spines in the fins; isocercal tail; low and long dorsal and anal fins (if present); absence of ventral fins; comparatively small gill-openings; scales lacking or rudimentary; slightly developed scapular arch; increased number of vertebræ; and various other skeletal pecularities. Of the dozen American families, 4 have local representatives and may be thus distinguished:

Key to the North Carolina families of eels.

i. Tongue present; pectoral fins present; gill-openings comparatively large, slit-like.
  a. Dorsal and anal fins confluent around the tail; pectoral fins well developed.
    b. Scales present, but embedded, linear in shape, and arranged in groups; species entering fresh water..ANGUILLIDÆ.
    bb. Scales entirely absent; species marine.........................LEPTOCEPHALIDÆ.
  aa. Dorsal and anal fins not confluent around the tail, the projecting tail without any rays; pectoral fins minute..OPHICHTHYIDÆ.
ii. Tongue absent; pectoral fins absent; gill-openings small, rounded........MURÆNIDAE.

Family ANGUILLIDÆ. The Common Eels.

The fishes of this family, which includes a single genus, pass much of their lives in fresh water, going to the sea to spawn. They are distinguished by having a conical head, well-developed opercles and branchial apparatus, distinct tongue, teeth in cardiform bands on jaws and vomer, gill-openings vertical, lateral line present, rudimentary scales, dorsal and anal fins that are continuous around the tail, and well developed pectorals. The young pass through a peculiar metamorphosis before attaining the adult form.

Genus ANGUILLA Shaw.　Common Eels.

Form elongate, rounded anteriorly, compressed posteriorly; head long, conical; mouth large, lower jaw projecting; teeth small, in bands in each jaw, and a patch on vomer; branchial opening a small slit, about width of base of pectorals; nostrils well separated, the anterior tubular; lateral line well marked; body covered with minute embedded scales arranged mostly in small groups, some of which are placed at right angles; dorsal and anal fins long, dorsal origin not near the head. One American species probably a variety of the European eel (*Anguilla anguilla*).

97. ANGUILLA CHRISYPA Rafinesque.
"Eel"; Common Eel; Fresh-water Eel.

Anguilla chrisypa Rafinesque, American Monthly Magazine and Critical Review, 1817, 120; Lake George, Hudson River, and Lake Champlain.　Linton, 1905, 351; Beaufort.

Anguilla sp. Cope, 1870b, 491; "all the Atlantic waters of North Carolina".

Anguilla bostoniensis, Yarrow, 1877, 216; Beaufort.

Anguilla vulgaris, Jordan & Gilbert, 1879, 385; Beaufort Harbor.

Anguilla anguilla rostrata, Jenkins, 1887, 86; Beaufort.　Jordan, 1889b, 129, 133, 139; Neuse, Cape Fear, and Catawba rivers.

Anguilla chrysypa, Smith, 1893a, 191, 195, 199; Pasquotank and Roanoke rivers, and Edenton Bay.　Evermann & Cox, 1896, 305; Neuse River.　Smith, 1901, 134; Lake Mattamuskeet.　Kendall & Smith, 1894, 21; Hatteras Inlet.　Jordan & Evermann, 1896, 348, pl. lv, fig. 143.

DIAGNOSIS.—Depth of body about .8 total length; head .12 length; eye about .6 length of snout; origin of dorsal fin behind branchial slit about twice length of head; anal origin about length of head posterior to dorsal origin; fins low; length of pectorals about .33 length of head Color: variable, usually greenish brown above, often brownish yellow, white below. (*chrisypa*, gold-bellied.)

The common eel has a wide distribution in the eastern part of North America; it is found from Canada to the West Indies and as far westward as the Rocky Mountains. It ascends all the coastwise streams, and is a permanent resident of the Great Lakes and Mississippi Valley. It occurs as a migrant in all the streams of North Carolina east of the Alleghenies and doubtless in the upper waters of the French Broad.

The maximum length of the eel is about 5 feet, although the average is under 3 feet. Eels of all sizes are found in the rivers and coastal waters at all times, but there are definite movements of adults from the fresh waters to the sea, and of young from salt water to the rivers. The eel belongs to the class of catadromous fishes—that is, those which go to the sea to spawn. There has been much mystery surrounding the spawning and other habits of eels, and some curious notions are entertained regarding the fish. Even at the present time much remains to be learned about this species, but the following facts seem to be established, based in part on the observations of the European eel, whose habits are similar to those of our own species.

Eels produce eggs like most of our common fishes; the eggs are, however, exceedingly small and numerous, and may easily be mistaken for the fatty tissue of the ovary in which they are embedded. The eggs are only a little more than .01 inch in diameter, and the number produced by a large fish has been estimated at over 10 millions. The female eel is larger than the male, the latter probably rarely exceeding 2 feet in length. The ovaries, two in number, are of a pale yellow color and extend along the vertebral column the whole length of the abdominal cavity; they are about half an inch wide and are thrown into numerous transverse folds. The two male organs are similarly situated, but have a different shape and appearance; each consists of about 50 lobules arranged in longitudinal rows, with a glistening white appearance. The male eel when sexually mature has very large eyes and a short, pointed snout, and its color is silvery gray.

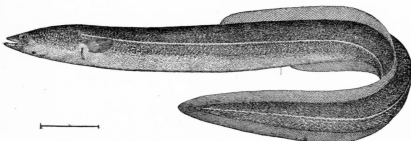

Fig. 33. COMMON EEL. *Anguilla chrisypa.*

Spawning normally occurs in salt water, in fall and winter. There is some evidence that eels may under exceptional circumstances spawn in fresh water, but it is not conclusive. The migration of the adult eels is said to take place mostly at night, and usually extends to mud banks off the mouths of rivers, the eggs being there laid and fertilized. The maturation of the reproductive organs takes place only after the eels reach salt water, and proceeds rapidly. It is thought by some authorities that all the individuals of both sexes die after once spawning.

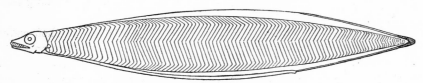

Fig. 34. LEPTOCEPHALUS OF THE COMMON EEL.

The eggs float at the surface, and are wafted about by wind and wave. They hatch into transparent, much-compressed, lanceolate creatures, with small head, large eyes, and large mouth armed with a few long, sharp teeth; these larval eels are called leptocephali, and are so different in form from the adults that the identification of this stage of the American eel has not been postively accomplished although it is probable that several leptocephali collected by the fishery steamer Albatross in fall about 100 miles off the New Jersey coast and studied by Prof.

C. H. Eigenmann* are referable to this species.   They were a little under 2 inches in length, and one of them is represented in the accompanying cut. The lepto-cephalus gradually changes into the eel shape, undergoing a reduction in size, so that when the young eel assumes the normal form it may be only half as long as when it was a leptocephalus.

The young eels, 2 to 3 inches long, come inshore and ascend the streams in spring; they are then frequently observed, as they have a dark color, swim at or near the surface, and are often in incredible numbers, extending for miles in almost unbroken lines along the edges of brooks and creeks.   They remain in the fresh waters until mature, and then descend to the sea.

Eels feed on all kinds of animal matter, whether living or dead, and are gener-ally recognized as destructive to other fish.   They are very injurious to the shad fishery in North Carolina, as in other waters.   When shad are caught in gill nets, the eels often destroy their market value by biting a hole in their abdomens and eating the eggs.   They also consume large quantities of eggs of shad and other fish after deposition.

While considerable quantities of eels are caught for market in North Caro-lina, this species does not rank among the important commercial fishes of the state.   In the Beaufort region it is common, but apparently not in sufficient abundance to support a special fishery.   About 1897 a religious band, called the "Arkites", went to Beaufort from Virginia in a houseboat or ark, taking with them eel pots; they began to fish for eels, marketing their catch in Newbern, but the business never met with much success.   Eels are caught for market in New River 50 miles from Beaufort, and at Newbern the eel fishery is growing; Oriental is also an important shipping point.   The fishermen use wire eel pots and also pots made from kegs, which they say are more successful.   The market is wholly in the north, owing to the widespread and deep seated local prejudice against eels. In Lake Mattamuskeet eels are abundant, but only sparingly utilized; at one time a religious sect, known as the "Sanctified", made a business of catching eels in the lake and shipping them north.

Eels have a very delicate, well-flavored flesh which is white when cooked, and rank high as food fishes, although many people refuse to eat them on account of their supposed snakish affinities.

In 1902 the North Carolina fishermen sold 507,111 pounds of eels, receiving $19,962 therefor.   The catch in recent years has been much larger than formerly; thus, in 1897, it amounted to 96,700 pounds worth $4,051, and in 1890 to 55,250 pounds worth $3,476.

Family LEPTOCEPHALIDÆ.   The Conger Eels.

Marine eels, characterized by scaleless, elongate body; extremity of tail surrounded by a fin as in the Anguillidæ; tongue anteriorly unattached; posterior

*The leptocephalus of the American eel and other American leptocephali.   Bulletin U. S. Fish Commis-sion 1901, pp. 81-92, 15 plates.

nostril near margin of eye; and well-developed pectoral fins. The best known genus, and the only one represented on the United States coast, is the following.

Genus LEPTOCEPHALUS Scopoli. Conger Eels.

Sea eels, similar to Anguilla and not always separated from it by fishermen, but attaining a much greater size and easily distinguished by the absence of scales, etc. A character in which this genus differs from the other American genera of this family (Congermuræna and Uroconger) is the origin of the dorsal fin posterior to the pectorals. Vomerine teeth in a band, none of them canine, and jaw teeth in several series, of which the outer are close together and form a cutting edge; the tail (i. e., the post-ventral part of the body) about half longer than the remainder of body; lateral line present; branchial openings large; eyes large. (*Leptocephalus,* slender head.)

98. LEPTOCEPHALUS CONGER (Linnæus).

Conger Eel; Sea Eel; Ocean Eel.

Muræna conger Linnæus, Systema Naturæ, ed. x, 245, 1758; Europe.
Conger conger, Jenkins, 1885, 11; Beaufort. Jordan, 1886, 26; Beaufort. Jenkins, 1887, 86; Beaufort.
Leptocephalus conger, Jordan & Evermann, 1896, 354, pl. lvii, fig. 148. Linton, 1905, 351; Beaufort.

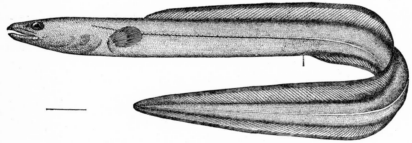

Fig. 35. CONGER EEL. *Leptocephalus conger.*

DIAGNOSIS.—Body elongate, rounded, depth .4 length of head; head flattened, pointed, somewhat more than .5 as long as trunk and .11 total length; mouth large, its angle under or beyond posterior margin of eye; lips thick, upper lip with prominent pores; eye .16 to .20 length of head and .66 length of snout; lateral line with conspicuous pores; dorsal fin arising over posterior extremity of pectorals; pectorals .3 length of head. Color: above black or dark olive green, beneath white; vertical fins with a narrow black border. (*conger,* ancient Latin name for this fish.)

A very widely distributed species, common in Europe, Asia, Africa, and on the east coast of America from Massachussetts to Brazil. In North Carolina it is not uncommon about Beaufort, in the harbor and in Newport and North rivers, and in the salt-water sounds. It reaches a very large size, European examples which weighed 90 to 100 pounds being recorded; 10 to 15-pound specimens are not infrequently taken on our coast.

The eggs of the conger, which are laid at sea during summer, are about .01 inch in diameter and float at the surface. The number produced by a single eel is enormous, exceeding 7 millions in certain large European specimens. A conger in the Berlin aquarium, weighing 22.5 pounds, had ovaries weighing 8 pounds which contained over 3 millions eggs (estimated). The young pass through a metamorphosis similar to that of the common eel.*

The conger subsists chiefly on fish, but also takes other animal food. Specimens examined at Beaufort in July and August contained fish, shrimp, and a small gastropod. Although an excellent food fish, extensively sought and eaten in Europe and Asia, the conger supports no fishery in the United States and is very sparingly utilized.

Family OPHICHTHYIDÆ. The Snake Eels.

These are tropical eels whose appearance suggests the serpents, some of the species being marked by bands or spots. The family contains about 100 species and 12 American genera (one local), and may be most readily recognized by the naked tail which projects beyond the dorsal and anal fins, if the latter are present (as in most genera). Body scaleless; tongue more or less closely adherent to floor of mouth; mouth small, moderate, or large; teeth various; anterior nostrils in upper lip and opening downward; gill-openings not united; fins either altogether absent or reduced in size and number.

Genus BASCANICHTHYS Jordan & Davis. Black-Snake Eels.

Small or moderate sized American eels, with cylindrical and very elongate body; included lower jaw; long dorsal and anal fins, the former beginning on head; rudimentary or minute pectorals; and small pointed tail destitute of rays. Three species, 2 known from single specimens (Gulf of Mexico and Gulf of California). (*Bascanichthys*, black-snake fish.)

99. BASCANICHTHYS SCUTICARIS (Goode & Bean).
Black-Snake Eel.

Sphagebranchus scuticaris Goode & Bean, Proceedings U. S. National Museum, 1879, 343; Cedar Key, Florida.
Bascanichthys scuticaris, Jordan & Evermann, 1896, 378, pl. lxiii, fig. 165.

DIAGNOSIS.—Trunk somewhat longer than tail; head contained 22 times in total length, 12 times in section anterior to vent; snout contained 5.3 times in head; diameter of eye rather less than .5 length of snout; tip of lower jaw under middle of snout; upper jaw .25 length of head; teeth blunt, in 1 series in jaws, in 2 series on vomer; origin of dorsal fin midway from tip of snout to gill-slit; pectoral fin .5 length of snout; lateral line arched over the opercle, with conspicuous pores. Color: above dark brown, below lighter, fins pale. (*scuticaris*, whip-like.)

The claims of this fish to a place in the North Carolina fauna depend on the taking of one specimen at the Beaufort laboratory in 1906. The habitat of the species has not heretofore been known to extend beyond the west coast of Florida, where it is said to be not rare.

Nothing has been recorded regarding the habits of the fishes of this genus; it is therefore interesting to note that the Beaufort specimen was dug out of the

*See "The egg and development of the conger eel," by C. H. Eigenmann, Bulletin U. S. Fish Commission 1901, in which eggs of this species found at the surface off the coast of Massachusetts are described and figured.

sand in the harbor by Dr. H. E. Enders on July 31, and was kept in an aquarium at the laboratory until August 18, when it died. While in captivity it remained most of the time with its body completely buried in sand, its head projecting just far enough to enable it to breathe. Small fishes and crab were supplied for food, but none were eaten so far as observed. This fish was 89 centimeters (about 36 inches) long; its head was 4 cm. long, its tail 40 cm., and its pectoral fins .4 cm.

Family MURÆNIDÆ. The Morays.

A very numerous family of sea eels, representing the most degenerate of the apodal fishes. They inhabit warmer waters, live largely in the crevices of coral reefs or rocks, and are pugnacious, some of the larger ones being able to inflict very painful and dangerous wounds. Distinguishing features of the family are absence of pectoral fins; thick, leathery, scaleless skins; and small round branchial openings. The posterior part of the head is elevated owing to the excessive development of muscles that move the jaw, and razor-like or crushing teeth are present in the narrow jaws. Of the dozen or more genera, only one is represented in North Carolina.

Genus LYCODONTIS McClelland. Morays.

Body compressed; dorsal fin beginning on the head, in front of branchial openings; jaw teeth all sharp; vomerine teeth in one or two series; posterior nostrils without a tube, anterior with a long tube. A numerous genus, many of the species beautifully marked, living among rocks in shoal water. One species strays to the North Carolina coast. (*Lycodontis*, wolf tooth.)

100. LYCODONTIS OCELLATUS (Agassiz).
Spotted Moray.

Gymnothorax ocellatus Agassiz, Pisces Brasilienses, 91, pl 50*b*, 1828; Brazil.
Lycodontis ocellatus, Jordan & Evermann, 1896, 399.

DIAGNOSIS.—Head contained 5.66 times in total length; lower jaw .5 head; jaws closing almost perfectly; teeth uniserial, large, weakly serrated on posterior edge; vomerine teeth small or wanting; eye .6 snout, .12 head. Color: dark brown, with numerous round, pale yellow spots, largest posteriorly; head lighter than body, reticulated, dark on occiput and between eyes; lower jaw pale, with reticulations; dorsal spotted like body, margined with elongated black blotches; anal pale, with a broad black edge. (*ocellatus*, covered with eye-like spots.)

The foregoing description is based on a specimen 18.5 inches long in the Beaufort laboratory, taken at this place in the summer of 1904. Another specimen 12.5 inches long, obtained on Bird Shoal, Beaufort Harbor, August 20, 1903, is also in the laboratory; the body is a rich brown, and some of the round yellow spots on the posterior part of body are as large as eye; spots on upper part of head smallest, those on cheeks elongate; head .14 total length; eye .7 snout, .12 head; lower jaw .4 head.

The species ranges from the coast of the Gulf States to Brazil, and has not heretofore been recorded from any point on the Atlantic coast of the United States. The large example represents about the maximum size attained by the species.

Order ISOSPONDYLI.   The Clupeoid and Salmonoid Fishes.

This order, which comprises some of the commonest and most valuable of our soft-rayed fishes, both marine and fresh-water, is divisible into two groups, characterized by the absence or the presence of an adipose dorsal fin.   The clupeoid, or herring-like, fishes do not possess this appendage, and constitute the families Elopidæ, Albulidæ, Hiodontidæ, Dorosomidæ, Clupeidæ, and Engraulidæ; the salmonoid, or trout-like, fishes have this fin, and include the family Salmonidæ.   The families of herring-like fishes having representatives in North Carolina may be distinguished as follows:

i. A bony plate between arms of the lower jaw...............................Elopidæ.
ii. No bony plate between the branches of the lower jaw.
    a. Lateral line present.
      b. Mouth small; base of tongue and roof of mouth covered with paved teeth; salt-water
        fishes ....Albulidæ.
    bb. Mouth large; teeth pointed, none forming a pavement; fresh-water fishes.
                                           Hiodontidæ.
    aa. Lateral line absent.
      c. Mouth small, inferior, without teeth; stomach gizzard-like. ......Dorosomidæ.
      cc. Mouth of moderate size, terminal, teeth small; stomach not gizzard-like.
                                             Clupeidæ.
      ccc. Mouth very large, inferior, lower jaw very long and slender ...... Engraulidæ.

Family ELOPIDÆ.   The Tarpons, Big-eyed Herrings, etc.

Large coastal fishes of southern waters, herring-like in appearance, with elongate body covered with large or small silvery scales, large terminal mouth, maxillary long and extending backward beyond orbit, a bony plate between the branches of the lower jaw, teeth in bands on jaws and also on tongue and roof of mouth, eye provided with an adipose lid, branchial membranes not united and free from the isthmus, gill-rakers long and slender, branchiostegals very numerous, lateral line present, bases of dorsal and anal fins surrounded by scaly sheath, a long accessory scale in axil of pectorals and ventrals, pyloric cœca numerous. Two American genera, easily distinguished by the size of the scales and the length of the last dorsal ray.

Genus TARPON Jordan & Evermann.   Tarpons or Tarpums.

Very large fishes found along the Atlantic coast of America.   The oblong and compressed body is covered with huge scales; the lower jaw is strong and projecting; the branchiostegals number 23; pseudobranchiæ are absent; lateral line present and straight; the dorsal fin is inserted behind ventrals and its last ray is produced as a long filament; anal fin long, its last ray elongate.   One species. (*Tarpon,* the local name for the fish in Florida, probably of Indian origin.)

101. TARPON ATLANTICUS (Cuvier & Valenciennes).
"Tarpon"; "Silver-fish"; "King-fish".

Megalops atlanticus Cuvier & Valenciennes, Histoire Naturelle des Poissons, xix, 398, 1846; Guadeloupe, San
    Domingo, Martinique, and Porto Rico.
Megalops thrissoides, Yarrow, 1877, 215; Beaufort.   Jordan & Gilbert, 1879, 384; Beaufort.
Tarpon atlanticus, Jordan & Evermann, 1896, 409, pl. lxvii, fig. 177.

Diagnosis.—Body elongate, compressed, dorsal outline but little elevated, the depth ther more than .25 total length; head .25 total length; mouth large, oblique, the maxillary tending far beyond eye; eye moderate, .16 length of head, .66 length of snout; bands of small eth on jaws, vomer, palatines, and tongue; scales very large, some nearly 3 inches in diameter, vered with a silvery epidermis, about 45 in lateral series and 12 in transverse series; dorsal ys 12, the last ray longer than head; anal rays 20 to 23; caual fin deeply forked. Color: ight silvery, darker above. (*atlanticus*, pertaining to Atlantic Ocean.)

This, the largest of the clupeoid fishes, ranges from Massachusetts to Brazil, d is most abundant in Florida and the West Indies. It reaches a length of 7 et and a weight of over 200 pounds. It is a powerful and active fish, and has e habit of leaping entirely out of the water. It feeds on small fish, and some-nes ascends fresh-water rivers, probably in pursuit of its prey. Its food value slight, as the flesh is very coarse, but the fish is much sought by anglers, being ught with rod and line by trolling and affording most exciting sport. The mense scales are objects of curiosity; they are sold as souvenirs in Florida and so are used in ornamental work.

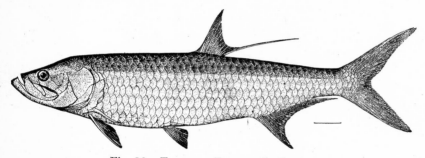

Fig. 36. Tarpon. *Tarpon atlanticus.*

The tarpon visits the North Carolina coast each season, and enters all the nds of the state as far north as Croatan Sound, in which stragglers are occa-nally observed. Yarrow reported it as very rare at Beaufort, and did not serve it; in recent years a few specimens have been taken in that vicinity. At pe Lookout this species is not uncommon in May, and large schools are some-nes noticed there, but the fish is seldom caught, as it is too strong for the nets; Cape Lookout fishermen call it "kingfish", "tarpon", and "silver-fish". July, 1906, Dr. E. W. Gudger observed a 5–foot specimen at Hatteras. The te Museum contains a specimen from Beaufort weighing 119 pounds and ther from Wilmington of 176 pounds.

Genus ELOPS Linnæus. Big-eyed Herrings.

Large sea fishes, with body elongate and rounded; head conical, jaws long; nchiostegals 30; pseudobranchiæ large; dorsal fin resting in a scaly sheath, last ray short; anal fin also in a sheath of scales; pectoral and ventral fins with g scale in axil. One American species. (*Elops*, ancient Greek name for some rine fish.)

102. ELOPS SAURUS Linnæus.

"Sea Pike"; "Horse Mackerel"; Big-eyed Herring; Ten-pounder.

Elops saurus Linnæus, Systema Naturæ, ed. x, 518, 1766; Carolina. Yarrow, 1877, 215; Beaufort. Jordan
Gilbert, 1879, 384; Beaufort. Jordan & Evermann, 1896, 410, pl. lxvii, fig. 178. Linton, 1905, 35
Beaufort.

DIAGNOSIS.—Form long, rather slender, cylindrical, the depth .16 to .20 total lengt
head conical, flattened above, its length contained 4.16 to 4.20 times in total length; upper ja
broad, maxillary extending far beyond eye; lower jaw included; eye .20 to .25 length of hea
scales small, 115 to 120 in lateral series, 36 in transverse series, lateral line straight; dorsal ra
20 or 21; anal rays 13. Color: bright silvery, greenish on back; bronze reflections on hea
dorsal and caudal light greenish brown, other fins tinged with pale yellow; all fins minute
spotted with black. (*saurus*, lizard.)

Fig. 37. BIG-EYED HERRING. *Elops saurus.*

The big-eyed herring is widely distributed in both Atlantic and Paci
oceans, and is found along the Atlantic coast as far north as Massachusetts.
occurs every year on the North Carolina coast, but is not common, at least
Beaufort, where Yarrow recorded the fish, noting the local name of "sea pike
and where Jordan and Gilbert reported it under the local name of "horse mac
erel". A length of 3 feet is attained, but the average is under 2 feet. T
young are long and transparent, and undergo a metamorphosis like the eel befo
attaining the adult form. The species has no food value, the flesh being d
and bony. A specimen examined at Beaufort in August, 1901, had in its stor
ach 6 large shrimp (*Peneus*).

Family ALBULIDÆ. The Lady-fishes.

This family includes a single genus and species of rather large-sized mari
fishes, found in the warmer parts of all seas. The moderately long body is b
slightly compressed, the head is large, naked, and marked by prominent lines a
ridges; the snout overlaps the small mouth; the short maxillary has a supp
mental bone which slips under the broad preorbital bone; the jaws and roof
mouth have small teeth in bands; the large eye has a circular adipose lid; pseu
branchiæ are present; the gill-rakers are very short and rounded; the branc
ostegals are numerous; the gill-membranes are not connected and are free fr
the isthmus; a lateral line is present; the pyloric cœca are numerous.

Genus ALBULA Scopoli. Lady-fishes.

The generic characters are shown under the family. The young undergo a peculiar metamorphosis; at first they are long, flat, ribbon-shaped, transparent, small-headed creatures, with little resemblance to the adult form; they then diminish in length, become stouter, and take on the shape of the adult. (*Albula*, whiting.)

103. ALBULA VULPES (Linnæus).

Lady-fish; Bone-fish; Wolf-fish.

Esox vulpes Linnæus, Systema Naturæ, ed. x, 313, 1758; Bahamas.
Albula conorhynchus, Yarrow, 1877, 215; Beaufort.
Albula vulpes, Jordan & Gilbert, 1879, 384; Beaufort (after Yarrow). Jordan & Evermann, 1896, 411, pl. lxviii, fig. 179.

DIAGNOSIS.—Depth .20 to .25 total length; head contained 3.75 times in length; eye .20 length of head, almost covered with a circular adipose lid; mouth small, horizontal, overhung by pig-like snout; branchiostegals about 14; preopercle with a broad membranous flap extending backward over base of opercle; scales in lateral series 71, in transverse series 16 (9 above lateral line), a band of long membranous scales on middle of back, a large scale in axil of ventrals; dorsal fin in front of ventrals, of 15 scaly rays; anal fin small, with 8 rays; caudal fin deeply forked, the upper lobe longer; pectorals and ventrals short. Color: brilliant silvery; greenish on back; faint streaks along back and sides; fins plain. (*vulpes*, fox.)

This species is found on the United States coasts as far north as southern California and Massachusetts. On the North Carolina coast it is only a straggler. Yarrow reported it at Beaufort on the authority of fishermen, but recent writers have not recorded it from the state. It attains a length of 3 feet, and has some value as food.

Family HIODONTIDÆ. The Moon-eyes.

Handsome American fresh-water fishes, with oblong, compressed body covered with silvery cycloid scales; head short, scaleless; mouth moderate, terminal, with small teeth on jaws, tongue, vomer, palatines, sphenoid, and pyterygoids; maxillary small, slender, forming lateral margin of jaw; jaws equal, lower jaw fitting within upper at sides; eye large, with adipose eyelid; nostrils large, 2 on each side separated by a flap; gill-membranes not united, and free from isthmus; branchiostegals 8 to 10; pseudobranchiæ rudimentary; gill-rakers few, short; air-bladder large; one pyloric cœcum; lateral line straight; dorsal fin short, posterior; anal long and low; caudal strongly forked. One genus.

Genus HIODON LeSueur. Moon-eyes, or Toothed Herrings.

There are 3 species of this genus, inhabiting the Great Lakes, Mississippi basin, and Canada. They are dazzling silvery in color, and are excellent game fishes, but are of little value as food, being dry and bony. Only one species is found within the limits of the State. (*Hiodon*, toothed hyoid.)

104. HIODON SELENOPS Jordan & Bean.
Moon-eye.

Hiodon selenops Jordan & Bean, Bulletin U. S. National Museum, x, 67, 1877; Chattanooga, Tenn.   Jorda
    & Evermann, 1896, 414, pl. lxviii, fig. 181.

DIAGNOSIS.—Body rather long, back slightly elevated, belly not keeled, depth .25 tot
length; head a little shorter than depth; eye .4 length of head; scales in lateral series 50; dors
rays 12; anal rays 27; pectorals not extending as far as ventrals.   Color: silvery.   (*selenop*
moon-eyed.)

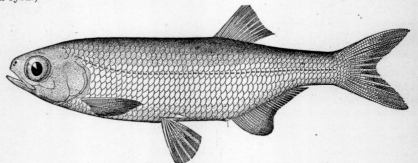

Fig. 38.   MOON-EYE.   *Hiodon selenops*.

This species, which is known from Tennessee, Cumberland, and Alaban
rivers, was only recently detected in North Carolina, a specimen having bee
forwarded to the National Museum in 1902 that had been taken at Bowman
Bluff, on the French Broad in Henderson County.   Length 1 foot.

Family DOROSOMIDÆ.   The Gizzard Shads.

This family is very closely related to the Clupeidæ.   The most evident cha
acters are a strongly-compressed, short, deep body; small, short head, wit
small inferior mouth; numerous slender gill-rakers; no lateral line; thin, decid
ous cycloid scales; very long, low anal fin; and a rounded, muscular stomac
Fishes of coasts, rivers, and lakes, with little food value.   Two American gener

Genus DOROSOMA Rafinesque.   Gizzard Shads; Mud Shads.

Medium-sized fishes, having in addition to the family characters note
above a thread-like prolongation of the last ray of the dorsal fin.   One Unite
States species.   (*Dorosoma*, lance-bodied.)

105. DOROSOMA CEPEDIANUM (LeSueur).
"Gizzard Shad"; "Mud Shad"; "Nanny Shad"; "Nancy Shad"; "Shiner";
"Winter Shad"; Hickory Shad.

Megalops cepediana LeSueur, Journal Academy Natural Sciences Philadelphia, i, 361, 1818; Delaware a
    Chesapeake bays.
Dorosoma cepedianum, Smith, 1893a, 191, 195, 199; Pasquotank and Roanoke rivers, and Edenton Bay.   J
    dan & Evermann, 1896, 416, pl. lxix, fig. 183.

DIAGNOSIS.—Body rather short, deep, greatly compressed, the back elevated, the ventr
edge sharp, depth contained 2.5 times in total length; head rather less than .25 total lengt

eye. 25 length of head, longer than snout; lower jaw included; scales in longitudinal series 56 to 65, in transverse series about 20; dorsal rays 10 to 12, the last ray about as long as head; anal rays 31; caudal forked, the lower lobe longer. Color: above bluish, sides silvery; North Carolina specimens often have dorsal and caudal fins uniformly dusky, and pectoral, ventral, and anal fins with dark edges; living fish are sometimes blackish-green all over. (Named after a celebrated French naturalist, Count Lacépède, whose Natural History of Fishes contains descriptions of many American species.)

This fish is found in brackish and fresh waters of the Atlantic coast from Massachusetts to Mexico, and is also a permanent resident throughout the Mississippi Valley and in several of the Great Lakes. While present in the larger coastal waters of North Carolina throughout the year, there is a special movement from salt water to the rivers in spring, and it is abundant in the sounds and streams at the time of the shad run. The young, 3 to 6 inches long, are also extremely numerous in spring; they are marked by a lustrous purple shoulder spot.

The local names are "gizzard shad," "mud shad", "nanny shad", "nancy shad", and "shiner", the one in most general use being "nanny shad".

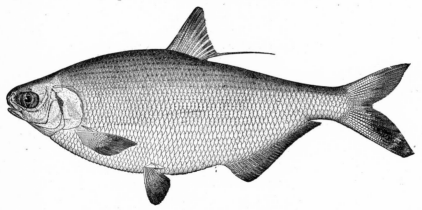

Fig. 39. GIZZARD SHAD; MUD SHAD. *Dorosoma cepedianum.*

The average weight is 1.5 to 2 pounds. The spawning season is summer. The stomach is a hard, rounded, muscular mass, like the gizzard of a chicken; and the food is chiefly bottom mud.

The gizzard shad has very little food value, the flesh being of poor quality and filled with numerous small bones. It is, however, sometimes consumed locally and also shipped to market, especially in winter.

Family CLUPEIDÆ. The Herrings, Sardines, Shads, and Alewives.

This, the most important family of fishes, contains several hundred species, found in all parts of the world, in both fresh and salt water; one species, the sea herring (*Clupea harengus*), having a greater value than any other fish, the annual product amounting to about $25,000,000. Most of the species occur in schools,

often of immense size. The clupeids are characterized by feeble jaws, inconspicuous or absent teeth, long, slender gill-rakers, no lateral line, forked tail, and
mostly silvery color. The North Carolina representatives of the family are 7*
in number and belong to 5 genera which may be distinguished as follows:

Key to the North Carolina genera of Clupeidæ.

i. Scales not closely imbricated, their posterior edge rounded; intestine of moderate length.
  a. Last ray of dorsal fin short.
    b. Scales (scutes) on medium line of abdomen weak; teeth on vomer........CLUPEA.
    bb. Scales on median line of abdomen strong; no teeth on vomer.
      c. Tip of upper jaw not notched for tip of lower jaw; cheeks longer than deep.
                                POMOLOBUS.
      cc. Tip of upper jaw notched to receive tip of lower jaw; cheeks deeper than long.
                                ALOSA.
  aa. Last ray of dorsal fin greatly elongated.............................OPISTHONEMA.
ii. Scales closely imbricated, their posterior edge vertical or fluted; intestine long; head large,
  back broad and rounded.......................................BREVOORTIA.

Genus CLUPEA Linnæus. Herrings.

Body long, compressed, with median line of abdomen armed with hard
scales or scutes; supplementary bone on maxillary broad; a permanent patch
of teeth on vomer. Two American marine species, one on the Pacific and one on
the Atlantic coast. (*Clupea*, herring.)

106. CLUPEA HARENGUS Linnæus.
Sea Herring.

Clupea harengus, Linnæus, Systema Naturæ, ed. x, 1758, 317; European seas. Jordan & Evermann, 1896, 421,
  pl. lxx. fig. 185; "chiefly north of Cape Hatteras".

DIAGNOSIS.—Form elongate, compressed, the ventral edge sharp, depth contained 4.5
times in total length; length of head equals depth of body; eye .25 length of head, longer than
snout; maxilla extending to middle of orbit; lower jaw projecting; minute teeth on vomer and
tongue, and often on palatines and jaws; gill-rakers long, thin, about 40 on lower arm of first
gill-arch; scales in lateral series 55 to 60, in transverse series 14; scutes on median line of abdomen anterior and posterior to ventral fins; dorsal rays 18; anal rays 17. Color: back rich blue,
opercles yellow, sides silvery. (*harengus*, herring.)

This most abundant and most valuable of all fishes inhabits the North
Atlantic Ocean, on the shores of America and Europe. In America it is especially numerous from Cape Cod to Newfoundland. It extends its range to the
coast of Maryland and Virginia, where it is perhaps to be found every winter;
and it doubtless goes as far as Cape Hatteras, although definite North Carolina
records are lacking. The average size is that of an alewife, although a length of
16 or 18 inches is attained. It is a valuable food fish in fresh, salted, smoked, or
canned condition, and one of the best bait fishes for use in the line fisheries for
cod, haddock, etc. In Maine the young are canned under the name of sardines.

Genus POMOLOBUS Rafinesque. Alewives, or River Herrings.

Anadromous or fresh-water herrings, scarcely separable generically from
the sea herrings; body long and compressed, the ventral scutes strong and sharp,

---

*Several other species may be looked for on the North Carolina coast; among these are the round herring
(*Etrumeus teres*) and the Spanish sardine (*Clupanodon pseudohispanica*).

gill-rakers long and numerous, teeth weak, cheeks longer than deep, an adipose eyelid, dorsal fin short and placed midway between tail and snout, scales cycloid, deciduous. Three of the four American species are found in North Carolina and may be distinguished as follows:

i. Membrane lining abdominal cavity pale.
  a. Head long (.25 total length); size large . . . .*mediocris.*
  aa. Head shorter (a little over .2 total length); size small . . . .*pseudoharengus.*
ii. Membrane lining abdominal cavity black. . . . .*æstivalis.*

(*Pomolobus,* lobed opercle.)

107. POMOLOBUS MEDIOCRIS (Mitchill).

"Hickory Shad"; "Hick"; "Jack"; "Skip-jack"; Tailor Herring; Tailor Shad;
Fall Herring; Mattowacca; Fall Shad; Fresh-water Tailor.

Clupea mediocris Mitchill, Transactions Literary and Philosophical Society New York, i, 1815, 450; New York. Smith, 1893a, 195, 199; Roanoke River and Edenton Bay.
Pomolobus mediocris, Yarrow, 1877, 215; Beaufort. Jordan & Gilbert, 1879, 385; Beaufort (after Yarrow). Jordan & Evermann, 1896, 425, pl. lxxi, fig. 188.

DIAGNOSIS.—Form elliptical, compressed, greatest depth contained 3.5 to 3.75 times in total length; head long and sharp, .25 total length, its superior profile straight and little elevated; lower jaw much longer than upper; eye somewhat less than .25 length of head and shorter than snout; scales in lateral series 50; fins small; dorsal origin anterior to middle of body; dorsal rays 15; anal rays 21. Color: back bluish silvery, sides with faint lengthwise lines; a longitudinal line of 6 to 8 brown spots posterior to head. (*mediocris,* mediocre, in allusion to its food value.)

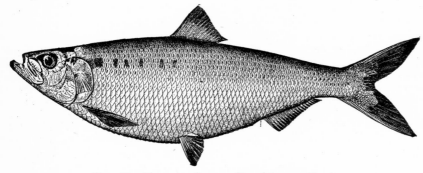

Fig. 40. HICKORY SHAD. *Pomolobus mediocris.*

The hickory shad ranges along the east coast from Massachusetts to Florida, often occurring in abundance at the extremes of its range. The region of greatest abundance is Chesapeake Bay. The species is common in the coast waters and rivers of North Carolina, coming in from the ocean in late winter or early spring, and ascending streams to spawn, going to the headwaters in company with the branch herring. It is usually present in large numbers in Pamlico and other salt-water sounds in winter, and the nets then in operation take many thousands.

It is known among the fishermen as "hickory shad" (sometimes shortened to "hick"), "jack", and "skip-jack".

The maximum length attained is 2 feet, and the maximum weight 5 pounds; but such large fish are now very rare, and the average weight is under 3 pounds.

The species is much inferior to the common shad, but nevertheless is often marketed at a fair price, sometimes being sold to the unsophisticated as a genuine shad. Dealers report that the larger ones are marketable in the north, where they are quoted as "jacks" and bring 10 to 20 cents each, sometimes even 25 to 50 cents each. The fish are also much used in the state trade. In 1897 the quantity marketed was 230,975 pounds, worth $7,583; but by 1902 the state catch had increased to 684,896 pounds, valued at $33,552.

108. POMOLOBUS PSEUDOHARENGUS (Wilson).

"Alewife"; "Goggle-eye"; "Big-eyed Herring"; "Wall-eyed Herring"; Branch Herring.

Clupea pseudoharengus Wilson, Rees's Cyclopedia, ix, about 1811; probably Philadelphia. Smith, 1893*a*, 191, 195, 199; Albemarle Sound and tributaries.
Clupea vernalis Mitchill, Report Fishes of New York, 22, 1814; New York.
Pomolobus pseudoharengus, Yarrow, 1877, 215; Beaufort, Neuse River and sounds to northward. Jordan & Evermann, 1896, 426, pl. lxxi, fig. 189.

DIAGNOSIS.—Body rather deep, the depth contained about 3 times in total length; head short, about as deep as long, contained 4.66 to 5 times in total length; lower jaw slightly longer; maxilla extending to pupil; tip of upper jaw with a slight concavity; eye large, longer than snout, contained 3.5 times in length of head; gill-rakers long, 30 to 40 on lower limb of first arch; scales 50 to 54 in lateral series; dorsal fin usually rather long, its height about .5 depth of body; dorsal rays 16; anal rays 17 to 19. Color: bluish on back, silvery white on sides; dusky longitudinal lines along center of scales; a small black spot behind head; fins plain; peritoneum pale. (*pseudoharengus*, false herring.)

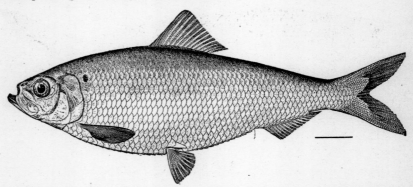

Fig. 41. BRANCH HERRING; GOGGLE-EYE. *Pomolobus pseudoharengus.*

The branch herring is found from North Carolina northward along the entire coast; if it exists at all in the rivers of South Carolina and Georgia it is very rare, and extensive collections of fishes in the St. Johns River, in Florida, have failed to disclose its presence. It is extremely abundant in Albemarle Sound, Chesapeake Bay, Delaware Bay, New York Bay, and their tributaries, and in the rivers, ponds, and bays of New England.

A. HOEN & CO.

BRANCH HERRING; GOGGLE-EYE (POMOLOBUS PSEUDOHARENGUS), MALE

The annual migration of alewives from the sea to the rivers is for the purpose of spawning. The time of their arrival in a given place is quite regular from season to season. The branch alewife usually precedes the other species by three or four weeks, and also arrives in numbers before the first run of shad. The Albemarle Sound fishermen refer to the "goggle-eye" as the forerunner of the "herring".

This species ascends the small streams to spawn, often pushing its way far to the headwaters of brooks and branches only a few feet wide and not more than 6 inches deep. After spawning very little is known of the fish; it is probable, however, that they gradually drop back to the bays and to salt water, and on the advent of cold weather withdraw from the shore waters and occupy an ocean area off the fresh water in which they spawn, but nothing is definitely known of the winter abode of the fish.

The alewives are very prolific. In Potomac River, 644 female branch herring yielded 66,206,000 eggs, an average of 102,800 per fish; and probably 100,000 eggs may be taken as a fair average for the species. The eggs are .05 inch in diameter, and are very glutinous when first laid, adhering to brush, ropes, stones, piling, and other objects. The hatching period is 6 days, in a mean water temperature of 60° F. The fry are very active, grow quickly, and by fall have reached a length of 2 to 3 inches; they feed on the fry of shad and alewives, mosquito larvæ, minute crustaceans, etc. As cold weather comes on they drop down stream, and pass the winter in salt water. The species attains its full size in 3 or 4 years, and then returns to spawn. The size of the mature alewives is quite uniform, averaging .4 of a pound. Examples weighing over half a pound are not common.

The alewives are the most abundant food fishes inhabiting the rivers of the eastern coast of the United States, and, next to the shad, are commercially the most valuable fish of those waters. Their abundance and cheapness make them of almost incalculable importance in many sections, and the annual catch in 14 states is 150 million fish, sold for food and bait, besides considerable quantities given away, used for home consumption, or put on the land as fertilizer.

North Carolina is the leading alewife state and for many years caught more of these fish than any other two states. Of late, however, Maryland has had a somewhat larger catch. Following are the statistics of the yield of both species of alewives in North Carolina for a term of years:

YEAR.	POUNDS (FRESH AND SALTED).	VALUE.	AVERAGE PRICE PER POUND.
1880	15,520,000	$142,784	$0.0092
1888	20,463,340	161,673	.0079
1890	16,481,063	164,636	.0099
1896	14,355,920	115,945	.0080
1897	15,790,437	127,055	.0080
1902	11,172,975	116,212	.0104
1904	10,492,000	124,408	0118

The leading fishing ground is Albemarle Sound and its tributaries, where millions of alewives are caught annually in seines, pound nets, and gill nets. More than half a million fish have here been taken at one haul of a seine, and hauls of 100,000 to 250,000 are not rare. Other important waters for alewives are Croatan and Pamlico sounds, and Neuse River. Many of the fish are sold fresh, but the principal trade is in salted fish, which are put up in various ways in barrels holding 200 pounds. There is little difference in the food value of the two species, but the branch herring is reputed to be somewhat better.

109. POMOLOBUS ÆSTIVALIS (Mitchill).*
"Herring"; "School Herring"; "Blueback"; "May Herring"; "Glut Herring".

Clupea æstivalis Mitchill, Transactions Literary and Philosopical Society of New York, i, 1815, 456; New York. Smith 1893a, 191, 195, 199; Albemarle Sound and tributaries.
Alosa cyanonoton Storer, Proceedings Boston Society of Natural History, ii, 242, 1848; Provincetown, Massachusetts.
Pomolobus æstivalis, Jordan & Evermann, 1896, 426 pl. lxxi, fig. 190.

DIAGNOSIS.—Similar to *P. pseudoharengus*, but with longer body (the depth contained 3.5 times in total length), somewhat shorter head, smaller eye (.25 length of head), less elevated dorsal fin, and black peritoneum. Color: back bluish, opercles and sides with coppery luster, below silvery; about 5 narrow dark lengthwise streaks along the upper rows of scales. (*æstivalis*, of the summer.)

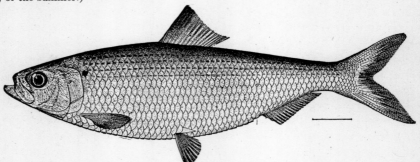

Fig. 42.   GLUT HERRING.   *Pomolobus æstivalis.*

The glut herring is found from St. Johns River, Florida, along the entire coast of the United States and also in the British maritime provinces. The great centers of abundance are Chesapeake Bay and Albemarle Sound.

The habits, size, etc., of this species are similar to those of the branch herring, and the remarks regarding the latter apply in general to this fish. The glut herring, however, comes later than the branch herring, usually appearing suddenly, in enormous schools, about the middle of the shad season; and it does not as a rule ascend the streams far above tide water. It spawns a shorter distance from the sea than does the branch herring, the number of eggs, spawning habits, movements and growth of young, etc., being the same in the two species.

*This fish has been called *æstivalis* by recent authors, in the belief that Mitchill's name applied to it. It is probable, however, as Dr. T. H. Bean has shown (Catalogue of the Fishes of New York, 1903), that the fish so designated by Mitchill was the hickory shad.

PLATE 4

A. HOEN & CO.

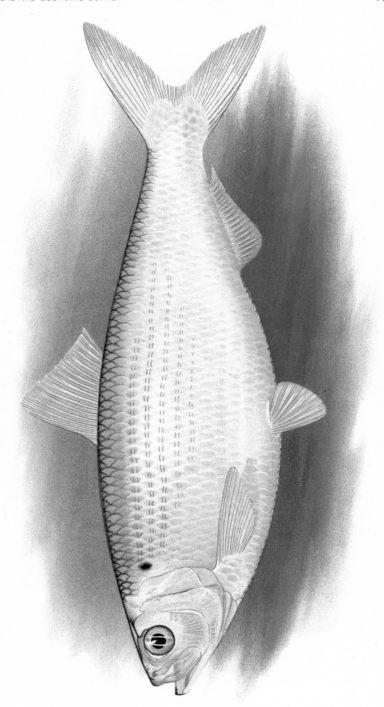

GLUT HERRING; MAY HERRING; BLUE-BACK (POMOLOBUS AESTIVALIS)

In April, 1892, numerous young glut herring, only 1.5 inches long, were found in Pasquotank River; they were apparently 3 months old, and their presence at that season is somewhat difficult to account for.   The adults had only just begun to run, and no spawning fish had as yet been observed in the river.

In the Albemarle region this fish is always distinguished by the fishermen, and is known under various names, such as "herring", "glut herring", "school herring", "blueback", and "May herring".   Features by which the two species of alewives may be readily separated are the color of the lining (peritoneum) of the abdominal cavity (pale in branch herring, black in glut herring), size of eye (larger in branch herring), and height of vertical fins (more elevated in branch herring).

Genus ALOSA Cuvier.   Shads.

Anadromous clupeids of comparatively large size; body deep and much compressed; cheeks deeper than long, jaws toothless in adults, upper jaw indented at tip to receive the tip of lower jaw.   Three American species, two of which inhabit rivers tributary to Gulf of Mexico and one the streams of the Atlantic coast.   (*Alosa*, from the Saxon *allis*, the European shad.)

110. ALOSA SAPIDISSIMA (Wilson).
"Shad"; "White Shad".

Clupea sapidissima Wilson, Rees' Cyclopedia, ix, about 1811; probably Philadelphia.   Smith, 1893a, 191, 195
    199; Albemarle Sound and tributaries.
Alosa præstabilis, Yarrow, 1874, 452; Beaufort Harbor.
Alosa sapidissima, Yarrow, 1877, 215; Beaufort Harbor and Neuse River.   Jordan & Evermann, 1896, 429,
    pl. lxxii, fig 191.

DIAGNOSIS.—Depth of body about .33 total length, the female being deeper than the male; head .23 to .29 total length; mouth large, jaws equal, teeth on jaws in young examples and sometimes in those over a foot long; eye .20 to .25 length of head; gill-rakers long and numerous, their number depending on size of fish, about 100 to 110 on the two arms of the first arch in full-sized examples; scales deciduous, in lateral series 60 to 65, in transverse series 16; fins small, vertical fins higher in male; dorsal rays 13 (+ 3 or 4 simple rays); anal rays 19 (+ several simple rays).   Color: dark green on back, silvery on sides, white below; a dusky blotch on side of body near head, and behind this several or numerous dark spots in one or two rows, these spots most distinct when scales are removed; fins plain.   (*sapidissima*, most palatable.)

The range of the shad is from Florida to Gulf of St. Lawrence.   Throughout this long stretch of seaboard, it ascends all suitable streams.   The species has also been introduced on the Pacific coast, and is now distributed from California to Alaska, being abundant in the San Francisco Bay region and Columbia River. The shad is the most valuable of all the anadromous fishes of the Atlantic coast and supports commercial fishing in every state,   In North Carolina the shad is numerous in nearly all the sounds and rivers, Pamlico and Albemarle sounds and the rivers which discharge into them and the bodies of water connecting these sounds having especially large runs.

The name "shad" is distinctive and is generally used in North Carolina as in the country at large; but owing to the fact that in this state the menhaden is called "shad" by some fishermen, the shad has in some localities acquired the unneccessary name of "white shad". The wide difference in market value of the sexes has resulted in their being kept as distinct in the fishing records as if they were entirely different species; and the males are always called "bucks" and the females "roes". Under the name "May shad" the fishermen of North Carolina recognize a shad which comes after the regular run, mostly in May, and is distinguished by its greater fatness, relatively deeper body, and thicker caudal peduncle, as compared with the ordinary fish, and, in addition, by its rich golden or brassy color. Dr. W. R. Capehart states that the names "short-tailed shad" and "golden-backed shad" also are sometimes applied to this form.

The female shad is larger than the male, the average difference being upward of a pound. The average weight of males is about 3 pounds and of females about 4.75 pounds. In the early years of the shad fishery, examples weighing 11, 12, and even 14 pounds were reported; but of late shad weighing more than 9 13.5 pounds have been very rare. There are certain seasons, however, when large

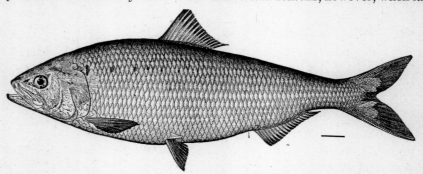

Fig. 43.　Shad.　*Alosa sapidissima.*

shad (7 to 9 pounds) are unusually numerous in some streams. One weighing 13.5 pounds was caught in a gill net in Roanoke Sound in 1899. On the Pacific coast, the shad averages at least a pound heavier than on the Atlantic coast, and occasionally attains a weight of 14 (perhaps more) pounds, while 9 to 12 pound fish have not infrequently been reported.

The shad passes most of its life in the ocean, and practically nothing is known of its habits before it enters bays and rivers in spring or after it has with drawn therefrom in fall. The movement of the shad from the ocean to the fresh waters is exclusively for reproduction purposes, and the time of the migration bears a close relation to the latitude, or, in other words, to the water temperature. Thus, in St. John's River, Florida, the southernmost shad stream, shad appear early in November, while in Miramichi River, New Brunswick, the run begins late in May, the intervening streams being entered in more or less regular order. This difference in the time of arrival of the shad in different sections does not imply that each year a great body of shad starts up the coast from Florida and sends detachments into the various streams as the main body

PLATE 5

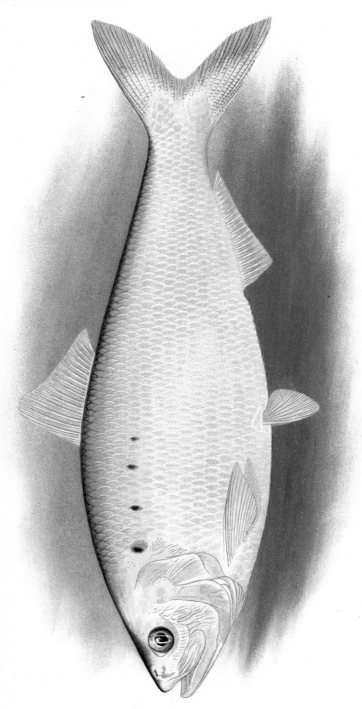

A. HOEN & CO.

SHAD (ALOSA SAPIDISSIMA)

continues its journey northward. This theory was at one time generally entertained and is still cherished by some people, although there are no facts to sustain it. Another theory which has had and still has many adherents is the so-called "instinct of nativity", by virtue of which an individual shad or other migratory fish, when mature, makes its way back to the particular stream in which it was hatched.

The facts seem to be that bodies of shad which are destined to enter a particular stream or hydrographic basin (such as Chesapeake Bay or the North Carolina sounds) occupy sea areas off these waters, and that when the fish reach maturity and are impelled by the spawning instinct to seek fresh water, they move inshore and pass up to their spawning grounds when the temperature of the water becomes favorable. In this way fish may and doubtless often do return to the stream in which they were hatched, but they are just as likely to enter adjacent streams. Thus, shad which were hatched in Roanoke River and went to sea during their first year, when they return to North Carolina waters and pass into Hatteras Inlet, might ascend Pamlico River, or, entering Albemarle Sound, might go up the Pasquotank or the Chowan. To claim anything else for the shad would be to ascribe to fish a higher order of intelligence than is possessed by any other class of animals.

Successive schools of shad arrive in a given stream during a period of several months, resulting in a rise and fall in the catch. The fish in the early runs are largely males, 90 per cent of some schools consisting of males, while later in the season males are often scarce. Shad may spawn anywhere in fresh water, but they prefer areas in rivers off the mouths of creeks or in sounds off the mouths of rivers, where the warmer water of the stream mingles with the cooler water below. While the eggs may be cast at any hour of the day or night, the largest percentage are deposited about the time the water on the spawning grounds reaches its highest daily temperature. This occurs about sunset, and it has been found that the bulk of the eggs are extruded between 5 and 10 p.m. The eggs are shot loosely in the water and quickly fall to the bottom, many escaping fertilization, many being killed by mud, and many being devoured by eels and other fishes. The average number of eggs produced by the shad is 25,000 to 30,000, although over 100,000 eggs (in one case 156,000) have been taken from large fish. The hatching period varies with the water temperature, but ordinarily is 6 to 10 days; when the water is very warm, the eggs may hatch in 3 days, but so short an incubatory period is likely to result in weak fry.

The newly-hatched shad are a little less than .4 inch long; they are very active from the outset, and feed freely and grow rapidly, so that their size doubles in 10 days, and by fall, when they leave the fresh waters, they are 3 to 7 inches long. Under especially favorable conditions, they may attain a length of 9 inches in 7 months.

Some years there is a small run of shad in fall, which naturally excites considerable interest. Thus in 1904 a full-grown shad was caught in North River, October 31, and another in Neuse River on the same date (described as "a fine

buck" in the New Bern Journal of November 2); a third was taken in Beaufort
Harbor November 2, and another, a female weighing 3.5 pounds, was seined on
Bird Shoal at Beaufort November 3.   Many more were doubtless taken at that
time.   Whether such fish have remained in the inshore water since spring or
whether they represent a fresh run from the ocean is not known.

The shad is the leading fish in North Carolina, its annual value being as much
as that of the two next important species combined.   Extensive fishing is prose-
cuted in Cape Fear, Neuse, Pamlico, Roanoke, Chowan, Pasquotank, and Perquimans rivers, but the principal operations are in Pamlico and Albemarle
sounds and the waters connecting them.   Dare County has by far the most
valuable fisheries, but in Tyrrell, Chowan, Washington, Bertie, and several other
counties the industry is also very important.   The fluctuations in the shad yield
of the state for a series of years, beginning 1880, are here shown:

Quantity and value of the North Carolina shad catch between 1880 and 1904.

YEAR.	POUNDS.	VALUE.
1880	3,221,263	$329,569
1887	4,746,226	298,069
1888	5,630,709	292,409
1889	5,356,386	280,198
1890	5,768,413	306,015
1896	8,842,708	417,243
1897	8,963,488	362,811
1902	6,566,724	384,808
1904	3,229,759	312,950

The leading kinds of apparatus used in taking shad are seines, pound nets,
stake nets, and drift nets.   The seines are especially important in Albemarle
Sound, Neuse, Roanoke and Chowan rivers; the pound nets in Albemarle Sound
and tributaries and about Roanoke Island; the stake nets in Pamlico and Albemarle sounds; the drifts nets in Cape Fear River.   In most of the rivers a peculiar
form of dip net known as the bow net is used.   In the interesting table here presented, the relative importance of the different kinds of apparatus in various
years is known.   A suggestive feature of the table is the decline of the seine
and the increase of the pound net.

Shad catch of North Carolina, by apparatus, for a term of years.

APPARATUS.	1887.		1889.		1890.	
	POUNDS.	VALUE.	POUNDS.	VALUE.	POUNDS.	VALUE.
Seines	1,677,112	$100,921	1,618,798	$81,580	1,844,729	$98,457
Gill nets	2,562,381	166,224	3,179,821	167,470	3,348,577	175,388
Pound nets	404,883	25,078	385,517	21,648	404,359	22,513
Other nets	101,850	5,846	172,250	9,500	170,748	9,657
Total	4,746,226	$298,069	5,356,386	$280,198	5,768,413	$306,015

LANDING A SHAD SEINE, ALBEMARLE SOUND.

SPLITTING AND SALTING HERRING AT A SEINE FISHERY ON ALBEMARLE SOUND.

Shad catch of North Carolina, by apparatus, for a term of years.—Continued.

APPARATUS.	1897.		1902.		1904.	
	POUNDS.	VALUE.	POUNDS.	VALUE.	POUNDS.	VALUE.
Seines	1,507,242	$60,235	996,181	$59,605	345,046	$30,810
Gill nets...........	4,916,952	205,079	3,660,410	218,860	1,147,268	104,010
Pound nets........	2,328,585	88,293	1,701,609	93,185	1,647,897	168,449
Other nets.........	210,709	9,204	208,524	13,158	89,548	9,681
Total	8,963,488	$362,811	6,566,724	$384,808	3,229,759	$312,950

The proportion of male and female shad varies considerably with the season; some years the sexes are about equally divided, while in other years two thirds of the catch may consist of one or the other. The following figures pertain to the North Carolina shad fishery in 1896:

ITEMS.	ROE SHAD.	BUCK SHAD.
Number of fish caught	942,843	1,153,961
Percentage	45	55
Weight......................................lbs.	4,804,508	4,038,200
Percentage	54	46
Value...	$246,676	$170,567
Percentage	59	41
Average weight...........................lbs.	5.09	3.49
Average value per fish	$.261	$.147
Average value per pound	$.051	$.042

The shad fishery of North Carolina steadily increased until a few years ago and at one time exceeded that of any other state. The climax was reached in 1896 and 1897; other years of maximum production were 1900 to 1902. Owing, however, to excessive fishing a decline has set in and the welfare of the fishery has become seriously threatened. The principal cause of the decrease has been the catching of disproportionately large quantities of fish in or near salt water, with a resulting diminution in the supply of fish on the spawning grounds. This matter received special attention at the hands of the legislature in 1904, and a law designed to afford greater protection to the shad was enacted and became effective in 1905.

Genus OPISTHONEMA Gill. Thread Herrings.

Small sea clupeids, chiefly distinguished by the elongated posterior dorsal ray; deep compressed body; long and numerous gill-rakers; no teeth in jaws; adherent scales; and strong scutes on median line of abdomen. (*Opisthonema*, thread-back.)

111. OPISTHONEMA OGLINUM (LeSueur).
"Hairy-back"; Thread Herring.

Megalops oglina LeSueur, Journal Academy Natural Sciences Philadelphia, i, 1817, 359; Newport, Rhode Island.
Opisthonema thrissa, Yarrow, 1877, 215; Beaufort Harbor. Jordan & Gilbert, 1879, 385; Beaufort Harbor.
Opisthonema oglinum, Jenkins, 1887, 85; Cape Lookout. Jordan & Evermann, 1896, 432.

DIAGNOSIS.—Form oblong, compressed, body depth .33 total length; head short, deep, its length .25 total length; lower jaw slightly projecting, upper jaw extending as far as middle of eye; jaws without teeth, small teeth on tongue; eye large, longer than snout, about .33 length of head; gill-rakers long and slender; scales in lateral series 50, in transverse series 15, ventral scutes strong; dorsal fin long, its origin in advance of ventrals and midway between snout and anal fin, the rays 19, the last ray extending to base of caudal; anal rays 24; paired fins small. Color: bluish above, silvery below; a dark spot at base of each scale on back, the spots forming longitudinal streaks; a bluish spot on shoulder; tip of anterior part of dorsal black in adult, dark in young. (*oglinum*, perhaps from ogle, in allusion to the prominent eyes.)

The thread herring is a regular visitant from the West Indies to the South Atlantic coast, and occasionally goes as far north as Massachusetts. In the Beaufort region it is usually not very abundant, but some seasons it occurs in considerable numbers. In August and September the young, 3 to 4 inches long, are sometimes very numerous in Beaufort Harbor; in 1902 many hundreds were seined about Bird Shoal and Town Marsh, but in the following year only a few were taken. In 1905, more than 75 were caught in the laboratory pound-net between July 18 and August 28, some being found in the net at nearly every haul. The fish reaches a length of a foot, and has little food value. It is caught incidentally with menhaden about Beaufort and is utilized at the fertilizer factories. The local name is "hairy-back".

Genus BREVOORTIA Gill. Menhadens.

Sea fishes of the western Atlantic, swimming in large schools. Head large, body short, compressed, tapering from head to tail; mouth large, lower jaw included, teeth absent; gill-rakers long, thin, and numerous; scales closely over-lapping, their posterior margin not convex; fins small; intestine long, the stomach an olive-shaped gizzard-like organ. Several species and varieties, found from Canada to Patagonia; the principal species abundant on Atlantic coast of the United States.   (Named for James C. Brevoort, an American ichthyologist.)

112. BREVOORTIA TYRANNUS (Latrobe).
"Menhaden"; "Bug-fish"; "Fat-back"; "Shad"; "Old-wife"; "Alewife"; "Yellow-tail".

Clupea tyrannus Latrobe, Transactions American Philosophical Society, v, 1802, 77, pl. i; Chesapeake Bay.
Brevoortia menhaden, Yarrow, 1877, 215; Beaufort.
Brevoortia tyrannus, Goode, History of the American Menhaden (in Report U. S. Fish Commission 1877), 1879, 6. Jenkins, 1887, 86; Beaufort. Smith, 1893a, 191, 195; Pasquotank River and Edenton Bay. Jordan & Evermann, 1896, 433, pl. lxxiii, fig. 195. Linton, 1905, 352; Beaufort.

DIAGNOSIS.—Body short, compressed especially below, back broad, depth .33 total length; head large, deep, less than .33 length of body; mouth large, weak, maxillary reaching beyond posterior border of eye; gill-rakers much longer than eye; scales irregularly arranged, their posterior edge vertical and fluted, number in lateral series 60 to 80; ventral plates 20 before vent, 12 behind; fins low, height of dorsal less than length of maxillary, height of anal less than half length of maxillary; dorsal rays 19; anal rays 20; caudal widely forked; ventrals very short, with a large axillary scale. Color: back greenish or bluish, sides brassy; a round black humeral spot, with a variable number of smaller black spots behind it; fins yellowish. (*tyrannus*, tyrant or ruler.)

The menhaden is probably the most abundant economic fish inhabiting the waters of the eastern coast of the United States, and is one of the most abundant of all ocean fishes. Its range extends from Maine and Nova Scotia to Florida, and thence through the West Indies to Brazil. The schools begin to arrive on our coast from the sea in spring and continue to appear throughout the summer, departing in fall, although in the extreme south there may be some fish present throughout the year. On the North Carolina coast large or small schools may be found from February to December, but the movements are irregular and not understood by the fishermen.

The full-sized menhaden is 12 to 14 inches long; the largest fish recorded, 18 inches long, was taken at Woods Hole, Mass. Fish of all sizes are found along the entire coast. The small fish, 1.5 to 5 inches long, are abundant throughout the season in harbors, rivers, bays, sounds, etc., swimming in serpentine schools and furnishing food for numerous other fishes.

In North Carolina, as in most other states, the menhaden is known by many aliases, some of which are very inappropriate, as will be seen from the foregoing list. To apply the name "shad" to this species, as is here done, is unfortunate,

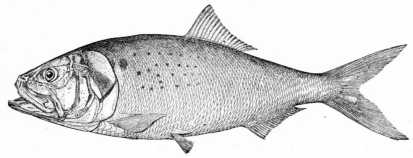

Fig. 44. MENHADEN. *Brevoortia tyrannus.*

and has led to the calling of the shad by the name of "white shad". It may be noted, as a matter of historic interest, that Lawson (1709) refers to this fish as "fat-back", a name still in general use in the state.

The menhaden feeds on minute floating plants and animals, which are taken into the gaping mouth while the fish is actively swimming. The well known whirling movements of the schools of both large and small fish are doubtless performed to facilitate feeding when the presence of an abundance of food has been determined. The mouth, with its numerous highly specialized gill-rakers, is admirably adapted for obtaining from the water the tiny organisms which swarm in the bays, sounds, estuaries, and inlets.

As is usually the case with fishes whose coastwise range is extensive, the spawning period of the menhaden is protracted. In New England spawning takes place in late spring or early summer, while from Chesapeake Bay southward the season is late fall or early winter. In the Beaufort region there is evidence that the eggs are deposited in November both in the open ocean and in the inside waters. Mr. S. G. Worth has supplied the following notes on the spawning and young of the menhaden at Beaufort:

Mr. Charles P. Dey, a Beaufort menhaden manufacturer of intelligence and large experience, asserts positively that this species deposits its eggs in November in the ocean a few miles distant from the inlet.   Mr. Bell, of Beaufort, also a fish-scrap manufacturer of intelligence and wide experience, maintains that a portion of the spawning is done in Newport and other inside rivers, as some of the large fish are annually taken in those waters in November and December. On November 7, 1903, Mr. Worth secured a menhaden in full roe, and on November 18 he found two males from which the milt was running freely.   On December 2 schools of menhaden from 1.5 inches long upward commenced running southward along the coast and were observable from Shackleford Bank; the run increased for 4 days and continued for a week, most of the schools remaining outside but some entering the harbor.   Mr. Joseph Lewis, proprietor of the Mullet Pond fishery on Shackleford Bank, states that schools of young menhaden winter in that vicinity, and that when the drum comes in February and March the menhaden are present in great quantities and constitute the principal food of the drum.

There is found in the roof of the mouth of southern menhaden a large crustacean parasite (*Cymothoa prægustator*), which clings tightly and considerably diminishes the capacity of the mouth.   One of the local vernacular names of the

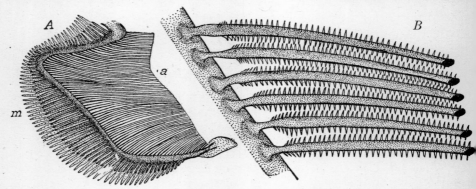

Fig. 45. GILL OF MENHADEN.

A. First gill-arch, natural size. *a.* Gill-rakers. *m.* Branchiæ, or gill proper. B. Six gill-rakers, enlarged 50 times, showing projecting rows of hooks.

menhaden ("bug-fish") is given in allusion to this fact.   In some schools practically every fish has a parasite in its mouth.   Another conspicuous crustacean parasite (*Lernæonema radiata*) is imbedded in the back muscles, the head parts having the form of a grapple and the long egg-sacs projecting beyond the surface.

The menhaden is one of the most valuable of the North Carolina fishes. Here as elsewhere it is caught chiefly for conversion into oil and guano, at factories located in the vicinity of Beaufort and Cape Fear.   Fishing is done with purse and haul seines in the ocean and sounds, and the industry gives employment to many people.   In recent years there have been about 10 such establishments, with upwards of 500 fishermen and shore hands connected therewith. In 1902, the last year for which statistics are available, 18,862,000 pounds of menhaden, worth $31,420, were taken by local fishermen, and about 30,000,000 pounds were caught by outside vessels to supply the factories in Brunswick County.

The menhaden is not extensively eaten, as its extreme oiliness is an objection; in fall, however, it is a very palatable fish when freshly caught and fried.   Every year many of the poorer people about Beaufort salt several barrels for winter use.   Recently the fish has begun to figure as a food fish in New England, and has at times sold fresh in Boston at ten cents apiece.   Nearly two centuries ago Lawson said of this fish in North Carolina:

Fat-backs are a small fish, like mullets, but the fattest ever known.   They put nothing into the pan, to fry these,   They are excellent sweet food.

Family ENGRAULIDÆ.   The Anchovies.

A numerous family of small sea fishes, closely related to the herrings (Clupeidæ), usually found in schools on sandy shores, and preyed on by many fishes. The species are for the most part too small to be economically important in the United States, but are rather extensively utilized in the Old World.   The anchovies are readily recognized by their peculiar head.   The mouth is very large, the gape wide, the upper jaw long, pointed, and extending far backward, the lower jaw weak, inconspicuous, and much shorter than the upper, and the eye large and placed anteriorly.   Other characters are the elongate compressed body, belly rounded or weakly compressed; teeth small, in a single row in each jaw; opercles thin, branchiostegals 7 to 14 in number, pseudobranchiæ present, gill-membranes free from isthmus, gill-rakers long and slender; scales thin, cycloid, no lateral line; a single dorsal fin; caudal fin forked.   Of the 6 American genera, only one is represented on our Atlantic coast.

Genus ANCHOVIA Jordan & Evermann.   Anchovies.

Anchovies of this genus are found in warmer waters in all parts of the world, going in large schools.   They have a silvery white color and usually a broad lateral silvery band.   The principal fatures of the genus are the oblong, compressed body; very long maxillary extending far beyond the eye; conical, compressed snout overhanging the oblique mouth; small teeth on jaws and roof of mouth; branchial membranes nearly or quite separated; dorsal fin small, anterior to anal; anal fin rather long (rays 12 to 40); and an axillary scale with each pectoral and ventral fin.   The two species known from North Carolina may be thus distinguished:

i. Anal rays 20; length 4 to 6 inches...*brownii.*
ii. Anal rays 25 to 28; length 2.5 inches.....................................*mitchilli.*

113. ANCHOVIA BROWNII (Gmelin).
"Smelt"; "Bait"; Anchovy; Striped Anchovy

Atherina brownii Gmelin, Systema Naturæ, 1397, 1788; Jamaica
Engraulis brownii, Yarrow. 1877, 215; Beaufort.
Engraulis vittatus, Jordan & Gilbert, 1879, 385; Beaufort.
Stolephorus brownii, Jordan, 1886, 26; Beaufort.   Jenkins, 1887, 86; Beaufort. Jordan & Evermann, 1896, 443.
     Linton, 1905, 353; Beaufort.

DIAGNOSIS.—Body compressed, not elevated, depth contained 4.75 times in length; head contained 3.75 times in length; snout .2 length of head; maxillary extending nearly to gill-opening; eye contained 3.5 times in length of head; gill-rakers .66 length of eye; scales in lateral series 40; dorsal rays 15; anal rays 20.   Color: back olivaceous, sides and belly silvery; a distinct lateral silvery band about width of eye.   (Named for Patrick Brown, who in 1756 published a History of Jamaica.)

This species of anchovy, which occurs in abundance from Massachusetts to Brazil, is very common in the Beaufort region; it enters the harbor, where numerous specimens have been seined in summer, but the largest schools remain outside.   On April 23, 1904, the author seined several specimens at Fort Beach and Bird Shoal.   The fish is too small to attract the special notice of the local fishermen, who know it only under the indefinite name of "bait"; Dr. Yarrow, in his Beaufort list, reported it as "smelt".   The appearance of schools of "bait" is welcomed by the fishermen as heralding the approach of Spanish mackerel and blue-fish, which feed on them extensively.

Anchovies are more important as food for other fishes than as food for man, and are but little utilized on the Atlantic coast of the United States.   In France, Japan, and other countries, however, they are canned after the manner of sardines and are preserved in various other ways.   In North Carolina they exist in sufficient abundance to support a canning industry, and ought to meet with a good sale if carefully preserved in oil and put on the market as anchovies.

114. ANCHOVIA MITCHILLI (Cuvier & Valenciennes).
Anchovy.

Engraulis mitchilli Cuvier & Valenciennes, Histoire Naturelle des Poissons, xxi, 50, 1848; New York; Carolina; Lake Pontchartrain, La.
Stolephorus mitchilli, Jordan & Evermann, 1896, 446.

DIAGNOSIS.—Body not very elongate, strongly compressed, depth .25 total length; head short, blunt, its length contained 3.75 times in total length; snout very short, about equal to pupil; maxillary extending nearly to gill-opening; eye very large, .33 length of head; scales thin, deciduous, 37 in lateral series; dorsal rays 12 to 14; anal rays 25 to 28; pectorals reaching ventrals.   Color: silvery with dark dots; a narrow silvery lateral band; fins yellowish. (Named after Dr. Samuel L. Mitchill, U. S. senator from New York and author of various papers on American fishes.)

Ranges along the entire Atlantic coast from Massachusetts to Texas, occurring in schools on sandy shores and in the bays and sounds.   There appears to be no published North Carolina record of the species, but it is doubtless an abundant form in that state as it is elsewhere throughout its range.   A number of specimens were collected at Morehead City on February 21, 1891, by Dr. W. C. Kendall, of the U. S. Bureau of Fisheries.   It rarely exceeds 3 inches in length and averages less.

Family SALMONIDÆ.   The Salmons, Trouts, and White-fishes.

A very numerous and important family of fresh-water and anadromous fishes restricted to the more northern parts of the world.   Although well represented in America, there is only a single native salmonid of North Carolina, the celebrated brook trout; the rainbow trout, however, has become so successfully established that it must now be considered among the fishes of the state.

The salmonids are characterized by a more or less elongate body; a terminal mouth, with the lateral margins of the upper jaw formed by the maxillary bone, to which is attached a supplemental bone; branchial membranes not connected and not attached to isthmus; gills 4 in number; gill-rakers of various form and number; pseudobranchiæ present; branchiostegals numerous; a single dorsal fin of soft rays placed near middle of body; behind this a small adipose fin; lateral line present; scales usually small, cycloid, covering body but not head; air-bladder large, pyloric cœca numerous; species oviparous, with large eggs.

The genera to which the brook trout and the rainbow trout belong are thus separated.

i. Body red-spotted; vomer boat-shaped, with a strongly depressed shaft containing no teeth. SALVELINUS.
ii. Body black-spotted; vomer flat, with its shaft not depressed and containing teeth in alternate rows. ....SALMO.

Genus SALVELINUS Richardson.   Charrs, or Red-spotted Trouts.

A numerous genus of moderate sized trouts, distinguished by having a rather large mouth; teeth on jaws, tongue, vomer, and palatines; a boat-shaped vomer without a central elevation; small scales; and rich coloration, with round red spots on body. Species inhabiting lakes and streams, sometimes running to the sea. (*Salvelinus*, charr.)

115. SALVELINUS FONTINALIS (Mitchill).

"Brook Trout"; "Speckled Trout"; Mountain Trout.

Salmo fontinalis Mitchill, Transactions Literary and Philosophical Society of New York, i, 1815, 435; vicinity of New York City. Cope, 1879*b*, 489; Catawba and French Broad rivers.
Salvelinus fontinalis, Jordan, 1889*b*, 139; Bucks Creek (tributary of Catawba) at Pleasant Garden and North Fork of Swannanoa River near Mt. Mitchell. Jordan & Evermann, 1896, 506, pl. lxxxii, fig. 218.

DIAGNOSIS.—Body moderately long, somewhat compressed, back slightly elevated, depth contained 4 to 4.5 times in total length; head large, broad between eyes, the length about equal to body depth; mouth large, the maxillary often extending beyond eye; eye about .5 length of snout and .16 length of head; scales very small, about 230 in lateral series; gill-rakers small, 17 on first arch; dorsal rays 10; anal rays 9. Color: variable, depending on local conditions; back usually grayish, mottled with dark green or black; lower parts in males often bright red; sides with numerous small vermilion spots on brownish background; dorsal and caudal fins barred or mottled with black; lower fins plain dusky, edged anteriorly with a creamy or orange stripe, behind which is a black stripe. (*fontinalis*, of the springs.)

This beautiful and excellent species is native to northern North America from Labrador to the Saskatchewan valley, throughout the Great Lakes region, and the eastern slope of Alleghany Mountains as far south as the headwaters of Chattahoochee River in Georgia. Its distribution has, however, been greatly extended by man; and the fish may now be found in nearly every suitable stream in the United States.

The natural distribution of the fish in North Carolina is the headwaters of the Catawba and French Broad rivers, although it has been introduced into various other waters, and is now quite generally found in the mountainous sections.   It is particularly abundant in the upper tributaries of the Catawba and in the Swannanoa and other affluents of the French Broad.

The brook trout is emphatically a cold-water fish, thriving best in clear mountain streams with a maximum temperature of 50° F., although in some places it flourishes in short coastal rivers and runs to salt water in winter. Its food consists largely of insects, worms, and crustaceans. While the species reaches a length of 18 to 24 inches, in North Carolina it is of comparatively small size.

The spawning time is in autumn, and the spawning beds are shallow places near the banks of streams. The female makes a kind of nest in the gravel, and guards the eggs during incubation. The eggs average about .15 inch in diameter, and the number laid varies from a few hundred to several thousand, depending on the size of the parent. The hatching period is about 50 days in water of 50 degrees temperature.

Fig. 46. BROOK TROUT. *Salvelinus fontinalis.*

This is a prime favorite with anglers in all parts of the country, and is one of the choicest of food fishes. Excellent trout fishing is afforded in the western part of North Carolina, and the number of fishermen coming from outside the state is increasing yearly. Trout streams are among the most valuable resources of a region; and it behooves the state to encourage the influx of sportsmen and tourists by keeping all suitable waters well stocked and protecting them in the interest of anglers. Mention should be made of the trout waters in the "Sapphire country". The three artificial lakes—Toxaway, Sapphire, and Fairfield—on the property of the Toxaway Company in Transylvania County have been stocked with both brook trout and rainbow trout, and the streams entering those lakes and in the vicinity also contain these fish.

Genus SALMO Linnæus. Salmons and Trouts.

Most of the fresh-water and migratory trouts of the Old World and America, together with the Atlantic salmon of Europe and America and the landlocked salmon* of Maine and Canada, belong in this genus. The elongate, compressed

---

*The introduction of the landlocked or Sebago salmon into the mountainous waters of the state is contemplated.

body is covered with small scales; the mouth is large, and in the adult male the jaws are more or less hooked; teeth grow on the jaws, tongue, vomer, and palatines; the vomer is flat; the fins are small, and the dorsal and anal contain only 10 to 12 rays. The general color is usually glistening silvery, and the markings are black; the young ("parrs") are dark barred. (*Salmo*, salmon.)

116. SALMO IRIDEUS Gibbons.
Rainbow Trout; California Trout.

Salmo irideus Gibbons, Proceedings California Academy of Sciences, 1865, 36; Alameda county, California
Jordan & Evermann, 1896, 500, pl. lxxxi, fig. 216.

DIAGNOSIS.—Body relatively short, the form more elongate in male, depth contained 3.5 to 3.75 in length; head short, about .25 length; snout rounded, .33 length of head; eye rather large, .2 head; mouth comparatively small, the maxillary longer in male, in which it extends beyond eye; vomerine teeth in 2 irregular series; scales in lengthwise series about 135, in crosswise series about 40; dorsal rays 10 to 12; anal rays 10 or 11; caudal fin concave or slightly forked. Color: variable; sea-run fish brilliant silvery with few markings; adult fresh-water examples dark bluish above, silvery on sides and below, a broad iridescent, red lateral band; back, sides, and top of head, together with vertical fins, profusely marked with small, round blackish spots. (*irideus*, like a rainbow.)

The waters of the Coast Range and Sierra Nevada mountains in California, Oregon, and Washington are inhabited by a numerous group of trouts collectively known as the rainbow trouts, which have become more or less differentiated and are probably to be regarded as distinct species. They are among the most beautiful, gamy, and deliciously-flavored of all trouts, and exhibit a wide variation in size, some in circumscribed waters never exceeding half a pound in weight, while others normally weigh from 5 to 12 pounds. The fish has long been cultivated, and has been planted by the general government in all suitable waters of the United States. The form most extensively cultivated is indigenous to the McCloud River and other streams south of Mount Shasta, and is called *Salmo irideus shasta*.

The rainbow trout has been introduced into various streams of North Carolina, and is now firmly established. As early as 1880, the planting of young fish in cold streams in the western counties was begun, and has been continued to the present time. This fish is adapted to warmer and more sluggish waters than the brook trout, and is in no sense a rival of the latter. Waters that have come unsuitable for brook trout through changed physical conditions may be advantageously stocked with the rainbow trout. This fish feeds by preference on insects, insect larvæ, worms, and crustaceans, and preys on minnows and other fishes only when its normal food is absent or insufficient in quantity. While inhabiting some of the waters in which the brook trout occurs, the rainbow is for the most part found lower in the streams.

Among the state waters which have been successfully stocked with rainbow trout are the lakes and streams of the Toxaway Company in Transylvania County, where excellent fishing is now enjoyed by many persons each year.

The spawning season is in spring, and the spawning grounds are the smaller tributaries of streams or the streams flowing into lakes.   At Toxaway, the U. S. Bureau of Fisheries has recently begun spawn-taking operations, the brood fish being caught while running into the feeders of the artificial lakes.   Spawning begins when the fish are 2 or 3 years old, and continues until they reach a considerable age.   The eggs are .2 inch or a little more in diameter, and from 500 to 3,000 are desposited by a single fish.

This is an excellent food fish, and one of the best of all the trouts.   In its native waters it has no superiors and few equals as a game fish, but in the east it has deteriorated in this respect and in general is inferior to the brook trout.

Order INIOMI.   The Lantern-fishes.

Family SYNODONTIDÆ.   The Lizard-fishes.

Chiefly small shore fishes, with elongate, cylindrical or little compressed body; cycloid scales; straight lateral line; very wide mouth provided with sharp teeth on the jaws, palatines, and tongue; an exceedingly long premaxillary bone which forms the entire margin of the upper jaw and conceals the rudimentary maxillary; branchial membranes not united or only slightly so and free from isthmus; short or obsolete gill-rakers; small or absent air-bladder; short dorsal fin; small adipose dorsal; forked caudal.

The typical and commonest genus, Synodus, is the only one as yet represented in the North Carolina fauna, although Trachinocephalus will no doubt eventually be found; this genus differs from Synodus in having a stouter body and a short, blunt, compressed head.   The only American species, *Trachinocephalus myops*, the ground spearing, is common from South Carolina southward and has been taken on a number of occasions as far north as Massachusetts.

Genus SYNODUS Gronovius.   Lizard-fishes.

The lizard-fishes are numerous in warm waters in various parts of the world. They are small or moderate in size, and have little food value.   They lie on or partly buried on shoal sandy shores and are very voracious.   They are distinguished by an elongate body nearly circular in cross-section; a depressed head; a pointed snout, a wide mouth, with a strong premaxillary more than half length of head, and a very complete and formidable set of teeth (2 series of large, knife-like teeth on premaxillaries, the larger inner row depressible; a band of similar teeth on lower jaw and another on palatine; and an area of strong, depressible teeth on tongue); a rather large eye placed above level of snout; spinous gill-rakers; branchiostegals 12 to 16; small cycloid scales on body, cheeks, and opercles, top of head naked; a long blind sac connected with stomach and numerous pyloric cœca; anal opening much nearer to base of caudal than to base of ventrals; a short dorsal fin placed well forward; a small adipose fin over anal; a short anal; rather small pectorals; moderately large ventrals, with inner rays longest; and a narrow, forked caudal.   A number of species known from both coasts of America, but only one ranging as far north as this state.   (*Synodus*, an ancient Greek name for some fish, meaning "teeth meeting".)

117. SYNODUS FŒTENS (Linnæus).
"Pike"; "Sand Pike"; Lizard-fish.

Salmo fœtens Linnæus, Systema Naturæ, ed. xii, 513, 1766; South Carolina.
Synodus fœtens, Jordan & Gilbert, 1879, 384; Beaufort Harbor. Jenkins, 1887, 86; Beaufort. Linton, 1905, 353; Beaufort.

DIAGNOSIS (based on specimen 12.5 inches long taken at Beaufort, November 1, 1904).— Body elongate, cylindrical, its depth .14 length; head long, depressed, lizard-like, .25 length of body; eye placed high, its diameter contained 6 times in head and 2.5 times in snout; mouth large and armed with numerous small, sharp, depressible teeth; snout long, sharp; premaxillary 2 times length of snout and equal to post-orbital part of head; scales in lateral series 63 to 65, in transverse series 7 or 8 + 11 or 12; dorsal rays 12 (including 2 unbranched rays), the longest .66 length of head; anal rays 12; caudal deeply forked; pectorals half length of head; ventrals large, their length about equal to height of dorsal. · Life colors: body and sides grayish, finely mottled with brownish green, the centers of the scales being lighter than the edges; head brownish with light vermiculations on top and sides, pale yellow below; about 8 very obscure dark blotches along sides; belly white; dorsal nearly plain, anal white, caudal dusky with black margin, pectorals dusky greenish above and white below, ventrals pale yellowish, adipose fin white anteriorly and black posteriorly. (*fœtens*, odorous.)

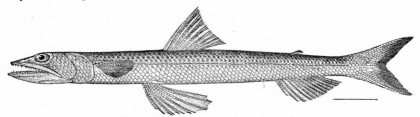

Fig. 47. LIZARD-FISH. *Synodus fœtens.*

The lizard-fish is found on sandy shores from Massachusetts to South America, and is common along the south Atlantic coast.   It is abundant in the North Carolina sounds, and is known locally as "pike" and "sand pike".   At Beaufort it is often caught in line fishing in the harbor.   The fishermen fear the lizard-fish's bite, which is said to "go to the bone".   The fish rarely attains a length of more than a foot, and the usual length is under 9 or 10 inches, but at Beaufort it is reported that 2-foot specimens are sometimes caught.   An example less than 2 inches long was dredged at a depth of 9 fathoms 2 miles east of Beaufort Inlet September 1, 1899, and another 2.25 inches long was seined in in Beaufort Harbor June 3, 1905.   The lizard-fish has a formidable mouth, and is a voracious feeder; small fish constitute its principal food, but crabs, shrimp, worms, and other animals are also eaten.   As a food fish it has no value.

Although Yarrow (1877) did not list this among the fishes of Beaufort harbor, it is probable that his remarks regarding the saury (*Scombresox saurus*) in reality apply to this fish.

Family AULOPIDÆ.

Bottom fishes, inhabiting moderate depths, similar to the Synodontidæ but with maxillary well developed, gill-rakers long and slender, ctenoid scales, etc. Only one genus represented in American waters.

Genus CHLOROPHTHALMUS Bonaparte.   Green-eyes.

Small smelt-like fishes, with terete, slightly compressed body, long head, large mouth, maxillary dilated behind and extending beyond front of large eye, projecting lower jaw, small teeth, short dorsal and anal fins, dorsal inserted anterior to middle of body, ventrals under dorsal, needle-shaped gill-rakers and silvery coloration.   Three known American species, in Atlantic Ocean, one recently detected off North Carolina.   (*Chlorophthalmus*, green-eyed.)

118. CHLOROPHTHALMUS CHALYBEIUS (Goode).
Green-eye.

Hyphalonedrus chalybeius Goode, Proceedings U. S. National Museum, iii, 1880, 484; Gulf Stream off Rhode Island, 85 to 167 fathoms.
Chlorophthalmus chalybeius, Goode & Bean, Oceanic Ichthyology, 1895, 60, fig. 71.

DIAGNOSIS.—Depth a little less than .16 length; head .25 length; eye .33 head and 4 times interorbital space; snout .25 head; maxillary broad, wider posteriorly, extending to opposite pupil; mandible protruding beyond snout; scales pectinate on margin, in regular rows, 48 in lateral series, 12 in crosswise series; dorsal rays 11, the fin inserted midway between end of snout and adipose fin; adipose dorsal over middle of anal; anal rays 8, anal base as long as snout; caudal forked; pectorals long, falcate, twice length of lower jaw; ventrals under middle of dorsal.   Color: grayish with discreet brown mottlings, the scales metallic silvery.   (*chalybeius*, steel blue.)

This species has heretofore been known only from the Gulf Stream in water of moderate depth.   It is entitled to a place in the North Carolina fauna from having been taken by the steamer Fish-Hawk in dredgings off Cape Lookout in August, 1902; 10 specimens, the largest 2.5 inches long, were secured.

Order HAPLOMI.   The Pikes and Pike-like Fishes.

In this order the fin-rays are soft, the single dorsal fin is placed more or less posteriorly (in some genera close to caudal), the ventral fins are abdominal, and the pectoral fins are placed low.   The body is elongate and covered with cycloid scales which extend also on the head.   There is no lateral line.   The terminal mouth contains teeth, and communicates by a duct with the air-bladder. Among the bony characters are the absent mesocoracoid; the separate hypercoracoid and hypocoracoid, with developed actinosts; the shoulder girdle joined to the skull by a post-temporal; distinct pharyngeal bones; and well developed opercles.

Of the 4 American families, 3 are strictly fresh-water and the other is largely so.   Among the members of one family are some of the largest and most predaceous of all fresh-water fishes, and among the members of another family are the smallest American fresh-water fishes.

i. Lateral margin of upper jaw formed by the maxillaries; premaxillaries not protractile.
  a. Size very small; jaws short, teeth villiform and of equal size..............UMBRIDÆ.
  aa. Size moderate to large; jaws produced and flattened, teeth cardiform and of unequal size.
                                                                                ESOCIDÆ.
ii. Lateral margin of upper jaw formed by the premaxillaries, which are more or less protractile.
  b. Vent placed well backward; premaxillaries very protractile...........POECILIIDÆ.
  bb. Vent placed near throat; premaxillaries slightly protractile.........AMBLYOPSIDÆ.

Family UMBRIDÆ.   The Mud Minnows.

A family of small fresh-water fishes, interesting on account of their habits and their peculiar distribution; of the three known species, one is found in Austria and two in the United States.   The body is long, but little compressed; the head broad; the lower jaw, premaxillaries, vomer, and palatines have bands of villiform teeth; the broad maxillaries, which form the lateral margins of the upper jaw, have no teeth; the branchial openings are wide, gill-rakers small, branchiostegals 6 to 8; pseudobranchiæ glandular; no lateral line; scales firm, regular, cycloid, covering body and head; fins small, dorsal single, placed well backward but in front of anal; pectorals close together; air-bladder simple. Oviparous, carnivorous fishes, inhabiting muddy ditches, and ponds and sluggish streams overgrown with weeds; very hardy and able to live buried in mud; sexes similar.

Genus UMBRA Müller.   Mud Minnows.

Characters of the genus are shown above.*   One species is found locally. (*Umbra*, shade.)

119. UMBRA PYGMÆA (DeKay).
"Mud-fish"; Mud Minnow.

Leuciscus pygmæus DeKay, New York Fauna, Fishes, 1842, 214; Rockland County, N. Y.
Umbra pygmæa, Jordan, 1889*b*, 126; Tar River at Rocky Mount.   Jordan & Evermann, 1896, 624, pl. xcix, fig. 268.
Umbra limi pygmæa, Evermann & Cox, 1896, 305; tributary of Neuse River near Raleigh

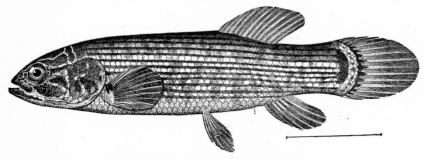

Fig. 48.   MUD MINNOW.   *Umbra pymæa.*

DIAGNOSIS.—Form compact, oblong, slightly compressed, depth contained 4.5 times in total length; head short and broad, .25 length of body; snout short, equal to eye, which enters 4.5 times in length of head; mouth moderate, jaws short; gill-slits wide; gill-rakers short and

*An interesting review of these fishes has recently been published by Dr. Theodore Gill under the title "A remarkable genus of fishes—the umbras", in Smithsonian Miscellaneous Collections, quarterly issue, vol. i, 1904.

numerous; scales in lateral series 35, in transverse series 13; dorsal rays 14; anal rays 7 or 8. Color: dark or yellowish green, with 10 or 12 pale, narrow lengthwise stripes; a dark stripe through eye; a black bar at base of tail; fins plain. Length, to 5 inches. (*pygmœa*, pygmy.)

The mud minnow, which exists in lowland streams, swamps, and ditches from New York to North Carolina, is known from only a few localities in the latter state, although it may be looked for in all waters from the Neuse northward. It is rather scarce in Tar River at Rocky Mount, and abundant in the vicinity of Raleigh. The National Museum has specimens collected in the Neuse at Goldsboro by James W. Milner in 1875. The writer did not find it in the Albemarle region in 1892, although it is known from the Virginia waters of the Dismal Swamp, from which some of the tributaries of Albemarle Sound flow. In mudholes about Lake Ellis in Craven County Mr. C. S. Brimley found it common in 1905 and 1906.

Family ESOCIDÆ. The Pikes, Pickerels, and Muskallunges.

A small family of fresh-water fishes of moderate to large size, peculiar to North America with the exception of one species found also in northern Europe and Asia. The body is very elongate, more or less compressed; the head long and flattened, and the mouth very large and fully provided with teeth on jaws, tongue, palatines, and vomer; lower jaw projecting; margins of upper jaw formed by maxillaries, which have a supplemental bone; body covered with fine scales, head naked above; lateral line present in adults; gill-slits wide, gill-membranes not united and free from isthmus; gill-rakers short and toothed; branchiostegals numerous; pseudobranchiæ glandular, concealed; dorsal and anal fins placed far back; pectorals close together; caudal forked; air-bladder simple. There is a single genus.

Genus ESOX Linnæus. Pikes, Pickerels, and Muskallunges.

The pikes in general have been thus referred to by Professor Goode:

They have been well described as mere machines for the assimilation of animal matter. They are the wolves of the ponds, the bluefish of the fresh waters, and nothing comes amiss to their ravenous maws. * * * * The hungry *Esox* is a sad foe to the proprietor of a fish preserve, and until it has been banished from a pond, no other species can be expected to live.* * * The enemies of *Esox* in America denounce him vigorously, and declare that he is bony, flavorless, and of trifling value. He has his friends, however, * * * Tough old pike, and those taken from muddy, sluggish water, are of course not to be desired, but as a rule any one of the species is to be chosen as a delicate morsel for the table.

The yield of the pikes in North Carolina in recent years has been from 30,000 to 100,000 pounds annually, for which the fishermen have received 2.5 to 4 cents a pound. The bulk of the catch comes from Craven and Beaufort counties.

Three representatives of this family and genus are found in the local waters, and they may be distinguished as follows:

i. Cheeks and opercles scaly; dorsal rays 11 to 15; branchiostegals 11 to 16, scales in lateral series 100 to 125.
    a. Dorsal rays 11 to 14, anal rays 11 or 12; branchiostegals 11 to 13, scales in lateral series 88 to 110; small fish with numerous blackish vertical bars on sides ......*americanus.*

aa. Dorsal rays 14 or 15; anal rays 13 or 14; branchiostegals 14 to 16; scales in lateral series about 125; medium sized fish with numerous dark lines, mostly horizontal and connected so as to form a loose network..*reticulatus.*
ii. Cheeks and opercles scaly above, naked below; dorsal rays 17; anal rays 15; branchiostegals 17 to 19; scales in lateral series about 150; very large fish with narrow indistinct bars which break up into ill-defined dark spots...............................*ohiensis.*

(*Esox,* a name applied by Pliny to some fish, probably the sturgeon.)

120. ESOX AMERICANUS Gmelin.
"Pike"; "Red-finned Pike"; "Jack"; Pickerel.

Esox lucius americanus Gmelin, Systema Naturæ, 1390, 1788; Long Island, N. Y.
Esox ravenelii, Cope, 1870*b*, 457; Catawba River.
Lucius americanus, Jordan, 1889*b*, 129, 133; Little River at Goldsboro; tributaries of Haw River in Guilford County. Smith, 1893*a*, 195, 199; cypress swamp near Edenton; Roanoke River at Plymouth and Weldon. Evermann & Cox, 1896, 305; Neuse River near Raleigh. Jordan & Evermann, 1896, 626. Smith, 1901, 134; Lake Mattamuskeet.

DIAGNOSIS.—Body long, robust, the depth about .2 total length; head large, more than .25 total length; snout broad and blunt, about .37 length of head; eye rather large, contained 5.5 times in length of head; lower jaw considerably longer than upper; maxillary extends to under pupil; dorsal and anal fins opposite, origin of former about equidistant from base of ventrals and caudal; ventrals about midway between end of snout and base of caudal. Color: dark green above, sides greenish yellow, with 18 to 20 dark, vertical curved bars; a dark bar below eye, and a dark stripe on side of head through eye; fins unspotted; lower fins in North Carolina specimens sometimes scarlet, upper fins dark, edged with carmine.

This little pickerel is found in streams and swamps of the eastern seaboard from Massachusetts to Alabama. It is known from numerous places in North Carolina. It is of small size, rarely exceeding a foot in length, and is of less importance as a food and game fish than *Esox reticulatus.* The food is chiefly minnows, with which the stomach is often gorged.

121. ESOX RETICULATUS LeSueur.
"Pike"; "Red-finned Pike"; "Black Pike"; "Duck-billed Pike"; "Jack"; Pickerel; Chain Pickerel.

Esox reticulatus LeSueur, Journal Academy Natural Sciences of Philadelphia, i, 1818, 414; Connecticut River, Mass.; Philadelphia.
Esox affinis, Cope, 1870*b*, 457; Neuse River.
?Lucius vermiculatus, Evermann & Cox, 1896, 305; Neuse River near Raleigh.
Lucius reticulatus, Jordan, 1889*b*, 126, 128, 133; Tar, Neuse (and Little), and Haw rivers. Smith, 1893*a*, 191, 195, 199; Pasquotank River, Edenton Bay, Roanoke River. Jordan & Evermann, 1896, 627. Smith, 1901, 134; Lake Mattamuskeet.

DIAGNOSIS.—Body long and slender, the depth .16 total length; caudal peduncle very slender, only .33 depth of body; head long, .4 total length; snout long, pointed, contained 2.25 to 2.33 times in length of head; eye small, .4 length of snout and .12 to .14 length of head. Color: varying from green to nearly black, sides lighter and with golden luster; entire body marked by narrow dark connecting lines which form a loose network; a dark bar below eye. (*reticulatus,* with mesh-like markings.)

This pike is an inhabitant of the eastern seaboard from Maine to Louisiana. It is common in the lower courses of North Carolina rivers flowing into the Atlantic Ocean. About Albemarle Sound, where all the local names in quotation marks are in use, it is very common, and is often caught in the nets of the com mercial fishermen.   Old examples living in deep, shady water are dark colored and are called "black pike".   In Lake Mattamuskeet the fish is numerous and reaches a large size (1.5 to 2 feet).   A weight of 7 or 8 pounds and a length of 3 or 4 feet have been attained in waters outside the state.

The chain pickerel is a voracious feeder, consuming minnows and other small fish in large numbers and also insects, frogs, and snakes.   Its favorite haunts are creeks, coves, and bayous with grasses and broad-leaved water plants, under which it lurks.   In spring about Albemarle Sound, the fish feeds chiefly on alewives.   Spawning occurs in late winter or early spring.   Lawson (1709) said of this species:

The jack, pike, or pickerel, is exactly the same, in Carolina, as they are in England. Indeed, I never saw this fish so big and large in America, as I have in Europe, these with us being seldom above two foot long, as far as I have yet seen.   They are very plentiful with us in Carolina, all our creeks and ponds being full of them.   I once took out of a ware, above three hundred of these fish, at a time.

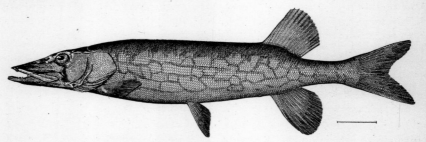

Fig. 49.   CHAIN PICKEREL; PIKE.   *Esox reticulatus.*

Considerable quantities of this fish are marketed, but it does not rank high, the flesh being coarse and filled with minute bones.   It bites freely at the still-baited hook or the trolling spoon, and affords much sport to anglers.

122. ESOX OHIENSIS Kirtland.
"Jack"; Ohio Muskallunge.

Esox ohiensis Kirtland, Proceedings Cleveland Academy of Natural Science, February 7, 1854, 85; Mahoning River, Ohio.   Jordan & Evermann, American Food and Game Fishes, 239, 1902.
Esox masquinongy, Jordan, 1889*b*, 150; French Broad River near Asheville.
Lucius masquinongy ohiensis, Jordan & Evermann, 1896, 629; Ohio River and tributaries.

DIAGNOSIS.—Body elongate and robust, the depth .16 total length; head large, more than .25 total length; snout .4 length of head; eye small, .09 length of head; gill-rakers "mere clumps of spiny tubercles".   Color: dark green on back, paler below, with brassy or golden reflections; 20 to 25 irregular, dark, vertical bars on upper half of body; unpaired fins with dark green spots or blotches.   (*ohiensis,* inhabiting Ohio.)

This species of muskallunge inhabits Ohio River and tributaries, and is entitled to a place in the North Carolina fauna by virtue of Dr. Jordan's record of its occurrence in French Broad River near Asheville.   It was there reported to be one of the food fishes of the section, and was locally known as "jack".

The species reaches a maximum length of 5 feet, and thus rivals the Great Lakes muskallunge (*Esox masquinongy*) with which it has until recently been identified.

Family PŒCILIIDÆ.   The Mummichogs, Top Minnows, etc.

A numerous family of small fresh-water, brackish-water, or salt-water fishes found in all parts of the world, with many representatives in the United States. They are of no value as food, but are of great importance as food for other fishes. The sexes are usually dissimilar in form and size, and many of the species bring forth their young alive.   The principal characters of the family are: Elongate body, compressed posteriorly, flattened anteriorly, covered with large cycloid scales; no lateral line; mouth terminal, premaxillary bones protractile and forming the margin of the upper jaw; jaws provided with cutting or villiform teeth; branchial membranes united, free from the isthmus; gill-rakers short and thick; pseudobranchiæ absent; dorsal fin single, composed only of soft rays and placed posteriorly; caudal fin square or concave, not forked; ventral fins abdominal; pectoral fins inserted close together.   Of the 20 or more American genera 5 are represented in North Carolina by 9 species.

Key to the North Carolina genera of killi-fishes.

i. Lower jaw strong and projecting; intestine comparatively short, with few convolutions; teeth slightly movable.
  a. Anal fins similar in both sexes; species oviparous.
    b. Teeth pointed (none compressed, tricuspid, or bicuspid).
      c. Teeth in bands or in more than one series; dorsal fin placed either before or behind anal; air-bladder well developed .... FUNDULUS.
      cc. Teeth in a single series; dorsal fin placed anterior to anal............. LUCANIA.
    bb. Teeth incisors, tricuspid, in a single row .... CYPRINODON.
  aa. Anal fin in male modified into a sword-shaped organ; teeth pointed, in bands; species viviparous .... GAMBUSIA.
ii. Lower jaw short and weak; intestine long, much convoluted; teeth freely movable, pointed, and in a single series; species viviparous: .... HETERANDRIA.

Genus FUNDULUS Lacépède.   Killi-fishes; Mummichogs.

This genus includes some of the best known and most abundant of our "minnows", and has numerous members in all parts of the country, 5 being in the local fauna.   Form elongate, posteriorly compressed, and back little or not at all elevated; mouth terminal, lower jaw projecting and rather heavy; a narrow band of teeth in each jaw; fins variable; dorsal origin in advance of, above, or behind anal origin; anal fin larger in male; caudal margin straight or rounded; sexes dissimilar in size, color, etc.   Several species abound in water of all degrees of density, while others are confined strictly to either fresh or salt water.   Some live on muddy bottom and feed on mud; others swim freely in creeks, rivers, and bays, and subsist largely on insects.   All the species go in schools, which sometimes contain thousands of individuals.

Key to the North Carolina species of Fundulus.

i. Dorsal fin inserted in advance of anal.
  a. Scales large, less than 40 in lateral series.
    b. Form elongate; branchiostegals 6; females with several black horizontal stripes, males with numerous black vertical bars .... *majalis.*

bb. Form robust; branchiostegals 5; females nearly plain brown; males darker, with pearly
    spots . . . .*heteroclitus.*
aa. Scales smaller, 44 to 48 in lateral series; body slender, depth about .2 length; color oliva-
    ceous, with numerous dark or light vertical bars. . . . .*diaphanus.*
ii. Dorsal fin inserted over or slightly behind anal; scales in lateral series 38 to 42.
    c. Olivaceous with brownish spots; a small mountain species . . . .*rathbuni.*
    cc. Olivaceous above, silvery on sides and belly, with 6 black longitudinal stripes from head
        to tail and (in male) 12 black crossbars; a small lowland species. . . . .*nottii.*

(*Fundulus,* from *fundus,* bottom.)

123. FUNDULUS MAJALIS (Walbaum).
"Minnow"; May-fish; Killi-fish.

Cobitis majalis Walbaum, Artedi Genera Piscium, iii, 12, 1792; Long Island.
Hydrargyra majalis, Yarrow, 1877, 214; Beaufort Harbor. Jordan & Gilbert, 1879, 384; Beaufort Harbor.
    Kendall & Smith, 1894, 21; Hatteras Inlet.
Fundulus majalis, Jenkins, 1887, 86; Beaufort. Jordan & Evermann, 1896, 639, pl. ci, figs. 271, 271a, 271b.
    Linton, 1905, 355; Beaufort.

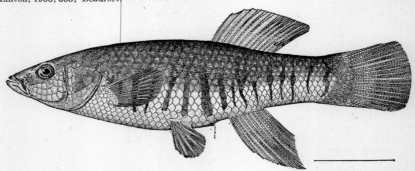

Fig. 50. MAY-FISH. *Fundulus majalis.* Male.

DIAGNOSIS.—Form oblong, back not elevated, the depth .25 total length; head long, more
than .25 length; mouth terminal, oblique, small; teeth in a broad band, the outer teeth enlarged;
eye .2 length of head and .66 length of snout; scales large, 35 or 36 in longitudinal series, 13 to
15 in transverse series; dorsal rays 12 to 14; anal fin higher in male, the rays 10 or 11; ventrals
longer in male, extending beyond origin of anal.   Color: Male (from Beaufort), back olive,
sides and belly bright salmon yellow, lower fins clear yellow, pectorals and anal partly dusky,
posterior edge of caudal dark, dorsal nearly all black, a large black ocellated spot on last rays;
opercles and under parts of head suffused with black; cheeks, top of head, and mouth bronze
yellow, about 18 narrow dusky vertical bars.   Female, olivaceous above, white below, 4 black
longitudinal stripes, 1 or 2 black crossbars at base of tail. (*majalis,* relating to May.)

The may-fish abounds from Massachusetts to Florida, in bays, salt-water
ponds, and the lower courses of rivers.   It reaches a length of 8 inches, and is the
largest of the killi-fishes; the usual length is less than 6 inches, the female being
larger than the male.   The fish is often found in large droves in shallow bayous
and coves, and marshy creeks, and a single haul of a fine-meshed collecting seine
may yield a thousand or more.   Spawning occurs in summer.   The young are
marked by black vertical stripes.

In Beaufort specimens, the young of both sexes are marked with 14 or 15
narrow vertical bars.   The external sexual characters appear at variable sizes.

In some specimens 1.25 inches long (taken July 25, 1900) the vertical bars have begun to fade, and the longitudinal stripes have appeared; the smallest male in this lot in which the dorsal ocellus is visible is 2 inches long. In this and other lots, there are males 2.25 inches long in which the ocellus has not appeared. Either the rate of growth is very irregular or the spawning time is protracted, as a lot of young fish seined in Beaufort Harbor July 25, 1900, varied from .5 to 2.5 inches in length.

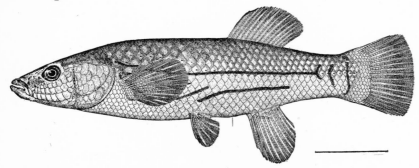

Fig. 51   MAY-FISH.   *Fundulus majalis.*   Female.

124. FUNDULUS HETEROCLITUS (Linnæus).
"Minnow"; Mud-fish; Mummichog.

Cobitis heteroclita Linnæus, Systema Naturæ, ed. xii, 500, 1766; Charleston, South Carolina.
Fundulus pisculentus, Yarrow, 1877, 214; Beaufort Harbor.
Fundulus heteroclitus, Jordan & Gilbert, 1879, 384; Beaufort Harbor.   Jenkins, 1887, 86; Beaufort.   Jordan
   & Evermann, 1896, 640, pl. cii, fig. 273.   Linton, 1905, 356; Beaufort.

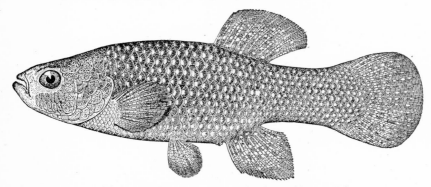

Fig. 52.   MUD-FISH.   *Fundulus heteroclitus.*   Male.

DIAGNOSIS.—Body rather short and deep, but little compressed, depth rather more than .25 length; head rather short and blunt, its length contained 3 to 3.5 times in total length; mouth small, very oblique; teeth pointed, in bands; eye .2 to .25 length of head, equal to snout and .5 width of interorbital space; scales in lateral series 35 to 38, in transverse series 13 to 15; dorsal rays 11; anal rays 10 or 11, oviduct attached to first ray; caudal fin rounded.   Color: Male, dark green above, yellow on belly; sides with narrow vertical silvery white bars, between which are numerous small, irregular whitish or yellow spots; head yellow below; vertical fins dark, with numerous pale spots; dorsal sometimes having a black spot posteriorly; anal and ventrals yellow anteriorly. Female, plain brownish green, lighter below, sides sometimes marked by about 15 dark crossbars narrower than the interspaces. (*heteroclitus*, irregular.)

The range of this killi-fish is from Maine to Mexico. It frequents chiefly brackish waters, but is also found in fresh water (as in the Potomac at Washington). It is very partial to shallow muddy waters, and one of its common names is mud-dabbler, in allusion to its mud-loving habit. Length, up to 6 inches. The species is an important bait fish, and is extensively eaten by squeteague, striped bass, and other fish, as well as by water birds.

125. FUNDULUS DIAPHANUS (LeSueur).
Killi-fish; Spring Minnow.

Hydrargyra diaphana LeSueur, Journal Academy of Natural Sciences Philadelphia, i, 130, 1817; Saratoga Lake.
Fundulus diaphanus, Smith, 1893a, 191, 195, 197; Pasquotank and Roanoke rivers and Edenton Bay. Smith, Notes on Fishes of Lower Potomac River (Bulletin U. S. Fish Commission 1890), 65, pl. xix, 1892. Jordan & Evermann, 1896, 645, pl. ciii, figs. 275, 275a.

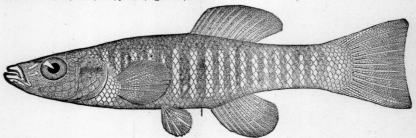

Fig. 53. SPRING MINNOW. *Fundulus diaphanus*. Male.

DIAGNOSIS.—Form elongated, slender, posteriorly compressed, depth contained 4.5 times in total length; head depressed, .25 to .4 total length; mouth nearly horizontal, on level with pupil, lower jaw projecting, angle of mouth half way between eye and tip of lower jaw; eye large, contained 3.5 times in head, 1.5 times in interorbital space, 1.33 times in snout; scales about 45 in lateral series and 15 in transverse; dorsal fin low, beginning considerably in advance of anal and nearer base of caudal than snout, rays 13; anal fin anteriorly sheathed by oviduct, short, higher than dorsal, rays 11; edge of caudal fin straight or slightly emarginate. Color: Male, uniformly olivaceous, darkest above, about 20 silvery vertical bars rather narrower than the interspaces, which are the color of the body; back may be dark-spotted; a dark purplish spot on opercle opposite eye; dorsal fin usually plain, occasionally faintly mottled with black and white spots; other fins plain. Female, body marked by 15 to 20 dark vertical bars, much narrower and shorter than silvery bars in male, the interspaces lighter than in male. (*diaphanus*, transparent.)

The southern limit of the range of this species appears to be North Carolina, whence it extends to Maine and the upper Mississippi, in rivers and lakes. It is found coastwise in abundance, in salt and fresh water, although it is less of a salt-water form than *Fundulus heteroclitus*, and often occurs in mountain brooks, in springs, and in clear cold lakes. It is very abundant in the lower stretches of the rivers debouching into Albemarle Sound; numerous small specimens (all under 2.5 inches) were collected by the writer in Pasquotank River and Roanoke River near Plymouth in April.   The maximum length is about 4 inches.

Many species of food and game fishes, in fresh and salt water, feed largely on this killi-fish, which, on account of its abundance, is one of the important "minnows".

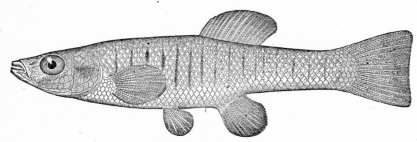

Fig. 54.   SPRING MINNOW.   *Fundulus diaphanus.*   Female.

The prominent external sexual differences in this species were first pointed out by the present writer in 1892, in the paper above cited, on fishes of the lower Potomac River, in which the figures of the two sexes here given were originally printed.   All immature specimens are marked by dark vertical bars on a pale olivaceous background; when the fish reaches a length of about 2 inches, the differential colors begin to appear.

126. FUNDULUS RATHBUNI Jordan & Meek.
Rathbun's Killi-fish.

Fundulus rathbuni Jordan & Meek, in Jordan, 1889a, 356, pl. xliv; Allemance Creek near Greensboro, N. C. Jordan. 1889b, 133, 134, pl. xiv, fig. 7; Reedy Fork, South Buffalo Creek, Little Allemance Creek and other tributaries of Haw River; and Jumping Run, tributary of Yadkin River, near Salisbury.   Jordan & Evermann, 1896, 649, pl. cv, fig. 280.

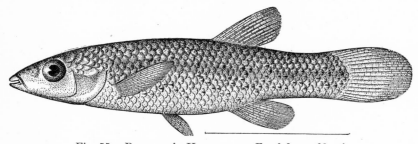

Fig. 55.   RATHBUN'S KILLI-FISH.   *Fundulus rathbuni.*

DIAGNOSIS.—Depth contained 4.5 times in total length, head 3.8 times in length; snout sharp; eye about .25 length of head; mouth small; scales in lateral series 38, in transverse series 12; two rows of scales on cheeks; fins small, dorsal rays 11, anal rays 11, caudal rounded. Color: pale green, with small irregular oblong dark brown spots scattered on head and body; male with scales dark-edged; fins yellowish with speckled base in male, plain in female. (Named for Dr. Richard Rathbun, formerly of the Bureau of Fisheries, now of the Smithsonian Institution.)

So far as known, this little killi-fish is peculiar to Cape Fear and Yadkin basins. It is common in small brooks, but is scarce in the larger streams. Its usual length is 2.5 inches.

127. FUNDULUS NOTTII (Agassiz).
Star-headed Minnow.

Zygonectes nottii Agassiz, American Journal of Science and Arts, 1854, 353; Mobile, Ala.
Fundulus nottii, Jordan & Evermann, 1896, 657, pl. cviii, fig. 288.

DIAGNOSIS.—Body comparatively long, compressed posteriorly, the depth contained 4.5 in length; head rather more than .25 length; eye very large, .37 length of head; interorbital space .5 length of head; snout obtuse, less than eye; outer row of teeth in each jaw enlarged and recurved; scales in lateral series 36, in transverse series 10; origin of dorsal fin more than .66 distance from snout to base of caudal, the rays 7 or 8, the longest ray about equal to distance from snout to posterior margin of pupil; anal similar to dorsal, its origin very slightly behind dorsal, the rays 9 or 10; caudal rounded behind, its length greater than head; pectorals short, acute, their length equal to height of dorsal; ventrals slightly shorter. Color: body from gill-opening to base of caudal marked by 6 narrow, horizontal black stripes, with several other obsolete ones above; 10 to 13 narrow, vertical black stripes of same width; a broad black bar through eye and on cheek; general ground color of body silvery; preorbital region, lower jaw, and upper part of opercle orange red; breast and lower half of opercle reddish yellow. (Named for Dr. Nott, who discovered the fish.)

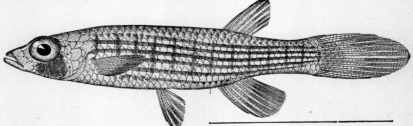

Fig. 56. STAR-HEADED MINNOW. *Fundulus nottii.*

This beautiful little killi-fish has heretofore been recorded from South Carolina, Georgia, Florida, and Alabama, in fresh-water streams and swamps. The National Museum contains one specimen collected in a pond at Wilmington, N. C., May 9, 1899, by Mr. William P. Seal. The maximum length of the species is about 2 inches. Nothing distinctive can be said of its habits.

Genus LUCANIA Girard. Rainwater-fishes.

Diminutive fishes inhabiting brackish and fresh-water swamps, lagoons, and ditches of United States. The body is rather short and much compressed, and covered with large scales; the small, oblique mouth has a single row of conical teeth in each jaw; the fins are small; and the species are oviparous. Of the 4 species known, the range of the following embraces the North Carolina coast. (*Lucania,* an ancient Italian province; a name having no known application to these fishes.)

128. LUCANIA PARVA (Baird & Girard).
Rainwater-fish.

Cyprinodon parvus Baird & Girard, Ninth Smithsonian Report, 345, 1855; Greenport, Long Island, N. Y.
Lucania parva, Jordan & Evermann, 1896, 665, pl. cix, fig. 292.

DIAGNOSIS.—Form rather short, the depth contained 3.25 times in total length; head equal to depth; eye large, .33 length of head; scales in lateral series 26, in crosswise series 8; dorsal rays 10 to 12; anal rays 10 or 11.   Color: olive, scales dark-edged; dorsal dull yellow with black spot surrounded by orange anteriorly; caudal yellow with black tip; anal and ventrals red with dusky edges; fins in female olive, unmarked.   (*parva*, small.)

Found in brackish ponds, ditches and bays, along the entire coast from Cape Cod to Key West.   It is known from Virginia and South Carolina, and undoubtedly occurs in suitable waters in North Carolina.   Its small size, 1.5 to 2 inches, enables it to be easily overlooked.

Genus CYPRINODON Lacépède.   Short Minnows.

Small, chubby brackish-water fishes found from United States to South America, usually going in schools; the males larger than the females; species oviparous.   Body short, back elevated, mouth small, teeth tricuspid incisors in a single row, scales large, origin of dorsal fin in front of anal, branchial aperture reduced, opercle superiorly fused with shoulder girdle.   Ten or twelve species known, one common along our Atlantic coast.   (*Cyprinodon*, carp-toothed.)

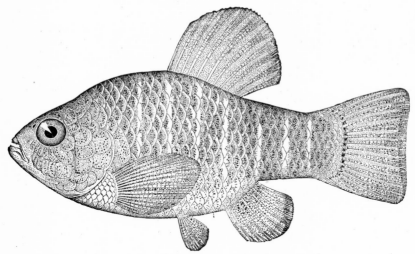

Fig. 57.   VARIEGATED MINNOW.   *Cyprinodon variegatus.*

129. CYPRINODON VARIEGATUS Lacépède.
"Sheepshead Minnow"; Variegated Minnow;   Short Minnow.

Cyprinodon variegatus Lacépède, Histoire Naturelle des Poissons, v, 486, 1803; South Carolina.   Yarrow, 1877, 214; Beaufort Harbor.   Jordan & Gilbert, 1879, 384; Beaufort Harbor.   Jenkins, 1887, 86; Beaufort. Jordan & Evermann, 1896, 671, pls. cxi, cxii, figs. 296, 296a.

DIAGNOSIS.—Form short and deep, back elevated, depth .43 to .50 total length; head wide, short, its length contained 3.25 to 3.6 times in length; snout sharp, mouth small, teeth large, eye contained 3.5 times in length of head and once in snout; caudal peduncle high and short, narrowing rapidly toward tail; scales large, 26 to 28 in lateral line, 13 in transverse line, a large scale on shoulder nearly half length of head; intestine nearly 3 times length of body; dorsal origin far in advance of anal, the fin higher in males than in females, the rays 11; anal rays 10. Color: Male, olive green, with a blue sheen anteriorly, the sides, abdomen, opercles, and cheeks salmon, dorsal black with orange anterior margin; anal dusky at base, with orange border; caudal dull green, marked by a black bar at tip and another at base; ventrals dusky, with orange margin; pectorals dull orange. Female, light olive, with about 7 or 8 dark crossbars on back and 14 on lower part of sides; whitish or yellowish below; lower jaw blue, cheeks brassy; dorsal dusky, with a black ocellus posteriorly; caudal dull reddish with black basal bar; other fins pale orange. (*variegatus*, variegated.)

This showy minnow, which occurs from Massachusetts to Mexico, is abundant in the brackish waters of the North Carolina coast. It is a very shy and active species, difficult to catch with a dip-net, however skilfully handled, but taken in large numbers in fine-meshed seines hauled in marshy creeks. It is carnivorous, and in captivity will devour its own young.

The name "sheepshead minnow", which is used in North Carolina and other states, arises from the resemblance between this fish and the sheepshead, and also from the belief, in some cases, that it is the young of the sheepshead. The full-grown male is 3 inches long and the female is considerably shorter.

Genus GAMBUSIA Poey. Top Minnows.

Very small viviparous fishes living in schools in fresh and brackish waters of United States, Mexico, Central America, and West Indies, the males smaller than the females and apparently much less numerous. Body elongate, deeper in female; mouth of moderate size, both jaws with a band of immovable pointed teeth; scales large; fins small, anal fin in male modified into a sexual organ; colors plain. One species found in North Carolina. (*Gambusia*, from the Cuban word *gambusino*, meaning "nothing".)

130. GAMBUSIA AFFINIS (Baird & Girard).
Top Minnow.

Heterandria affinis Baird & Girard, Proceedings Academy Natural Sciences Philadelphia, 1853, 390; Rio Medina and Rio Salado, Texas.
Haplochilus melanops Cope, 1870*b*, 457; "Still water of Neuse basin, Wake County, N. C."
Zygonectes atrilatus Jordan & Brayton, 1878, 84; Little River at Goldsboro. Jordan & Gilbert, 1879, 368; Neuse River.
Gambusia patruelis, Jenkins, 1885, 11; Beaufort. Jordan, 1886, 26; Beaufort. Jenkins, 1887, 86; Beaufort Jordan, 1889*b*, 126, 129; Tar and Neuse rivers. Smith, 1893*a*, 191, 195, 199; Pasquotank and Roanoke rivers and Edenton Bay
Gambusia affinis, Evermann & Cox, 1896, 305; Neuse River near Raleigh Jordan & Evermann, 1896, 680, pl. cxiii, figs. 289, 289*a*.

DIAGNOSIS.—Form plump, depth abruptly reduced posterior to dorsal and anal fins; greatest depth a little less than .25 length; head about .25 length; eye .33 length of head; snout with upward inclination, less marked in male; scales in lateral series 27 to 32, in transverse series 7 to 10; dorsal fin placed far back, its origin posterior to or over last anal ray, dorsal rays 7 to 9; anal rays 8 to 10. Color: light olive, each scale with a dark edge, a fine dark line along sides, sometimes a dark blotch below eye, a dark purplish blotch on side above vent (absent in male), dorsal with 2 or 3 transverse rows of black spots, anal dark-edged (plain in male), caudal with 3 or 4 irregular transverse rows of dark spots, other fins dusky; examples from ditches and drains are very pale, those from dark-colored water of swamps are dark green, with a distinct purple bar below eye. (*affinis*, related.)

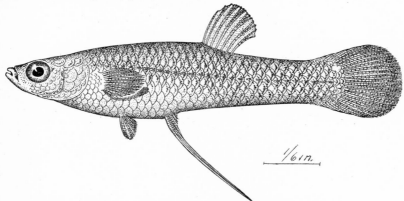

Fig. 58. TOP MINNOW. *Gambusia affinis*. Male.

The top minnow is found along the coast from Delaware to Mexico and reaches inland as far as Illinois. In North Carolina it is excessively abundant in the lowlands, in swamps, ditches, creeks, and also in the open waters of the rivers. Roadside ditches and drains in the Albemarle region teem with the species, and it is there that the aptness of the name top minnow is readily appreciated. It also abounds in the Wilmington region, and doubtless along the entire coastal region of the state.

The length of the adult female is 1.25 to 2.5 inches, while that of the male rarely exceeds 1 inch and is often under .75 inch. The proportion of males to females in a lot of specimens collected by the writer in Pasquotank River was 1 to 3, but there is usually a greater disparity, the males sometimes representing only 2 or 3 per cent.

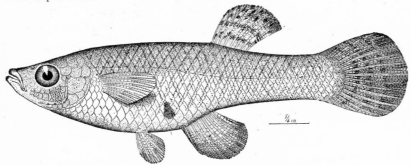

Fig. 59. TOP MINNOW. *Gambusia affinis*. Female.

This is one of the most interesting of our fishes because it brings forth its young alive. The young are born in spring and summer, and probably several broods are produced in one season. From 10 to 30 are expelled at one time;

these are .37 inch long and are able to swim at once.   The old fish, at least in aquaria, often devour the young as soon as born.

The top minnow feeds on mosquitoes and other insects, the larvæ of mosquitoes being the principal food in some places at proper season.   Because of its mosquito-eating propensity, the species plays an important rôle, and its introduction into malarious and yellow-fever regions is strongly advocated   Vegetable matter, in the form of diatoms, desmids, and filamentous algæ, is also eaten.

Genus HETERANDRIA Agassiz.   Top Minnows.

Very small, viviparous fishes inhabiting swamps, ditches, and sluggish streams of southern United States, Central America, and West Indies; similar to Gambusia in form and habits.   Mouth small, jaws weak, a single row of slender, movable teeth in each jaw, lower jaw short; fins small; anal fin in advance of dorsal, modified in the male as in Gambusia.   One species is found in South Atlantic States.   (*Heterandria*, different male.)

131. HETERANDRIA FORMOSA Agassiz.
Top Minnow.

Heterandria formosa Agassiz, Ms., 1853; Girard, Proceedings Academy Natural Sciences, Philadelphia, 1859, 62; Charleston, S. C., Palatka, Fla.   Jordan & Evermann, 1896, 687, pl. cxiv, fig. 302.

DIAGNOSIS.—Body short, slightly compressed, depth .25 total length; length of head contained 3.5 to 3.6 times in total length; mouth terminal, lower jaw slightly projecting; eye .33 length of head and 1.5 times snout; scales in lateral series 24 to 28; dorsal fin with 7 rays, its origin over middle of anal; anal rays 6 to 9; caudal long, .2 length of body.   Color: brownish green; a dark band from mouth to caudal, ending at base of latter in a black spot; 6 to 9 vertical dark streaks; a black spot at base of dorsal and anal.   (*formosa*, comely.)

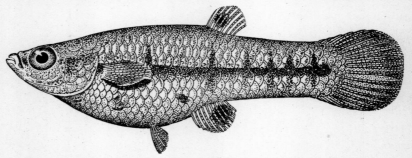

Fig. 60.   TOP MINNOW.   *Heterandria formosa.*

This is one of the smallest of fishes, the female being only 1 inch long and the male .75 inch.   The ascribed range is from South Carolina to Florida in blackwater swamps and ditches, but it has recently been found in the vicinity of Wilmington, N. C., by Mr. W. P. Seal, who has forwarded a number of specimens to the National Museum.   Mr. Seal states that the species abounds in cypress ponds and tidal ditches in that region, in company with Umbra, Fundulus, Gambusia, and other small fishes characteristic of the lowland waters.

Family AMBLYOPSIDÆ.   The Blind-fishes.

This singular American family is composed of small, ovoviviparous fishes with primitive or rudimentary eyes, living in caves, swamps, and ditches of the Southern and South Central states.   Superficially these fishes resemble the Pœciliidæ, but the mouth is much larger, the scales are finer, the ventral fins are absent or rudimentary, and the vent is placed far forward.   Other characters of this family are an elongate body, compressed posteriorly; long, flat head; projecting under jaw; edge of upper jaw formed by a long premaxillary; jaws and palatines with bands of sharp, slender teeth; short gill-rakers; branchial membranes connected with the isthmus; lateral line absent; air-bladder present; ovary single; single dorsal fin with few rays, placed about midway between end of snout and end of tail; anal similar to and opposite dorsal; caudal rounded, pointed or truncate; and pectorals rather long and pointed.   Of the 4 or 5 known genera, only one is represented coastwise, and that has functional eyes and a pigmented skin, all the others having skin-covered eyes and colorless body.

Genus CHOLOGASTER Agassiz.   Swamp Minnows.

Eyes small; pyloric cœca 2; ventral fins absent.   Three or more species, one found coastwise in the South Atlantic region.   (*Chologaster*, maimed belly.)

132. CHOLOGASTER CORNUTUS Agassiz.
Fish of the Dismal Swamp.

Chologaster cornutus Agassiz, American Journal Science and Arts, 1853, 135; Waccamaw, S. C., in rice-field
  ditch.   Jordan & Evermann, 1896, 703, pl. cxv, fig. 305; Dismal Swamp to Okefinokee Swamp.
Chologaster avitus Jordan & Jenkins, in Jordan, 1889*a*, 356, pl. 44; outlet of Lake Drummond, Dismal Swamp,
  near Suffolk, Va.

DIAGNOSIS.—Body elongate, depth about .16 length; head .33 length; eye .10 to .12 head, .5 snout; maxillary reaching to front of eye; gill-membranes covering the vent; scales in lateral series about 70; dorsal rays 8 or 9, the longest but little more than half length of head; anal rays 8 or 9, shorter than dorsal; caudal pointed, about length of head; pectorals .66 length of head.   Color: body and head dark brown above, white below; sides with 3 narrow longitudinal black stripes, the middle one extending across eye and snout; dorsal white with dark spots; a black blotch at base of tail, beyond which a white area or bar, the posterior .5 to .6 of tail black.   (*cornutus*, horned, in allusion to the flaps of the nostrils.)

Although long known from Virginia, South Carolina, and Georgia, this species has only recently been reported from North Carolina.   Mr. Wm. P. Seal has collected the fish in a large cypress pond near Wilmington where it is "about as abundant as non-gregarious species generally are—such as Umbra and Aphredoderus"; he has also found it in tidal ditches in the same section, in company with Gambusia and Heterandria,   In Lake Ellis, Craven County, the fish is common, according to Mr. C. S. Brimley; and it may be looked for in other parts of North Carolina in suitable situations.   The maximum length does not exceed 2.5 inches.

Order SYNENTOGNATHI.   The Gars, Half-beaks, and Flying-fishes.

Family BELONIDÆ.   The Needle-fishes and Marine Gars.

The fishes of this family are easily distinguishable by a very elongate, slender body covered with minute scales; jaws produced so as to form a long, sharp bill, and armed with numerous sharp teeth; and long, falcate dorsal and anal fins occupying about the posterior fourth of the body length.   They resemble the gar pikes (Lepisosteidæ), but are more attenuated, have much thinner scales, and are typically salt-water fishes.   The lower jaw is slightly longer than the upper, and in the young is relatively much longer; the maxillaries and premaxillaries are firmly united; the teeth are in a band in each jaw and in patches on the upper and lower pharyngeal bones; the distinct and continuous lateral line is placed very low on the side and forms a kind of fold.   The needle-fishes are voracious devourers of small fish, which they catch with great facility.   Some of the species have the habit of rushing from the water and making a series of prodigious leaps, renewing their impetus by a powerful flexion of the tail as it comes in contact with the surface.   Such species are known as hound-fish, and are dangerous to fishermen, as their speed is such that they may penetrate the fishermen's body like an arrow.   The two American genera are thus distinguished:

i. Body only slightly compressed, the width more than .66 the depth . . . . TYLOSURUS.
ii. Body greatly compressed, the width less than .5 the depth . . . . ATHLENNES.

Genus TYLOSURUS Cocco.   Gar-fishes; Bill-fishes; Needle-fishes; Hound-fishes.

Large or moderate sized marine fishes, entering bays and estuaries, and some species often found in fresh water.   The slender body is either about as thick as deep or is very slightly compressed; the color is plain green or blue above, white below, with a silvery reflection; the gill-rakers are mere rudiments; the lateral line extends along the side of the belly and becomes median on the slender caudal peduncle; the caudal fin is more or less deeply forked; the ventrals and pectorals are small, the former inserted posterior to middle of body but well separated from the anal.   The numerous species are American, and 4 are known from the North Carolina coast, while several others may from time to time straggle there from the tropics.

Key to the North Carolina species of Tylosurus.

i. Dorsal rays 1,14 or 1,15; anal fin larger than dorsal, its rays 1,17 or 1,18; scales in lateral series about 300 . . . . *marinus.*
ii. Dorsal rays 1,21 to 1,24; anal rays 1,21 to 1,24; scales in lateral series 350 or more, or less than 275.
    a. Bill comparatively short and strong, its length less than twice that of remainder of head; scales in lateral series about 350 . . . . *raphidoma.*
    aa. Bill long, at least twice length of remainder of head.
        b. Upper jaw not arched at base; no lateral stripe; greatest depth of body .66 length of pectoral; scales in lateral series about 380 . . . . *acus.*
        bb. Upper jaw conspicuously arched at base; a bluish lateral stripe; greatest depth of body .75 length of pectoral; scales in lateral series about 255 . . . . *caribbæus.*

(*Tylosurus,* callous-tailed.)

133. TYLOSURUS MARINUS (Walbaum).
"Bill-fish"; "Gar-fish"; "Green Gar"; "Doctor-fish".

Esox marinus Walbaum, Artedi Genera Piscium, iii, 88, 1792.
Belone longirostris, Yarrow, 1877, 214; Beaufort. Jordan & Gilbert, 1879, 383; Beaufort. Jordan & Gilbert, 1879, 368; Neuse River at Goldsboro.
Tylosurus marinus, Jordan, 1886, 26; Beaufort. Jenkins, 1887, 86; Beaufort. Smith, 1893a, 191, 195; Pasquotank River and Edenton Bay. Linton, 1905, 356; Beaufort.

DIAGNOSIS.—Body slender, its greatest depth contained about 5.5 times in head; head more than .3 total length; upper jaw (anterior to eye) .22 total length and twice length of remainder of head; eye large, .4 postorbital part of head; maxillary only partly concealed by preorbital; scales in lateral series about 300; lateral line forming a slight keel on caudal peduncle; dorsal fin slightly falcate, the rays 1,14 or 1,15, the last rays not elongated; anal fin shaped like dorsal, the rays 1,17 or 1,18; caudal slightly forked; pectorals about length of post-orbital part of head; origin of ventrals midway between preopercle and base of caudal. Color: uniform green above, silvery on sides, white below; a narrow silvery lengthwise stripe; a dark bar on opercle; fins olivaceous; keel on tail not black. (*marinus,* of the sea.)

Fig. 61. GAR-FISH; BILL-FISH. *Tylosurus marinus.*

This fish, which is found from Massachusetts to Texas, is common on the North Carolina coast, where it is the most abundant and most familiar member of the family. The local name most often heard is "gar-fish". Dr. Yarrow's note on the species at Beaufort in 1873 is:

Quite abundant; appearing in Beaufort Inlet in February. At this time it swims in schools and many are taken in nets. When swimming near the surface of the water it will readily take the hook. Is eaten by poor fishermen and negroes, and the flesh is said to be good. The largest specimen seen measured 24 inches in length.

The well known habit of the species of entering fresh water is strikingly exhibited in North Carolina. During spring it runs into Albemarle Sound, and is not rare in the lower part of its tributaries, being often caught in nets and seines; it is there known as "green gar", and is sometimes called "doctor-fish" by the Edenton fishermen. Jordan & Gilbert record the fish from the Neuse at Goldsboro. The maximum length of the species is about 4 feet, the average about 1.5 to 2 feet.

The gar is a surface swimmer and feeder, and preys chiefly on small fish like anchovies and silversides. Its movements are very swift, and it seldom fails to catch the luckless minnow to which it gives chase.

Little is known of the spawning of the gars, except that the eggs are deposited in summer in the bays and estuaries.

The flesh of the gar is very palatable, and should be generally eaten; but at present the fish has no commercial value, and in North Carolina, when utilized at all, is eaten only by negro fishermen. The peculiar green color of the skeleton may perhaps account for the prejudice which many people entertain.

134. TYLOSURUS RAPHIDOMA (Ranzani).
Hound-fish.

Belone raphidoma Ranzani, Novi Commentarii Academiæ Scientiarum Instituti Bononiensis, v, 1842, 359, pl. 37, fig. 1; Brazil.
Tylosurus raphidoma, Jordan & Evermann, 1896, 715, pl. cxvi, fig. 308.   Linton, 1905, 357; Beaufort.

DIAGNOSIS.—Body slightly compressed, comparatively short, the depth about .08 total length with caudal, equal to postorbital part of head and contained less than 4 times in total length of head; head less than .33 length, broad; space between eyes about .66 length of post-orbital part of head, with a broad shallow groove; jaws comparatively short, strong, upper jaw (anterior to eye) less than 2 times remainder of head; teeth large, strong, knife-like; eye less than .33 postorbital part of head and contained 1.8 times in interorbital space; maxillary entirely covered by preorbital; scales in lateral series about 350; cheeks closely scaled, opercles scaled only anteriorly; dorsal rays 21 to 24, height of longest rays about equal to postorbital region; anal rays 22 to 24, the fin similar to dorsal; caudal deeply concave, the upper lobe much longer than lower; ventrals inserted halfway between eye and base of caudal, their length less than pectorals.   Color: green above, silvery on sides and below, no lateral stripe; dorsal, caudal, and pectorals blackish; caudal keel black. (*raphidoma*, from *raphis*, a sharp instrument.)

This large hound-fish is a rare straggler to the United States coast north of Florida, its normal range being the West Indies and northern South America. The only North Carolina record is that of a 3–foot specimen taken at Beaufort August 26, 1901.   The species attains a length of 5 feet, and is a hound-fish *par excellence*, its leaps out of the water making it dangerous to fishermen.

135. TYLOSURUS ACUS (Lacépède).
Hound-fish; Gar-fish.

Sphyræna acus Lacépède, Histoire Naturelle des Poissons, v, 6, pl. 1, fig. 2, 1803; Martinique.
?Belone hians, Jordan & Gilbert, 1879, 383; Beaufort.
Tylosurus caribbæus, Jordan, 1886, 26; Beaufort.
?Tylosurus acus, Jordan & Evermann, 1896, 717, pl. cxvi, fig. 309; Beaufort, etc.

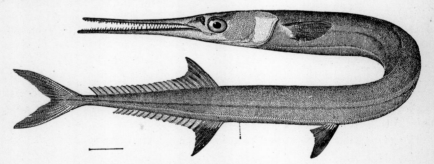

Fig. 62. HOUND-FISH. *Tylosurus acus.*

DIAGNOSIS.—Body slightly compressed, its depth .05 total length and .66 length of pectorals; head flattened above, with a median groove expanding posteriorly into a triangular space, length of head contained a little more than 3 times in total length; beak strong, about twice length of remainder of head; eye .1 length of head, equal to interorbital width; teeth large, sharp, about 60 in each jaw; scales in lateral series about 380; caudal keel strong; several folds of skin across opercle; dorsal fin arising slightly in advance of anal, falcate, the developed rays 23 or 24; anal fin falcate, the rays 21 or 22, the last ray considerably anterior to last dorsal;

caudal deeply forked; length of pectorals a little less than postorbital part of head; ventrals short, about .14 length of head, their base midway between eye and caudal base.   Color: green above, silvery white on sides and below; no lateral stripe; caudal keel black; anterior dorsal and pectoral rays blackish, other fins whitish.   (*acus*, needle.)

A large West Indian gar-fish, straying to the east coast of the United States as far north as Massachusetts.   The North Carolina records are somewhat uncertain, owing to the difficulty in determining just what species were represented by *Belone hians* of Jordan & Gilbert (1879) and *Tylosurus caribbæus* of Jordan (1886). There is no doubt, however, that the present species properly belongs in the state list, for on June 17, 1904, a specimen 4.5 inches long was seined in Beaufort Harbor and is preserved in the laboratory; this little example is green above, silvery on the sides, and white below, with all the fins white except the posterior division of the dorsal, which is black, this color extending on the tail.   Later in the season a second specimen was taken at Beaufort by Dr. G. W. Gudger.

Jordan & Evermann (1896) base a Beaufort record for *Tylosurus acus* on Jordan's *Tylosurus caribbæus* of 1886, which in turn was founded on Jordan & Gilbert's *Belone hians* of 1879.   Under the last name Jordan & Gilbert recorded one specimen obtained by them at Beaufort in 1877, and stated that Professor Goode had received a number of others from the North Carolina coast in the same summer.

136. TYLOSURUS CARIBBÆUS (LeSueur).
"Gar-fish"; Hound-fish.

Belone caribbæa LeSueur, Journal Academy Natural Sciences, Philadelphia, ii, 1821, 127; Caribbean Sea.
Tylosurus caribbæus, Jordan & Evermann, 1896, 717, West Indies.   Linton, 1905, 358; Beaufort.

DIAGNOSIS.—Body compressed, broad, very long, the depth .05 total length with caudal; head contained 3.4 times in length; jaws long, slender, and not closing completely; upper jaw (anterior to eye) more than 2 times length of remainder of head; teeth rather weak; eye about .10 length of entire head and .5 postorbital region; scales in lateral series 250 to 260; dorsal rays 24, the origin slightly behind anal, lobe low, posterior rays slightly elevated; anal rays 22, the fin similar to dorsal; caudal fin moderately forked, upper lobe longer; a strong keel on peduncle; ventrals inserted half-way between pupil and base of caudal.   Color: green above, bluish white on sides and below; a faint bluish lateral stripe; fins bluish. (Named after Caribbean Sea.)

This gar-fish has heretofore been known only from the West Indies.   In August, 1902, 8 specimens were obtained in the bight of Cape Lookout by assistants of the Bureau of Fisheries.   One of the examples, examined by Professor Linton, had been feeding on small crustaceans and insects.

Genus ATHLENNES Jordan & Fordice.   Flat-sided Gars.

From Tylosurus this genus may be easily distinguished by the much compressed body and the strongly arched base of the upper jaw.   One species. (*Athlennes*, without slime.)

137. ATHLENNES HIANS (Cuvier & Valenciennes).
Gar-fish.

Belone hians Cuvier & Valenciennes, Histoire Naturelle des Poissons, xviii, 432, 1846; Havana; Bahia.
Tylosurus hians, Jenkins, 1885, 11; Beaufort.   Jordan, 1886, 26; Beaufort.   Jenkins, 1887, 86; Beaufort.
Athlennes hians, Jordan & Evermann, 1896, 718.

DIAGNOSIS. —Body elongate, strongly compressed, the depth more than twice breadth and .9 length; jaws long, slender, twice length of remainder of head, upper jaw with an upward curve at base; maxillary covered by preorbital; eye .4 length of postorbital part of head; scales minute, over 500 in lateral series; a fold of skin across preopercle; dorsal fin falcate, beginning in advance of anal, the rays 1,24; anal fin falcate, the rays 1,25; caudal deeply forked; pectorals long and falcate; ventrals inserted nearer to anterior edge of eye than to base of caudal. Color: green above, silvery on sides; no lateral stripe; fins black-tipped; young with dark blotches. (*hians*, gaping.)

The normal range of this gar in the Atlantic is from Florida to Brazil, but stragglers have from time to time been reported to the northward as far as Massachusetts (whence the present writer recorded the species). The first North Carolina record was that of Dr. Jenkins, who reported the species as common at Beaufort in 1885, not being distinguished from *Tylosurus marinus* by the fishermen. A specimen 14 inches long was taken at Beaufort in the summer of 1903, and in 1905 various others were caught in a pound net in the harbor: 1 August 11, and other August 21, and 5 young August 23. The maximum length attained is about 3 feet, and the habits are similar to those of the related gars.

Family HEMIRHAMPHIDÆ.   The Half-beaks or Balaos.

Small shore fishes, the typical forms readily distinguished by their greatly produced lower jaw. The general shape is similar to that of the gars. Body elongate, compressed; upper jaw short and forming a flexible, flat, triangular plate; lower jaw (in local species) very long and slender, with a membranous flap below, toothed only at the base where it is in contact with upper jaw; maxillary firmly united to premaxillary; teeth small, tricuspid; gill-rakers long and slender; lateral line placed low on side; scales large, cycloid, in regular rows; air-bladder large; dorsal and anal fins small, on posterior third of total length; caudal forked or lunate; ventrals small, posterior, placed nearer to anal fin than to gill-opening; pectorals small. Species numerous, surface-swimming, and herbivorous; some Old World forms are viviparous. Of the 4 American genera 2 are represented in North Carolina, and may be thus distinguished:

i. Sides of body convex; air-bladder not cellular; ventrals inserted considerably in advance of dorsal; dorsal and anal similar and opposite ..................HYPORHAMPHUS.
ii. Sides of body flat, vertical; air-bladder cellular; ventrals inserted but little anterior to dorsal; dorsal larger than anal and beginning anterior to anal .............HEMIRHAMPHUS.

Genus HYPORHAMPHUS Gill.   Half-beaks.

Form slender, compressed, the sides more or less bulging; body scales large, deciduous, top of head covered with large plate-like scales; dorsal and anal fins low, and alike in size and relative position; caudal fin slightly forked or deeply incised, the lobes of about equal length; ventrals very small, inserted about midway between gill-opening and caudal base; air-bladder large and simple; sides with a bright silvery band. Three or four American species, only one of which ranges along our east coast. (*Hyporhamphus*, beaked below.)

138. HYPORHAMPHUS ROBERTI (Cuvier & Valenciennes).
"Red-billed Gar"; Half-beak.

Hemirhamphus roberti Cuvier & Valenciennes, Histoire Naturelle des Poissons, xix, 24, 1846; Cayenne.   Jordan,
    1886, 26; Beaufort.
Hemirhamphus unifasciatus, Yarrow, 1877, 214; Beaufort.   Jordan & Gilbert, 1879, 383; Beaufort.
Hyporhamphus roberti, Jordan & Evermann, 1896, 721, pl. cxvii, fig. 312; Beaufort, etc.   Linton, 1905, 358;
    Beaufort.
Hyporhamphus unifasciatus, Jenkins, 1887, 86; Cape Lookout.

DIAGNOSIS.—Dorsal and ventral outlines similar; depth contained 12 or 13 times in total
length and 9 times in length without lower jaw; head with lower jaw contained 2.3 times in
total length, head without lower jaw 4.3 times; lower jaw (shorter in young) .25 total length;
premaxillary plate (upper jaw) rather broader than long; eye large, more than .25 length of
head without lower jaw; scales in lateral series 54; dorsal and anal fins opposite and of the same
size, posterior rays not produced; dorsal rays 14 to 16; anal rays 15 to 17; caudal moderately
forked; pectorals short, about equal to postorbital part of head; ventrals small, but little
longer than diameter of eye, inserted about half-way between gill-opening and posterior end of
dorsal base.   Color: green above, silvery white on sides, a bright silvery longitudinal stripe
narrower than eye; scales of back dark-edged; anterior dorsal and anal rays and tips of caudal
blackish; filamentous tip of lower jaw red; peritoneum black.   (Named for Mons. Robert, a
Frenchman who collected fish for Valenciennes at Cayenne.)

Fig. 63.   HALF-BEAK.   *Hyporhamphus roberti.*

Inhabits both coasts of North and South America, and is common on our
Atlantic and Gulf coasts.   It appears to visit the North Carolina coast in spring
and remains throughout the summer.   In Beaufort Harbor it is abundant about
shoals and sandy islands.   Yarrow, who gives it the name of red-billed gar, has
the following note regarding it in that region:

Abundant during the latter part of August and entire month of September.   This species
appears to feed along the beach in shallow water, and may be readily taken at night with a
torch and scoop net.   It is also found in the channel and along the edges of shoals where blue-
fish congregate, this fish devouring enormous numbers.

On April 23, 1904, the writer caught about 50 specimens, 7 to 10 inches long,
in two seine-hauls on Bird Shoal, Beaufort Harbor, in company with gars, silversides, anchovies, mullets, pin-fish, spots, etc.   In August, 1899, many examples
3 to 4 inches long were cast up on Shackleford Beach near Beaufort Inlet.

The food of this and other half-beaks consists almost exclusively of green
algæ.   A few small crustaceans are sometimes found in the stomach, but these
are probably eaten incidentally with the seaweed.

The fish reaches a length of a foot or a little more, and is quite palatable, but
is only sparingly eaten in the United States.

Genus HEMIRHAMPHUS Cuvier.   Half-beaks; Balaos.

Similar to Hyporhamphus, but the body stouter, the sides more compressed
and flat, the dorsal larger than the anal and inserted in advance of it, the ven-

trals inserted only slightly in front of dorsal and much nearer to base of caudal than to branchial opening, the air-bladder divided by many partitions, and the caudal more deeply forked. One Cuban species and the following, which has been described under many names. (*Hemirhamphus*, half-beak.)

139. HEMIRHAMPHUS BRASILIENSIS (Linnæus).
Half-beak; Balao.

Esox brasiliensis Linnæus, Systema Naturæ, ed. x, 1758, 314; Jamaica.
Hemirhamphus brasiliensis, Jordan & Evermann, 1896, 722, pl. cxvii, fig. 313.

DIAGNOSIS.—Depth contained 6.75 in length (excluding lower jaw); head with lower jaw contained 2.66 in total length, head without lower jaw 5 times in length; lower jaw (from tip of upper jaw) nearly half longer than head and contained 4.5 times in total length; upper jaw broader than long; eye large, .25 length of head (without lower jaw) and more than half length of postorbital part of head; scales in lateral series about 53; dorsal rays 14, the longest less than twice diameter of eye, the posterior rays somewhat produced; anal fin beginning about under middle of dorsal, the rays 12, the posterior rays produced; caudal deeply forked, the lower lobe much longer than upper; ventrals very small, inserted in advance of dorsal about length of longest dorsal ray; length of pectorals about equal to depth of body. Color: above rich bluish green, sides silvery, no lateral stripe; bill blackish with a scarlet or orange tip, the membrane white-edged; dorsal lobe and upper caudal lobe orange yellow; ventrals yellow-edged. (*brasiliensis*, inhabiting Brazil.)

Fig. 64. HALF-BEAK. *Hemirhamphus brasiliensis.*

On the coast north of Florida this fish is a straggler and heretofore has been recorded only from Chesapeake Bay and Woods Hole, Mass. A specimen one foot long was taken in Beaufort Harbor in July, 1899, and is included in the laboratory record on the authority of Prof. H. V. Wilson. Another, about 10 inches long, was taken in the harbor on June 9, 1904, by Mr. Barton A. Bean, of the U. S. National Museum. This species is abundant from Florida to Brazil, reaches a length of 15 inches, and is said to be a good food fish.

Family SCOMBRESOCIDÆ. The Sauries.

Pelagic fishes of temperate regions, having a strong superficial resemblance to the mackerels (Scombridæ) in shape, color, and habits. The elongate body is compressed; one or both jaws are prolonged to form a very weak, slender beak, with feeble teeth; the maxillary and premaxillary are strongly united; the numerous gill-rakers are long and slender; the scales are small, thin, and decid-uous; the fins are small, the dorsal and anal being similar, and posterior to each is a series of finlets as in the mackerels. Several genera, of which only one is found in the Atlantic.

Genus SCOMBRESOX Lacépède. Sauries; Skippers.

Both jaws prolonged, forming a slender bill longer than remainder of head, the lower jaw the longer; the jaws short in the young; air-bladder large; lateral line near ventral edge of body, formed of minute rounded pores; opercle partly covered with small scales. One American species. (*Scombresox*, mackerel-pike.)

140. SCOMBRESOX SAURUS (Walbaum).

Skipper; Saury.

Esox saurus Walbaum, Artedi Genera Piscium, iii, 93, 1792; Cornwall.
Scombresox scutellatus, Yarrow, 1877, 214; Beaufort.
Scombresox saurus, Jordan & Evermann, 1896, 725, pl. cxvii, fig. 314.

DIAGNOSIS.—Body elongate, compressed, the depth .11 total length, .13 length without bill; head broad on top, tapering evenly to the beak, its length contained 3.4 times in total length of body, head without bill contained 5 times in length; eye .33 length of postorbital part of head; jaws very slender, distance from eye to end of lower jaw .2 total length; scales in lateral line about 115, 8 rows of scales on upper part of opercle; dorsal fin small and low, the rays 10 or 11, followed by 5 finlets; anal similar to dorsal, but longer and beginning slightly in advance of it, the rays 12 or 13, with 6 finlets; caudal well forked, the peduncle slender; pectorals shorter than postorbital part of head; ventrals about twice diameter of eye, their base half-way from front of eye to caudal base. Color: greenish brown on back to upper level of eye, sides and belly silvery, a silvery lateral band about width of eye. (*saurus*, lizard.)

Fig. 65. SKIPPER; SAURY. *Scombresox saurus.*

A species of the open sea, going in immense schools and preyed on by mackerel, tunny, etc.; rare south of Cape Cod. Recorded from Beaufort by Yarrow, but not found by others and evidently only a straggler. Yarrow's references to the size of this species and to taking it with hook-and-line, and his use of the name "sea pike", indicate a mistaken identification. That the fish he had in mind may have been the lizard-fish (*Synodus foetens*) is suggested by the omission from his list of that very common species, which bites freely at the baited hook and is known as "pike" in the Beaufort region.

Family EXOCŒTIDÆ. The Flying-fishes.

The flying-fishes are found in the warmer parts of all seas, and are familiar to all persons who have cruised in temperate or tropical waters, being numerous in both species and individuals. They for the most part inhabit the open seas, but sometimes come close inshore, and are often found in abundance about isolated islands.

These fishes may be instantly recognized by their enormously developed filmy pectoral fins, which are inserted high on the side of the body and when expanded suggest wings. The form of body is elongate, and not greatly compressed; head rather short; mouth small, terminal, margin of upper jaw formed chiefly by the premaxillaries, which are not joined to the maxillaries; jaw teeth small and weak; eye large; nostrils large, double, and close to eye; gill-membranes not connected, and free from isthmus; pseudobranchiæ glandular; airbladder large and extending far backward; scales rather large, cycloid, covering entire body and most of head; lateral line on level with ventral fins; dorsal fin placed posteriorly, relatively small, and containing only soft rays; anal opposite and similar to dorsal, but smaller; caudal deeply forked, the lower lobe much the longer; ventrals abdominal, usually large and placed posteriorly.

The "flight" of the flying-fishes has been much discussed. Many people have contended that the greatly enlarged pectoral fins are veritable wings and are used as birds' wings are, while others have held that the propelling force is in the tail and that the pectorals are incapable of rapid and active flapping. With regard to this question it may be stated that the shape and structure of the pectorals, the nature of their insertion, and the position and character of their muscular attachments prevent the use of these fins in the air except as sailing or balancing organs. The flight of *Cypselurus californicus*, the largest and most powerful of the family, has been studied under particularly favorable circumstances, and is thus described by Jordan and Evermann (1896, p. 730):

> The flying-fishes live in the open sea, swimming in large schools. They will "fly" a distance of from a few rods to more than an eighth of a mile, rarely rising more than 3 or 4 feet Their movements in the water are extremely rapid; the sole source of motive power is the action of the strong tail while in the water. No force is acquired while the fish is in the air. On rising from the water, the movements of the tail are continued until the whole body is out of the water. While the tail is in motion, the pectorals seem to be in a state of rapid vibration, but this is apparent only, due to the resistance of the air to the motions of the animal. While the tail is in the water, the ventrals are folded. When the action of the tail ceases, the pectorals and ventrals are spread and held at rest. They are not used as wings, but act rather as parachutes to hold the body in the air. When the fish begins to fall, the tail touches the water, when its motion again begins, and with it the apparent motion of the pectorals. It is thus enabled to resume its flight, which it finishes finally with a splash. While in the air it resembles a large dragon-fly. The motion is very swift, at first in a straight line, but later deflected into a curve. The motion has no relation to the direction of the wind. When a vessel is passing through a school of these fishes, they spring up before it, moving in all directions, as grasshoppers in a meadow.

In addition to the species actually known from the coast of North Carolina, various others undoubtedly occur and will in time be detected. The genera represented by these species are thus differentiated:

i. Pectoral fins of moderate length, not extending beyond middle of dorsal fin; dorsal fin very high; body elliptical in cross section .... PAREXOCŒTUS.
ii. Pectoral fins very long, extending beyond base of dorsal and in some species to base of caudal; dorsal fin low; body angular in cross section.
    a. Ventral fins small and inserted nearer tip of snout than base of caudal, their ends not extending as far as dorsal .... EXOCŒTUS.
    aa. Ventral fins large and inserted nearer base of caudal than end of snout, their ends reaching beyond origin of dorsal .... CYPSELURUS.

Genus PAREXOCŒTUS Bleeker. Flying-fishes.

Small flying-fishes with sides of body rounded, not angular; snout short; lower jaw not projecting; teeth on jaws and on vomer, palatines, and pterygoids; dorsal fin elevated; pectorals not reaching beyond middle of dorsal base; ventrals long and placed behind middle of body. (*Parexocœtus*, near *Exocœtus*.)

141. PAREXOCŒTUS MESOGASTER (Bloch).

Flying-fish.

Exocœtus mesogaster Bloch, Ichthyologie, 1795, pl. 399; Martinique.
Parexocœtus mesogaster, Jordan & Evermann, 1896, 728.

DIAGNOSIS.—Depth .2 total length; head narrow, its length a little greater than body depth; snout pointed, its length contained a little over 4 times in length of head; eye .33 length of head and equal to the flat interorbital space; gill-rakers long and numerous; scales in lateral series about 38; dorsal rays 12, the longest longer than head and longer than dorsal base; anal rays 13; length of pectorals .5 to .6 length of body, the tips extending to middle of dorsal fin; ventrals inserted midway between eye and base of caudal, their length more than .2 total length, and their tips extending beyond beginning of anal. Color: blue on upper half of body, silvery below; dorsal white, except upper part of anterior rays, which is black; anal with small black dots; caudal dusky reddish; pectorals and ventrals white, dusky in young. (*mesogaster*, middle belly, in allusion to position of ventrals.)

A widely distributed species, known from the Atlantic, Pacific, and Indian oceans. On the east coast of the United States it has been found as far north as Rhode Island. Although there are no definite North Carolina records, Jordan and Evermann say "it is the commonest flying-fish of the Carolina region", and it will doubtless eventually be taken in the state. The size is small, probably not exceeding 7 inches.

Genus EXOCŒTUS Linnæus. Flying-fishes.

Body quite elongate, with flattened sides; head rather short; snout blunt; pectorals exceedingly long, extending to base of caudal; ventrals short, inserted anteriorly, their tips not reaching as far as dorsal. (*Exocœtus*, sleeping outside.)

142. EXOCŒTUS VOLITANS Linnæus.

Flying-fish.

Exocœtus volitans Linnæus, Systema Naturæ, ed. x, 316, 1758.
Exocœtus evolans Linnæus, Systema Naturæ, ed. xii, 521, 1766.
Halocypselus evolans, Jordan & Gilbert, 383, 1879; Beaufort. Jordan, 1886, 26; Beaufort. Jordan & Evermann, 1896, 729.

DIAGNOSIS.—Greatest depth of body contained 5.3 times in total length; head .25 total length; snout less than eye, contained 4.5 in head; eye large, about .25 length of head; interorbital region flattened, .33 length of head; gill-rakers long and slender; scales in lateral series about 40; dorsal rays 13, the longest less than half length of head; anal similar to dorsal in size and shape, its rays 13; lower caudal lobe .25 longer than head; pectorals .75 length of body, tips extending to base of caudal; first ray simple, second ray divided, ventrals only half length of head, inserted midway between tip of snout and last anal ray. Color: upper parts olivaceous; dorsal and anal pale, a white streak on anal base; caudal dusky; pectorals dark above, with white lower margins; ventrals white; young with 2 dark cross-bands. (*volitans*, flying.)

A very widely distributed and abundant species, found on both shores of the Atlantic and also in parts of the Pacific. According to Jordan & Evermann (1896), it is not uncommon on our Atlantic coast, where it spawns in summer. One young specimen was taken in Beaufort Harbor by Jordan & Gilbert in 1878.

Genus CYPSELURUS Swainson. Flying-fishes.

This genus includes numerous species, found in warm seas in all parts of the world. The elongate body is broad above, with sides compressed and flattened; the head is short, blunt, with small mouth and feeble teeth; the pectoral fins extend at least as far as beginning of anal; the long ventrals are inserted nearer to base of caudal than to end of snout, and reach beyond the origin of the anal. Besides the two following species recorded from the state, three or four others (*rondeletti, vinciguerræ, heterurus, furcatus*) may be looked for:

i. Anal rays 11 or 12; longest dorsal ray .4 head; ventrals inserted about midway from posterior margin of preoperele to base of caudal; depth contained 6.2 times in length.. *speculiger.*
ii. Anal rays 8 or 9; longest dorsal ray .5 head; ventrals inserted about midway from center of pupil to base of caudal; depth contained 5.2 to 5.5 times in length ....*lutkeni.*

(*Cypselurus,* swallow-tailed.)

143. CYPSELURUS SPECULIGER (Cuvier & Valenciennes).
Flying-fish.

Exocœtus speculiger Cuvier & Valenciennes, Histoire Naturelle des Poissons, xix, 93, 1846; Indian Ocean Pacific Ocean, etc.
Exocœtus volitans, Jordan & Evermann, 1896, 734, pl. cxviii, fig. 318. (Not *E. volitans* Linnæus.)
Exocœtus melanurus, Yarrow, 1877, 214; Beaufort. Jordan & Gilbert, 1879, 383; Beaufort (after Yarrow).
Exonautes speculiger, Jordan & Evermann, 1898, 2836.

DIAGNOSIS.—Form slender, the depth less than one sixth length; length of head contained 4.25 times in total length; snout .25 length of head; eye contained a little less than 3 times in head; scales in lateral series about 55; dorsal rays 11 to 13, the longest .4 length of head; anal rays 11 to 13, the longest .33 length of head; pectorals extending beyond dorsal and anal, their length .7 length of body, first ray simple, second divided, third and fourth longest; ventrals long, inserted rather nearer to base of caudal than to eye, their length nearly .3 length of body. Color: back bluish green, below white; pectorals dark brown, an oblique white band extending backward from axil to middle of fin, the edges whitish; dorsal, anal, and ventrals whitish. (*speculiger,* mirror-bearing.)

This flying fish, which inhabits the open seas, is known from a number of points on the east coast of America as far north as Newfoundland. At Woods Hole, Mass., it is common some seasons and is caught in nets; young specimens from 1.5 inches upward have been seined there in September and October, and even the smallest have been observed to "fly". Yarrow recorded the fish as "occasionally seen" at Beaufort, but his identification was uncertain and his note might have applied to various other species. This fish reaches a length of a foot, and is a very superior food fish.

144. CYPSELURUS LUTKENI (Jordan & Evermann).
Flying-fish.

Exocœtus robustus, Jordan & Meek, Proceedings U. S. National Museum, 1885, 61; "Cape San Antonio" (not
    E. robustus Günther from Australia).
Exocœtus lutkeni Jordan & Evermann, 1896, 736; "Cape San Antonio, Cuba".
Cypsilurus lutkeni, Jordan & Evermann, 1898, 2836.
Cypselurus lutkeni, Smith, Science (N. Y.), May 12, 1905; Beaufort.

DIAGNOSIS.—Depth contained 5.5 times in length to end of vertebral column; head
broad, contained 4.5 times in length; snout .66 eye and less than .25 length of head; eye very
large, more than .33 head and greater than interorbital width; scales in lateral series about 50,
rows of scales between dorsal fin and lateral line 7 or 8; dorsal rays 14, anal rays 8 or 9; the
longest anal ray .66 longest dorsal; lower caudal lobe much the longer, 1.25 times head; pectorals very broad and long, their tips extending to posterior end of base of anal, .66 total length;
first pectoral ray simple and .6 length of fin, second ray branched, third ray longest; ventrals
.33 length of body, their tips extending as far back as those of pectorals, the center of the base
midway between base of caudal and pupil. Color: brownish above, silvery below; dorsal and
anal fins white, caudal dusky; pectorals white anteriorly, black posteriorly, the white extending
as a broad oblique band from base, across middle, nearly to upper margin, posterior edge of fin
pale; ventrals blackish posteriorly. (Named after the European ichthyologist Christian
Lütken, author of an important paper on the flying-fishes.)

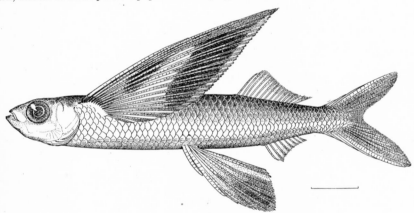

Fig. 66. FLYING-FISH. *Cypselurus lutkeni.*

Only 2 specimens of this fish are known. The type is in the Academy of
Natural Sciences, Philadelphia, and bears a label which is obviously incorrect—
"near Cape San Antonio, California, Dr. H. C. Yarrow"—for there is no such
cape in California, and Dr. Yarrow has informed the author that he never collected fishes at Cape San Antonio or elsewhere in Cuba. It is quite probable
that this fish was obtained at Beaufort, N. C., by Dr. Yarrow and was one of the
numerous collection of fishes from that region presented by him to the academy.
In this view Mr. Henry W. Fowler, curator of fishes, concurs. The second
specimen was caught in a mullet net in Beaufort Harbor, October 3, 1904, and
presented to the laboratory by Mr. J. H. Potter. It has been compared with the
type and found to agree in every essential particular. The type, however,
lacks the blackish area on the posterior part of the ventrals, and has a well
defined dark vertical bar at base of caudal.

Order HEMIBRANCHII.   The Half-Gills.

Family FISTULARIIDÆ.   The Trumpet-fishes.

This is the only family of the order represented in North Carolina, and it has but a single genus.   The body is very elongate, depressed, destitute of scales but with series of bony shields partly covered by skin.   The head is very long, owing to the prolongation of the bones of the anterior part of the skull; these form a tube at the end of which is the small mouth.   Minute teeth exist on the jaws and roof of mouth.   The gills are 4 in number on each side, the gill-rakers are obsolete, and the basal parts of the gills are absent; the branchial membranes are separate, and not joined to the isthmus; pseudobranchiæ are present.   The intestine is short, the pyloric cœca are few, and the air-bladder is large.   The spinous dorsal, which is small or rudimentary in other families of this order, is entirely lacking here; the soft dorsal is small and placed for backward as in Hemirhamphus, and the anal is similar to it in size and position; the caudal is forked and from its middle a long, slender filament proceeds; the pectorals and ventrals are quite small, and the latter are abdominal, wide apart, 6–rayed, and far in advance of dorsal.

Genus FISTULARIA Linnæus.   Trumpet-fishes.

Large shore fishes of warm seas, with characters as given above.   The bony plates or shields are a strip in the median line of the back, a dorso-lateral pair posterior to the head, a pair on the sides anteriorly, and a ventral pair extending far backward.   The snout has longitudinal ridges which are more or less serrated.   The skin is either rough or smooth.   The pectoral fins are broad-based and inserted low.   Three American species, two on east coast and one on both coasts; only one known from United States waters.   (*Fistularia*, from the Latin *fistula*, a tube or pipe.)

145. FISTULARIA TABACARIA Linnæus.
Trumpet-fish.

Fistularia tabacaria Linnæus, Systema Naturæ, ed. x, 312, 1758; tropical America.   Yarrow, 1877, 205; Beaufort.   Jenkins, 1887, 87; Beaufort.   Jordan & Evermann, 1896, 757; "occasional northward to Carolina."

DIAGNOSIS.—Greatest depth of body about .03 total length and .66 width; head rather more than one third length; mouth oblique, lower jaw overlapping upper; snout very long, contained 3.75 times in total length; upper lateral edges of snout usually with a few fine serrations; width of eye about equal to length of lower jaw and rather more than .1 length of head; sharp points on anterior and posterior margins of orbit; dorsal rays 14, the longest .25 length of snout; anal opposite dorsal, its rays 13, the longest equal to longest dorsal; caudal forked, the lobes equal, the slender median filament a little longer than snout; pectorals short, .5 length of head posterior to snout; ventrals very small, inserted about midway between tip of snout and end of caudal lobes.   Color: reddish brown above, with many large oblong blue spots on back and sides, the spots arranged in series but of unequal size; under parts pale.   (*tabacaria*, having shape of a pipe.)

The trumpet-fish is a straggler from the West Indies to the United States coast, where it has been recorded from as far north as Massachusetts by the author.   Dr. Yarrow recorded two specimens taken at Beaufort in September and November, 1871; Dr. McMurrich observed a specimen there in 1884; and it has of late been collected there on several occasions.   On August 14, 1902, the steamer Fish-Hawk collected a specimen off the harbor, and on November 12, 1902, Mr. J. H. Potter, of Beaufort, presentd to the laboratory a specimen that had been taken in the vicinity.   Another specimen, 12 inches long, was taken on the north side of Bird Shoal in 1903.   In June, 1905, Mr. Barton A. Bean seined several specimens along the inner beach at Fort Macon.   This species reaches a length of 6 feet.   It has no economic value.

Order LOPHOBRANCHII.   The Tuft-gilled Fishes.

Family SYNGNATHIDÆ.   The Pipe-fishes and Sea-horses.

The members of this family are among the most peculiar of marine fishes as regards both form and habits.   The body is more or less elongated, often slender, and has no scales but is covered with bony plates which form a kind of armor. The snout is long, tubular, and terminates in a small mouth without teeth. The gill-opening is very small and at the upper posterior border of the opercle; the gills are tufted and consist of small, rounded lobes; the gill-covers are simple, composed of a single plate.   The tail is either stiff or prehensile, and is or is not surmounted by a small caudal fin.   The dorsal fin, inserted about the middle of the body, is rather small and composed only of soft rays, the anal is either rudimentary or well developed; the pectorals are small or lacking; the ventrals are absent.   The male is provided with an abdominal pouch in the median line, into which the eggs are laid pending hatching.   The genera are numerous and the number of species is large, abounding in warmer waters, but some species occur well to the north.   Of the 5 American genera, 2 are represented on the east coast of the United States:

i. Body very long, slender, with long axis of head in line with long axis of body; trunk not conspicuously larger than adjoining parts of body; caudal fin small; tail not prehensile; anal fin minute; head not like that of a horse.............................SIPHOSTOMA.
ii. Body moderately elongate, the tail slender, with long axis of head at right angles to long axis of body; trunk conspicuously larger than adjoining parts of body; caudal fin absent; tail prehensile; anal fin well developed; head strongly resembling that of a horse.
HIPPOCAMPUS.

Genus SIPHOSTOMA Rafinesque.   Pipe-fishes.

Small, very slender, weak fishes inhabiting shoal bays and other sheltered localities, and nearly always found among eel-grass and algæ.   The 6 or 7 sided body tapers into a very long tail, and is protected by longitudinal series of keeled, bony plates which form numerous rings on the body and tail.   The head is long slender, with a tube-like snout, which is longer in the female.   All the fins are small; the dorsal low and over or immediately anterior to vent, the anal minute, the pectorals short and broad.   The egg-pouch, formed of two folds of skin, is on the under side of the tail in the male.   There are many American species, six being known from the Atlantic coast from Key West northward.   Three species are recorded from North Carolina, and several others may be looked for as stragglers from the south.

Key to the North Carolina pipe-fishes.

i. Body rings 17 to 19, caudal rings 31 to 33; dorsal rays 29 to 31, dorsal base covering 1,
    rarely 2, dorsal rings; snout contained 1.66 to 1.8 times in head.............*floridæ.*
ii. Body rings 20 or 21, caudal rings 36 to 38; dorsal rays 32 to 41, dorsal base covering 3 to 5
    dorsal rings.
  a. Snout more than half length of head; belly flat or concave; dorsal fin shorter than head,
      its rays 32 to 37 and its base covering 3 dorsal and 5 caudal rings......*louisianæ.*
  aa. Snout half length of head; belly convex; dorsal fin longer than head, its rays 38 to 41 and
      its base covering 4 or 5 dorsal rings and 4.5 or 5 caudal rings.............*fuscum.*

(*Siphostoma*, tube-mouthed.)

146. SIPHOSTOMA FLORIDÆ Jordan & Gilbert.

Pipe-fish.

Siphostoma floridæ Jordan & Gilbert, Proceedings U. S. National Museum, 1882, 263; Pensacola, Fla. Jordan,
    1886, 30; Beaufort.   Jenkins, 1887, 87; Beaufort.   Jordan & Evermann, 1896, 766; Beaufort.   Wilson,
    1900, 355; Beaufort.   Gudger, 1905a, 449; Beaufort.

DIAGNOSIS.—Bony rings 17 to 19 on body, 31 to 33 on tail (i. e., posterior to vent); head
contained 6 to 6.5 times in total body length; snout contained 1.66 to 1.8 times in length of
head; dorsal fin low, shorter than head, its rays 29 to 31, covering 1 to 2 body rings and 5 to 6.5
caudal rings; tail longer than trunk and .55 total length; pouch involving about 18 caudal
rings; caudal fin about .4 length of dorsal base.   Color: dark or light green; sides with gray specks;
tail marked with dark bars and pale oblong spots; snout mottled; dorsal yellowish as base;
anal plain; caudal yellow with dusky tip.

Inhabits sandy shores from North Carolina to Texas.   It is abundant at
Beaufort, and is probably the most numerous species in that region.   A favorite
locality is about Bird Shoal, but it may be found almost everywhere in eel-grass.
The color is subject to considerable variation, depending on that of the plants
among which the fishes live.   The food consists of minute organisms, mostly crustacea.

The breeding habits of this species at Beaufort have been described in a
paper by Gudger (1905b).   The breeding season of this and other pipe-fishes in
that region is June to August, and the transfer of eggs from the female to the
male takes place at night, so far as observed.   The egg-laying occurs while the
bodies of the two fishes are mutually entwined in such a way as to bring the
oviduct into relation with the marsupial pouch at its anterior end, the eggs
being fertilized as they enter the cavity.   The transfer of eggs is repeated from
time to time until the pouch is well filled; in one pair of fishes under observation in
an aquarium at the Beaufort laboratory, the copulatory act was repeated 4
times in an hour.   The eggs are at first loose in the male's pouch, but later they
become attached in several rows on each side.   Hatching ensues in about 10
days.

Adult fish reach a length of 9 inches, but may be only 3 inches long, the
females being a little the larger.   Among a dozen mature specimens from Beaufort, the body rings number 18 or 19, and the caudal rings 31 to 33 (34 in one
specimen); the dorsal fin covers 16 dorsal rings and 5 to 6.5 caudal rings; and the
dorsal rays number 29 to 31.   In 2 males, one with eggs and the other with
young, the dorsal base covers 2 dorsal and 5.5 caudal rings.

147. SIPHOSTOMA LOUISIANÆ (Günther.)
Pipe-fish.

Syngnathus louisianæ Günther, Catalogue of the Fishes of the British Museum, viii, 160, 1870; New Orleans.
Siphostoma louisianæ, Jordan, 1886, 30; Beaufort. Jordan & Evermann, 1896, 770; North Carolina to Texas.

DIAGNOSIS.—Trunk broader on ventral surface, which is flat or slightly concave and has a median keel; bony rings 20 or 21 on body, 36 to 38 on tail; head contained 7 to 7.6 times in total length; snout contained 1.6 times in length of head; tail longer than trunk and .56 total length; dorsal fin shorter than head, its rays 32 to 37, covering 3 body rings and 5 caudal rings; caudal fin longer than pectoral and .4 length of dorsal base. Color: brownish, lighter on under parts; a well marked brown band on sides extending through eye to middle of snout; fins plain.

The range of this species coincides with that of *Siphostoma floridæ*. In Beaufort Harbor it is found in the same localities and at the same time as *Siphostoma floridæ*, but is less abundant. Dr. W. C. Kendall collected specimens at Morehead in April, 1891. In the first half of June, 1905, Mr. B. A. Bean found the fish abundant on grassy shoals in all parts of Beaufort Harbor, many of them containing eggs about ready to hatch.

148. SIPHOSTOMA FUSCUM (Storer.)
Pipe-fish.

Syngnathus fuscus Storer, Report on Fishes of Massachusetts, 162, 1839; Nahant, Mass.
Syngnathus peckianus, Yarrow, 1877, 204; Bird Shoal, Beaufort Harbor.
Siphostoma fuscum, Jordan & Gilbert, 1879, 368; Beaufort. Jordan & Evermann, 1896, 770; Cape Ann to Virginia. Linton, 1905, 359; Beaufort.

DIAGNOSIS.—Ventral surface convex, with a very slight keel; bony rings 18 to 21 on trunk, 36 to 40 on caudal part; head short, its length contained 7.5 to 9 times in total length; snout half length of head; tail much longer than trunk and .6 total length; dorsal fin longer than head, its rays 36 to 41, its base covering 4 to 5 trunk rings and 4 to 5 caudal rings. Color: dark green or brown above, lighter below; irregularly mottled with brown; snout pale beneath; opercles silvery below. (*fuscum*, brown.)

Yarrow (1877) records a pipe-fish from Beaufort under a name now referred to the synonymy of *Siphostoma fuscum*, and Jordan and Gilbert (1879) also list the species; but Jordan and Evermann (1896) assign to this species a range which extends no farther south than Virginia. However, 2 small pipe-fishes now in the U. S. National Museum, collected by Yarrow at Beaufort in 1872, are *Siphostoma fuscum*, as is also another specimen 6.25 inches long in the museum, collected by Mr. Earll in Middle Sound, near Wilmington, in 1880. Specimens now in hand, 5.25 and 6.37 inches long, obtained at Beaufort in the summer of 1902, are clearly referable to this northern species. In one, a female, the rings are 21+36, of which 5 body rings and 4.5 caudal rings are covered by the dorsal fin, which has 41 rays; in the other, a male containing eggs, the rings are 20 + 38, of which 4 + 5 are under the base of the dorsal fin, which has 38 rays; in both the snout is half the length of head.

This is the only species of pipe-fish mentioned by Linton (1905) in his paper on the parasites of the fishes of Beaufort; he lists 90 specimens taken in July and August, but it is probable that most of them were the much commoner species, *louisianæ* and *floridæ*.

Genus HIPPOCAMPUS Rafinesque. Sea-horses.

The sea-horses are singular creatures which depart greatly from the popular idea of the conventional fish; their head and neck bear a striking resemblance to a horse's; the fish move through the water in an erect position; and when resting they usually curl their prehensile tail about a bit of seaweed or blade of grass. Additional interest attaches to these fishes because the male fish receives the eggs in a pouch and carries them until they are hatched, and the young occupy the pouch until they are of considerable size, going out in search of food and returning for shelter.   The sea-horses are dried and sold as curiosities, becoming familiar objects in all parts of the country.   The body is much compressed, and just back of the dorsal fin tapers abruptly to a long, angular, flexible tail; the belly protrudes; the head is set at right angles to the body, and is separated therefrom by a constricted, arched neck; a compressed occipital crest is surmounted by a star-shaped process; the trunk and tail are completely encased in bony plates which have 6 spines on the body and 4 on the tail, and form rings; the head is more or less thickly beset with spinous processes; the male has an egg-pouch at the base of the tail, in the median line; the dorsal fin, of moderate size, is placed about the middle of the back, opposite the vent; the anal fin is very small; the caudal fin is deficient; the pectoral fins are short and broad.   Many species, none of large size, exist in warmer waters of all parts of the world.   Two are known from our Atlantic coast which may be thus distinguished:

i. Dorsal rays 19, covering 3.5 trunk rings and no caudal rings; color, ashy or brown, sometimes with sharply marked pale blotches but no spots....................*hudsonius.*
ii. Dorsal rays 17 or 18, covering 1.5 trunk rings and 2 caudal rings; color, dark brown with dark marbling and numerous light blue spots..........................*punctulatus.*

(*Hippocampus*, the ancient Greek name for the sea-horse.)

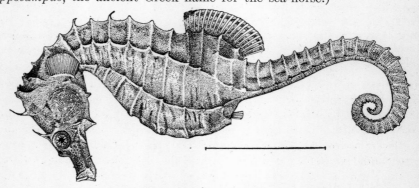

Fig. 67. SEA-HORSE. *Hippocampus hudsonius.*

149. HIPPOCAMPUS HUDSONIUS DeKay.

Sea-horse; Horse-fish.

Hippocampus hudsonius DeKay, New York Fauna, Fishes, 322, pl. 53, fig. 171, 1842; New York.   Yarrow, 1877, 204; Beaufort.   Jordan & Evermann, 1896, 777, pl. cxxi, fig. 327.
Hippocampus antiquorum, Jordan & Gilbert, 1879, 367; Beaufort.   Jordan, 1886, 30; Beaufort.   Jordan & Gilbert, Synopsis of the Fishes of North America, 1883, 907; Beaufort.   Wilson, 1900, 355; Beaufort.

DIAGNOSIS.—Rings on trunk 12, on tail 32 to 35; snout less than half total length of head; spines on body short and blunt, those on head with cirri; diameter of eye equal to half length of snout; dorsal rays 19, covering 3.5 trunk rings. Color: varying from light ashy to dark brown, with pale grayish blotches having paler or blackish edges; dorsal with a dark zone near the margin. (*hudsonius*, relating to Hudson River.)

This is a rather uncommon species, found from Massachusetts to South Carolina. It is not common on the North Carolina coast. Yarrow lists the fish as doubtless rare, in 1871, as several were presented to him by the fishermen as great curiosities. Jordan and Gilbert found it uncommon in 1878, being preserved by the fishermen as curiosities and sold to visitors at about 25 cents per specimen. Specimens have occasionally been brought to the Beaufort laboratory, and a few examples 3 to 6 inches long have recently been collected about Bird Shoal, Perry Island, and Town Marsh. Dr. R. E. Coker reports that a large male taken August 18, 1902, had a pouch full of young and delivered them in the laboratory aquarium August 20. The opening in the pouch is at its anterior end and is slit-like when closed but round when the young are about to be extruded. When liberating the young, the fish swam upright, and made a peculiar effort resembling peristalsis. The young emerged several at a time and were forced some distance from the parent; they swam in a cluster near the surface and on the side of the aquarium nearest the light.

150. HIPPOCAMPUS PUNCTULATUS Guichenot.

Spotted Sea-horse.

Hippocampus punctulatus Guichenot, in Sagra, Cuba Poissons, 174, pl. 5, fig. 2, 1850; Cuba. Jenkins, 1885, 11; Beaufort. Jordan, 1886, 30; Beaufort. Jenkins, 1887, 87; Beaufort. Jordan & Evermann, 1896, 777; "occasionally northward in Gulf Stream as far as Beaufort, N. C."

DIAGNOSIS.—Rings on trunk 10, on tail about 35; snout .4 length of head; eye .5 length of snout; spines on body obtuse and blunt; the coronet low; filaments usually absent on head; dorsal rays 17 or 18, the base of fin covering 1.5 trunk rings and 2 caudal rings. Color: dark brown, with darker marblings, the entire body marked by light blue spots (rarely wanting), most numerous posteriorly. (*punctulatus*, dotted.)

A rare species on the United States coast, but not uncommon in the West Indies, whence it ranges to Brazil and West Africa. Four specimens were collected at Beaufort by Dr. Jenkins in 1885, and one was taken by Mr. Barton A. Bean on Bird Shoal, June 8, 1904. Mr. Charles Hatsel, of the Beaufort laboratory, collected a specimen in Bogue Sound on August 8, 1905, which lived in a laboratory aquarium until October 10 of the same year.

Order ACANTHOPTERYGII. The Spiny-rayed Fishes.

Most of the salt-water fishes and numerous fresh-water ones are included in this order, whose members may be regarded as representing the highest development among fishes. The order is very complex, comprising such different families as the perches and mullets, the mackerels and flounders; typically it is distinguished by the presence of spiny rays in the anterior part of the dorsal and anal fins, but in some groups this feature is lacking, and the more constant characters of the order must be sought in the formation of the border of the mouth solely by the premaxillaries, in the anterior attachment of the ventral fins (which normally have 1 spine and 5 rays), in the absence of a duct connecting the air-bladder with the mouth cavity, in the laminated gills, and in various cranial and pelvic peculiarities.

Family APHREDODERIDÆ.   The Pirate Perches.

This family, which contains a single genus, has the following leading characters: Oblong body, compressed posteriorly, elevated in front of dorsal fin; depressed head; moderate-sized, oblique mouth, with projecting lower jaw; villiform bands of teeth on jaws, vomer, palatines, and pterygoids; serrated margins to preopercle and preorbital; spine on posterior part of opercle; ctenoid scales on body, opercles, cheeks, and top of head; short, dentate gill-rakers; obsolete pseudobranchiæ; imperfect or absent lateral line; vent placed far forward, beneath preopercles in adult; single, high dorsal fin with 3 or 4 spines; 2 anal spines; thoracic ventral fins, with 1 short spine; rounded caudal fin; large simple air-bladder; about 12 pyloric cœca.

Genus APHREDODERUS LeSueur.   Pirate Perches.

Characters of the genus indicated in family description.   One small species, confined to United States.   (*Aphredoderus*, excrement throat, in allusion to the position of the vent.)

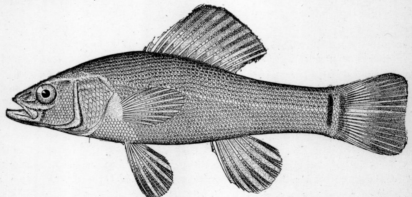

Fig. 68.   Pirate Perch.   *Aphredoderus sayanus.*

151. APHREDODERUS SAYANUS (Gilliams.)
Pirate Perch.

Scolopsis sayanus Gilliams, Journal Academy of Natural Sciences of Philadelphia, iv, 81, 1824; near Philadelphia.
Aphredoderus sayanus, Cope, 1870b, 455; tributaries of Neuse River in Wake County.   Jordan, 1889b, 126,
   129; Tar River at Rocky Mount, Little River at Goldsboro.   Smith, 1893a, 199; Roanoke River at Plymouth.   Evermann & Cox, 1896, 305; Neuse River near Raleigh.   Jordan & Evermann, 1896, 786, pl
   cxxii, fig. 331.

DIAGNOSIS.—Depth .33 total length; head equal to depth; maxillary reaching anterior
edge of eye; eye equal to snout, a little less than .2 length of head; scales in lateral series 45 to
55, those on opercle rather larger than on body, those on cheeks smaller; origin of dorsal fin

over ventrals, dorsal rays III,10 to IV,11, the soft rays much longer than the longest (3rd) spine; anal rays II,5 or 6.   Color: dark brown or dark olive, sometimes with numerous dark specks forming longitudinal rows along scales; 2 black transverse bars at base of caudal with a light area between them.   (*sayanus*, after Thomas Say, an American naturalist.)

The pirate perch inhabits sluggish waters, from New York to Texas and throughout the Mississippi valley.   Its maximum length is 5 inches.   It is reported to be voracious, and to feed chiefly at night.   In North Carolina it is known from various streams.   Jordan reported it as rather scarce in Tar River near Rocky Mount, and not rare in Little River at Goldsboro, and Cope found it abundant in tributaries of the Neuse in Wake County.   The National Museum contains specimens collected in a pond at Wilmington in 1899 by Mr. W. P. Seal. The writer collected but one specimen in Albemarle Sound and tributaries, this being an example 2.5 inches long, of a rich brown color, taken in the Roanoke near Plymouth; depth .28 length, head .33 length; eye 4.25 in head; dorsal rays III,11; anal rays II,5; scales in lateral line 51; outer parts of dorsal and caudal fins white, inner parts reddish purple; pectorals and anal faintly spotted with purple. Mr. C. S. Brimley reports the species as not uncommon in Lake Ellis, Craven County.

Family ATHERINIDÆ.   The Silversides.

Elongate, shapely fishes, with a silvery lateral stripe, most of them of small size, inhabiting fresh or salt waters in temperate or tropical latitudes.   They usually go in large schools, and in some regions are among the most abundant of fishes.   The body is more or less compressed, without lateral line, and is covered with regularly arranged scales, of moderate or small size and usually cycloid. The mouth is terminal, rather small and weak; the premaxillaries are protractile in most of the genera; the jaws and vomerine teeth, if present, are small.   The branchial aperatures are wide; the gill-membranes not connected and free from the isthmus; the gill-arches 4 in number; the opercular bones without spines. A thin-walled air-bladder is present.   There are 2 dorsal fins entirely disconnected; the anterior, placed in about the middle of the back, has a few (3 to 8) very slender, feeble spines, united by a delicate membrane; the posterior contains soft rays, which are more numerous than the spines.   The anal fin contains one spine and rather numerous soft rays, and is usually larger than the second dorsal. The caudal fin is usually deeply forked; the ventrals are small, placed anterior to the first dorsal, and consist of one spine and 5 soft rays; the pectorals are of moderate size and inserted rather high.   The flesh is firm, white, and palatable; and some of the species are important food fishes.   Of the 10 or more North American genera only the following 2 are represented on the Atlantic coast north of Florida.

i. Scales cycloid; dorsal and anal fins for the most part scaleless . . . . MENIDIA.
ii. Scales laciniate; dorsal and anal fins with large scales. . . . . KIRTLANDIA.

Genus MENIDIA Bonaparte.   Silversides.

Small American fishes, most of them inhabiting salt or brackish water; body elongate, compressed, belly rounded; head compressed; mouth small, oblique, the angle usually not extending as far back as eye; jaws weak, each with a band of small teeth; maxillary slipping behind preorbital, premaxillaries very protractile; scales rather large, with entire margins, no scales on dorsal and anal fins; dorsal fins short, the first with 4 to 6 spines, the second with one spine and 6 to 11 soft rays.

The silversides of this genus found on the east coast are considered in detail in an interesting paper by Kendall, in the Report of the U. S. Fish Commission for 1901 (pp. 241–267, 6 plates of species).   Silversides are eaten on the Middle Atlantic coast under the name of "whitebait", but their direct economic value is small.   Owing, however, to their great abundance and wide distribution they must be among the most important foods of many of the common food fishes of the coast.   There are numerous species, and at least two occur in North Carolina waters, as follows:

i. Anal rays 1+22 or 23; beginning of dorsal fin nearer to base of caudal than to tip of snout.
menidia.
ii. Anal rays 1+17 or 18; beginning of dorsal nearer to tip of snout than to base of caudal.
beryllina.

(*Menidia*, an old Latin name for some small silvery fish.)

152. MENIDIA MENIDIA (Linnæus).
"Sardine"; Silverside; Smelt.

Atherina menidia Linnæus, Systema Naturæ, ed. xii, 519, 1766; Charleston, S. C.
Chirostoma menidium, Jordan & Gilbert, 1879, 383; Beaufort.
Menidia menidia, Jenkins, 1885, 11; Beaufort Harbor.   Jordan, 1886, 27; Beaufort.   Jenkins, 1887, 87; Beau-
    fort Harbor.   Jordan & Evermann, 1896, 800.   Kendall, Silversides of Genus Menidia of East Coast of
    United States, 1902, 264–267, text cut; Fort Macon and Wilmington, N. C.   Linton, 1905, 360; Beaufort.

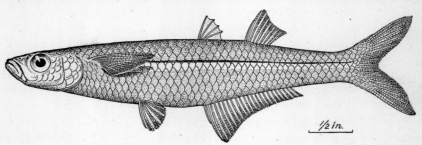

Fig. 69. SILVERSIDE. *Menidia menidia.*

DIAGNOSIS.—Depth .2 length; head contained 4.6 to 5 in length; mouth large; eye equal to snout and contained 3.25 times in head; scales in lateral series 40 to 45, in transverse series 7 to 9; dorsal rays IV or V+1,7 to 1,9; anal rays 1,21 to 1,25.   Color: light olivaceous, with minute brown dots on top of head, jaws, and edge of scales on back; silvery lateral band .66 width of scales; fins plain.

The typical form ranges northward from Florida, beginning to intergrade in North Carolina with the variety *notata*, which predominates further north, ranging to Nova Scotia.   This silverside abounds on sandy shores in salt and brackish water, and exceeds a length of 6 inches.   It is common on the North

Carolina coast, and is doubtless a permanent resident, as it is taken at Beaufort in midwinter.

The spawning season extends from early in April in the south to July in Massachusetts. At Woods Hole, Massachusetts, a good-sized fish yielded 1,413 eggs 2 millimeters in diameter. The eggs are peculiar in having at one pole a tuft of about 50 elastic filaments, 8 times the diameter of the egg, by means of which the eggs are attached in clusters to marine plants. The incubatory period is about 10 days, the newly-hatched fish being 6 millimeters long and having a small yolk-sac.

At Beaufort in the second week of April, 1904, the silversides were spawning freely. The average length (without caudal) of 14 spawning fish of each sex was 3.12 inches for males and 3.56 inches for females.

The food consists largely of free-swimming crustacea, such as copepods, together with algæ, diatoms, and mud.

This silverside is large enough to serve as human food, and is sometimes eaten, being excellent when fried plain or rolled in cracker-crumbs or corn meal. The chief value of the fish, however, is as food for blue-fish, squeteague, barracuda, etc.

153. MENIDIA BERYLLINA (Cope), var. CEREA Kendall.
"Sardine"; Silverside.

Chirostoma beryllinum Cope, Transactions American Philosophical Society, 1866, 403; Potomac River at Washington.
Menidia beryllina, Smith, 1893a, 192, 195; Pasquotank River and Edenton Bay, Kendall & Smith, 1894, 21; Albemarle Sound. Smith, 1901, 134; Lake Mattamuskeet.
Menidia beryllina cerea Kendall, Silversides of Genus Menidia of East Coast of United States, 1902, 261, text cut; Albemarle Sound, Lake Mattamuskeet, Massachusetts, South Carolina, etc.
Menidia gracilis, Jordan & Evermann, 1896, 797.

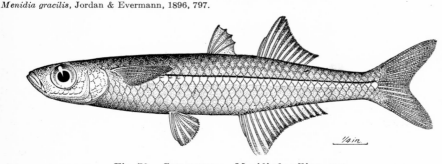

Fig. 70. SILVERSIDE. *Menidia beryllina cerea.*

DIAGNOSIS.—Depth contained 5.8 to 6 times in length; head contained about 4.3 times in length; eye large, its diameter greater than snout and .33 length of head; scales in lateral series 40 to 42, in transverse series 8 or 9; dorsal rays IV to VI + 1,9 to 1,11; anal rays 1,17 or 1,18. Color: translucent waxy, the back and top of head thickly spotted with minute black dots; snout and chin blackish; silvery lateral band narrow, less than .5 diameter of eye, on fourth row of scales. (*beryllina*, having the color of emerald; *cerea*, waxy.)

The typical form of this species is restricted to the fresh waters of the Potomac; the variety occurs from Massachusetts to South Carolina, in fresh and salt water. It is a small species, rarely exceeding 3 inches in length, and is abundant in most parts of its range. The writer found it common in the Albemarle region; it is also recorded from Lake Mattamuskeet, and is doubtless to be found throughout the state coastwise.

Genus KIRTLANDIA Jordan & Evermann. Rough Silversides.

This genus is scarcely separable from Menidia, as the characters on which it is based—gashed scales on the body and scaly dorsal and anal fins—are possessed in some degree by species of Menidia. The genus contains perhaps only a single species, which is variable. (Named for Dr. J. P. Kirtland, an early student of American fishes.)

154. KIRTLANDIA VAGRANS (Goode & Bean).
"Sardine"; Silver-fish; Silverside.

Chirostoma vagrans Goode & Bean, Proceedings U. S. National Museum, 1879, 148; Pensacola, Fla.
Menidia vagrans laciniata Swain, in Jordan & Gilbert, Synopsis of the Fishes of North America, 908, 1883, Beaufort, N. C.
Menidia laciniata, Jordan, 1886, 27; Beaufort.
Kirtlandia vagrans et laciniata, Jordan & Evermann, 1896, 794, 795, pl. cxxiv, fig. 336.
Kirtlandia vagrans laciniata, Jordan & Evermann, 1898. 2840.

DIAGNOSIS.—Depth contained 5.5 to 6 times in length; head contained 4.4 times in length; eye large, .33 head and greater than snout; scales firm, rough to the touch, edges crenate, some with 12 points, number in lateral series 48 to 50, in transverse series 6 or 7, large scales on vertical fins and head; spinous dorsal fin small, its origin slightly in advance of anal, the rays IV + 1,7 or V + 1,7; anal base equal to length of head, the rays 1,14 to 1,19; caudal fin slightly forked, the lobes equal; pectorals about length of head, their tip extending slightly beyond origin of ventrals. Color: pale green on back, silvery on sides and belly, with a broad silvery band covering parts of third and fourth rows of scales; scales of back dark spotted on edge; muzzle yellowish; caudal yellow, dorsal and pectorals dusky, other fins plain. (vagrans, wandering).

This silverside is abundant on sandy shores from Virginia to Texas, and is also known from New Jersey and New York. Swain's type of his supposed variety laciniata came from Beaufort, N. C., where the fish is common. Jordan & Evermann consider the typical form as inhabiting the Gulf coast, and the variety laciniata as representing the fish found on the Atlantic coast. The species reaches a length of 4 inches, and is largely consumed by other fishes. Owing to the peculiar laciniate scales along the back, this fish is rough to the touch. Many specimens collected by Dr. W. C. Kendall at Morehead City in April, 1891, were all males; they were in company with Menidia menidia, of which all the specimens observed were spawning females.

Family MUGILIDÆ. The Mullets.

A numerous family of fresh-water and marine fishes, usually going in schools and inhabiting the warmer regions of the world; in North and South America, Europe, Asia, Africa, and Australia, the mullets are important food fishes. The body is moderately elongate, or oblong, and is slightly to considerably compressed; the cycloid scales with which the body is covered are rather large; there is no lateral line.   The head is rather short, the mouth small, the jaws weak, the premaxillaries protractile, the teeth small or absent.   The gill-arches number 4 on each side, the gill-openings are wide, the gill-membranes are free from the isthmus, the gill-rakers are long and slender, and the pseudobranchiæ are large. The intestine is long, the peritoneum black, the air-bladder large and simple. The caudal fin is large and usually forked; the other fins are of moderate size; the two dorsal fins are widely separated, the anterior having 4 stiff spines, the posterior a single spine and a few soft rays; anal similar to second dorsal, with 2 or 3 spines; the ventrals are abdominal and contain 5 rays preceded by a spine.

Only a single genus, the type of the family, is known from the east coast of the United States.   Dr. T. H. Bean (Catalogue to the Fishes of New York, 1903) contends that the genus Querimana, which was established by Jordan & Gilbert in 1883 for certain small mullets with only 2 anal spines and no adipose eyelid, represents simply the young of Mugil, and that all the species of Mugil pass through a Querimana stage.

Genus MUGIL Linnæus.   Mullets.

In this genus the form is robust, the body only slightly compressed, the back and belly rounded; the head obtuse, broad, and scaly; the mouth terminal, the jaws equal, the lower jaw with a median projecting angle; the jaw teeth short, flexible, and hair-like; the eye large, with a conspicuous fatty lid in the adult covering part of the iris; scales large; anal spines 3 (2 in young).   The mullets are the most valuable fishes of the South Atlantic and Gulf States.   In North Carolina and Florida, especially, they support exceedingly important fisheries.   They go in vast schools along the ocean shores, in bays, and in estuaries, and feed chiefly on minute animal matter extracted from the mud.   Of the 10 or 12 American species, 2 range along our Atlantic coast; these, while quite similar, may be thus distinguished:

 i. Soft dorsal and anal fins scarcely scaly; scales in lateral series about 41 or 42; anal rays III,8; sides and back marked with distinct dark lengthwise stripes along the rows of scales.
cephalus.

ii. Soft dorsal and anal fins very scaly; scales in lateral series about 38 or 39; anal rays III,9; sides and back not marked with dark stripes (these sometimes evident after death).
curema.

The annual yield of these 2 fishes in North Carolina in the past 25 years has not fallen below 2,500,000 pounds, and in the last year for which statistics are available was more than double that amount.   The product during 5 years as determined by the U. S. Bureau of Fisheries was as follows:

YEARS.	POUNDS FRESH AND SALTED.	VALUE.
1880	3,368,000	$80,500
1889	3,053,305	85,085
1890	3,585,980	97,408
1897	3,409,525	90,338
1902	6,705,490	187,643

Mullets are caught in every county bordering on salt water, the bulk of the yield coming from Brunswick, New Hanover, Pender, Onslow, Carteret, Pamlico and Dare counties. (*Mugil*, mullet.)

155. MUGIL CEPHALUS Linnæus.

"Mullet"; "Jumping Mullet"; Striped Mullet.

Mugil cephalus Linnæus, Systema Naturæ, ed. x, 316, 1758; Europe. Jordan, 1886, 27; Beaufort. Jenkins, 1887, 87; Beaufort. Jordan & Evermann, 1896, 811, pl. cxxvi, fig. 343. Linton, 1905, 361; Beaufort.
Mugil lineatus, Yarrow, 1877, 212; Beaufort.
Mugil plumieri, Jordan & Gilbert, 1879, 381; Beaufort.
?Querimana gyrans Jordan & Gilbert, Proceedings U. S. National Museum, 1884, 26; Key West. Jenkins, 1885, 11; Beaufort. Jordan, 1886, 27; Beaufort. Jenkins, 1887, 87; Beaufort Harbor. Smith, 1893a, 192, 195, 199; Pasquotank River, Edenton Bay, and Roanoke River.

DIAGNOSIS.—Form stout, slightly compressed, depth rather more than .25 length; head about equal to depth; snout short, less than eye; gape short, extending only to anterior margin of eye; interorbital space wide, convex; scales in lateral series about 41 or 42, in transverse series 14, about 23 scales on median line between tip of snout and beginning of dorsal, few scales on soft dorsal and anal fins; dorsal rays III+I,8 the first spine about .5 length of head; soft dorsal and anal fins similar, their margin incised; caudal fin deeply forked; pectorals rather long, extending nearly to opposite origin of dorsal; longest ventral rays about equal to first dorsal spine. Color: dark greenish or bluish on back, silvery on sides, and whitish beneath; a dark area on each scale of the 7 or 8 upper rows, forming distinct longitudinal stripes; fins dusky, the ventrals yellowish. (*cephalus*, head.)

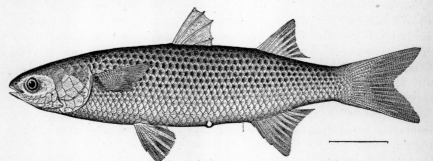

Fig. 71. STRIPED MULLET; JUMPING MULLET. *Mugil cephalus.*

The striped mullet is of wide distribution; in the new world it is found coastwise from Massachusetts to Brazil and from California to Chile; in the old world it inhabits the waters of southern Europe and northern Africa. On the south Atlantic coast of the United States it occurs in immense numbers, being one of the most abundant food fishes from North Carolina southward. It attains a length of 2.5 feet, but averages less than 1.5 feet. Mr. George N. Ives states that the largest North Carolina mullet seen by him weighed 10 pounds.

This is by far the most abundant and important salt water fish of North Carolina, this state ranking next to Florida in the extent of the mullet fishery. It is found on the ocean beaches and in the sounds and estuaries during a large part of the year, and is caught mostly with drag nets. Dr. Yarrow has left the following note on the fish in the Beaufort region in 1871:

This species is the most abundant of the locality, and affords sustenance and employment to thousands of persons on the coast of North Carolina. From the month of May, when small-sized individuals appear, fishing continues during the entire summer with gill and small draw nets, and in the latter part of August, as the fish commence to school preparatory to migration, the regular seine fishing commences, and continues frequently until November. The schools appear to come from the northward through Albemarle, Pamlico, and Core sounds, gradually working their way to the southward. Their departure through the various inlets seems to depend upon a favorable state of the wind, which should be from the northward, for it has been noticed frequently that when the wind hauled, the schools of mullet already without the harbor have suddenly turned, re-entering the inlet, and pursued their course southward through Bogue Sound. Their movements through the water are quite slow, and a person without exertion may keep pace with them walking upon the beach. The numbers taken are simply enormous, sometimes as many as 500 barrels being secured at a single haul. It was estimated by competent observers that not less than 12,000 barrels of mullet were captured on the coast of North Carolina Friday, September 22, 1871. Regarding the spawning grounds of *M. lineatus* considerable uncertainty exists. At the time of their arrival at Fort Macon, in August and September, the females are enormously distended with roe, some, however, being more so than others and it is supposed that the process of oviposit takes place from July until December, many remaining in the sounds for the purpose. Many schools of young mullet have been seen in Beaufort harbor during December and January, which could have been but a few weeks old. These young fishes suffer from a curious disease, which is characterised by the presence of a gradually increasing film upon the eyes, which finally destroys the sight, and myriads perish from this cause.

Observations on the spawning habits of the mullet in the vicinity of Beaufort, conducted in the years 1903–6 by Mr. S. G. Worth, superintendent of the hatchery at Edenton, indicate that the species deposits its eggs during November and December. A specimen 22 inches long and 4.75 pounds in weight taken at the Mullet Pond fishery on November 20, 1903, yielded a 12-ounce roe. The cultivation of this species on the coast of North Carolina will doubtless soon be taken up by the general government.

The food of the mullet is varied. Twelve fish examined by Dr. Coker at Beaufort in June and July contained amphipods, annelids, small shrimps and ophiurans, and bivalve mollusk shells.

In winter and spring there occur in the salt, brackish, and fresh waters of the North Carolina coast multitudes of small mullet, mostly under 1.5 inches long, with a dark bluish or greenish back and lustrous silvery sides and belly. These fish have only 2 anal spines, no adipose eyelid, 28 to 33 scales in lateral series, and various other characters in which they differ from the adult mullet; and they have usually been identified as the whirligig mullet, *Querimana gyrans* Jordan & Gilbert, which is recorded from Massachusetts to Florida. According to Dr. Bean (op. cit.), however, this nominal species in reality represents the young stage of the fan-tail mullet (*Mugil trichodon* Poey), the differences noted being due to age. This author states that the third anal spine in young mullets is only a simple articulated ray until the fish reach a length of 40 to 50 mm. (1.6 to 2.00 inches); then an articulation breaks off, the point becomes sharpened, and hard material is deposited, so that a slender but perfect spine is formed. The range of the adult fan-tail mullet is from the

Florida Keys to Brazil; the fish is abundant about Key West, but is not known from the coast north of Florida, while the so-called whirligig mullet is found from Key West to Massachusetts, in salt, brackish, and fresh water. The present writer is inclined to accept Dr. Bean's general conclusion in this matter, but regards it unfortunate that *Querimana gyrans* has not been shown to be the young of the striped mullet or the silverside mullet. The chief obstacle to such an identification is the difference in the number of scales in the lateral series, and until this is overcome the question must be considered unsettled.

156. MUGIL CUREMA Cuvier & Valenciennes.

"Silverside Mullet"; "Mullet"; White Mullet; Blue-back Mullet.

Mugil curema Cuvier & Valenciennes, Histoire Naturelle des Poissons, xi, 87, 1836; Brazil; Martinique; Cuba. Jordan, 1886, 27; Beaufort. Jenkins, 1887, 87; Beaufort. Jordan & Evermann, 1896, 813, pl. cxxvi, fig. 344. Linton, 1905, 360; Beaufort.
Mugil brasiliensis, Jordan & Gilbert, 1879, 381; Beaufort.

DIAGNOSIS.—Form similar to that of *Mugil cephalus*, the depth about equal to length of head and contained about 4 times in total length; snout .2 length of head; interorbital space .5 length of head; scales in lateral series about 38, in transverse series 12, about 22 between tip of snout and origin of dorsal; soft dorsal and anal thickly scaled; dorsal rays IV+1,8, the longest spine more than half length of head, the margin of soft dorsal incised; anal fin similar to and opposite soft dorsal, the rays III,9; caudal deeply forked; pectorals reaching about .75 distance to spinous dorsal. Color: dark greenish or bluish above, silvery on sides, white beneath; no dark streaks along sides in life; two yellow blotches on side of head; a small dark blotch at pectoral base; fins mostly pale, with small dark spots; caudal yellowish at base, with a black margin; anal and ventrals yellowish. (*curema*, a Portuguese name for this or a similar fish.)

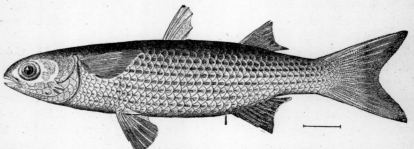

Fig. 72. WHITE MULLET. *Mugil curema.*

The range of the white mullet is from Cape Cod to Brazil, and also extends to the west coast of America. It is an abundant species on our South Atlantic coast, but is less numerous than the jumping mullet, with which it associates. At Beaufort it is called "silverside mullet". The usual length is about one foot. The habits of the two fish are quite similar, and much that is said of the jumping mullet applies also to this species. As a general thing this fish is not distinguished by the local fishermen.

Family SPHYRÆNIDÆ. The Barracudas.

The barracudas are elongated pike-like fishes, more or less circular in cross section, with very long, pointed head and large mouth armed with formidable teeth.   Lower jaw the longer; upper jaw not protractile, its margin formed by the premaxillaries; maxillaries broad; teeth of unequal size on jaws and palatines, a single large canine at tip of lower jaw; gill-openings wide, gill-membranes not connected and free from isthmus, gill-arches 4, gill-rakers short or rudimentary, pseudobranchiæ large, branchiostegals 7; no spines on opercular bones; air-bladder large, divided anteriorly; pyloric cœca numerous; lateral line well developed, straight; scales small, cycloid, the head scaly on top and sides; 2 dorsal fins widely separated, first dorsal with 5 strong spines; second dorsal and anal similar, opposite, and rather short; caudal widely forked; pectorals short, attached low on side; ventrals abdominal, under first dorsal.   The barracudas inhabit the warm seas; some of them attain a large size (6 feet or more); in some countries they are food fishes of some importance.   They are powerful, active fishes, carnivorous, and voracious.   A score or more of species are known, all belonging in one genus.

Genus SPHYRÆNA Bloch & Schneider.   Barracudas.

Only one small species is known from North Carolina, but two others may occur as stragglers; these are the great barracuda, *Sphyræna barracuda*, which ranges from Brazil to Pensacola, Charleston, and Bermuda, and has occasionally wandered to Massachusetts, and the guaguanche, *Sphyræna guachancho*, which inhabits the West Indies, but has been noted in southern Massachusetts in at least two instances.   (*Sphyræna*, hammer-fish.)

157. SPHYRÆNA BOREALIS DeKay.

Barracuda.

Sphyræna borealis DeKay, New York Fauna, Fishes, 37, pl. 60, fig. 196, 1842; New York.   Yarrow, 1877, 212;
Cape Lookout.   Jordan, 1886, 27; Beaufort.   Jordan & Evermann, 1896, 825; Cape Cod to Cape Fear.
Linton, 1905, 361; Beaufort.
Sphyræna spet, Jordan & Gilbert, 1879, 381; Beaufort harbor.

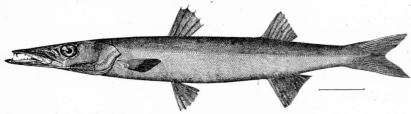

Fig. 73. BARRACUDA. *Sphyræna borealis.*

DIAGNOSIS.—Body slender, subterete, depth about .12 total length; head large, .33 in total length; maxillary rather small, not extending as far as orbit; lower jaw with a fleshy tip; premaxillary teeth small, about 40 in number, 2 pairs in front large and canine; the anterior teeth smallest and directed downward, the posterior directed downward and backward; about 10 teeth in lower jaw; anterior palatine teeth larger than premaxillary, wide-set; posterior teeth small and close-set; eye small, a little wider than interorbital space, interorbital area slightly convex, with a shallow median groove divided by a ridge; scales in lateral series 115 to 130; cheeks, opercles, and top of head scaly; dorsal rays v + 9, the distance between the fins a little less than .2 total length of fish; anal rays 1,9. Color: dark greenish above, silvery below; the young marked with dark transverse blotches. (*borealis*, northern.)

North Carolina appears to be the southern limit of the range of this species, which is the common barracuda of the Middle Atlantic coast of the United States. The species is small, rarely exceeding a foot in length. Yarrow reported it as "uncommon, a few taken occasionally near Cape Lookout". The young are at times not uncommon in the harbor of Beaufort; in July, 1902, many examples 1.5 to 3 inches long were taken, and in July, 1903, 7-inch specimens, mostly on Bird Shoal.

The barracuda is an active, voracious species, subsisting largely on small fishes—silversides at Beaufort. It is, however, not a hardy species, and dies very quickly after being caught in a seine, so that it is difficult to carry specimens to the aquarium.

Family MULLIDÆ. The Goat-fishes or Surmullets.

These fishes have a head that suggests that of a goat, the principal point of resemblance being 2 large barbels on the throat. They are marine fishes of rather small size, some of them gaily colored, found primarily in the tropics but occasionally well to the north. Body elongate, somewhat compressed, back arched; upper profile of head strongly curved; mouth small, terminal; premaxillaries slightly protractile; maxillaries rather broad and partly concealed by the preorbitals; lower jaw small, with 2 long barbels attached just behind the symphisis; teeth small, variously placed on jaws, vomer, and palatines; eyes rather large and placed high on side of head; branchiostegals 4; pseudobranchiæ present; opercular margin smooth or with a single broad spine; peropercle smooth or somewhat serrate; scales large, slightly ctenoid, largest on head; lateral line complete; pyloric cœca numerous; air-bladder simple if present; 2 dorsa' fins, widely separated, short, the anterior with 6 to 8 rather high spines depressible in a groove; anal fin similar to second dorsal; ventrals attached below pectorals. The American species number 8 or 10 and belong to 3 genera, of which only one has a place in the state fauna, although another, *Mullus auratus* Jordan & Gilbert, ranges as far northward as Cape Cod and may sometime be detected here.

Genus UPENEUS Cuvier. Goat-fishes.

This, the most numerous genus of Mullidæ in our waters, is distinguished by having one or two series of strong teeth on both jaws but none on the vomer and palatines; a narrow concave interorbital space; a short, deep opercle with a posterior spine; long and numerous gill-rakers; first dorsal placed near head, with 7 or 8 spines; anal with 2 spines and a few soft rays; caudal forked. Several of the West Indian and Floridan species are valuable food fishes. (*Upeneus*, an ancient Greek name for some undetermined fish.)

158. UPENEUS MACULATUS (Bloch).
Goat-fish.

Mullus maculatus Bloch, Ichthyologie, pl. 348, 1797; Brazil.
Upeneus maculatus, Jordan & Evermann, 1896, 858, pl. cxxxii, fig. 362.   Linton, 1905, 361; Beaufort.

DIAGNOSIS.—Body moderately elongate, depth rather less than .25 length, back strongly curved; length of head slightly less than depth of body, upper profile very steep; mouth horizontal; upper jaw not extending as far as orbit; teeth coarse; those in upper jaw in a single series or an incomplete double series; teeth in lower jaw in one series; eye large, .25 length of head and .5 length of snout; barbels slender, .75 length of head; gill-rakers on first arch 30, the longest about .5 eye; lateral line high, following arch of back; scales in lateral series about 30; dorsal rays VII or VIII+1,8, the longest spine (second) .66 length of head; anal rays II,6; longest dorsal and anal soft rays a little shorter, pectorals and ventrals a little longer, than longest dorsal spine.   Color: bright red above, yellow on sides, greenish below; 3 or 4 dark red blotches on sides, one over opercular spine, one under each dorsal fin, and one behind dorsal; scales on sides with a small blue spot on base, the spots forming longitudinal lines; sides of head with blue streaks; first dorsal mostly pale blue, with some red and yellow areas; anal pale red; caudal blue, with some yellow and red on base; pectorals mostly yellow, with red on rays; ventrals pale blue, with red and yellow lines on anterior part; barbels yellow, with pink base; under side of head pink.   (*maculatus*, spotted.)

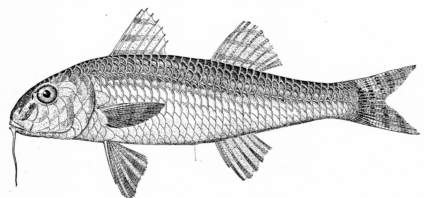

Fig. 74.   GOAT-FISH.   *Upeneus maculatus.*

The red or spotted goat-fish is common in the West Indies, but north of Florida is only a straggler and has rarely been taken.   One specimen, 3 inches long, was taken at Bird Shoal in Beaufort Harbor July 19, 1902.   The species attains a length of about a foot, and is a food fish of some importance in the tropics.   In Porto Rico it is extensively eaten and highly esteemed.

Family SCOMBRIDÆ.   The Mackerels.

The mackerels are fishes of the high seas, with compact, fusiform bodies adapted for rapid movement.   They swim more or less in schools, some of which are of immense size.   Most of the species are of wide distribution.   The family includes species that are among the most important food fishes of the new and old worlds.   The family characters are a rather elongate body, cylindrical or slightly compressed; a conic head; large mouth with large or small sharp teeth in jaws; unarmed opercle; wide gill-openings; gill-membranes unconnected, and free from the isthmus; long gill-rakers; large pseudobranchiæ; 4 gill-arches; 7 branchiostegals; 2 dorsal fins, the anterior of weak spines, the posterior like the anal; posterior rays of dorsal and anal fins separated and known as finlets; caudal peduncle slender and keeled; caudal fin large and forked; stomach sac-shaped, with numerous cœca; air-bladder small or absent; color usually blue above, with metallic sheen.   Eight genera and 15 species are represented in American waters; and of these 6 genera and 8 species are known from North Carolina.   Doubtless other wide-ranging species have from time to time been taken on the North Carolina coast and may be looked for again.   The common mackerel (*Scomber scombrus*) of the Middle Atlantic and New England coast, the most valuable member of the family in American waters and also in the world, is first met with in spring off Cape Hatteras, but is not common in the inshore waters.

Key to the North Carolina genera of mackerels.

i. Caudal peduncle with a median keel on each side, with a smaller keel above and below this.
   a. Body without scales, except on lateral line and corselet.
      b. Dorsal fins separated by more than half length of head; dorsal spines 10; teeth on vomer, none on palate bones ....AUXIS.
      bb. Dorsal fins separated by a space less than .2 length of head; dorsal spines 15; teeth on palate bones, none on vomer................................GYMNOSARDA.
   aa. Body entirely covered with small scales.
      c. Jaw teeth slender; gill-rakers numerous; pectoral fins placed low.
         d. Vomer and palate bones with villiform teeth; body robust, size very large. THUNNUS.
         dd. Vomer without teeth; palate bones with a single row of strong conic teeth; body elongate, size small..SARDA.
      cc. Jaw teeth strong, triangular or knife-like; gill-rakers few; pectoral fins inserted near level of eyes...SCOMBEROMORUS.
ii. Caudal peduncle without median lateral keels.............................SCOMBER.

Genus AUXIS Cuvier. Frigate Mackerels.

Small scombrids, intermediate in form between the common mackerel and bonito, with elongate, plump body, destitute of scales except along lateral line and in region of pectoral and ventral fins; small mouth, very small jaw teeth mostly in single series, short snout; slender, depressed peduncle with strong lateral keel; small fins, the second dorsal and anal especially so; long and numerous gill-rakers.   The single species is pelagic, swims in large schools, and is very erratic in its movements.   (*Auxis*, ancient Greek name for the young tunny.)

159. AUXIS THAZARD (Lacépède).
"Bonito"; Frigate Mackerel.

Scomber thazard Lacépède, Histoire Naturelle des Poissons, iii, 9, 1802; coast of New Guinea.
Auxis thazard, Jordan & Evermann, 1896, 867, pl. cxxxiii, fig. 365.

DIAGNOSIS.—Body very slightly compressed, its depth a little less than .25 total length; head .25 length, the snout conic; maxillary bone beneath the preorbital and almost concealed by it; eye .2 length of head, equal to snout; gill-rakers on lower limb of first arch about 33; dorsal fins separated by a space nearly equal to length of head, the rays x + 12, with 7 or 8 finlets; anal rays 13, with 7 or 8 finlets.   Color: back blue with darker vermiculations; sides and below silvery white.   (*thazard*, from the French *tassard*, a name given to fishes like the Spanish mackerel.)

This species inhabits all the warm seas. It was not observed in United States waters until 1880, when it came in countless numbers to the southern New England coast. It has since been reported from time to time at various points on our Atlantic coast. Two long-established and well-informed fish dealers at Beaufort report that this species occurs there as a straggler, and is not

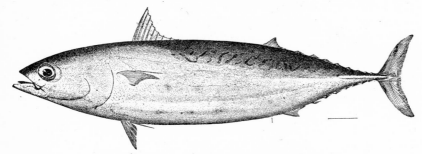

Fig. 75. FRIGATE MACKEREL. *Auxis thazard.*

distinguished by fishermen from the related species locally called "bonito". The frigate mackerel reaches a weight of 3 or 4 pounds, probably averaging only 2 pounds; and is of very inferior quality as food. The posterior muscles are white, but those near the head are black and rank.

Genus GYMNOSARDA Gill. Little Tunnies.

Large oceanic fishes, with robust form, destitute of scales except about pectorals, ventrals, and spinous dorsal; with dorsal fins close together, the anterior with 15 or 16 spines; and with no teeth on vomer. Of the 2 species occasionally found on our coasts, only 1 is known from North Carolina, but the other (*Gymnosarda pelamis*, the oceanic bonito) is likely to be taken any season. (*Gymnosarda*, naked bonito.)

160. GYMNOSARDA ALLETERATA (Rafinesque).

"Bonito"; "Bolter"; Little Tunny.

Scomber alleteratus Rafinesque, Caratteri di alcuni nuovi generi e nuovi specie di animali e piante della Sicilia, 46, 1810; Palermo.
Gymnosarda alleterata, Jordan & Evermann, 1896, 869, pl. cxxxiv, fig. 366.

DIAGNOSIS.—Body stout, fusiform, the depth .25 length; head contained 3.75 times in length; eye small, .16 to .2 length of head, about .5 length of snout; dorsal rays xv or xvi + 12, with 8 finlets; anal rays 12, with 7 finlets; pectorals about .5 length of head. Color: back blue, with wavy, oblique dark stripes; sides and belly silvery; 5 round black spots, size of pupil, below pectoral fin. (*alleterata*, an Italian name for this fish.)

The little tunny has at times been seen in abundance in southern Massachusetts and elsewhere on our east coast, going in large schools. It is very irregular in its appearance, and may not be recorded during several years. Dr. Coker reports that this fish is known to the Beaufort fishermen as "bonito" or, sometimes, "bolter".

Although eaten in Bermuda, southern Europe, and other places, it is not highly regarded in the United States, and is seldom sent to market. Its usual weight is 30 to 40 pounds. It has been observed at times in numbers in the

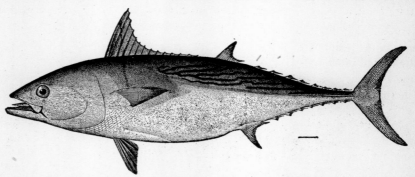

Fig. 76. LITTLE TUNNY. *Gymnosarda alleterata.*

ocean off Roanoke Island, and is known to the fishermen of that section as "bonito"; those taken have weighed 15 to 30 pounds. The fish is not regarded with any favor as food in North Carolina.

Genus THUNNUS South. Great Tunnies, or Albacores.

This genus has as its only member an immense pelagic species, the largest of the family, having a stout, scaled body, with well developed corselet; large mouth, small conical teeth in a single series on jaws and bands of minute teeth on roof of mouth; dorsal fins very close together, the anterior with 12 to 15 spines; dorsal and anal finlets about 9. (*Thunnus*, tunny.)

161. THUNNUS THYNNUS (Linnæus).
Tunny; Horse Mackerel; Albacore.

Scomber thynnus Linnæus, Systema Naturæ, ed. x, 297, 1758; Europe.
Orcynus secundi-dorsalis, Yarrow, 1877, 207; Beaufort.
Orcynus thunnus, Jordan & Gilbert, 1879, 375; Beaufort. Jenkins, 1887, 88; Beaufort.
Thunnus thynnus, Jordan & Evermann, 1896, 870

DIAGNOSIS.—Body cylindrical, the depth .25 length; head large, contained 3.75 times in total length; mouth large, the maxillary extending as far back as pupil; eye small, .16 length of head; dorsal and anal fins short and falcate; dorsal rays xii to xv + 13, with 8 to 10 finlets; anal rays 12, with 8 to 10 finlets; ventrals longer than anal; pectorals short. Color: dark blue above, grayish below with silvery blotches. (*thynnus*, a classical name for this fish, whence tunny, tuna, etc.)

This magnificent species is found in warm and temperate regions of the globe, and is not rare on our coasts. It reaches a weight of 1,500 pounds or more and a length of 10 feet or upwards. It is a first-class food fish, and supports important fisheries in southern Europe, but has been regarded with little favor in the United States. It is caught chiefly in pound nets, and is usually thrown away. It feeds on menhaden and other school fishes, and is exceedingly voracious and destructive.

From the account of this fish at Beaufort as given by Yarrow, it is evident that he had some other species in mind. Jordan & Gilbert frequently heard of the tunny, but did not see it; Jenkins, however, saw two specimens there in 1885.

Genus SARDA Cuvier. Bonitoes.

Moderate-sized, very active, pelagic fishes, swimming in large schools and often coming inshore in pursuit of food. The elongate body is covered with scales, which in the pectoral region are modified and form a corselet; the caudal peduncle is very slender and strongly keeled; the jaws contain strong, conical teeth, and the palate bones have similar teeth; the gill-rakers are long and stout; the dorsal fins are separated only by a short notch; the anterior dorsal has 18 to 22 spines; the dorsal finlets number 8 or 9 and the anal usually less. Two American species, one on each coast. (*Sarda*, the ancient Greek and Latin name for the fish, from the island of Sardinia.)

162. SARDA SARDA (Bloch).

"Bonito".

Scomber sarda Bloch, Ichthyologie, x, 35, pl. 334, 1797; Europe.
Sarda pelamys, Yarrow, 1877, 207; Shackleford Banks.
Sarda sarda, Jordan & Evermann, 1896, 872.

DIAGNOSIS.—Body slightly compressed, depth .25 length; head contained 3.75 times in length; mouth large, maxillary extending beyond eye and not concealed by preorbital; about 30 teeth in each jaw; corselet small, not extending beyond pectorals; lateral line wavy; gill-rakers 11 or 12 on lower arm of first arch; dorsal rays xxi or xxii + 13, with 8 finlets, the spines becoming gradually shorter from front to back; anal rays 14, with 7 finlets. Color: steel blue above, with numerous parallel, oblique black stripes which form v's on back; sides and below silvery white. (*sarda*, an ancient name for the bonito, from the island of Sardinia.)

The bonito is one of the best known species of the mackerel family in our waters, being abundant in summer on the Atlantic coast from Massachusetts southward. It is taken in large numbers in pound nets and other nets, and may also be caught by trolling with blue-fish tackle. A weight of 12 pounds is attained, but the average does not exceed 4 or 5. When seen in the water the bonito may be readily recognized by its back being strikingly marked by a series of black v's pointed forward.

At Beaufort this fish is known to most of the fishermen as "bonito", but it is not caught in noteworthy numbers. Yarrow noted that it was "tolerably abundant near Shackleford banks". Goode (1884) notes that the fish is occasionally observed off Cape Hatteras.

Although the bonito does not rank high as a food fish in our markets, it is really an excellent fish when eaten soon after capture. From abundant personal experience, the present writer endorses the following opinion of Professor Goode:

Tested side by side with the blue-fish, at the same table, the bonito seems not much inferior, though the flesh is somewhat softer and more perishable. The bonito may be ranked among the many excellent food fishes of our coast, and, in any other country not so abundantly supplied with finely-flavored fishes, it would be considered of the highest value. Its vitality is so great and its supply of blood so abundant that unless bled immediately after capture the flesh, especially in warm weather, is apt to deteriorate,

Statistics of the North Carolina fisheries show a catch of only a few thousand pounds of "bonito" annually, mostly in the gill-net fishery of Carteret County, and this small quantity probably includes 1 or 2 other species besides *Sarda sarda*. The price received by the fishermen is only 1 or 1.5 cents a pound.

Genus SCOMBEROMORUS Lacépède. Spanish Mackerels, Ceroes, etc.

These are among the most graceful, most beautiful, and most valuable of the mackerels. Some species enter our bays and estuaries, others remain at sea. The form is very elongate and considerably compressed, the body being entirely covered with rudimentary scales not forming a corselet; the head is short and pointed; the mouth is large, with strong knife-like teeth in jaws and with villiform teeth on vomer and palate bones; there is a single keel on the caudal peduncle; the gill-rakers are few in number; the dorsal fins are almost continuous, the anterior low and containing 14 to 18 feeble spines; the soft dorsal and anal are similar and are followed by 7 to 10 finlets. Of the 5 American species, 3 occur on the Atlantic coast and are known from North Carolina.

Key to the North Carolina species of Scomberomorus.

i. Origin of soft dorsal fin in advance of anal fin; 24 to 32 teeth in each jaw..*maculatus*.
ii. Origin of soft dorsal fin over origin of anal fin.
  a. Depth more than .2 length; about 40 teeth in each jaw....................*regalis*.
  aa. Depth about .16 length; about 30 teeth in each jaw........................*cavalla*.

(*Scomberomorus*, near *Scomber*.)

163. SCOMBEROMORUS MACULATUS (Mitchill).
"Spanish Mackerel".

Scomber maculatus Mitchill, Transactions Literary and Philosophical Society of New York, i, 1815, 426; New York.
Cybium maculatum, Yarrow, 1877, 208; Beaufort, Shackleford Banks, Cape Lookout. Jordan & Gilbert, 1879, 375; Beaufort; Albemarle Sound (?).
Scomberomorus maculatus, Jordan, 1886, 27; Beaufort. Jenkins, 1887, 88; Beaufort. Jordan & Evermann, 1896, 874, pl. cxxxiv, fig. 368.

DIAGNOSIS.—Depth contained 4.5 times in total length; head equal to depth, small, pointed; profile from snout to dorsal fin straight; mouth large, maxillary extending to posterior edge of eye; teeth large, sharp and compressed; gill-rakers on first arch, 2 above and 11 below angle; lateral line wavy, with about 175 pores; dorsal rays about XVII+18, with 9 finlets; anal rays II,17, with 9 finlets; soft dorsal inserted in advance of anal a distance equal to diameter of eye. Color: dark blue above, silvery below; 2 rows of rounded, dull yellow or yellowish brown spots on sides above lateral line, one row below; anterior dorsal with white base and black distal portion; soft dorsal yellow-tinged, with black edge; anal white; pectorals black posteriorly, yellow anteriorly with black border; caudal blackish. (*maculatus*, spotted.)

On the Atlantic coast of America this species is known from Brazil to Massachusets. It is especially abundant in the Gulf of Mexico, about the Florida keys, and on the coast of the Carolinas; and was once very numerous in Chesapeake Bay, but is now much less abundant than it was 25 years ago.

The fish attains a large size, 9 or 10 pounds being the normal maximum. Very exceptionally, however, it becomes larger; and a few years ago one was found in the Washington (D. C.) market from Chesapeake Bay which was 41 inches long and weighed 25 pounds; it was seen and identified by Professor B. W. Evermann and others from the United States Bureau of Fisheries.

The fish doubtless spawns throughout its entire range on the United States coast, but, as shown hereafter, apparently very few remain on the North Carolina coast during the spawning season. The lower part of Chesapeake Bay was formerly and is still a favorite spawning ground. The eggs are about 1mm. (.04 inch) in diameter, and float at the surface; they are laid mostly at night, and the hatching period is about 25 hours in a water temperature of 77° or 78° F. All the eggs of a given fish do not ripen at one time, and the spawning may thus extend over several weeks during which several hundred thousand eggs may be deposited.

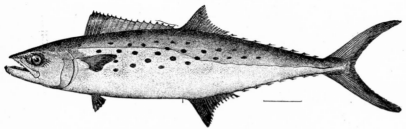

Fig. 77. SPANISH MACKEREL. *Scomberomorus maculatus.*

As a food fish the spanish mackerel is one of the choicest species of our east coast, being hardly surpassed by any species except the pompano. Dr. Coker contributes the following interesting account of its economic importance on the North Carolina coast:

The spanish mackerel are, regularly, the highest priced fish of our waters, the fishermen not infrequently receiving 40 cents each for them. They are practically all shipped to markets north of North Carolina, except that when not abundant enough for separate shipment, they are put into boxes of assorted fish for state markets.

The mackerel season commences in May and the best catch is in early June; mackerel contracts used to close June 10, but now run somewhat later. Few fish, however, are caught after the middle of June, and while all during the summer there are a few scattered mackerel about, there is no fishing again until fall, when they reappear in large numbers, in September, and especially October. After the first of November it is unusual to find any number of mackerel.

The view of the fish-shippers as to the movements of this fish is probably correct. In the spring the schools of mackerel are coming from the south. At this season they are comparatively poor and have a roe that is not quite ripe. A few remain here but the mass pass on north, and somewhere north of us spawn and fatten. With the first "shift of wind" (to the north) in September, the scattered mackerel here school up and start south. They are succeeded by schools from farther north, which are accountable for the later fall catches. Now they are without roe and fat—with an average weight of about 3 pounds, as opposed to barely over 2 pounds in the spring. The largest mackerel caught are a little over 11 pounds.

The spring catch is greater than that of the fall, but this is doubtless due to weather conditions. Apparently spanish mackerel run before the wind, so that, since all the fishing is done within a comparatively short distance from the shore, the fish are not expected when an offshore wind prevails. Thus, a southeast breeze is quite favorable, while a northwest breeze is most unfavorable for fishing. To the prevailing southerly winds of the spring and summer is, therefore, to be attributed the better catch in May and June.

On the night and morning of October 19 and 20, 1903, one dealer at Morehead City received 15,000 pounds of mackerel—an unprecedented day's catch for the fall, though larger catches are sometimes made in the spring. The number of mackerel taken varies much from year to year; during the fall of 1903 it has been high; a year ago there were not many, some being taken 10 miles off Cape Lookout.

The yield of this excellent fish in 1902 aggregated 354,085 pounds, valued at $19,948. The bulk of the catch came from the seine and gill-net fisheries of Carteret, Pamlico, Hyde, and Dare counties. In 1897 the product was 330,840 pounds, worth $18,017; and in 1890 was 91,500 pounds, valued at $6,252.

164. SCOMBEROMORUS REGALIS (Bloch).
"Cero"; King-fish; King Cero; Spotted Cero; Spotted Mackerel.

Scomber regalis Bloch, Ichthyologie, pl. 333, 1797; Martinique.
Cybium regale, Yarrow, 1877, 208; Beaufort. Jordan & Gilbert, 1879, 375; Beaufort (after Yarrow).
Scomberomorus regalis, Jordan & Evermann, 1896, 975, pl. cxxxv, fig. 369. Linton, 1905, 362; Beaufort.

DIAGNOSIS.—Depth contained 4.5 times in total length; length of head slightly greater than depth; maxillary reaching to below eve; teeth triangular, compressed; lateral line descending obliquely, wavy along tail; pectoral fins scaly; dorsal rays about xviii + 15, with 8 finlets; anal rays ii,14; caudal fin less widely forked than in *S. maculatus*. Color: silvery, darker on back; 2 blackish longitudinal stripes across lateral line under soft dorsal, these broken into numerous spots posteriorly; similar spots in rows above and below the others; spinous dorsal fin black anteriorly. (*regalis*, royal, kingly.)

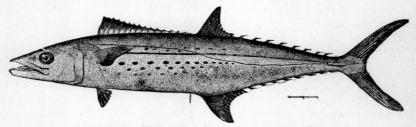

Fig. 78. KING-FISH. *Scomberomorus regalis.*

Although the king-fish ranges northward on our east coast as far as Massachusetts, it is not abundant north of Florida. Its similarity to the spanish mackerel and cero is such that the fishermen often do not distinguish between them. Yarrow reported the fish as not abundant at Beaufort, only one being seen by him, and Jordan, Gilbert, and Jenkins did not find it there. It occurs regularly in summer, however, in company with *Scombermorus cavalla*, but its relative abundance has not been determined. The usual weight is 15 to 35 pounds. Its habits are like those of the cero, and its food and game qualities are similar.

165. SCOMBEROMORUS CAVALLA (Cuvier).

"Cero"; King-fish.

Cybium cavalla Cuvier, Regne Animal, ed. 2, ii, 200, 1829; Brazil.
Scomberomorus cavalla, Jordan & Evermann, 1896, 875.

DIAGNOSIS.—Depth .16 total length; head .2 length; eye .5 length of snout; maxillary extending under eye; teeth triangular, compressed; gill-rakers short, less than .33 diameter of eye, 8 below angle of first arch; lateral line descending abruptly below soft dorsal fin; dorsal rays xvi + 15, anal rays ii,15, each with 8 finlets. Color: iron gray above, lighter below; adults almost or quite unspotted; young with dark yellow spots on sides; no black blotch on anterior part of first dorsal fin. (*cavalla*, a Spanish name meaning horse.)

The cero inhabits both coasts of the tropical Atlantic, extending its range as far northward as Massachusetts. It occurs in large schools, and is especially abundant from South Carolina to Key West. It is a powerful, active ocean marauder, its large mouth being provided with sharp teeth which work havoc among the schools of small fishes.

Although the species is common on the North Carolina coast, it has rarely been recorded therefrom, and ichthyological literature contains few or no North Carolina references. Yarrow, Jordan, Gilbert, Jenkins, and others did not find the fish in the Beaufort region, but it occurs there at the same time as the spanish mackerel, May, June, September, and October being the best months for it. It does not, however, go into the estuaries and rivers like the latter, but remains outside, although sometimes occurring in the inlet and occasionally in the channels along Shackleford Banks and Fort Macon. It is much less abundant and less valuable than the spanish mackerel, bringing only half as much per pound; and, as its sharp teeth and great strength make it disastrous to ordinary nets, it is not sought by the market fishermen, who, however, catch it incidentally in drift nets, set nets, and purse seines used for spanish mackerel. Dr. Coker states that 15 or 20 is a good catch to a boat in a day, but that on one occasion 160 were received by a local dealer as the day's catch of one boat. Mr. George N. Ives reports that when he operated large seines in the bight of Cape Lookout he sometimes landed 1,500 to 2,000 ceroes at a haul, the largest weighing 40 pounds. At the present time many fish could be caught there if especially strong seines were used, but the cero brings a very small price and is rarely marketed in the north.

In the channels near the "banks", ceroes are likely to be found among menhaden; and 2 or 3 to 10 or 20 are not infrequently caught by the menhaden boats in schools of menhaden. The fish thus taken are eaten on board the boats, not being considered of sufficient value to ship. In the line fishing for "trout" and other species, the cero is sometimes troublesome, and may then be readily caught by baiting a large hook on a stout line with a young croaker or trout.

At Beaufort the cero is the most highly prized of the game fishes, being caught by trolling. The usual weight of those thus taken is 15 to 30 pounds, some being larger. Dr. Coker has seen 24 cero brought in as the result of one day's fishing, this being considered a good catch, but doubtless this number has at times been greatly exceeded. Mr. M. B. Claussen, of New York, who has angled much in the Beaufort region, reports that a few years ago he caught a cero there that weighed 54 pounds.

Opinion differs at Beaufort as to the quality of the fresh meat, but it has not good keeping qualities and soon becomes soft even in ice; as a salted fish, however, the cero is good. One of the most successful of the anglers who visit Beaufort is Mr. McLung, of Tennessee, who regards the cero as one of the most delicious of sea food fishes when eaten within a few hours after being caught, but useless when shipped home, as the flesh losses its fine flavor and becomes soft.

The cero catch of North Carolina in 1902 was 45,380 pounds, for which the fishermen received $455. Nearly this entire quantity is to be credited to the seine fisheries in Carteret County.

Genus SCOMBER Linnæus.   Common Mackerels.

This genus contains a few moderate sized, wandering marine fishes characterized by an elongate, fusiform body; slender caudal peduncle with 2 lateral keels on each side; wide, weak mouth, with small teeth on jaws, vomer, and palatines; maxillary slipping behind preorbital; very small scales; long and slender gill-rakers; numerous pyloric cœca; small or deficient air-bladder; widely separated dorsal fins, the anterior with 9 to 12 weak spines; 5 to 9 finlets behind dorsal and anal fins; rather small forked caudal fin; and small pectoral and ventrals fins. Two American species, both widely distributed and valuable for food. (*Scomber*, a name based on the ancient Greek name for the common mackerel.)

166. SCOMBER SCOMBRUS Linnæus.
"Round Mackerel"; Common Mackerel.

Scomber scombrus Linnaeus, Systema Naturæ, ed. x, 297, 1758; Atlantic Ocean.   Jordan & Evermann, 1896, pl. cxxxiii, fig. 363; south to Cape Hatteras.   Goode, 1884, 281; sounds about Cape Hatteras.

Fig. 79.   COMMON MACKEREL.   *Scomber scombrus.*

DIAGNOSIS.—Depth contained 4.5 times in length; head somewhat less than .25 length; maxillary reaching vertical from anterior edge of orbit; eye .2 length of head and .66 snout; snout long and pointed; air-bladder absent; dorsal rays XI + 12; the fins separated by a space somewhat less than length of head; anal rays I,11, opposite and similar to soft dorsal; 5 finlets behind dorsal and anal fins; caudal fin deeply forked; pectorals about .5 length of head; ventrals shorter. Color: above dark blue, with numerous transverse wavy, parallel black bars; below glistening white; fins dusky, dorsals edged with white. (*scombrus*, ancient Mediterranean name for the fish.)

There are no definite North Carolina records for this species, although it has been frequently cited as occurring "off Cape Hatteras", "as far south as Cape Hatteras", etc. As is well known, it often happens that the first schools of mackerel met with by the New England fishermen in spring are off Cape Hatteras, and in one or two instances the fish have been seen off Cape Hatteras in December or late fall.

The writer's recent observations have shown that this is the species known to the fishermen of Cape Lookout and other North Carolina localities as "round mackerel". The fish is caught in bottom gill nets at Cape Lookout in spring and fall, and one specimen was taken there in the third week in April, 1904. The largest numbers come with the spanish mackerel in May. During summer the mackerel is absent, but in fall it reappears and at that time is sometimes caught in pound nets in Pamlico Sound and about Roanoke Island. Mr. George N. Ives, however, one of the very best informed fish men in North Carolina, says he has never seen this fish in the state and doubts its occurrence.

Family TRICHIURIDÆ. The Hair-tails.

These fishes frequent the warmer parts of the ocean and swim near the surface. They are exceedingly elongate, with closely compressed sides and body tapering posteriorly to a point. The head is large, with wide mouth, powerful jaws, and prominent teeth. The gills are 4 in number, the gill-membranes are not connected and are free from the isthmus. The body is destitute of scales, but there is a lateral line. The air-bladder is present. The fin development is peculiar: The dorsal fin is very long, and usually without differentiation of the spinous and soft rays, all of which are short; the anal is likewise long and very low; the caudal is absent; the pectorals are small; and the ventrals are either absent or rudimentary. The family is represented in American waters by a single genus and species.

Genus TRICHIURUS Linnæus. Cutlass-fishes.

Body band-like; head long, lower jaw strong and projecting; teeth on jaws and palatines, those on jaw of unequal size, strong and sharp; margin of maxillary partly covered by preorbital; lateral line decurved; dorsal fin extending without a break from nape to end of tail; anal consisting of short, detached spines nearly concealed by the skin; posterior extremity of body produced as a long filament; pectorals very short; ventrals absent. (*Trichiurus*, hair-tail.)

167. TRICHIURUS LEPTURUS Linnæus.

"Sword-fish"; Cutlass-fish; Scabbard-fish; Sabre-fish; Hair-tail.

Trichiurus lepturus Linnæus, Systema Naturæ, ed. x, 246, 1758; America. Yarrow, 1877, 207; Beaufort. Jenkins, 1887, 88; Beaufort. Jordan & Evermann, 1896, 889, pl. cxxxvii, fig. 375.

DIAGNOSIS.—Greatest depth of body about .06 total length; head pointed, comparatively large, contained 7.5 times in total length; upper jaw with about 4 large lancet-like teeth and others smaller; lower jaw with numerous sharp teeth; mandible reaching to posterior margin of eye; eye large, .5 length of snout and .16 length of head; posterior margin of opercle forming a rather sharp angle; lateral line beginning opposite upper margin of eye, dropping suddenly behind pectoral, and continued to tail near and concurrent with belly; dorsal rays about 135, of nearly uniform length, the longest not twice diameter of eye; anal spines about 100, scarcely evident, the anterior directed backward, the posterior forward; pectorals short, pointed, slightly longer than eye.   Color: uniformly glistening silvery; dorsal fin with a dark margin. (*lepturus*, slender tailed.)

This curious and easily recognized fish of the warm seas comes northward on our east coast as far as Massachusetts, and is not rare from Chesapeake Bay southward.   It attains a length of 5 feet, and in Jamaica and other places is eaten, although it has little value in the United States.   On the North Carolina coast it enters all the inlets and sounds during summer and fall, and sometimes at least in winter.   At Beaufort it is often caught in line fishing at the inlet and inside the harbor, the hooks being baited with mullet and sunk to the bottom; the fish is said to pull very hard when caught.   Many are taken in mullet nets as late as the second half of November, 40 to 50 being sometimes taken at one haul; they tangle the nets badly, and are not liked by the fishermen.   On December 13, 1890, Dr. W. C. Kendall found a cutlass-fish stranded on the beach at Hatteras Inlet.

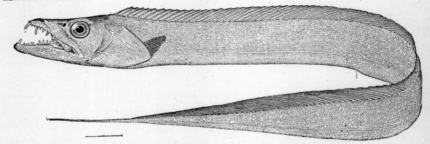

Fig. 80. CUTLASS-FISH; HAIR-TAIL. *Trichiurus lepturus*.

The cutlass-fish has an exceedingly formidable mouth, and, being an active swimmer, must be a terror to small fishes.   Spawning occurs in summer.   In August, 1906, Dr. E. W. Gudger obtained ripe eggs from a 30-inch fish caught at Beaufort.   The ovary is single, and in this specimen was about 6.5 inches long.

Family XIPHIIDÆ.   The Sword-fishes.

This family contains a single species of large size and great power, inhabiting the high seas.   Body elongate, compact, smooth, and destitute of scales. Upper jaw greatly prolonged and forming a flat sword, the bones entering into it being the premaxillaries, ethmoid, and vomer; lower jaw large; teeth absent in adult.   Gills 4, the laminæ of each united into a single plate; gill-membranes separate, not connected with isthmus.   Intestine long, pyloric cœca numerous, air-bladder large and simple.   Two dorsal fins, the anterior large and beginning opposite gill-opening, the posterior very small and situated near the caudal; 2 anal fins, the anterior rather large, the posterior small and opposite second dorsal; caudal very large and widely forked; pectorals long, narrow and pointed;

ventrals absent; all the fins shark-like, the rays developed in the skin; caudal peduncle slender, with a keel on each side; young with both jaws produced, the dorsal and anal fins continuous, the head spinous, and body with rudimentary scales.

Genus XIPHIAS Linnæus.   Sword-fishes.

Characters of the genus noted above.   (*Xiphias*, ancient Greek name for the sword-fish, from *xiphos*, a sword.)

168. XIPHIAS GLADIUS Linnæus.
Sword-fish.

Xiphias gladius Linnæus, Systema Naturæ, ed. x, 248, 1758; Europe.   Yarrow, 1877, 207; off Cape Lookout. Jenkins, 1887, 88; Beaufort   Jordan & Evermann, 1896, 894.

DIAGNOSIS.—Body very slightly compressed, tapering uniformly from head to tail, the greatest depth (at anterior dorsal fin) contained 5.5 to 6 times in total length (to base of caudal fin); head with sword longer than remainder of body; snout about .33 total length to tip of caudal lobes; mouth large, the cleft extending far beyond eye; eye .25 postorbital part of head; first dorsal fin very high and falcate anteriorly, its height nearly as great as depth of body; dorsal rays 40+2 to 4; first anal fin falcate like dorsal but smaller, its origin about midway between pectorals and base of caudal; anal rays 18 to 21+3; length of caudal lobes measured from end of keel greater than depth of body; pectorals placed very low, their length about equal to that of first dorsal.   Color: lustrous blackish purple above, whitish beneath; the fins dark bluish; upper side of sword purplish blue like the head, under side lighter; iris blue. (*gladius*, sword.)

This large inhabitant of the high seas is common off the entire east coast of the United States, occasionally coming into the inshore waters.   Yarrow did not see this species at Fort Macon, but received "reliable information of its occasional appearance off Cape Lookout".

Jenkins lists it as "occasionally reported by fishermen", and cites Prof. W. K. Brooks as authority for the statement.   Goode (1884) quotes a Mr. A. W. Simpson as reporting that sword-fish have at times been seen in large numbers off Cape Hatteras in November and December, sometimes entering the sounds.

The sword-fish is one of the largest, most powerful, and most dangerous fishes sought by man.   The average weight is 400 to 500 pounds, and the maximum more than 800 pounds, the length of the largest being 15 feet.   On the New England coast there is an important fishery for the sword-fish, which is killed by harpooning.   The flesh is firm and palatable, and usually brings a good price; it is sold in the form of steaks.

Family ISTIOPHORIDÆ.   The Sail-fishes and Spear-fishes.

These are large, pelagic fishes, similar in appearance and habits to the much commoner sword-fish (Xiphias), but readily distinguishable therefrom by the compressed body, elongate dorsal fin, well-developed ventral fins, shorter sword, complex air-bladder, etc.   The body is elongate and covered with linear scutes. The bones of the upper jaw are fused and elongated to form a long and strong sword or spear.   The mouth is provided with small granular teeth on jaws and palatines. There are 2 anal fins. On each side of the caudal peduncle are 2 fleshy ridges. The intestine is short and but slightly convoluted, and the large air-bladder has numerous divisions. The family contains 2 genera, which are thus distinguished:

i. Dorsal fin much higher than depth of body, and not divided in middle; ventral fins formed of 2 or 3 rays...ISTIOPHORUS.
ii. Dorsal fin less than height of body, and separated in middle by aborted rays; ventral fins formed of a single spine..TETRAPTURUS.

Genus ISTIOPHORUS Lacépède.   Sail-fishes.

Form slender, much compressed, caudal peduncle narrow; skin rough and covered with small, elongate scales; sword flattened, tapering to a point, its upper and lower surfaces rounded; dorsal fin continuous, beginning on head and extending nearly to caudal, the anterior three-fourths very high, the posterior rays low; anal fin double, small; caudal lobes widely flaring; ventral rays very long. Several species, 1 American. (*Istiophorus*, sail-bearing.)

169. ISTIOPHORUS NIGRICANS (Lacépède).
Sail-fish.

Makaira nigricans Lacépède, Histoire Naturelle des Poissons, iv, 688, 1803; Rochelle, France.
Istiophorus nigricans, Jordan & Evermann, 1896, 891, pl. cxxxii, fig. 376.

DIAGNOSIS.—Depth greatest over gill-opening, .14 length from tip of sword to base of tail; head (including upper jaw) 2.5 times depth; eye small, .09 to .10 length of head, midway between tip of lower jaw and gill-slit; upper jaw 3 times length of postorbital region; lateral line straight, with a marked arch over pectoral; dorsal rays about XL,7, the longest spines more than twice body depth, the last rays much reduced; anal rays 9+7; caudal deeply forked, the lobes very slender and about length of upper jaw; ventrals long and pointed, longer than upper jaw; pectorals .5 ventrals. Color: above bluish black, below pale; dorsal fin bluish, with numerous round black spots; caudal with black blotches; other fins dark. (*nigricans*, becoming black.)

The sail-fish, so named because of the immense dorsal fin, is not uncommon in the West Indies and about the Florida Keys, but occurs only as a rare straggler along the east coast of the United States. The only specimen recorded from North Carolina was caught by a Morehead City fisherman in the summer of 1884 and was handled by Mr. George N. Ives, then in business at that place. The specimen finally reached Mr. H. H. Brimley, by whom it was preserved for the State Museum at Raleigh. This example is 71 inches long, with upper jaw 15 inches long.

Genus TETRAPTURUS Rafinesque.   Spear-fishes.

Body elongate, sides much compressed, caudal peduncle contracted; scales rudimentary and embedded; dorsal fins separate; the first beginning over gill-slit and extending beyond first anal, with anterior rays elevated and others very low, the second dorsal small and opposite second anal; caudal fin widely forked; ventral fins consisting of a single slender ray. Two American and several old world species. (*Tetrapturus*, four-winged tail.)

170. TETRAPTURUS ALBIDUS Poey.

Spear-fish; Bill-fish.

Tetrapturus albidus Poey, Memorias sobre la historia natural de la isia de Cuba, ii, 237, 1858; Havana.   Goode, 1884, 357, pl. 116.
Tetrapturus imperator, Jordan & Evermann, 1896, 892.

DIAGNOSIS.—Greatest depth of body, under anterior lobe of dorsal fin, .15 total length; depth of caudal peduncle .25 depth of body; head (with upper jaw) about .3 length; eye small, .25 postorbital part of head; length of snout about twice length of remainder of head; dorsal rays III,35+6, the anterior elevated rays about .75 depth of body; anal rays II,8+6; each caudal lobe as long as upper jaw, the fork making an angle of 70 to 80 degrees; pectorals longer than ventrals and nearly .5 length of head. Color: back and fins dark blue, sides and below white; anterior dorsal fin dark-spotted. (*albidus*, whitened.)

This species, whose center of abundance is the West Indies, occasionally ranges as far north as Massachusetts. There is a single North Carolina record which has been communicated by Mr. H. H. Brimley. This is a specimen found on the beach on Bogue Bank in the summer of 1892 by Mr. Thomas C. Harris, then curator of the State Museum. The head of this specimen is now in the museum; it is 41 inches long, with upper jaw 29 inches long, spear at tip of lower jaw 2 inches wide and 1.45 inches deep, width of head between eyes 7.25 inches, and diameter of eye 2.5 inches. These dimensions indicate a fish more than 10 feet long.

The spear-fish sometimes attains a very large size, one 26 feet long having been reported from the island of Mauritius, where the species is highly esteemed as food. Like the sword-fish, this species occasionally attacks vessels without any provocation, and may cause serious leaks; it is also dangerous to fishermen in small boats. It often floats listlessly at the surface, but is also known to swim at a depth of 100 fathoms.

Family CARANGIDÆ.   The Cavallies, Pompanoes, etc.

A numerous and important family of marine fishes, found in warm and temperate latitudes. They are for the most part active swimmers, and many of the species go in schools. The carangids differ much in form, some being elongate and not greatly compressed, while others are deep and much compressed. The body is usually covered with thin cycloid scales, but is sometimes naked; the lateral line is arched anteriorly, straight posteriorly, and may be armed with bony plates; the dorsal fins are more or less separated, the spines rather weak and depressible in a groove; the anal fin is long, with 2 stiff spines; the caudal fin is widely forked, the peduncle slender; the pectoral fins are usually long and narrow; the gill-rakers are usually long; the gill-membranes are free from the isthmus and usually not united; the air-bladder is present, the pseudobranchiæ are large, and the pyloric cœca are numerous. There are about 20 American genera, of which 8 are known to be represented in the state fauna.

Key to the North Carolina genera of carangids.

i. Body covered with linear, embedded scales, giving the skin a peculiar leathery appearance; premaxillaries not protractile; pectoral fins short and rounded..........OLIGOPLITES.
*ii.*Body either naked or covered with small cycloid scales; premaxillaries protractile; pectoral fins either long and falcate or short and pointed.

  a. Anal fin much shorter than soft dorsal, its base not longer than abdomen...SERIOLA.
 aa. Anal fin as long as soft dorsal, its base longer than abdomen.
    b. Pectoral fins long and falcate; maxillary with a supplemental bone; lateral line usually
      with bony plates.
      c. Dorsal outline more strongly curved than ventral outline.
        d. Lateral line with bony plates only on posterior part.
          e. Body elongate, moderately compressed, back somewhat elevated; jaw teeth
            in a few series or in one series; no fin-rays produced; plates of lateral
            line strongly developed...................................CARANX.
            first 5 or 6 dorsal and anal rays produced as long filaments; plates of
         ee. Body short and deep, greatly compressed; jaw teeth in villiform bands;
            lateral line well developed ....ALECTIS.
        eee. Body broad ovate, strongly compressed, anterior profile nearly vertical,
           forehead bulging; teeth weak; dorsal and anal fins very low, no rays pro-
           duced; plates of lateral line almost obsolete................VOMER.
        dd. Lateral line without any bony plates...........................SELENE.
      cc. Dorsal outline less strongly curved than ventral; no plates on lateral line.
                                             CHLOROSCOMBRUS.
    bb. Pectoral fins short and not falcate; maxillary without supplemental bone; lateral line
      without bony plates. ....TRACHINOTUS.

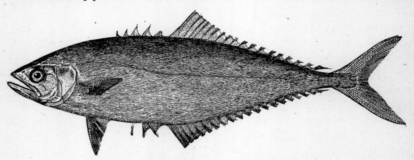

Fig. 81. LEATHER-JACKET. *Oligoplites saurus.*

Genus OLIGOPLITES Gill. Leather-jackets.

The leather-jackets are easily recognizable by their greatly compressed,
more or less elongate body covered with very narrow scales embedded in the skin
with little regularity of arrangement, the scales being very different from ordinary ones. Head short, compressed; mouth large, with bands of small, sharp
teeth on jaws, tongue, palatines and vomer; upper jaw not protractile; maxillary
narrow; gill-rakers long; lateral line with a slight curve anteriorly, unarmed;
caudal peduncle without keel; dorsal spines low, separated, 3 to 5 in number;
second dorsal long, anterior rays highest, posterior rays low, separated, and
forming finlets; anal spines well separated from soft part, the latter similar to
soft dorsal; caudal widely forked; pectorals and ventrals short, the latter depressible in a groove. The few species are of small size and are found only in
warmer American waters. (*Oligoplites,* poorly armed.)

171. OLIGOPLITES SAURUS (Bloch & Schneider).

Runner; Leather-jacket.

Scomber saurus Bloch & Schneider, Systema Ichthyologiæ, 1801, 321; Jamaica.
Oligoplites saurus, Jordan & Evermann, 1896, 898, pl. cxxxviii, fig. 378.

DIAGNOSIS.—Depth .25 length; head .2 length; maxillary extending beyond pupil; eye slightly less than snout, .25 head; head naked, the body covered with linear, obliquely arranged, embedded scales; dorsal rays v +1,20; anal rays ii +1,20; caudal lobes equal, about length of head; pectorals and ventrals about .66 length of head. Color: bluish on back and top of head, silvery on sides and belly; iris and fins yellow. (*saurus*, lizard.)

Although the leather-jacket ranges regularly from the tropics along our east coast to New York, it has not heretofore been recorded from North Carolina. On May 17, 1904, a Beaufort fisherman brought a 10-inch specimen to the laboratory, and reported that he had met with the fish before. The species rarely exceeds a foot in length, and has no food vaue.

Genus SERIOLA Cuvier. Amber-fishes.

Rather large, shapely fishes, usually with a good deal of greenish-yellow on body and fins, whence the name of amber-fish. They are found on the coasts of America, Europe, and Asia, and in some countries are important food fishes. Body rather elongate, slightly compressed, back not elevated; head conical; mouth large, with bands of small teeth on jaws, tongue, vomer, and palatals; premaxillaries protractile; supplemental maxillary broad; body and sides of head covered with very small scales; lateral line greatly arched anteriorly, forming a keel on side of peduncle; anterior dorsal fin low, with about 7 spines connected by a membrane; posterior dorsal long, elevated in front; anal similar to soft dorsal but smaller, preceded by 2 very small free spines (disappearing with age); ventrals rather long; pectorals short. About 10 American species, 7 of which occur on our east coast; 3 known from North Carolina.*

Key to the North Carolina species of amber-fishes.

i. Body marked by 5 or 6 broad black cross-bands, very distinct in smaller specimens, becoming obsolete with age; size moderate.
  a. Body rather stout, the depth .33 length to end of scales; length of head much less than depth of body; a dark band from eye to spinous dorsal; ventrals and spinous dorsal black...*zonata.*
  aa. Body slender, the depth .21 length; length of head greater than depth of body; a horizontal yellow band from opercle to end of tail; ventral and spinous dorsal not black.
                                                           carolinensis.
ii. Body not marked by black cross-bands; form slender, depth of body about .25 length to end of scales; length of head equal to or less than depth of body; a golden stripe from eye to spinous dorsal; size large...*lalandi.*

(*Seriola*, an Italian name for one of the fishes of this genus.)

172. SERIOLA ZONATA (Mitchill).†

Rudder-fish; Shark Pilot.

Scomber zonatus Mitchill, Transactions Literary and Philosophical Society of New York, 1815, 427; New York Bay.
Seriola zonata, Jordan & Evermann, 1896, 902, pl. cxxxix, fig. 381; Cape Cod to Cape Hatteras.

    *Several other amber fishes (*S. fasciata*, *S. rivoliana*) are known from South Carolina and may be looked for further north.
    †The pilot-fish (*Naucrates ductor*) was recorded from Beaufort by Yarrow on the authority of a fisherman; but no specimen has been obtained from North Carolina, and it is probable that the fish Yarrow noted was the young of this species.

DIAGNOSIS.—Body rather deep, the depth contained 3 times in total length; back and top of head compressed; head .75 depth of body; supplemental maxillary bone about as broad as eye; lower jaw somewhat projecting; eye rather large, .66 snout; dorsal rays VII+1,38, the longest spine about equal to eye; anterior soft dorsal rays somewhat elongate but less than half length of eye; origin of anal fin under tenth ray of soft dorsal, the anal rays 1,21; pectorals less than .5 length of head; ventrals .6 head. Color: above dull bluish-gray, below white; back and sides with 5 or 6 broad black crossbands, 3 of which extend on dorsal and 2 on anal, the bars becoming more indistinct with age and disappearing in largest fish; a dark oblique stripe from eye to spinous dorsal; spinous dorsal black; tips of caudal white; ventrals black above, pale below. (*zonata*, banded).

Ranges from Cape Hatteras northward to Massachusetts, and will doubtless be found well represented on the North Carolina coast when properly sought. The deep, banded body enables one to recognize the species readily. The young are interesting aquarium fish. This species and the next associate with sharks or other large fish, and are also often found about the rudders of vessels. Attains a length of 3 feet, and is an excellent food fish.

173. SERIOLA CAROLINENSIS Holbrook.

Rudder-fish; Shark Pilot.

Seriola carolinensis Holbrook, Ichthyology of South Carolina, 72, 1860; Charleston.
Halatractus zonatus, Yarrow, 1877, 209; Beaufort.
Seriola zonata, Jordan & Gilbert, 1879, 377; Beaufort.
Seriola zonata carolinensis, Jordan & Evermann, 1896, 902; north to Cape Hatteras.

DIAGNOSIS.—Body slender, the depth about .21 total length; head .28 length; eye small, .16 head; dorsal rays V to VII+1,36 or 37; anal rays 1,19 to 1,21. Color: bluish above, whitish below, a greenish-yellow band extending from opercle to caudal; fins mostly greenish, the ventrals whitish; young with about 6 black cross-bands which become fainter with age, the bands extending on dorsal and anal fins. (*carolinensis*, inhabiting Carolina.)

This species is closely related to *Seriola zonata* and has been regarded by recent writers as a variety of that species; it is a much more elongate form, however, with smaller eye and somewhat different color, and may be recognized as a distinct species until it is found to intergrade with *zonata*.

The fish is found from Cape Hatteras to Texas, but is not common in North Carolina. Yarrow in 1871 observed only a single specimen at Beaufort; Jordan and Gilbert in 1878 and Jenkins in 1885 did not find it there; and of late it has rarely been seen. The fish is not known to the Beaufort fishermen.

174. SERIOLA LALANDI Cuvier & Valenciennes.

Amber-fish; Yellow-tail.

Seriola lalandi Cuvier & Valenciennes, Histoire Naturelle des Poissons, ix, 208, 1833; Brazil. Jordan & Evermann, 1896, 903, pl. cxl, fig. 382. Linton, 1905, 363; off Cape Lookout.

DIAGNOSIS.—Depth .25 total length to fork of caudal; caudal peduncle slender, its depth but little more than diameter of eye; head about equal to depth; maxillary reaching to pupil; eye small, less than .5 length of snout and .16 length of head; scales in lateral series about 160; dorsal rays about VI+1,34, the anterior dorsal very low, the posterior elevated in front, the longest soft ray being .5 head; anal fin similar to but much smaller than second dorsal, its rays 1,21 to 1,24. Color: grayish or purplish golden above, whitish below; a bright bronze horizontal stripe extending from snout, through eye, to caudal; an oblique bronze stripe from eye to spinous dorsal; ventrals white below, anal blackish, other fins dusky yellow. (*lalandi*, after a French naturalist named Delalande.)

This amber-fish, which is found from Brazil to southern New England, is common southward and is sometimes taken in considerable numbers on the New Jersey coast. There appear to be no published records of its capture in North Carolina, but it undoubtedly occurs there every year and could be found if sought for with proper apparatus on the outer shores.

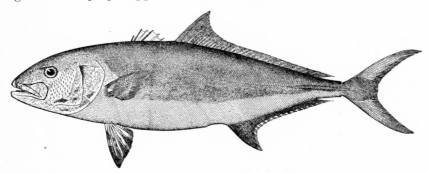

Fig. 82. AMBER-FISH. *Seriola lalandi.*

A number of years ago, some New Jersey fishermen set pound-nets off the beach at Nags Head and for some time caught numbers of fine, large amber-fish, and 20 boxes of the fish were sent to market from Skyco, Roanoke Island. The steamer Fish-Hawk caught a specimen about 28 miles off Cape Lookout, August 21, 1902.

Genus CARANX Lacépède. Crevallés; Cavallies.

A numerous genus of rather small marine species, found in all warm seas, some of them valuable food fishes. Form ovate, considerably compressed; back sometimes arched; head large or moderate; mouth rather large, maxillary reaching to below or beyond eye; jaw teeth not in villiform bands, usually present on vomer, tongue, and palatines; premaxillaries protractile; gill-rakers long; eye large, with adipose eye-lid; anterior dorsal fin rather low, the spines connected by membrane, soft dorsal elevated in front, both fins depressible in a groove; anal fin similar to soft dorsal, preceded by 2 strong spines; pectoral fins falcate; posterior part of lateral line with strong bony plates, each plate with a spine; a short dorsal branch of lateral line usually present. The American species number a dozen or more; the 5 known from the east coast of the United States have been noted in local waters.

Key to the North Carolina species of Caranx.

i. Soft dorsal and anal fins only slightly elevated in front, their rays about 27 and 23 respectively; teeth in a narrow band in each jaw, without canines.
  a. Greatest depth of body contained 2.8 times in length; straight part of lateral line about as long as curved part; color pale, mostly golden ....*bartholomæi.*
  aa. Greatest depth of body contained 3.5 times in length; straight part of lateral line much longer than curved part; color dark, mostly bluish ....*ruber.*

ii. Soft dorsal and anal fins much elevated in front, the rays less numerous than above; teeth in upper jaw in a band, in lower jaw in single series.
  b. Breast without scales, except small patch before ventrals; outer teeth in upper jaw canine; bony plates in lateral line 30...................................*hippos.*
  bb. Breast entirely covered with scales; outer teeth in jaw not canine.
    c. Body rather elongate, depth less than .33 length; bony plates in lateral line 50; soft dorsal rays 1,24...*crysos.*
    cc. Body shorter, depth .4 length; bony plates in lateral line 35; soft dorsal rays 1,22...*latus.*

The cavallies do not figure prominently in the fisheries of the state, being held in little esteem and not especially sought. The total catch in 1902 was 13,900 pounds, which sold for $164.

(*Caranx*, a corruption of a Portuguese or French name for these fishes).

175. CARANX BARTHOLOMÆI Cuvier & Valenciennes.
Yellow Jack.

Caranx bartholomæi Cuvier & Valenciennes, Histoire Naturelle des Poissons, ix, 106, 1833; St. Bartholomew Island. Jenkins, 1885, 11; Beaufort. Jordan, 1886, 27; Beaufort. Jenkins, 1887, 88; Beaufort; Jordan & Evermann, 1896, 919; West Indies to North Carolina.
Caranx beani Jordan, Proceedings U. S. National Museum, iii, 1880, 486; Beaufort.

DIAGNOSIS.—Body deep, compressed, the depth contained 2.8 times in length; head not much compressed, .33 length; maxillary not extending to pupil; eye shorter than snout; gill-rakers long; soft dorsal, anal, and caudal fins densely scaled; plates in lateral line 28; dorsal rays VIII+1,27, soft part slightly falcate; anal rays II+1,23; pectorals falcate, a little shorter than head and extending beyond front of anal. Color: bluish silvery, with golden suffusion; fins pale yellow; young with golden spots. (Named after the island of St. Bartholomew.)

This species, which is common in the West Indies, occasionally strays to the coast of Florida and North Carolina. Two small specimens seined in Beaufort Harbor by Drs. Jordan and Gilbert in 1878 were made the basis of a new species, *Caranx beani*, which is now considered synonymous with *Caranx bartholomæi*. Dr. Jenkins obtained several specimens at Beaufort in the summer of 1885. On August 4, 1905, Mr. C. B. Wilson seined in the harbor a specimen now preserved at the laboratory.

176. CARANX RUBER (Bloch).
Crevallé; Carbonero.

Scomber ruber Bloch, Ichthyologie, pl. 342, 1793; island of St. Croix.
Caranx ruber, Jordan & Evermann, 1896, 919.

DIAGNOSIS.—Depth contained about 3.5 times in total length; head about equal to depth; maxillary barely reaching front of eye and contained 2.75 times in head; no canine teeth in jaws; diameter of eye less than .25 head; snout more than .3 head; scutes 25 to 30, lateral line not strongly arched; dorsal rays VII+1,26 to 28, the anterior rays of soft dorsal more than .3 head; anal rays II+1,22; pectoral fins as long as head. Color: bluish above, silvery below; an obscure horizontal blue stripe below dorsal; dorsal yellowish; lower lobe of caudal with a blackish bar; other fins plain. (*ruber*, red, an inappropriate name based on a drawing erroneously colored.)

In August, 1906, a specimen of this fish about 8 inches long was caught in Beaufort Harbor, and is now in the laboratory collection. This species has not heretofore been recorded from the United States, but is common in the West Indies.

177. CARANX HIPPOS (Linnæus).

"Olbacore"; "Albacore"; "Horse Mackerel"; Crevallé; Cavally; Horse Crevallé (S.C.);
Jack; Jack Crevallé (S. C.)

Scomber hippos Linnæus, Systema Naturæ, ed. xii, 494, 1766; Charleston, S. C.
Carangus hippos, Yarrow, 1877, 208; Beaufort.
Caranx hippos, Jordan, 1886, 27; Beaufort.   Jordan & Evermann, 1896, 920, pl. cxli, fig. 387.   Linton, 1905,
    365; Beaufort.

DIAGNOSIS.—Depth .4 length; head large and deep, .28 length of body, anterior profile
strongly curved; mouth large, lower jaw prominent, maxillary extending to or beyond posterior
border of eye; two canine teeth in front of lower jaw; eye .2 length of head; gill-rakers long and
stout, 15 on lower arm of first arch; plates on lateral line 30; dorsal rays VIII+1,20; anal rays
II+1,17; pectorals slightly longer than head.   Color: olive green above, golden on sides and
abdomen; a large black opercular blotch; axil of pectorals with a black blotch; margin of soft
dorsal black.   (*hippos*, horse.)

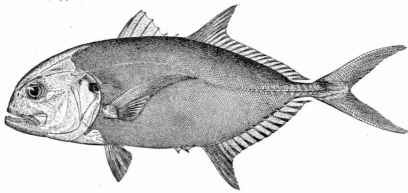

Fig. 83.   CAVALLY.   *Caranx hippos.*

This species of cavally is found on both coasts of America, and occurs
regularly on the eastern seaboard of the United States as far north as Massachusetts.   On the North Carolina coast it is the commonest species of the genus.   At
Beaufort, where the general name for the cavallies is "albacore" or "olbacore",
these fishes were formerly caught in considerable quantities in spring, but are
not now abundant; occasionally a shipment of 25 to 30 boxes is made.   The
local opinion is that the fish has a thick skin and tough flesh, and does not have
high rank as a food fish; although at Key West, Florida, and at other places it
has some commercial importance.   Its weight is usually under 5 pounds, but
often reaches 10 or 12 pounds and occasionally 20 pounds.   Lawson's note on
the cavallies doubtless applies primarily to this species:

Cavallies are of a brownish color, have exceeding small scales and a very thick skin; they
are as firm a fish as ever I saw; therefore will keep sweet (in the hot weather) two days, when
others will stink in half a day, unless salted.   They ought to be scaled as soon as taken; otherwise you must pull off the skin and scales, when boiled; the skin being the choicest of the fish.
The meat, which is white and large, is dressed with this fish.

178. CARANX CRYSOS (Mitchill).

"Horse Mackerel"; "Sun-fish"; "Albacore"; "Olbacore"; Cavally; Crevallé; Horse
Crevallé (S. C.); Jack Crevallé (S. C.); Hard-tail; Runner; Jurel;
Yellow Mackerel.

Scomber crysos Mitchill, Transactions Literary and Philosophical Society of New York, i, 1815, 424; New York.
Carangus chrysos, Yarrow, 1877, 208; Beaufort.　Jordan & Gilbert, 1879, 376; Beaufort.
Carangus pisquetus, Jordan & Gilbert, 1879, 376; Beaufort (after Yarrow).
Paratractus pisquetos, Yarrow, 1877, 208; Beaufort.
Caranx chrysus, Jordan, 1886, 27; Beaufort.　Jenkins, 1887, 88; Beaufort.
Caranx crysos, Jordan & Evermann, 1896, 921, pl. cxlii, fig. 388.

DIAGNOSIS.—Depth contained 3.25 times in total length; head contained 3.75 times in
length; maxillary extending to pupil; eye shorter than snout, contained 3.5 times in head;
gill-rakers long and numerous; plates covering entire straight part of lateral line, 50 in number;
dorsal rays VIII+1,24; anal rays II+1,19; pectorals about length of head.　Color: light green
above, golden yellow or silvery below; a black opercular spot; fins pale.　(*crysos*, gold.)

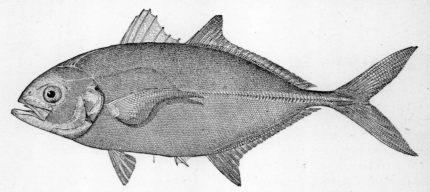

Fig. 84.　CAVALLY; HARD-TAIL.　*Caranx crysos*.

The range of this cavally extends from Brazil to Massachusetts.　On the
North Carolina coast it is ordinarily less common that *Caranx hippos*.　Yarrow
reported a few seen at Fort Macon in early fall, and took one 14 inches long in
May.　Jenkins noted the fish as common in the summer of 1885.　One or two
specimens have been obtained in recent years for the Beaufort laboratory, and
in 1905 the species was very common, upward of 240 specimens being caught
between July 18 and August 28 in a pound net operated in the interest of the
laboratory.　The local name in most general use is "olbacore".　In the Gulf of
Mexico the species is very abundant and highly esteemed as food.　The length
rarely exceeds 15 inches.

179. CARANX LATUS Agassiz.
Jurel; Horse-eye Jack.

Caranx latus Agassiz, Pisces Brasilienses, 105, 1829; Brazil.　Jenkins, 1885, 11; Beaufort.　Jordan, 1886, 27;
　　Beaufort.　Jenkins, 1887, 88; Beaufort.　Jordan & Evermann, 1896, 923.
Caranx richardi Holbrook, Ichthyology of South Carolina, 96, pl. 13, fig. 1, 1860; South Carolina.

DIAGNOSIS.—Shaped like *C. hippos*, but with less strongly curved profile; depth .4 length;
head contained 3.4 times in length; maxillary extending as far as posterior edge of pupil; canine

teeth in front of lower jaw; gill-rakers long, 12 below angle of first arch; scutes in lateral line 35; dorsal rays VIII+1,22; anal rays II+1,16 to 18; pectorals length of head. Color: bluish above, with silvery or golden sides and abdomen; a small black opercular spot; young with black cross-bands; caudal yellow; no spot on pectorals. (*latus*, broad.)

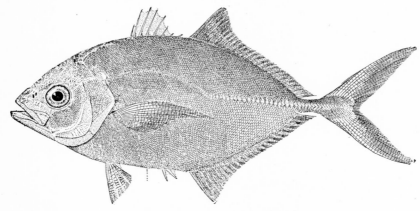

Fig. 85. JUREL. *Caranx latus.*

From the West Indies and South America, this species ranges northward to Virginia; it is also found on the west coast of Mexico. It was first recorded from North Carolina in 1885, when Jenkins obtained a few specimens at Beaufort. Specimens have recently been obtained at Perry Island and Bird Shoal, and outside the harbor by the Fish-Hawk on August 14, 1902. A pound net belonging to the Beaufort laboratory caught 19 specimens in the second and third weeks of August, 1905, but took none during the remainder of the season. From time immemorial the sale of this fish has been prohibited in Cuba because of the numerous cases of illness (ciguatera) which have followed its use.

Genus ALECTIS Rafinesque. Thread-fishes.

Body deep, rhomboid, much compressed; scales minute, embedded; bony plates on straight part of lateral line; teeth in villiform bands on jaws, tongue, vomer, and palatines; dorsal spines short and rudimentary, mostly disappearing with age; soft dorsal and anal fins similar, the first 5 or 6 rays thread-like; ventrals short; pectorals falcate. In the young, the body is more orbicular, the thread-like rays are longer, and the ventrals are longer than in the adult. Several species, only one American. (*Alectis*, chicken-cock, in allusion to the names sea-cock, sea-hen, and fish-cock applied to these and similar fishes in olden times.)

180. ALECTIS CILIARIS (Bloch).
"Moon-fish"; "Shoemaker"; Thread-fish; Cobbler-fish.

Zeus ciliaris Bloch, Ichthyologie, vi, 29, 1788; East Indies.
Blepharichthys crinitus, Yarrow, 1877, 208; Beaufort.
Alectis crinitus, Jordan & Gilbert, 1879, 376; Beaufort (after Yarrow).
Caranx crinitus, Jordan, 1886, 27; Beaufort.
Alectis ciliaris, Jordan & Evermann, 1896, 931.

DIAGNOSIS.—Depth varying with age, .5 total length in adult, equal to length in young; head .33 length; a sharp keel on occiput; mouth horizontal in adult, oblique in young; lateral line with a wide arch anteriorly, the plates on posterior part numbering about 12; dorsal rays VI+1,19; anal rays II+1,16; pectorals falcate, longer than head; ventrals broad. Color: above bluish, below golden yellow; a dark blotch on opercle, another on dorsal, and another on anal. (*ciliaris*, with long threads or lashes.)

Fig. 86. THREAD-FISH. *Alectis ciliaris*.

From the tropical seas this species ranges northward on our east coast as far as Massachusetts; it is, however, not common north of Florida. At Beaufort a few specimens are taken nearly every year in summer and fall. The largest seen there are 12 inches long, which is about the maximum size of the species. The names "moon-fish" and "shoemaker" are applied to this species in the Beaufort region, the former name being shared by several related fishes.

The dorsal and anal rays in the thread-fish are enormously extended, especially in the smaller individuals, and must at times prove a decided inconvenience. Two specimens 8 inches long taken at Beaufort September 14, 1904, by Mr. S. G. Worth had dorsal and anal filaments 15 inches long.

Genus VOMER Cuvier & Valenciennes. Moon-fishes.

Body ovate, much compressed, forehead gibbous, lateral line strongly arched anteriorly, weak plates on the lateral line posteriorly, scales rudimentary, anterior dorsal obsolete, soft dorsal and anal low. In young, the form is deeper and the fins are higher. Several American species, one occurring in United States waters. (*Vomer*, plowshare, in allusion to the shape of the body.)

181. VOMER SETIPINNIS (Mitchill).

"Moon-fish"; "Sun-fish"; Horse-fish.

Zeus setipinnis Mitchill, Transactions Literary and Philosophical Society of New York, 1815, 384; New York.
Vomer setipinnis, Yarrow, 1877, 208; Beaufort.   Jordan & Gilbert, 1879, 376; Beaufort.   Jordan, 1886, 27;
    Beaufort.   Jenkins, 1887, 88; Beaufort.   Jordan & Evermann, 1896, 934, pl. cxliv, fig. 392.

DIAGNOSIS.—Depth in adult .5 total length, in young .6 to .8 length; head contained 3.5 times in length, anterior profile steep, forehead very prominent, snout projecting, mouth oblique, maxillary extending to front of eye; plates on lateral line about 20; dorsal rays VIII + I, 21 or 22; anal rays II + I, 19 or 20; these fins very low in adults; ventral fins very small; pectorals about length of head.   Color: pale green above, silvery on sides; a black blotch at angle of lateral line in young.   (*setipinnis,* bristle-finned.)

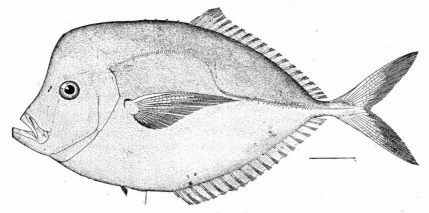

Fig. 87.   MOON-FISH; HORSE-FISH.   *Vomer setipinnis.*

Found along the entire east coast of the United States, but not common northward; its range extends through the West Indies to Brazil, and, on the Pacific coast, from Mexico to Peru.   Yarrow records it from Beaufort as "abundant in the fall, numbers being taken on the outer beach in company with mullet". Its local North Carolina names are "moon-fish" and "sun-fish", and it is not distinguished by the fishermen from *Selene vomer.*   It reaches a length of a foot, and is a good food fish, but is seldom marketed.

Genus SELENE Lacépède.   Moon-fishes.

Marine fishes of very peculiar shape, body greatly compressed and much elevated, anterior profile very steep, edges of body sharp; head short and deep with a prominent angle at nape; mouth small, with protractile premaxillaries and broad maxillaries with supplemental bone; jaws, tongue, vomer, and palatals with minute teeth; gill-rakers long and slender; scales small, lateral line without bony plates; soft dorsal and anal fins with anterior rays much elongated, spinous dorsal rays filiform in young, anal spines becoming obsolete in adult, ventrals very long in young and minute in adult.   Two American species, one found on the east coast.   (*Selene,* moon.)

182. SELENE VOMER (Linnæus.)

"Moon-fish"; "Sun-fish"; "Horse-fish"; Lookdown; Horsehead.

Zeus vomer Linnæus, Systema Naturæ, ed. x, 1758, 266; America.
Selene argentea, Yarrow, 1877, 208; Beaufort. Jordan & Gilbert, 1879, 376; Beaufort.
Argyriosus vomer, Yarrow, 1877, 208; Beaufort. Jordan & Gilbert, 1879, 376; Beaufort.
Argyriosus capillaris, Yarrow, 1877, 208; Beaufort.
Selene vomer, Jordan, 1886, 27; Beaufort. Jenkins, 1887, 88; Beaufort. Jordan & Evermann, 1896, 936, pls.
    cxliv, cxlv, figs. 393, 393a. Linton, 1905, 365; Beaufort.

DIAGNOSIS.—Depth in adult about .66 total length; head .33 length; profile from tip of snout to occiput straight; mouth horizontal, the lower jaw small; diameter of eye about equal to length of opercle and to distance from eye to anterior profile; lateral line with a well marked arch anteriorly, the length of arch greater than that of straight part; dorsal rays VII + 1,23, the spines very low; anal rays II + 1,18, the 2 anterior spines immovable and sometimes absent; pectorals long, falcate. Color: uniform silvery. (*vomer*, plowshare.)

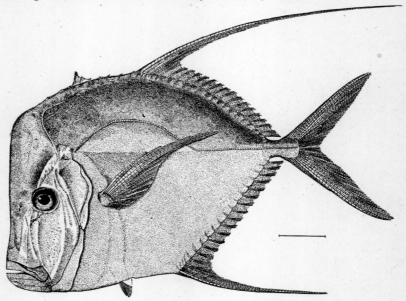

Fig. 88. MOON-FISH; LOOKDOWN. *Selene vomer.*

This species is found on both coasts of America, its range on the east coast being from Brazil to Massachusetts; it is rather common from Chesapeake Bay southward. In the Beaufort region, where it is known as "moon-fish", "sun-fish", and "horse-fish", it is common from May throughout the summer, specimens 2 to 6 inches long often being taken in the harbor and on the outer beaches in company with mullets and *Vomer setipinnis*. The food consists chiefly of shrimp, other small crustaceans, and small gastropods and bivalves.

The young differs greatly from the adult in appearance, the body being much deeper, the profile less vertical, the ventral fins much longer, and the dorsal rays more produced. An example in the Beaufort laboratory 1.25 inches long taken in the summer of 1900 has the ventral fins 1 inch long and the anterior dorsal rays 2.37 inches long.

Genus CHLOROSCOMBRUS Girard. Bumpers.

Small American marine fishes, with much compressed, elliptical body, the ventral curve being greater than the dorsal; caudal peduncle very slender; small smooth scales covering body, head nearly naked; lateral line arched anteriorly, plates wanting; mouth small, oblique, upper jaw protractile, the maxillary bone concave behind and with a large supplemental bone; feeble teeth, mostly in one series, on jaws and roof of mouth; dorsal spines weak, joined by membrane; soft dorsal and anal similar, low, slightly elevated in front, anal spines strong; pectorals long and falcate; ventrals small. Two species, one in Atlantic, the other in Pacific Ocean. (*Chloroscombrus*, green mackerel.)

183. CHLOROSCOMBRUS CHRYSURUS (Linnæus).
Bumper.

Scomber chrysurus Linnæus, Systema Naturæ, ed. xii, 494, 1766; Charleston, S. C.
Chloroscombrus chrysurus, Jenkins, 1885, 11; Beaufort. Jordan, 1886, 27; Beaufort. Jenkins, 1887, 89; Beaufort. Jordan & Evermann, 1896, 936, pl. cxlv, fig. 394.

DIAGNOSIS.—Depth .4 total length; head deeper than long, about .25 length; eye longer than snout, .33 length of head; maxillary extending as far as anterior margin of eye; dorsal rays VII+1,26; anal rays II+1,26; pectorals .33 length of body; depth of caudal peduncle less than diameter of eye. Color: above green, below golden; a dark spot on upper part of opercle and in axil of pectoral; inside of mouth black; caudal peduncle black above; dorsal and anal fins plain, with a narrow dark margin; pectorals and caudal pale greenish-yellow. (*chrysurus*, gold-tailed).

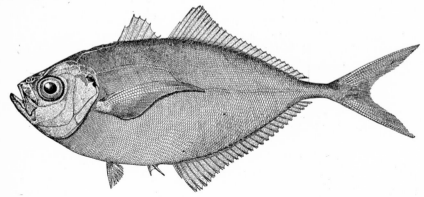

Fig. 89. BUMPER. *Chloroscombrus chrysurus.*

While the bumper is found from Cape Cod to Brazil, it is not common north of Charleston and has rarely been taken in North Carolina waters. One small specimen was collected at Beaufort by Dr. Jenkins in the summer of 1885, and another 1.87 inches long, now in the Beaufort laboratory, was obtained in the harbor Sept. 4, 1901, from the bell-cavity of a medusa (Dactylometra.) Three other specimens, the largest 4.25 inches long, were taken in the laboratory pound net in Beaufort Harbor, in July and August, 1905. The species reaches a length of a foot and is very handsome, but has no food value, the flesh being dry and bony. The North Carolina fishermen do not appear to know the species.

Genus TRACHINOTUS Lacépède. Pompanoes.

A numerous genus of subtropical marine fishes, some of them excellent food. The body is ovate, compressed, the edges rounded; head blunt, snout truncate; mouth rather small, horizontal, maxillary extending about to middle of eye, premaxillaries protractile; vomer and palatals with villiform teeth in bands, teeth usually absent in adults; preopercle entire in adult, spinous in young; gill-rakers short; scales small, smooth; lateral line not strongly arched, unarmed; dorsal spines low, 6 in number, connected by membrane in young but free in adult; soft dorsal and anal falcate, anal preceded by 2 stout spines which become obsolete with age.   Of the 10 or 12 American species, 5 are known from the east coast of the United States, and 4 of these have been taken in local waters.

Key to the North Carolina species of pompanoes.

i. Soft dorsal rays 19 or 20; soft anal rays 17 to 19.
   a. Body very strongly compressed; sides with 4 narrow black vertical bars; anterior soft
       rays of dorsal and anal very long, extending to or beyond middle of caudal....*glaucus.*
   aa. Body moderately compressed; no black cross-bars on sides; anterior dorsal and anal soft
       rays rarely reaching base of caudal.
       b. Body broad, depth about .66 length; anterior soft rays of dorsal and anal fins con-
           siderably elongated, the dorsal lobe much longer than head; size small ....*falcatus.*
       bb. Body oblong, depth about .4 length; anterior soft rays of dorsal and anal fins shorter;
           size large...*goodei.*
ii. Soft dorsal rays 25 to 27; soft anal rays 22 to 26..........................*carolinus.*

(*Trachinotus,* rough-back.)

184. TRACHINOTUS GLAUCUS (Bloch)
"Gaff-topsail Pompano".

Chætodon glaucus Bloch, Ichthyologie, pl. 210, 1787; Martinique.
Trachinotus glaucus, Jordan & Evermann, 1896, 940, pl. cxlvi, fiig. 395.

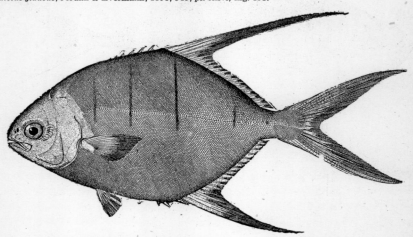

Fig. 90. Gaff-topsail Pompano. *Trachinotus glaucus.*

Diagnosis.—Depth .5 length; head .25 length; eye contained 3.6 times in length of head; dorsal rays vi+1,19, anal rays ii+1,18; caudal lobes long, nearly half length of body.   Color:

bluish above, golden below, 4 narrow black vertical bars on back and sides, a fifth bar represented by a spot on lateral line on peduncle; dorsal and anal lobes dark, caudal bluish, pectorals golden and bluish, ventrals whitish. (*glaucus*, hoary blue.)

This pompano is peculiar in having the anterior soft rays of the dorsal and anal fins very much elongated, and in having 4 black vertical bands on back and sides. The species is found from Chesapeake Bay to Caribbean Sea, and is not uncommon in Florida. It has not been reported from North Carolina waters, but nevertheless occurs there irregularly, and is known locally as "gaff-topsail pompano". In the summer of 1903 a specimen 9 inches long was taken at Beaufort. Ten or twelve years ago, according to Mr. J. H. Potter, a local fish dealer, a great many were caught at Beaufort. The species somewhat exceeds a foot in length, but does not rank high as a food fish.

185. TRACHINOTUS FALCATUS (Linnæus).

"Allovericore"; Round Pompano.

Labrus falcatus Linnæus, Systema Naturæ, ed. x, 1758, 284; America.
Trachynotus ovatus, Jordan & Gilbert, 1879, 376; Beaufort.
Trachynotus rhomboides, Jordan, 1886, 27; Beaufort. Jenkins, 1887, 89; Beaufort.
Trachinotus falcatus, Jordan & Evermann, 1896, 941, pl. cxlvi, fig. 396.

DIAGNOSIS.—Body very broad, the depth more than .5 total length; head contained 3.75 times in length; snout shorter than eye; dorsal rays VI+1,19, dorsal spines thick and short; anal rays II+1,18; anterior rays of dorsal and anal reaching nearly to posterior margin of fins; ventrals short, .33 length of head. Color: bluish above, silvery below; fins bluish with lighter tips; dorsal black in young. (*falcatus*, scythe-shaped.)

The principal habitat of the round or ovate pompano is the West Indies, whence it extends to Massachusetts and Brazil. The young are sometimes abundant in southern Massachusetts, where they are transported by the Gulf Stream, but the adults are not common anywhere in the northern part of the species' range. Jenkins obtained one specimen at Beaufort in the summer of 1885; Jordan & Gilbert took a single young specimen there in 1878; and in 1902 a 1–inch example was taken at Town Marsh, Beaufort harbor, on August 23, and additional specimens were collected at the bight of Cape Lookout. The maximum length of the species is 15 inches.

186. TRACHINOTUS GOODEI Jordan & Evermann.

"Pompano"; Permit.

Trachinotus goodei Jordan & Evermann, 1896, 431; West Indies, north to west Florida.

DIAGNOSIS.—Depth contained 2.6 times in total length; head .33 length; dorsal rays VI+1,19; anal rays II+1,17; ventrals .5 length of head. Color: bluish silvery above, silvery white below; dorsal, anal, and caudal lobes black. (Named after Prof. George Brown Goode, former U. S. Commissioner of Fisheries.)

This large pompano is a West Indian form which ranges regularly to Florida and sometimes strays to points on the east coast north of Florida. It is occasionally taken by the Beaufort fishermen, the examples weighing 25 pounds or more; and many years ago one weighing 28 pounds was caught at Cape Lookout and forwarded to Professor Baird at Washington by Mr. George N. Ives. In the State Museum at Raleigh there is a fine example of this fish taken in New Hanover County in 1884 by Mr. H. H. Brimley, and in the same collection there are several others from the southern part of the state; all of these are about 2.5 feet long. In July, 1906, Dr. E. W. Gudger saw a 20-pound specimen at Hatteras. The local fishermen have no more for it except "pompano". As a food fish it is inferior to the smaller species.

187. TRACHINOTUS CAROLINUS (Linnæus.)
"Pompano"; "Sun-fish".

Gasterosteus carolinus Linnæus, Systema Naturæ, ed. xii, 490, 1766; Carolina.
Trachynotus carolinus, Yarrow, 1877, 209; Beaufort.   Jordan & Gilbert, 1879, 377; Beaufort.   Jordan, 1886, 27; Beaufort.
Trachinotus carolinus, Jenkins, 1887, 89; Beaufort.   Jordan & Evermann, 1896, 944, pl. cxlvii, fig. 398.   Linton, 1905, 366; Beaufort.

DIAGNOSIS.—Depth contained 2.33 to 2.4 times in total length; head .25 length; eye equal to snout, contained 4.5 times in length of head; dorsal rays vi+1,25; anal rays ii+1,23; ventrals about .5 length of pectorals and .4 length of head.   Color: bluish or greenish on back silvery on sides, rich golden yellow below; fins with bluish or yellowish shades.

Fig. 91.   POMPANO.   *Trachinotus carolinus.*

This well-known food fish occurs on our Atlantic coast between Massachusetts and Texas, and is common from Chesapeake Bay southward. Its present abundance on the North Carolina coast is not nearly so great as formerly. Yarrow, referring to the year 1871, stated that it was abundant at Beaufort in fall, and Jordan & Gilbert reported it as very abundant on the outer banks, the young going in great schools in the surf. Examples from .5 inch to 4 inches long are taken in Beaufort Harbor in summer, but spawning fish have not yet been reported from that region. The local names for the species are "pompano" and "sun-fish". The latter has been in use here since early colonial days, and was employed in 1709 by Lawson, who wrote:

Sun-fish are flat and rounder than a bream, and are reckon'd a fine-tasted fish, and not without reason. They are much the size of angel-fish.

The pompano ranks as one of the choicest of our salt-water food fishes, and by many people is regarded as the best. The catch in the state in 1902 was 19,590 pounds, for which the fishermen received $965, the bulk of the yield coming from Carteret, Beaufort, and Pamlico counties. In 1897 more than 53,000 pounds, valued at $1,728, were credited to the state, while in 1890 only 9,750 pounds, worth $780, were reported. With regard to the pompano in the Beaufort region Dr. Coker reported:

The scarcity of the pompano at Beaufort prevents its being counted an important fish. During the years 1902–3 the catch amounted to only a few hundred pounds. A few years ago a good many boxes were shipped, and in the days of the Cape Lookout fishery quantities were taken. The average weight is 2.5 to 4 pounds, the largest being about 5 pounds. Fish of 3 to 5 pounds weight bring prices which compare with those for mackerel, 20 to 25 cents, sometimes 40 cents a pound, while the smaller ones are of much less value, hardly selling so well as spots.

Family POMATOMIDÆ. The Blue-fishes.

This family, which is related to the Carangidæ, contains a single genus. Body elongate, compressed, covered with weakly ctenoid scales; head large; mouth large, oblique, lower jaw projecting, premaxillaries protractile, maxillary with a large supplemental bone; jaws with a single series of strong, wide-set teeth; upper jaw with an inner row of small depressed teeth; a patch of villiform teeth on vomer and on base of tongue, a band of such teeth on palatines; opercle terminating in a flat point, preopercle produced and serrated; gill-membranes free from isthmus and not connected; gill-rakers few and slender; branchiostegals 7; pseudobranchiæ large; lateral line present; cheeks and opercles scaly; air-bladder present; pyloric cœca numerous; dorsal fins 2, the anterior with weak, low spines, the posterior dorsal long, elevated anteriorly; anal similar to second dorsal, with 2 small free spines; dorsal and anal scaly; ventrals thoracic; pectorals small; caudal widely forked.

Genus POMATOMUS Lacépède. Blue-fishes.

The generic characters are included in the family description. There is only a single species, found in both old and new worlds. (*Pomatomus*, with cutting opercles.)

188. POMATOMUS SALTATRIX (Linnæus).

"Blue-fish"; "Tailor"; "Green-fish"; "Skip-jack"; Snapping Mackerel.

Perca saltatrix Linnæus, Systema Naturæ, ed. x, 293, 1758; Carolina.
Pomatomus saltatrix, Yarrow, 1877, 210; Beaufort. Jordan & Gilbert, 1879, 380; Beaufort. Jordan, 1886, 27; Beaufort. Jenkins, 1887, 89; Beaufort. Jordan & Evermann, 1896, 946, pl. cxlviii, fig. 400. Linton, 1905, 368; Beaufort.

DIAGNOSIS.—Body elongate but stout, depth .25 total length; head contained 3.3 times in length; cheeks long; eye small, .5 length of snout and .12 length of head; maxillary extending beyond eye; scales in lateral series about 95; top of head and a ridge above cheek naked; dorsal rays VIII + I,25; anal rays II + I,25; pectorals about .5 length of head. Color: green above, silvery below; the young brilliant silvery. (*saltatrix*, leaper.)

The blue-fish is widely distributed in the Atlantic Ocean, and is also known from the Mediterranean Sea and the Indian Ocean. It is, however, nowhere more abundant and valuable than in the United States, where it is one of the most highly esteemed and economically important of food fishes.

"Blue-fish", "green-fish", and "skip-jack" are among the names applied to the fish in North Carolina, and of late "tailor", a Chesapeake Bay name, has come into use at Beaufort. Lawson (1709) lists both "blue-fish" and "taylors" among the fishes of the state.

Fig. 92. BLUE-FISH. *Pomatomus saltatrix.*

The species attains a large size. Some schools consist of fish weighing 8 or 10 pounds or even more, while other schools may be composed of 1–pound, 3–pound, or 5–pound fish. The larger fish remain at sea, while the smaller ones enter bays, sounds, and rivers. Fish weighing more than 15 pounds are rare, and the maximum authentic weight is less than 30 pounds. In "Forest and Stream" for October 10, 1903, the writer published a note on what appears to have been the largest recorded blue-fish; it was taken at the Maddequet Life-saving Station, Nantucket, in the latter part of September, 1903, and was 3 feet 9 inches long and weighed 27 pounds. Professor Goode, in his "Natural History of Useful Aquatic Animals" (1884), gives the following data showing the relation between the length and weight of the blue-fish:

Length.		Weight.	
14 inches		1	pound
17 "		2	"
21 "		3	"
24 "		4	"
26 "		5	"
26–27 "		6	"
29 "		8	"

The blue-fish probably spawns offshore in summer, but ripe examples have rarely been observed and nothing definite is known as to the spawning time and habits. At Woods Hole, Massachusetts, well-developed spawn is found in the fish when they first arrive from the south about June 1, and young fish about 3 inches long appear in July. The young, 3 to 6 inches long, are abundant in Beaufort harbor in summer.

The blue-fish is one of the most voracious and destructive of fishes. Compared with its ravages, the work of man in killing fishes is utterly insignificant. The remarks of Professor Baird on this subject may appropriately be quoted:

There is no parallel in point of destructiveness to the blue-fish among the marine species on our coast, whatever may the case among some of the carnivorous fish of the South American waters. The blue-fish has been well likened to an animated chopping-machine, the business of which is to cut to pieces and otherwise destroy as many fish as possible in a given space of time. All the writers are unanimous in regard to the destructiveness of the blue-fish. Going in large schools, in pursuit of fish much inferior to themselves in size, they move along like a pack of hungry wolves, destroying everything before them. Their trail is marked by fragments of fish and by the stain of blood in the sea, as, where the fish is too large to be swallowed entire, the hinder portion will be bitten off and the anterior part allowed to float or sink. It is even maintained, with great earnestness, that such is the gluttony of the fish that when the stomach becomes full the contents are disgorged and then again filled. It is certain that it kills many more fish than it requires for its own support.

The youngest fish, equally with the older, perform this function of destruction, and although they occasionally devour crabs, worms, etc., the bulk of their sustenance throughout the greater part of the year is derived from other fish. Nothing is more common than to find a small blue-fish of six or eight inches in length under a school of minnows making continual dashes and captures among them. The stomachs of the blue-fish of all sizes, with rare exceptions, are found loaded with the other fish, sometimes to the number of thirty or forty, either entire or in fragments.

As already referred to, it must also be borne in mind that it is not merely the small fry that are thus devoured, and which it is expected will fall a prey to other animals, but that the food of the blue-fish consists very largely of individuals which have already passed a large percentage of the chances against their attaining maturity, many of them, indeed, having arrived at the period of spawning. To make the case more clear, let us realize for a moment the number of blue-fish that exist on our coast in the summer season. As far as I can ascertain by the statistics obtained at the fishing stations on the New England coast, as also from the records of the New York markets, kindly furnished by Middleton & Carman, of the Fulton Market, the capture of blue-fish, from New Jersey to Monomoy, during the season, amounts to not less than one million individuals, averaging five or six pounds each. Those, however, who have seen the blue-fish in his native waters, and realized the immense number there existing, will be quite willing to admit that probably not one fish in a thousand is ever taken by man. If, therefore, we have an actual capture of one million, we may allow one thousand millions as occuring in the extent of our coasts referred to, even neglecting the smaller ones, which perhaps should also be taken into the account.

An allowance of ten fish per day to each blue-fish is not excessive, according to the testimony elicited from the fishermen and substantiated by the stomachs of those examined; this gives ten thousand millions of fish destroyed per day. And as the period of the stay of the blue-fish on the New England coast is at least one hundred and twenty days, we have in round numbers twelve hundred million millions of fish devoured in the course of a season. Again, if each blue-fish, averaging five pounds, devours or destroys even half its own weight of other fish per day (and I am not sure that the estimate of some witnesses of twice this weight is not more nearly correct), we will have, during the same period, a daily loss of twenty-five hundred million pounds, equal to three hundred thousand millions for the season.

This estimate applies to three or four year old fish, of at least three to five pounds in weight. We must, however, allow for those of smaller size, and a hundred-fold or more in number, all engaged simultaneously in the butchery referred to.

We can scarcely conceive of a number so vast; and however much we may diminish, within reason, the estimate of the number of blue-fish and the average of their captures, there still remains an appalling aggregate of destruction. While the smallest blue-fish feed upon the diminutive fry, those of which we have taken account capture fish of large size, many of them, if not capable of reproduction, being within at least one or two years of that period.

North Carolina has long been famous for its blue-fish, which support special market fisheries and also afford excellent sport to many hundreds of persons annually. The species is subject to great variations in abundance quite independent of human influence. Yarrow has left the following note on the fish during 1871:

This species appears in Beaufort Inlet in early spring, but is taken only in nets. In June it commences to take the hook, but the months of August and September are the best for trolling. At this time enormous numbers may be found in schools, swimming alongside shoals in tolerably rough water. On the 23rd day of September, 1871, four persons, in four hours, took by trolling 660 blue-fish. During the latter part of this month, in the same year, enormous schools were noticed in and near the ship channel, feeding upon the red-billed gar, so-called (*Hyporhamphus roberti*). The stomachs of individuals taken were literally crammed with these fishes. The very large specimens of blue-fish occasionally met with in the markets in January never enter Beaufort Inlet; they are taken on the beach from Cape Lookout northward, the run lasting sometimes two months, occasionally only a week or ten days. During the last week of December, 1871, large schools of young blue-fish were noticed in Beaufort Inlet swimming from the southward, apparently making for the sea; their size about four inches.

Mr. R. Edward Earll (in Goode, 1884) gave the following account of the blue-fish in North Carolina in the years preceding 1880:

The large fish are most abundant between Cape Hatteras and New Inlet. Small fish frequently enter the sounds during the summer months, and have long been taken by the residents. The larger ones seldom enter the inlets, but remain near the outer shore, where they feed upon the menhaden, shad, and alewives, during the season of their migrations to and from the larger sounds in fall and spring..

Apparently the first that was known of the presence of large blue-fish in this region was in 1842, when a quantity was taken in a haul-seine near New Inlet. Gill-nets were first used for the capture of the species in this locality in 1847, though they were not generally adopted till several years latter. The first vessel visited the region in 1866, and from that date to 1879 six to twelve sail came regularly to the locality. The fishery reached its height between 1870 and 1876, when in addition to the vessels fully one hundred crews of five men each fished along the shores. The catch varies greatly from time to time as the fish are constantly on the move and often go beyond reach of the seines and gill-nets. Some seasons each boat's crew has averaged four or five thousand fish weighing ten to fifteen pounds each, and again they have taken almost nothing. Frequently the bulk of the catch of an entire season is taken in three or four days.

Since the winter of 1877 and 1878 the fish are said to have been much less abundant and of smaller size. In the winter of 1879 and 1880 about seventy-five crews were engaged in the fishery from the first of November till Christmas. The total catch did not exceed fifty thousand fish averaging six pounds each. The small number taken is partially accounted for by the fact that many of the fish were so small as to readily pass through the meshes without being caught.

During my visit in May, 1880, large schools of blue-fish were reported along the shore, and a considerable number of shad and other species were found upon the beach where they had been driven by their pursuers. A good many blue-fish were also stranded while in pursuit of their prey. It seemed that there is no reason to believe that the fish have permanently left the coast, or that they are even so scarce as is at present claimed, for the men have fished with little regularity, and have gone a short distance from the shore, while the bulk of the blue-fish may have been farther out.

Lawson's note on the blue-fish in North Carolina waters in the first decade of the eighteenth century has some historic interest:

The blue-fish is one of our best fishes and always very fat. They are as long as a salmon, and indeed, I think, full as good meat. These fish come (in the fall of the year) generally after there has been one black frost, when there appear great shoals of them. The Hatteras Indians, and others, run into the sands of the sea and strike them, though some of these fish have caused sickness and violent burnings after eating them, which is found to proceed from the gall that is broken in some of them, and is hurtful. Sometimes many cartloads of these are thrown and left dry on the seaside, which comes by their eager pursuit of the small fish, in which they run themselves ashore, and the tide leaving them, they cannot recover the water again. They are called blue-fish, because they are of that colour, and have a forked tail, and are shaped like a dolphin.

Among the salt-water fishes of North Carolina, the blue-fish is exceeded in value by only the mullets and the squeteagues. The general trend of the fishery is upward, but the catch shows seasonal fluctuations here as elsewhere. Following are the official statistics for 5 years:

YEARS.	POUNDS.	VALUE.
1880	600,000	$12,000
1889	895,110	20,877
1890	1,345,115	33,603
1897	1,696,175	46,752
1902	977,140	34,268

Gill nets take the largest quantities, followed by seines, pound nets, and lines, the last being used principally in Dare County. The fishermen of Carteret County conduct the most extensive fishery, closely followed by those of Dare County; noteworthy fishing is also done in Beaufort, Craven, Hyde, New Hanover, Onslow, and Pamlico counties. In recent years about 8 or 10 per cent of the product has been salted.

Family RACHYCENTRIDÆ. The Crab-eaters.

This family includes a single genus related to the scombroid fishes. The body is elongate, cylindrical, and covered with small, smooth scales; head broad, somewhat depressed; mouth horizontal, wide, maxillary reaching front of eye; short, sharp teeth in villiform bands on jaws, tongue, vomer, and palatines; premaxillaries not protractile; preopercular margin entire; gill-rakers short and stout; air-bladder absent; dorsal fin consisting of 8 short, stout spines, not connected by membrane and each depressible in a groove, and a long, low soft portion; anal fin similar to soft dorsal, with 2 spines; caudal strongly forked.

Genus RACHYCENTRON Kaup. Crab-eaters.

The peculiarities of this genus are indicated in the family definition. One species, of wide distribution, superficially resembling the common remora. (*Rachycentron,* spiny back.)

189. RACHYCENTRON CANADUS (Linnæus).

"Cabio"; Crab-eater; Sergeant-fish.

Gasterosteus canadus Linnæus, Systema Naturæ, ed. xii, 491, 1766; Carolina.
Elacate canada, Yarrow, 1877, 212; Beaufort. Jenkins, 1885, 11; Beaufort. Jordan, 1886, 27; Beaufort. Jenkins, 1887, 88; Beaufort.
Rachycentron canadus, Jordan & Evermann, 1896, 948, pl. cxlviii, fig. 401. Linton, 1905, 370; Beaufort,

DIAGNOSIS.—Depth contained 5.6 times in length; head contained 4.25 times in length; lateral line wavy, nearly parallel with back, descending posteriorly; dorsal rays VIII+I,26; anal rays II,25; caudal deeply concave, upper lobe longer; pectorals broad and pointed. Color: dark brown on back, silvery white below; a dark lateral band, about width of eye, extending from snout to tail; below this a narrower dark band. (*canadus,* Canada, where the species does not occur.)

Fig. 93. CRAB-EATER. *Rachycentron canadus.*

In summer this species is found on the middle and south Atlantic coast of the United States, being especially common in Chesapeake Bay, where it is a food fish of some importance under the name "bonito"; in winter it withdraws to the West Indies. It also occurs in the East Indies. Dr. Yarrow inserted this species in his Beaufort list but does not mention having seen an example; there is, however, a specimen in the National Museum obtained at Beaufort by Dr. Yarrow, and there is a second specimen forwarded from Fort Macon by Dr. Weyrich in 1872. Drs. Jordan and Gilbert failed to find it and omitted it altogether from their list. Dr. Jenkins, however, found it in 1885. Dr. Coker reports that when the large seines were used in the Cape Lookout fisheries, crab-eaters were often taken, some of them weighing 40 to 50 pounds; they were shipped chiefly to the state markets, where they brought a fair price, sometimes being sold as cero. The fish was found occasionally in the Beaufort market in 1901, and a number of specimens were collected for the laboratory in the summer of 1903, one on an oyster reef in the harbor, another, 10 inches long, on Bird Shoal. The regular name for the fish at Beaufort is "cabio", allied to the Bermuda name "cubby-yew"; the book name "cobia" is possibly a misprint.

The fish is known to spawn in Chesapeake Bay in summer, and its eggs have been artificially hatched. It feeds largely on crabs, but also eats shrimp and small fish of all kinds, and is very voracious. It attains a length of 5 feet or more and a weight of upwards of 60 pounds.

Family STROMATEIDÆ. The Butter-fishes.

Small marine fishes, some of them food fishes of importance. Body compressed, depth moderate or extreme; head more or less blunt; mouth small or moderate, with weak teeth in jaws; tongue, vomer, and palatines rarely or never toothed; esophagus with lateral sacs in which are hooked teeth; nostrils double; opercles entire or serrate; gill-membranes free from isthmus; gill-rakers long or moderate; **pseu**dobranchiæ present; branchiostegals 5 to 7; lateral line present and continuous; body and more or less of head covered with small, thin cycloid scales, which extend on vertical fins; air-bladder usually lacking; pyloric cœca numerous; dorsal fin single, preceded by a few weak or obsolete spines, the soft rays numerous; anal similar to dorsal, usually with 3 spines; ventrals thoracic, present in young but sometimes absent in adults. Following the revision of this family by Regan (Annals and Magazine of Natural History, vol. x, 7th series, 1902), 4 genera are represented in the local fauna. In addition thereto at least one other, Palinurichthys, may be provisionally inserted; the rudder-fish, *Palinurichthys perciformis* (Mitchill), is often observed on the Middle Atlantic coast under floating boxes, logs, etc., or about rudders of vessels, and doubtless will be found to occur in North Carolina waters.

Key to the North Carolina genera of Stromateidæ.

i. Ventral fins present in adult as well as in young; esophagus with longitudinal folds; dorsal spines 7 to 11.
    a. Lateral line concurrent with outline of back; dorsal spines high, 10 or 11 in number.
        b. Teeth on vomer and palatines..NOMEUS
        bb. No teeth on palatines..PSENES
    aa. Lateral line curved anteriorly, straight posteriorly; dorsal spines low, 7 to 9 in number.
                                    PALINURICHTHYS.
ii. Ventral fins absent in adult; esophagus without longitudinal folds; dorsal spines 3.
        c. Dorsal and anal fins very high and falcate in front; body almost as deep as long; no series of pores along back above lateral line........................PEPRILUS.
        cc. Dorsal and anal fins moderately elevated in front and not falcate: body not half as deep as long; a series of conspicuous pores along back above lateral line.
                                              PORONOTUS.

Genus NOMEUS Cuvier. Portuguese-man-of-war-fishes.

In this genus the body is moderately compressed; head rather flat above; teeth on jaws, vomer, and palatines, in a single series on jaws; pseudobranchiæ large; air-bladder present; about 10 dorsal spines and 3 anal spines; ventrals long and attached to abdomen by a membrane; caudal strongly forked. One species. (*Nomeus*, pastor.)

190. NOMEUS GRONOVII (Gmelin).

Portuguese-man-of-war-fish.

Gobius gronovii Gmelin, Systema Naturæ, xiii, 1205, 1788; tropical America.
Nomeus gronovii, Jenkins, 1885, 11; Beaufort. Jordan, 1886, 27; Beaufort. Jenkins, 1887, 89; Beaufort. Jordan & Evermann, 1896, 949. Wilson, 1900, 355; Beaufort.

DIAGNOSIS.—Depth contained 3.8 times in total length, the dorsal and ventral outlines equally curved; head contained 3.4 times in length; maxillary extending under anterior part of eye; eye contained 3.2 times in head, snout 4 times; scales in lateral series 65; dorsal rays IX or X+1,25 to 27; anal rays III,25 to 27; ventrals extending to front of anal, a little shorter than head; pectorals extending beyond front of anal.   Color: light brown above, silvery below, sides with large brown spots; caudal with brown spots; anal with 3 brown spots; ventrals black with silvery margin; pectorals brown above, white below.   (Named for the celebrated Dutch ichthyologist, Gronovius, contemporary with Linnæus.)

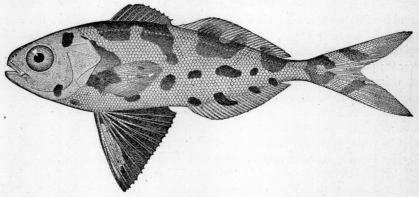

Fig. 94.   PORTUGUESE-MAN-OF-WAR-FISH.   *Nomeus gronovii.*

This native of tropical waters (West and East Indian) is abundant in the Sargasso Sea and not uncommon in southern Florida; at more northern points on the United States coast it occurs as a straggler.   Dr. Jenkins took an example half an inch long in a tow net at Beaufort in the summer of 1885, and states that in fall the fish is common, "then found only in a medusa, the medusa never being found without a Nomeus".   Prof. Wilson also records the fish as occurring at Beaufort in the bell-cavity of the medusa Stomolophus.   The present author has noted the occurrence at Woods Hole, Mass., of as many as 12 of these fish under a single specimen of the medusa known as the "Portuguese man-of-war" (Physalia).   The usual length attained is 5 or 6 inches.

Genus PSENES Cuvier and Valenciennes.

Body rather deep and compressed; mouth small, overhung by the swollen snout; jaw teeth in a single series; no teeth on tongue and vomer in young; scales of small or moderate size, covering body; first dorsal with 10 or 11 spines; second dorsal and anal long and similar; anal spines 3, not separate from soft part.   There are 5 or 6 American species, some found in very deep water and some at the surface; 1 known from North Carolina coast.   (*Psenes*, osprey or fish-hawk, a name of no obvious application.)

191. PSENES REGULUS Poey.

Psenes regulus Poey, Synopsis piscium cubensium, 375, 1868; Cuba.   Jordan & Evermann, 1896, 951.

DIAGNOSIS.—Body oval, much compressed, depth .4 length; head about equal to depth; eye large, more than .3 head; teeth on jaws in one row, short, slender; dorsal rays x,16 to x,18;

anal rays III,15; caudal rounded; ventrals much shorter than pectorals. Color: silvery white, with large irregular dark spots and blotches. (*regulus*, little king.)

A 1-inch specimen of this species, heretofore known only from the coast of Cuba, was obtained by the steamer Fish-Hawk off Beaufort in the summer of 1902; it was doubtless a mere straggler, wafted there by the Gulf Stream. The maximum length is about 3.5 inches.

Genus PEPRILUS Cuvier. Harvest-fishes.

Body much compressed, orbicular; head short, anterior profile obtuse; caudal peduncle slender, without keel; mouth terminal, oblique, jaws about equal; lateral line arched, continuous; dorsal fin long, with anterior rays much elongated, anal fin similar; caudal fin large and strongly forked; pectorals long and narrow; ventrals absent, represented by a single sharp spine attached to pubic bone. One species on the Atlantic coast of the United States.

192. PEPRILUS ALEPIDOTUS (Linnæus).
"Star"; "Star-fish"; Harvest-fish.

?Stromateus paru Linnæus, Systema Naturæ, ed. x, 248, 1758; Jamaica.
Chætodon alepidotus Linnæus, Systema Naturæ, ed. xii, 460, 1766; Charleston.
Rhombus paru, Jordan & Evermann, 1896, 965; 1898, 2849; pl. cl, fig. 404.
Stromateus alepidotus, Kendall & Smith, 1894, 21; Hatteras Inlet

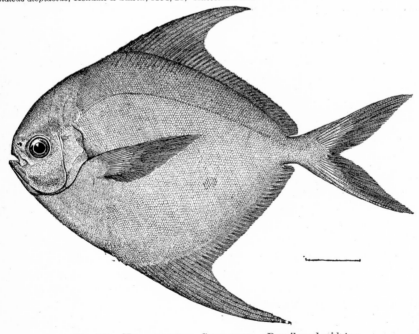

Fig. 95. HARVEST-FISH; STAR-FISH. *Peprilus alepidotus.*

DIAGNOSIS.—Depth .66 to .75 length; caudal peduncle very short and narrow, its depth equal to distance from pupil to end of snout; head small, .25 to .28 length; mouth very small;

maxillary reaching to front of orbit; eye longer than snout, .33 length of head; scales thin, deciduous, about 90 in lateral series; dorsal fin falcate, the rays III,45; anal fin similar to dorsal, the rays III,43; caudal fin long, very deeply forked; pectorals 1.4 to 1.6 times length of head. Color: pale green above, golden yellow or silvery below. (*alepidotus*, unscaled.)

The harvest-fish ranges from Massachusetts to South America, and is not uncommon in Chesapeake Bay and southward. Although it has not often been recorded from North Carolina, it is not rare there. About Roanoke Island, in Croatan and Pamlico sounds, it is well known under the name of "star" or "star-fish". It is often taken in pound nets in Pamlico Sound, and is there considered an excellent food-fish. On December 13, 1890, Dr. Kendall found several live specimens stranded on the beach at Hatteras Inlet. During July and August, 1905, more than 500 specimens were reported as being caught in Beaufort Harbor in a pound net operated for the laboratory. Eight inches appears to be about the maximum length attained. The young are often found beneath the "Portuguese man-of-war" and other large medusæ.

Genus PORONOTUS Gill. Butter-fishes.

Similar to *Peprilus*, but with depth of body much less, the dorsal and anal fins less elongated, and a series of large, wide-set pores along the back; lateral line arched and placed high on the side; pectorals long; ventrals wanting. One species. (*Poronotus*, pore-back.)

193. PORONOTUS TRIACANTHUS (Peck).

"Butter-fish"; "Butter-perch"; Dollar-fish; Harvest-fish.

Stromateus triacanthus Peck, Memoirs American Academy, ii, part 2, 48, pl. 2, fig. 2, 1800; Piscataqua River, New Hampshire. Jordan, 1886, 27; Beaufort.
Poronotus triacanthus, Yarrow, 1877, 209; Beaufort. Jordan & Gilbert, 1879, 377; Beaufort (after Yarrow). Jordan & Evermann, 1898, 2849, pl. cl, fig. 405.
Rhombus triacanthus, Jordan & Evermann, 1896, 967.

DIAGNOSIS.—Body oval, dorsal and ventral curves similar, depth contained 2.3 times in total length; head .25 length; maxillary not extending as far as anterior margin of eye; lower jaw somewhat the longer; snout very short and obtuse; eye .25 length of head; gill-rakers .6 diameter of eye; scales very small; a row of conspicuous pores on back near base of dorsal fin; dorsal rays III,45; anal rays III,38; pectorals longer than head; caudal deeply forked. Color: bluish silvery, with numerous irregular, discreet, dark spots (not evident after death). (*triacanthus*, three-spined.)

Ranges along the entire east coast of the United States, and is abundant from Massachusetts to North Carolina from spring to fall. Yarrow reported the species as not abundant at Beaufort; Jordan & Gilbert and Jenkins did not find it there. It occurs, however, in the inside waters near Beaufort and Morehead from April to fall, being most common during the latter season. According to Dr. Coker it is caught in large numbers in some parts of Pamlico Sound (as in the vicinity of Portsmouth), and is also taken about Cape Lookout. It is common about Roanoke Island from May through the summer. In June, 1899, one was found in the bell-cavity of a jelly-fish (Stomolophus) at Beaufort. On

December 13, 1890, Dr. W. C. Kendall found one stranded on the beach of Hatteras Inlet.

The butter-fish goes in schools, sometimes of large size, and when swimming leisurely has a peculiar undulatory movement. Its maximum size is under a foot. In North Carolina, as elsewhere, it is considered an excellent pan fish. The local names are "butter-fish" and "butter-perch". The species is not always distinguished from *Peprilus alepidotus* by the fishermen.

Fig. 96. BUTTER-FISH. *Poronotus triacanthus.*

Commercially this fish is worth several thousand dollars annually to the North Carolina fishermen. In 1897 a catch of 94,750 pounds sold for $1,758, and in 1902 a catch of 83,218 pounds brought $1,357.

Family CORYPHÆNIDÆ. The Dolphins.

A family of large oceanic fishes found chiefly in warm seas, noted for their beautiful, evanescent hues. The body is elongated and much compressed, tapering gradually from head to tail; the forehead is elevated owing to a crest on the skull; the mouth is large, with cardiform teeth on jaws, vomer, and palatal bones, and with villiform teeth in a patch on tongue; there is a single many-rayed dorsal fin beginning over eye and extending nearly to caudal fin; the anal fin is similar to dorsal and about half its length; the pectoral fins short and small; the ventrals rather large; the caudal long and very deeply forked; a lateral line is present, and the body is covered with small cycloid scales; the gill-membranes are free from isthmus; the branchiostegals number 7; the pseudobranchiæ are absent; the pyloric cœca are numerous; the air-bladder is lacking. One genus.

Genus CORYPHÆNA Linnæus. Dolphins.

This genus, the characters of which have been given in the family definition, contains probably only 2 species. Both are now recorded from North Carolina, although only one has heretofore been reported from the coasts of the United States. The two are very much alike:

i. Frontal profile nearly vertical in adult; maxillary reaching to or beyond middle of eye; dorsal rays 55 to 65; anal rays 26 to 30; size very large.....................*hippurus.*
ii. Frontal profile convex in adult; maxillary reaching front of pupil; dorsal rays 51 to 55; anal rays 24 to 26; size small...*equisetis.*

(*Coryphæna*, a name given by Aristotle to the following species.)

194. CORYPHÆNA HIPPURUS Linnæus.

Dolphin.

Coryphæna hippurus Linnæus, Systema Naturæ, ed. x, 261, 1758; open seas.   Jordan & Evermann, 1896, 952, pl. cxlix, fig.402.   Linton, 1905, 372; Beaufort.

DIAGNOSIS.—Depth .2 length; length of head contained 4.6 to 5.75 times in length; profile varying with age and sex, that of adult male nearly vertical; maxillary extending to or beyond middle of orbit; dorsal rays 55 to 65; anal rays 26 to 30.   Color: brilliant, changing rapidly after death; general hue light green, darker above; white or golden below; back and head with a series of about 15 bright blue spots which extend on snout and form bands; dorsal fin purplish blue, with paler oblique lines; caudal yellow; other fins tinged with blue; small black spots on lower parts.   (*hippurus*, horse-tail.)

Fig. 97.   DOLPHIN.   *Coryphæna hippurus.*

The dolphin is known from both sides of the Atlantic Ocean and from the western Pacific.   On our east coast it ranges as far as Cape Cod, where a number of small specimens have been collected by the writer, and is not rare from South Carolina to Texas.   It reaches a length of 6 feet, and is a good food fish, although reputed to be poisonous at times.   It is a powerful swimmer, and preys on other fishes which live near the surface.

This species has not heretofore been recorded from North Carolina.   A specimen was caught by a Beaufort fisherman on August 1, 1902, and sent to the laboratory by Mr. Charles S. Wallace, of Morehead City.   It measured 28.5 inches over all, had 56 dorsal and 27 anal rays, and contained fish, among which silversides and a small lizard-fish were recognizable.   In the summer of 1903 at least one dolphin was taken near Beaufort, but did not reach the laboratory.   Two examples about 15 inches long from Carteret County are in the State Museum at Raleigh.

195. CORYPHÆNA EQUISETIS Linnæus.

Small Dolphin.

Coryphæna equisetis Linnæus, Systema Naturæ, ed. x, 261, 1758; high seas. Jordan & Evermann, 1896, 952. Linton, 1905, 375; off Cape Lookout.

DIAGNOSIS.—Depth contained 3.4 to 4 times in length; head contained 4.2 to 4.6 times in length; profile of head oblique; maxillary extending to front of pupil; dorsal rays 51 to 55; anal rays 24 to 26. Color: brilliant and evanescent; brownish green on back, white or golden below, back and sides with blue spots; dorsal blue, with pale stripes; caudal yellow; other fins blue tinged. (*equisetis*, horse-tail.)

This small species inhabits the open Atlantic, and apparently has not previously been recorded from the coast of the United States. On August 21, 1902, 3 specimens 20 to 24 inches long were caught by the steamer Fish-Hawk about 28 miles off Cape Lookout. They agree very well with the published descriptions as regards frontal profile, length of maxillary, dorsal and anal rays, etc.

Family CENTRARCHIDÆ. The Fresh-water Basses and Sun-fishes.

This strictly American family includes some of the best known and most useful of our fresh-water fishes, and is represented by numerous species east of the Rocky Mountains, only a single species being found beyond the mountains. Nearly all the species have nests and guard their eggs and young with great care. Anatomical characters by which the family is distinguished are a compressed and rather short body; a large or small terminal mouth well supplied with villiform teeth in bands on jaws, vomer, palatines, etc.; protractile premaxillaries; maxillaries with a supplemental bone, obsolete in small-mouthed species; opercular margin with 2 points or with a single long flap; preopercle entire or slightly serrate; pseudobranchiæ small; branchiostegals usually 6; gill-membranes not connected (except in Elassoma) and not attached to isthmus; gill-rakers mostly short, with teeth; body, opercles, and cheeks scaly; lateral line present and usually perfect; two dorsal fins connected, the anterior with 6 to 13 spinous rays (4 or 5 in Elassoma); anal fin large, with 3 to 8 spines and numerous soft rays; intestine short; pyloric cœca 5 to 10 (absent in Elassoma). Of the 12 or 13 genera recognized, the following 10 are represented in North Carolina by 17 species:

Key to North Carolina genera of basses and sun-fishes.

i. Dorsal spines 4 or 5; pyloric cœca absent ....ELASSOMA.
ii. Dorsal spines 6 to 13; pyloric cœca present.
  a. Dorsal fin about same size as anal.
    b. Dorsal spines 6 to 8; anal spines 6; body and fins profusely and irregularly spotted with black...POMOXIS.
    bb. Dorsal spines 11 or 12; anal spines 7 or 8 ....CENTRARCHUS.
  aa. Dorsal fin much larger than anal.
    c. Body comparatively short and deep, depth usually exceeding .4 length; no deep notch between two dorsal fins.
      d. Teeth on tongue and pterygoids; mouth moderate, the maxillary extending beyond middle of eye.
        e. Scales cycloid; caudal fin rounded........................ACANTHARCHUS.
        ee. Scales ctenoid; caudal fin concave.

f. Anal spines 5 to 8; opercular margin with 2 flat points; preopercle serrate
    at angle ....AMBLOPLITES.
ff. Anal spines 3; opercular margin with a long flap; preopercle entire.
                                         CHÆNOBRYTTUS.
dd. No teeth on tongue and pterygoids; mouth small, the maxillary barely extending
    to pupil or not reaching anterior margin of eye.
    g. Caudal fin rounded; opercle with no flap; fishes small (3 inches or less).
      h. Dorsal spines 9; maxillary extending to anterior edge of pupil. .ENNEACANTHUS.
      hh. Dorsal spines 10; maxillary not reaching anterior edge of eye.MESOGONISTIUS.
    gg. Caudal fin concave; opercle prolonged into a flap, always black; supplementary
         maxillary bone rudimentary or lacking..............................LEPOMIS.
cc. Body elongate, depth about .33 length; dorsal fins separated by a deep notch; fishes
    of comparatively large size ....MICROPTERUS.

Genus ELASSOMA Jordan. Pygmy Sun-fishes.

This genus is by some authorities made the type of a separate family,
Elassomidæ. It is characterized by a reduced number of dorsal spines (4 or 5);
a rather long, compressed body covered with large scales; conical teeth in a few
series in jaws, weak teeth on vomer; gill-membranes connected, not joined to
isthmus; knob-like gill-rakers; obsolete lateral line; small fins; no pyloric cœca.
The genus contains 2 species, which are among the smallest of known fishes,
inhabiting swampy districts in the Southern and South Central States. They
are dwarfed sun-fishes, bearing the same relation to the other sun-fishes that the
darters do to the perches. The 2 species are quite similar, but typical examples
may be thus distinguished:

    a. Scales in longitudinal series 38 to 45; a round black spot as large as eye on side below
      anterior part of dorsal fin; numerous dark narrow vertical bars on sides .... *zonatum.*
    aa. Scales in longitudinal series 27 to 30; no round black spot on side; no dark cross-bars.
                                                   evergladei.

(*Elassoma*, diminution.)

196. ELASSOMA ZONATUM Jordan.
Pygmy Sun-fish.

Elassoma zonata Jordan. Bulletin U. S. National Museum, x, 50, 1877; Little Red River, Judsonia, White
    County, Arkansas.
Elassoma zonatum, Jordan & Evermann, 1896, 982; 1898, 2851 (Waccamaw River at Whiteville, N. C.).

DIAGNOSIS.—Depth contained 3.5 times in total length; head .33 length; mouth small,
oblique, the maxillary barely reaching pupil; eye large, .33 length of head; scales in lateral
series about 40, in transverse series 19; dorsal rays IV,9, V,9, or V,10: anal rays III,5; caudal
rounded. Color: olive green; 10 or 12 dark vertical bands on sides; a large rounded black spot
on side under anterior part of dorsal; a black bar at base of caudal; fins obscurely barred.
Length, 1.5 inches. (*zonatum*, banded.)

There is only a single North Carolina record for this species, Prof. Harrison
Garman having collected a specimen at Whiteville, Columbia County, on the
Waccamaw River. It is probable that the species will be found to be not uncom-
mon in that section. It ranges southward from Illinois in sluggish waters.

197. ELASSOMA EVERGLADEI Jordan.
Pygmy Sun-fish.

Elassoma evergladei Jordan, Proceedings U. S. National Museum, 1884, 323; Indian River and Lake Jessup,
    Florida. Jordan & Evermann, 1896, 982, pl. cliii, fig. 414.

DIAGNOSIS.—Body less compressed than in *zonatum*, the depth contained 3.5 times in total length; head 3.1 times in length; mouth very small, upper jaw reaching only to anterior margin of eye, lower jaw slightly projecting; eye large, its diameter greater than snout and .33 head; scales in lengthwise series about 30, in transverse series 13; cheeks and opercles scaly; dorsal rays III,8 to IV,9; anal rays iii,5 to iii,7; caudal rounded. Color: variable, usually dark brown, with darker spots; some of the body scales blue; vertical bands on sides either faint or absent; no black spot on shoulder; dorsal and anal fins with several rows of dark (red) spots; caudal usually with vertical rows of dark spots and 2 red spots at base. Length, to 1.3 inches. (*evergladei*, of the Everglades.)

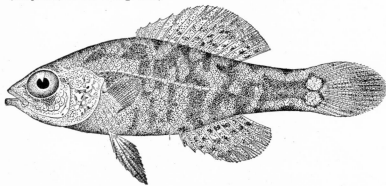

Fig. 98. PYGMY SUN-FISH. *Elassoma evergladei.*

Heretofore known from swampy regions in Georgia and Florida. In January, 1906, the U. S. Bureau of Fisheries received from Mr. W. P. Seal a specimen taken by him in a large cypress swamp near Wilmington, N. C. He reports the species as not rare in that locality and found in the same situations as the mud minnow (Umbra) and various cyprinodonts (Gambusia, Heterandria, etc.).

Genus POMOXIS Rafinesque. Crappies.

A strongly marked genus of rather large sun-fishes, distinguished by a compressed and deep body; large, oblique mouth; projecting, upturned snout; broad maxillary with large supplemental bone; projecting lower faw; long and slender gill-rakers; finely toothed preopercle and preorbital; large scales, with complete lateral line; well developed dorsal and anal fins, the anal larger; ventral fins close together, with a strong spine. Two species, very similar but quite distinct; only one definitely detected in North Carolina, although the other may be looked for and will eventually be introduced. The two are distinguished as follows:

i. Dorsal spines 7 or 8; depth .5 length; 6 rows of scales on cheeks; dark markings not forming vertical bars on sides. ....*sparoides.*
ii. Dorsal spines 5 or 6; depth .42 to .45 length; 4 or 5 rows of scales on cheeks; dark markings forming vertical bars on sides...*annularis.**

(*Pomoxis*, sharp opercle.)

**Pomoxis annularis* Rafinesque. Crappie. In 1865, under the name *Pomoxis protacanthus*, Dr. Gill described a fish supposed to be from Tarboro, on Tar River, N. C. This species is now referred to the synonymy of *P. annularis*, the crappie, as an examination of the types in the National Museum indicates that it is undoubtedly that species. As there is considerable doubt, however, as to the locality in which the specimen was really collected, and as *P. annularis* is not known from North Carolina (although it may be looked for in the French Broad), it is thought best to disregard these specimens.

198. POMOXIS SPAROIDES (Lacépède).

"Speckled Perch"; "White Perch"; Calico Bass; Strawberry Bass; Crappy.

Labrus sparoides Lacépède, Histoire Naturelle des Poissons, iii, 517, 1802; South Carolina.
Pomoxys hexacanthus, Cope, 1870b, 451; Neuse River.
Pomoxis sparoides, Jordan, 1889b, 126, 130; Tar and Neuse rivers. Smith, 1893a, 192, 196, 199; Pasquotank
    River, Edenton Bay, Roanoke River. Evermann & Cox, 1896, 305; Neuse River. Jordan & Ever-
    mann, 1896, 987, pl. cliv, fig. 416.

DIAGNOSIS.—Body much compressed, back elevated, the depth .5 length; head .33
length; snout somewhat upturned; mouth large, maxillary extending beyond pupil; eye large,
equal to snout, .25 length of head; scales in lateral series 40 to 45, in transverse series 22;
dorsal and anal fins high; dorsal rays VII,15 or VIII,15; anal rays VI,17 or VI,18. Color: body
light silvery green, sometimes with a delicate pink or purple suffusion; back and sides irregularly mottled with dark green or black; dorsal, anal, and caudal fins marked by pale and dark
green or black spots in more or less regular rows. (*sparoides*, like *Sparus*, the sea bream.)

Fig. 99. CALICO BASS; STRAWBERRY BASS; CRAPPY. *Pomoxis sparoides.*

The calico bass is found coastwise from New Jersey to Texas, and throughout the Great Lakes and upper Mississippi basin. Its range has been greatly
extended by transplanting, the Potomac and various other streams having been
successfully stocked. This fish is common in Albemarle Sound and tributaries,
in Tar and Neuse rivers, and in other suitable waters of the coastal plain and
Piedmont regions. The name "speckled perch" is in use on Albemarle and
Pamlico sounds, and the name "white perch" is applied near Raleigh. The
fish mentioned by Lawson in 1709 as the "flat, mottled perch, or Irishman", is
doubtless this species.

This bass ranks high as a game fish, and in fall affords sport to the people of
Edenton and other points, minnows and grubs being used for bait. The flesh is
firm, white, and of fine flavor when the fish are taken from cool, pure waters.
The maximum weight is 3 pounds, but the average is not over 1 pound.

The calico bass spawns in March in Cape Fear River, several weeks later in the Albemarle section. The mated fish prepare their nest, and zealously guard their eggs and brood in the same manner as the black basses, remaining with the fry until the latter begin to take food; at times they have been observed to show great pugnacity in defence of their progeny.

Genus CENTRARCHUS Cuvier & Valenciennes.   Fliers; Round Sun-fishes.

This genus embraces a single small species which is one of the most beautiful of the sun-fishes. Among the generic characters are the short, deep, and compressed body; projecting lower jaw; well developed supplemental bone on maxillary; teeth on jaws, tongue, vomer, palatines, and pterygoids; long, slender, numerous gill-rakers; large fins; large ctenoid scales; and complete lateral line. (*Centrarchus*, spiny vent.)

199. CENTRARCHUS MACROPTERUS (Lacépède).

"Flier"; "Mill-pond Perch"; "Sun-fish".

Labrus macropterus Lacépède, Histoire Naturelle des Poissons, iii, 447, 1802; Charleston, S. C.
Centrarchus irideus, Cope, 1870b, 451; Neuse River.
Centrarchus macropterus, Jordan, 1889b, 130; Neuse River at Millburnie, Little River at Goldsboro. Smith, 1893a, 199; Roanoke River at Plymouth. Jordan & Evermann, 1896, 988, pl. clv, fig. 417.

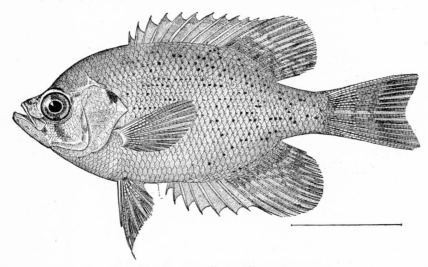

Fig. 100. FLIER. *Centrarchus macropterus.*

DIAGNOSIS.—Body comparatively short, profile from dorsal fin to eye very steep, depth .5 length; head contained 2.75 to 3 times in length; mouth oblique, rather small, the maxillary extending to pupil; eye contained 3.5 to 4 times in head; scales in lateral series 38 to 45, in transverse series 21, 4 to 6 rows on cheeks; dorsal rays xi to xiii,12 to 14; anal rays vii,15 or viii,15. Color: bright yellowish green or pea green, with longitudinal rows of small dark-brown spots; a dark spot below eye; soft dorsal and anal obscurely mottled or with narrow blackish bars. (*macropterus*, large-finned.)

This exceedingly beautiful sun-fish inhabits lowland waters from Virginia to Louisiana, and the Mississippi basin as far north as Illinois. It is common in Roanoke and Neuse rivers, is also known from Tar River, and doubtless occurs in all other coastal streams. Its small size, 6 or 7 inches, renders it unimportant as a food fish, but it is used locally, at Plymouth and other places, being caught in slat-weirs, seines, etc. It shares with other species the name of "sun-fish" but is also known locally as "flier" and "mill-pond perch", designations which seem to be used only for this species and in this state.

Genus ACANTHARCHUS Gill. Mud Sun-fishes.

In this genus the form is oblong, rather stout, and but little compressed; mouth moderate, maxillary broad, supplemental bone large, lower jaw slightly projecting; teeth on jaws, vomer, palatines, pterygoids, and tongue; gill-rakers few, long; preopercular margin not serrate; scales large, lateral line complete; dorsal spines 11 or 12, anal spines 5; caudal rounded. One small species. (*Acantharchus*, spiny vent.)

200. ACANTHARCHUS POMOTIS (Baird).

"Mud Perch"; "Perch"; Mud Sun-fish; Mud Bass.

Centrarchus pomotis Baird, Ninth Smithsonian Report, 325, 1854; New York and New Jersey.
Acantharchus pomotis, Jordan, 1889b, 126, 130; Tar River near Rocky Mount, Neuse River at Millburnie.
Evermann & Cox, 1896, 305; Neuse River near Raleigh. Jordan & Evermann, 1896, 989, pl. clv, fig. 418

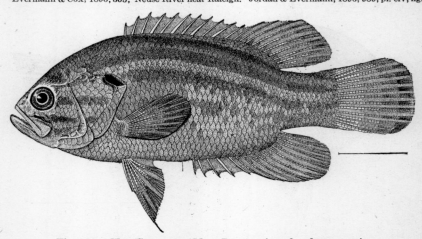

Fig. 101. Mud Sun-fish; Mud Bass. *Acantharchus pomotis*.

DIAGNOSIS.—Depth .4 total length; head .37 length; mouth wide, maxillary extending to posterior third of eye; snout short; eye .25 head, exceeding snout; developed gill-rakers about 5; scales in lateral series about 43, in transverse series 18, rows of scales on cheeks 5; dorsal rays xi,10 to xii,11, the spines very low, only half length of soft rays; anal rays v,10; caudal rounded; pectorals .6 length of head. Color: dark greenish, with 5 blackish lengthwise bands on side and back; several dark horizontal bands on cheeks, the lowermost extending on mandible; a black spot on upper part of opercle. (*pomotis*, a genus of sun-fishes synonymous with *Lepomis*.)

PLATE 7

A. HOEN & CO.

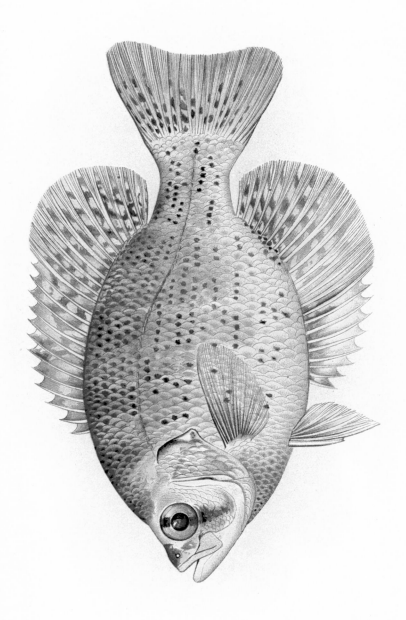

FLIER (CENTRARCHUS MACROPTERUS)

The mud bass, which lives in sluggish fresh waters along the coast from New York to South Carolina, is known from the Neuse near Raleigh and at Kinston; from the Tar near Rocky Mount; and from Lake Ellis in Craven County. It doubtless exists in various other state waters in which no collections have been made. Its length is about 6 inches, and its food value is slight. It lives mostly in muddy water, and is said to be nocturnal in its habits.

Genus AMBLOPLITES Rafinesque. Rock Basses.

Body oblong, compressed, back somewhat elevated; mouth large, a large supplemental maxillary; teeth in bands or patches on jaws, tongue, vomer, and pterygoids; preopercular angle serrate; gill-rakers long, strong, and toothed; scales large, lateral line complete; dorsal fin longer than anal, with 10 or 11 low spines. One species. (*Ambloplites*, blunt armature.)

201. AMBLOPLITES RUPESTRIS (Rafinesque).

Rock Bass; Red-eye.

Bodianus rupestris Rafinesque, American Monthly Magazine, 1817, 120; lakes of New York, Vermont, and Canada.
Ambloplites rupestris, Cope, 1870b, 451; French Broad River and head of Cumberland. Jordan, 1889b, 153; Swannanoa River near Asheville and Spring Creek at Hot Springs. Jordan & Evermann, 1896, 989, pl. clvi, fig. 419.

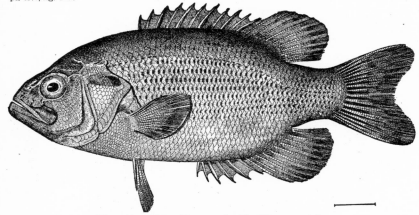

Fig. 102. ROCK BASS. *Ambloplites rupestris.*

DIAGNOSIS.—Depth .4 to .5 total length; head large, contained 2.75 times in length; mouth large, maxillary reaching to posterior edge of pupil; eye large, about equal to snout, contained 3.5 times in head; gill rakers on lower arm of first arch 7 to 10; scales in lateral series 40, in transverse series 17, scales on cheeks in 6 to 8 rows; dorsal rays x,10 or xi,10, spines low, the longest less than .5 length of head; anal rays v,10 to viii,10; caudal concave, with rounded ends. Color: pale green, with dark mottlings and a dark spot on each scale; a dark spot on upper part of opercle; fins dark mottled. (*rupestris*, inhabiting rocks.)

From Vermont this species ranges through the Great Lakes to Manitoba, thence to the lower Mississippi valley, being abundant in the Great Lakes and the Mississippi basin. In North Carolina the rock bass is naturally confined to the French Broad and tributaries, where it is reported as abundant by both Cope and Jordan, the latter remarking that it ascends the mountain streams farther than other sun-fishes.   A specimen in the State Museum was caught near Raleigh about 1892; this, however, was probably an introduced example.

The rock bass reaches a length of 12 or 14 inches and a weight of 2 pounds. It is a good table fish, and also ranks high as a game fish, being a free biter and vigorous fighter.   It is a desirable fish for ponds, and has been extensively planted in all parts of the country; one of the principal hatcheries is at Wytheville, Virginia.   The fish spawns in spring, on gravelly bars, the parents guarding the eggs and young.

Genus CHÆNOBRYTTUS Gill. Warmouths.

This genus resembles Ambloplites in general shape, teeth, dorsal and caudal fins, but it has only 3 anal spines and the preopercle is not serrated.   There is only one known species.   (*Chœnobryttus*, yawning sun-fish.)

202. CHÆNOBRYTTUS GULOSUS (Cuvier & Valenciennes).

"Goggle-eye"; "Chub"; "Mud Chub"; "Red-eyed Bream"; Warmouth; Red-eye.

Pomotis gulosus Cuvier & Valenciennes, Histoire Naturelle des Poissons, iii, 498, 1829; Lake Pontchartrain and lagoons near New Orleans.
Chœnobryttus gillii, Cope, 1870b, 452; all streams of North Carolina east of Alleghenies.
Chœnobryttus gulosus, Jordan, 1889b, 130, 133; Neuse River near Raleigh, Moccasin Swamp near Goldsboro, Reedy Fork of Haw River (tributary of Cape Fear).   Smith, 1893a, 196, 199; Edenton Bay, Roanoke River at Plymouth and Weldon.   Evermann & Cox, 1896, 305; Neuse River near Raleigh.   Jordan & Evermann, 1896, 992, pl. clvii, fig. 421.

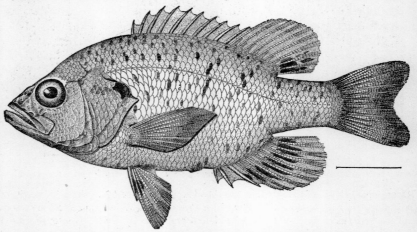

Fig. 103. WARMOUTH; GOGGLE-EYE.   *Chœnobryttus gulosus*

DIAGNOSIS.—Body stout, depth .4 to .5 length; head large, about .4 length; mouth large, maxillary extending as far as posterior margin of eye; eye equal to snout, contained 4 to 4.5 times in head; 8 or 9 gill-rakers fully developed; scales in lateral series 40 to 46, in transverse series 17 or 18, 6 to 8 rows on cheeks; dorsal rays x,9 or x,10, the spines short, less than .5 length of head; anal rays iii,8 or iii,9; caudal concave, the ends rounded; pectorals pointed, rather long, extending to or beyond anal origin.   Color: above dark green, clouded with red, blue, or bronze; below yellow; dusky spots on each scale or on many scales; a black spot on opercle; 3 dark bars radiating from eye; vertical fins with dusky mottlings; a large dark spot on posterior part of soft dorsal. (*gulosus*, large-throated.)

This fish is distributed from the Great Lakes to North Carolina and Texas, being particularly numerous in the South Atlantic and Gulf States. Cope (1870) stated that "this species is exceedingly common in all the streams of North Carolina east of the Allegheny Mountains", but that "it does not occur in the French Broad". Jordan, in his explorations in 1888, found the fish only in the Neuse and Cape Fear basins. The present writer in 1892 found it common in Albemarle Sound and abundant in the lower Roanoke. The National Museum contains specimens from Tar River at Tarboro and Yadkin River at Salem, and Mr. W. H. Yopp reports it from the Cape Fear and tributaries about Wilmington.

Warmouth is a distinctive name for this species, but the North Carolina names are "goggle-eye", "chub", and "mud chub" on Albemarle Sound and tributaries; "red-eyed bream" on the Catawba, according to Cope; and "goggle-eye perch" at Wilmington. In South Carolina and Georgia the vernacular names are warmouth perch, more-mouth bream, yaw-mouth perch, warm-mouth perch, and sun trout. Bream, sun-fish, and perch are southern names which this species shares with other centrarchids.

The warmouth rarely exceeds 10 inches in length. In the Albemarle region it is caught in gill nets and other nets, and is sold in the local markets. It is in the Wilmington markets throughout the year, but is not very abundant; it there ranges from one-fourth of a pound to one pound in weight, and brings the fishermen 7 cents a pound on an average. The fish takes the hook readily and is often caught by North Carolina anglers.

Genus ENNEACANTHUS Gill. Little Sun-fishes.

Small fishes, with rather short, deep, compressed body; small mouth, with teeth on jaws, vomer, and palatines, but none on tongue; short maxillary with supplemental bone well developed; margin of preopercle entire; 2 flat points on opercular margin; large scales; lateral line usually complete; short and not numerous gill-rakers; about 9 dorsal spines, 3 anal spines; convex caudal fin. Two species are now recognized, both found in North Carolina:

i. Dark spot on opercle more than half diameter of eye; 5 to 8 persistent black vertical bars on sides; body and fins with purplish or golden spots...........................*obesus*.
ii. Dark spot on opercle less than half diameter of eye; vertical bars narrower and less distinct (disappearing with age); body and fins with sky-blue spots.................*gloriosus*.

(*Enneacanthus*, nine-spined.)

203. ENNEACANTHUS OBESUS (Baird).
Little Sun-fish.

Pomotis obesus Baird, Ninth Smithsonian Report, 324, 1854; Beesley Point, N. J.
Enneacanthus guttatus, Cope, 1870b, 452; Neuse River.
Enneacanthus obesus, Smith, 1893a, 199; Roanoke River at Weldon. Jordan & Evermann, 1896, 993.

DIAGNOSIS.—Body compressed, elliptical, depth more than .5 length; head .37 to .4 total length of body; eye rather large, its diameter contained 3 to 3.25 times in head; snout less than eye; mouth oblique, comparatively small, the maxillary extending as far back as center of pupil; gill-rakers on lower arm of first arch 10 to 12, those on short arm 3 or 4, usually rudimentary; scales in lateral series about 32, in transverse series 14 or 15; scales on cheek in 4 rows; dorsal rays ix,10 or ix,11, the longest spine .5 length of head, the longest soft ray .66 length of head; anal fin large, the rays iii,10, the third spine about .5 length of head, the soft part of fin larger than soft dorsal; caudal fin rounded; pectorals rather long, .75 length of head, reaching beyond anal spines; ventrals extending to second anal ray.   Color: body olive green, with 5 to 8 dark transverse bars; body, cheeks, and fins with small purple or golden spots; opercular flap with a velvety black spot edged with purple; a black bar beneath eye. (*obesus*, fat.)

This diminutive sun-fish, which occurs along the coast from Massachusetts to Florida in sluggish waters, has been reported in North Carolina only from Neuse and Roanoke rivers, and is much rarer than the next species.   It lives among weeds in quiet water.   Its maximum length is 3.75 inches, but it rarely exceeds 3 inches.

204. ENNEACANTHUS GLORIOSUS (Holbrook).

"Speckled Perch"; Little Sun-fish; Blue-spotted Sun-fish.

Bryttus gloriosus Holbrook, Journal Academy Natural Sciences of Philadelphia, 1855, 51; Cooper River, S. C.
Enneacanthus pinniger Jordan, Bulletin x, U. S. National Museum, 27, 1877; Neuse River at Kinston.
Enneacanthus simulans, Smith, 1893a, 196; Edenton Bay.
Enneacanthus gloriosus, Jordan, 1889b, 126, 130; Tar and Little rivers.   Smith, 1901, 134: Lake Mattamuskeet.
    Evermann & Cox, 1896, 305; Neuse Basin near Raleigh.   Jordan & Evermann, 1896, 993, pl. clviii, fig.
    422

DIAGNOSIS.—Form very similar to that of *obesus*, but its depth equal to or less than .5 total length; head .37 length; eye a little less than .33 length of head; snout short, .66 diameter of eye; maxillary extending to anterior margin of pupil; gill-rakers on lower arm of first arch 10 or 11, on upper arm 3 (of which only 1 is developed); scales in lateral series 30 to 32, in transverse series 12 to 14; dorsal rays ix,10 to x,11, the longest spine equal to postorbital part of head, the longest soft rays equal to head minus snout; anal rays iii,9 to vi,10, the first spine less than eye, the third spine equal to postorbital region of head, the longest soft rays about equal to those of dorsal; caudal fin rounded, the longest rays .66 length of head; pectorals extending to above base of second or third anal soft ray, about .75 length of head; ventrals about .66 length of head.   Color: males, dark olive green, with numerous small round blue spots on body, head, and fins, the spots having a tendency to form irregular cross stripes; opercular spot pearly blue, with a blue margin; a black bar below eye; females duller, the spots large and less distinct; young with narrow dark crossbars, more or less indistinct.   (*gloriosus*, glorious.)

This handsome little sun-fish, whose maximum length is only 3 inches, ranges from New York to South Carolina, in clear coastal streams, and is common in North Carolina.   The types of Jordan's nominal species, *Enneacanthus pinniger*, came from Neuse River at Kinston.   Other North Carolina localities where the species has been collected are Little River at Goldsboro, Neuse River near Raleigh, Tar River at Rocky Mount, Edenton Bay, Lake Ellis, and Lake Mattamuskeet. The fish is too small to have any economic value, but is most desirable and attractive for the aquarium.

Genus MESOGONISTIUS Gill.   Banded Sun-fishes.

Form short and compressed; mouth small, the maxillary not reaching as far as anterior margin of eye, the supplemental bone very small; small teeth on jaws, vomer, and palatines; opercular margin with 2 flat points covered with skin; preopercular margin entire; gill-rakers long and toothed; scales large; dorsal spines 10, the middle spines rather long; anal fin smaller than dorsal, the rays longer; caudal and pectorals rounded. A single small species. (*Mesogonistius*, middle-angled dorsal.)

205. MESOGONISTIUS CHÆTODON (Baird).

Black-banded Sun-fish.

Pomotis chætodon Baird, Ninth Smithsonian Report, 324. 1854; Cedar Swamp Creek, N. J.
Mesogonistius chætodon, Jordan & Evermann, 1896, 995, pl. clviii, fig. 423.

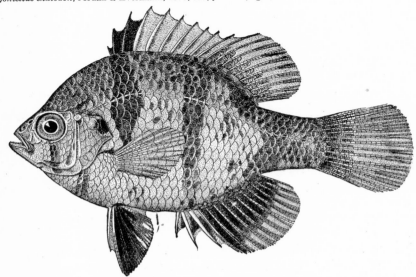

Fig. 104. BLACK–BANDED SUN–FISH. *Mesogonistius chætodon.*

DIAGNOSIS.—Body rather short, much compressed, depth contained 1.7 to 2 times in total length; head .33 total length; eye large, .33 length of head; mouth small; gill-rakers short, 10 or 11 on lower arm of first arch; lateral line unbroken; scales in lateral series about 28, in transverse series 14; fins large; dorsal rays x,10; anal rays iii,12. Color (of specimens from Wilmington): body dirty white or pale straw color, often with silvery purplish reflections, marked by 6 to 8 black vertical bars; the first of these, through the eye, is the narrowest, most intense, and most sharply defined, the part below the eye being jet black and usually the most conspicuous part of the fish; second bar anterior to pectorals, represented on opercle by a black spot; third bar extends on spinous dorsal, forming a bluish black blotch on first three interradial membranes and a similar central stripe on ventrals; fourth bar at front of soft dorsal; fifth bar under posterior edge of soft dorsal, last bar at base of caudal; fourth spinous dorsal membrane with white pigment, sometimes orange in male; soft dorsal with about 5 transverse rows of dark brown spots on rays; caudal similarly marked; anal with dark edge and about 4 longitudinal rows of dark brown spots; anal in some specimens with a purplish suffusion and spots; pectorals colorless, unmarked; opercle and posterior edge of orbit with brilliant golden reflections; iris anterior to black bar orange, posterior section white. Length, to 3 inches. (*chætodon*, a genus of salt-water fishes many of which resemble this species in coloration.)

This is one of the smallest, most beautiful, and most interesting of the sun-fishes.   Although it ranges from New Jersey to southern North Carolina and is abundant in the latter state, there are no published records of its occurrence south of Maryland.   Specimens in the National Museum were collected in Neuse River at Kinston about 1874, and in ponds along the Cape Fear River at Wilmington in 1899 by W. P. Seal.   The species has no common name except banded or black-banded sun-fish, and this exists only in books, as the fish is unknown to fishermen.

According to Mr. Seal, who has collected many specimens of this fish in New Jersey and North Carolina for aquarium purposes, in the latter state it is abundant in rice ditches, creeks, and ponds connected with Cape Fear River.   It is always found among water plants, and occupies very circumscribed areas in the waters in which found, differing markedly in this respect from Enneacanthus, which is distributed throughout the waters.

In 1901 Mr. Seal forwarded to the United States Bureau of Fisheries from Wilmington 50 living examples of this fish, which were kept in aquaria for nearly a year and proved very attractive and interesting.   One peculiarity of behavior was their habit of clustering on the leaves or branches of water plants and remaining perfectly quiet for long periods.   Sometimes, every fish would be thus situated, and, if the vegetation was profuse, very effectively concealed.   On one occasion 14 of them were packed on the top of a tall narrow spray of Myriophyllum with their heads turned outward.   The fish often rest with the long axis of the body vertical, the head being up.   When disturbed, even when touched, they leave the hiding or resting place with reluctance, and proceed to a new place with a few short rapid darts.

Judging by its behavior in captivity, this dainty little fish eats only living, moving food.   Even when very hungry, it refused chopped meat.   When supplied with white-fish fry and trout fry it ate them promptly, but without great avidity.   One fish which struck at a trout fry failed to grasp it, and, although the fry dropped to the bottom dead, the sun-fish did not notice it further.   Another stopped following a trout fry to pursue a gammarid.   Insect larvæ and small crustacea were always eaten readily, and such animals are doubtless the usual natural food.

The species spawns in North Carolina in March.   Some of the specimens forwarded by Mr. Seal were in spawning condition, he having expressed ripe eggs from them before shipment.   In the aquarium, however, they did not spawn.

Genus LEPOMIS Rafinesque.   Common Sun-fishes.

These are the typical "sun-fishes" which in the Southern States are usually called "bream", "brim", or "perch", with or without qualifying names.   They are numerous as to both species and individuals, and are among the best known of American lake, pond, river, and creek fishes.   Their brilliant coloration and the avidity with which they take the baited hook make them very popular with youthful anglers and compensate for their comparatively small size.   The

BANDED SUN-FISH.   *Mesogonistius chætodon.*

From a painting by Charles B. Hudson of living specimens from Wilmington, N. C.

species are difficult to distinguish, and even the numerous genera which have from time to time been recognized are separated by no constant characters of importance. In the present account, the genus Lepomis is regarded as embracing all the species found in North Carolina, and may be defined as follows:

Body ovate, compressed, the dorsal outline in adults rather more strongly arched than the ventral; mouth of moderate size, jaws equal, maxillary narrow and not extending beyond pupil, supplemental bone small or wanting; no teeth on tongue or pterygoids; pharyngeal bones narrow or broad, with sharp or blunt paved teeth; preopercular margin entire; opercle ending in a more or less elongated flap which is conspicuously colored; gill-rakers usually short and feeble; dorsal spines 10, anal spines 3; caudal fin concave or emarginate behind; pectorals long or short, pointed or rounded.

Five species recorded from North Carolina, typical adult specimens of which may be thus identified:

Key to the North Carolina species of Lepomis.

i. Pectoral fins rather short, rounded, not extending to first anal spine; opercular flap very long and narrow.
  a. Scales in lateral series 43 to 48...*auritus.*
  aa. Scales in lateral series 35 to 45......................................*megalotis.*
ii. Pectoral fins longer, pointed, and reaching to or beyond first anal spine; opercular flap short and broad.
  b. Gill-rakers on lower arm of first arch 11 to 13; opercular flap without pale margin; a black blotch at base of dorsal and anal fins posteriorly....................*incisor.*
  bb. Gill-rakers on lower arm of arch 10, of moderate length; opercular flap with a broad orange margin posteriorly and inferiorly; no black blotch on dorsal or anal..*holbrooki.*
  bbb. Gill-rakers on lower arm of first arch 8 to 10, very short and feeble; opercular flap with bright red margin: no black blotch on dorsal or anal.................*gibbosus.*

(*Lepomis,* scaly opercle.)

206. LEPOMIS AURITUS (Linnæus).

"Yellow-belly"; "Red-belly"; "Leather-ear"; "Red-bellied Bream"; "Robin Perch"; "Robin"; "Leather-ear Robin"; "Leather-ear Perch"; Long-eared Sun-fish.

Labrus auritus Linnæus, Systema Naturæ, ed. x, 283, 1758; Philadelphia.
Lepomis rubricauda, Cope, 1870b, 452; Catawba, Yadkin, and Neuse basins
Lepomis auritus, Jordan, 1889b, 126, 130, 133, 139; Tar, Neuse, Little, Cape Fear, Yadkin, and Catawba basins.
    Smith, 1893a, 196; Edenton Bay. Evermann & Cox, 1896, 305; Neuse River near Raleigh. Jordan & Evermann, 1896, 1001, pl. clix, figs, 425, 425a.

DIAGNOSIS.—Body moderately elongate, the depth about .5 length; head (exclusive of flap) .33 length; mouth oblique, comparatively large, maxillary extending nearly to anterior margin of pupil; eye .22 to .25 length of head, .66 length of snout; gill-rakers on lower arm of first arch 8 or 9, strong, short, the longest .33 diameter of eye; scales in lateral series about 45, in transverse series 6 or 7+13 to 15; scales on cheeks in 5 or 6 rows; opercular flap very long and narrow (in full grown fish), its width rather less than eye; dorsal rays x,10 to x,12, the longest spine .33 length of head and .66 longest soft ray; anal rays III,8 to III,10, the spines stout, the longest (3rd) equal to snout and .66 longest soft ray; caudal rather short and moderately incised behind; pectorals broad, rounded, reaching to vent; ventrals reaching to or beyond vent, the spine .5 length of fin. Color: light olive above, the belly orange, brightest in breeding males; scales on sides pale bluish with reddish centers; bluish stripes on head; opercular flap usually with pale lower margin; dorsal, anal, and caudal fins yellow or orange. (*auritus,* eared.)

In the streams of the Atlantic and Gulf coasts, from Maine to Louisiana, this well known sun-fish abounds. Both typical *auritus* and the southern variety, *solis*, are represented in North Carolina, the latter distinguished by having larger scales on cheeks and breast, and a dusky blotch on the posterior part of dorsal fin. Cope (1870), under the name *Lepomis rubricauda*, records the species as very common in the basins of the Catawba, Yadkin, and Neuse. More recent collectors have reported it as common in the same waters and in addition in Tar and Cape Fear rivers and Albemarle Sound. The National Museum contains specimens from the lower Neuse at Kinston, collected by J. W. Milner; and at New Bern, collected by Marshall McDonald.

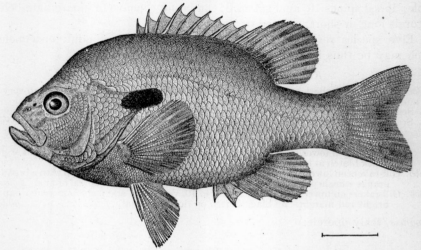

Fig. 105. Long-eared Sun-fish; Red-belly; Robin. *Lepomis auritus.*

The species bears numerous names in North Carolina; some of them are peculiar to it, while others are sometimes applied to related species. The most generally used names are given above, but various other combinations of "robin", "perch", "bream", "red-belly", "leather-ear", etc., are heard. On Albemarle and Currituck sounds and their tributaries the names most often used are "leather-ear", "red-belly", "yellow-belly", and "robin".

The long-eared sun-fish rarely exceeds 8 inches in length. It is often caught by anglers using angleworms, grubs, and grasshoppers as bait; and is sometimes taken in the nets of the commercial fishermen and sent to market.

207. LEPOMIS MEGALOTIS (Rafinesque).

Large-eared Sun-fish.

Ichthelis megalotis Rafinesque, Ichthyologia Ohiensis, 29, 1820; Ohio River.
Lepomis megalotis, Cope, 1870b, 452; upper waters of French Broad. Evermann & Cox, 1896, 305; Neuse River near Raleigh. Jordan & Evermann, 1896, 1002, pl. clx, fig. 426.

DIAGNOSIS.—Body rather short and compressed, back arched, profile becoming steeper over eye, depth .4 to .6 total length; head .33 length; eye .25 length of head, a little less than snout; mouth small, the maxillary extending as far as pupil; gill-rakers short and feeble, 8 or 9 on lower arm of first arch; width of opercular flap equal to eye, its length nearly twice width; scales in lateral series 35 to 45, in transverse series 5+14; rows of scales on cheek, about 5; dorsal rays x̄,10 to x,12, the longest spine about .33 head; anal rays III,8 to III,10, the longest spine about length of longest dorsal spine; pectorals .66 to .75 head; ventrals very long, extending beyond anal origin. Color: back blue, under parts orange, the sides with orange spots and blue streaks; opercular flap with pale blue or red margin, sometimes wanting; cheeks orange with blue stripes; lips and stripes before eye blue; soft dorsal and anal rays blue, membranes yellow. (*megalotis*, large-eared.)

The long-eared sun-fish is an abundant species throughout most of its range, from the Great Lakes region to Texas, but in North Carolina, which marks its southeastern limit, it is not common. Evermann & Cox record a single specimen from Neuse River near Raleigh. The only other record is that of Cope from "the upper waters of the French Broad", which, however, may refer to another species, although there is nothing improbable in the reference. A length of 8 inches is reached.

208. LEPOMIS INCISOR (Cuvier & Valenciennes).

"Blue Joe"; "Blue Perch"; Blue Bream (S. C.); Blue Sun-fish; Copper-nosed Bream; Blue-gill.

Pomotis incisor Cuvier & Valenciennes, Histoire Naturelle des Poissons, vii, 466, 1831; New Orleans.
? *Lepomis notatus*, Cope, 1870b, 453; French Broad River.
Lepomis purpurescens Cope, 1870b, 454; Yadkin River in Roane County, N. C
Lepomis pallidus, Jordan, 1889b, 152; Spring Creek (tributary of French Broad). Smith, 1893a, 196, 200; Edenton Bay, Roanoke River at Weldon. Jordan & Evermann, 1896, 1005, pl. clx, fig. 427. Smith, 1901, 134; Lake Mattamuskeet. (Not *Labrus pallidus* Mitchill.)
Lepomis incisor, Smith, Science, May 12, 1904, 746.

DIAGNOSIS.—Body very short and deep in old examples, more slender in young, the depth contained 1.8 to 2.25 times in total length; length of head contained about 3 times in total length; mouth small. oblique, the lower jaw slightly longer, maxillary reaching as far as anterior margin of eye; eye about equal to snout and rather less than .25 length of head; opercular flap of moderate length and broad; gill-rakers rather short, stout, about 11 or 12 on long arm of first arch, the longest .25 diameter of eye; scales in lateral series about 42 to 52, of which 40 to 50 have pores; scales in transverse series 7+15 or 16; scales on cheeks in 5 rows; dorsal rays x,11 or x,12, the spines strong, the first as long as snout and half as long as the fifth, the longest soft rays about half length of head; anal rays III,10 to III,12, the spines stout, the first less than eye, the longest soft rays .5 length of head; caudal notched; pectorals very long and pointed, about length of head, reaching beyond origin of anal; ventrals extending nearly to anal, the spine nearly as long as the third anal. Color: adults light or dark green, with a beautiful purplish luster in life, the belly coppery red; sides with dark transverse bars, most distinct when the fish is in the water; cheeks and jaws bright purplish blue; opercular flap black; a black blotch on base of dorsal and anal posteriorly; young duller, the sides silvery, the fin blotches obscure. (*incisor*, cutter.)

The blue-gill has a wide distribution, extending from western New York throughout the Great Lakes to Florida and Texas. In North Carolina it has been collected at various points. In creeks near Edenton and in Roanoke River at Weldon it was found to be common by the present writer. Jordan reported it as scarce in Spring Creek (tributary of the French Broad) at Hot Springs. A specimen collected at Wilmington by Prof. S. F. Baird in April, 1877, is in the National Museum.   The fish described by Cope as *Lepomis purpurescens*, from the Yadkin, is referred to this species; and the fish he called *Lepomis notatus* from the French Broad is probably also referable to it.

This is the largest and finest of the sun-fishes.   It attains a length of 12 to 14 inches and a weight of a pound and a half, and when full grown is a magnificent species.   As a game and food fish it stands high.   In the Albemarle region it is often sought by anglers, and is also sold in the local markets; the names "blue joe" and "blue perch" are applied to it in that section.   In Lake Mattamuskeet, where the blue bream is common, it ranks next to the white perch in popular estimation as a food fish.

This fish has for many years been called *Lepomis pallidus* in the belief that Mitchill's name of *Labrus pallidus* applied to it; but a close examination of Mitchill's description shows that it could not have been intended for this species, and furthermore the blue-gill is unknown in the locality from which the type of *pallidus* came.   The earliest available name is *incisor* of Cuvier & Valenciennes.

209. LEPOMIS HOLBROOKI (Cuvier & Valenciennes).
Holbrook's Sun-fish.

Pomotis holbrooki Cuvier & Valenciennes, Histoire Naturelle des Poissons, vii, 466, 1831; Charleston, S. C.
Lepomis holbrooki, Jordan, 1889b, 130; Little River at Goldsboro.
Eupomotis holbrooki, Jordan & Evermann, 1896, 1008.

DIAGNOSIS.—Body stout, the depth about .5 total length; head contained 3 to 3.5 times in length; snout rather long, .25 length of head; maxillary extending to front of eye; eye equal to snout; opercular flap short and broad; gill-rakers rather short, distinctly dentate, about 10 on long arm of first arch; scales in lateral series about 45, in transverse series 6+15, 5 rows on cheek; dorsal rays x,10 to x,12 the spines and soft rays equally high, the longest .5 length of head; anal rays iii,9 to iii,11; pectorals as long as head.   Color: dark green above, silvery below; breast yellow; opercular flap dark, with a broad orange-red margin; fins dark, with yellow rays.   (Named for Dr. Holbrook, author of Ichthyology of South Carolina.)

This sun-fish is peculiar to the lowland streams between Virginia and Florida, and is especially numerous in South Carolina and Florida.   The only North Carolina record is that of Jordan (1889b), who reported the fish as scarce in Little River near Goldsboro.   One large specimen was collected by the writer a number of years ago at the western end of Albemarle Sound.   The fish attains a length of 10 or 11 inches, and is of some importance in the southern part of its habitat.   In size, habits, food value, and gameness it closely resembles the blue-gill.

210. LEPOMIS GIBBOSUS (Linnæus).
"Sand Perch"; "Robin"; "Robin Perch"; "Red-belly"; "Yellow-belly"; Pumpkin-seed; Tobacco-box.

Perca gibbosus Linnæus, Systema Naturæ, ed. x, 292, 1758; Carolina.
Pomotis maculatus, Cope, 1870b, 455; all North Carolina rivers east of Alleghenies.
Lepomis gibbosus, Jordan, 1889b, 130; Neuse River near Raleigh.   Smith, 1893a, 192, 196, 200; Pasquotank River, Edenton Bay. Roanoke River at Plymouth and Welden.   Evermann & Cox, 1896, 305; Neuse River near Raleigh.
Eupomotis gibbosus, Jordan & Evermann, 1896, 1009, pl. clxi, fig. 429.   Smith, 1901, 134; Lake Mattamuskeet.

BLUE-GILL; BLUE JOE (LEPOMIS INCISOR). FEMALE

DIAGNOSIS.—Body ovate, the depth .5 to .7 total length, the thickness .33 the depth; length of head contained 3 times in length; a slight depression in the profile above eye; mouth oblique, small, the maxillary barely extending to front of orbit; eye equal to snout, rather less than .25 length of head; opercular flap very broad, short; gill-rakers very short, 8 to 11 on lower arm of first arch, the longest not .25 diameter of eye; scales in lateral series 40 to 45, in transverse series 6+3, 4 rows of scales on cheek; dorsal rays x,10 to x,12, the first spine about equal to eye, the longest twice diameter of eye, the longest soft ray equal to distance from eye to end of flap; anal rays III,10, the first spine half length of third, which is less than twice diameter of eye, the soft rays shorter than those of dorsal; caudal notched; pectorals long but less than head, extending as far as anal origin; ventrals reaching beyond vent. Color: above olive with bluish reflection, sides spotted with orange; cheeks orange, with wavy blue streaks; lower fins orange, dorsal and caudal fins bluish with orange spots; opercular flap black, with lower posterior margin bright scarlet. (*gibbosus*, hunched or humped.)

This species is found along the entire Atlantic seaboard of the United States, in the Great Lakes, and in the northern part of the Mississippi basin. Jordan & Evermann (1896) say the fish is rather rare in the Carolinas and Florida, but it is very common in the Neuse and abundant in Albemarle Sound and tributaries, being the most numerous of the sun-fishes in the latter section. Cope ascribes the fish to "all the rivers of North Carolina east of the Allegheny range", but Jordan did not find it in any stream west of the Neuse.

The breeding habits of this sun-fish have been studied by the writer and others, and are now well known. The "nest" is a slight depression on the bottom made by the fins, and after the eggs are laid and attached to stones or weeds, the male stands guard and repels intruding fishes or other animals; the care of the young also devolves on the male, which at this season is in his brightest colors and even in the water can be readily distinguished from his mate.

The names borne by this fish in North Carolina are "robin", "robin perch", "red-belly", and "yellow-belly", all used about Albemarle Sound; "sand perch", on the Neuse near Raleigh; and "robin" on the Neuse about New Bern. It is likely that the fishermen do not always distinguish this species from *Lepomis auritus*, as both are sometimes given the same names in the same places. Pumpkin-seed and tobacco-box are very old names given to the fish in other states. In his list of the fresh-water fishes of North Carolina, Lawson (1709) mentions "pearch, small and flat, with red spots, call'd round robins", and elsewhere in his work he makes the following reference to this species:

We have another sort of pearch, which is the least sort of all, but as good meat as any. These are distinguished from the other sorts [i. e., yellow perch, white perch, crappy, and black bass] by the name of round-robins; being flat, and very round-shap'd; they are spotted with red spots very beautiful, and are easily caught with an angle, as all the other sorts of pearches are.

The pumpkin-seed is one of the commonest fishes which fall to the lot of youthful anglers, as it abounds in ponds and streams, is a ready biter, and is not very fastidious in its tastes. As it does not exceed 8 inches in length and usually does not exceed 6 inches, it has little commercial value. On Roanoke River it is caught in gill nets with Chænobryttus and Centrarchus, and is regularly exposed for sale in the Plymouth market. In Currituck, Camden, Dare, and

244 FISHES OF NORTH CAROLINA.

other counties in the extreme eastern section, comparatively large quantities
of "robins" are taken in seines, fykes, and other nets, the principal catch being
in Currituck Sound. The annual product is now 40,000 to 50,000 pounds, for
which the fishermen receive 1.5 to 3 cents a pound.

Genus MICROPTERUS Lacépède. Black Basses.

The largest and most highly developed fishes of the family, characterized
by an elongate, moderately compressed body; stout caudal peduncle; long head;
large, oblique mouth, with long and broad maxillary and strong, projecting
lower jaw; supplementary maxillary very broad; bands of fine teeth on jaws,
vomer, and palatines; posterior margin of opercle with 2 broad points; preopercle
entire; gill-rakers long and slender; scales small, ctenoid; lateral line complete;
dorsal fins continuous, a deep notch at their junction; dorsal spines 10, rather
low; anal fin similar to soft dorsal, the spines 3; caudal fin concave behind.
The genus has only 2 members, both represented in the North Carolina fauna;
they closely resemble one another but may be distinguished as follows:

i. Inhabits cold, clear running water; maxillary not reaching beyond eye; scales in lateral
series 70 to 85, in transverse series about 36; scales on cheek small, in about 17 rows; color
nearly uniform green, the young barred or spotted.........................*dolomieu.*
ii. Inhabits chiefly sluggish, warmer waters; maxillary reaching beyond eye; scales in lateral
series 65 to 70, in transverse series 23 to 28; scales on cheek large, in about 10 rows;
a distinct black lateral band in young and in adults of moderate size, being obsolete in old
specimens...*salmoides.*

(*Micropterus*, small-finned, an inappropriate name based on a specimen with
mutilated dorsal fin.)

211. MICROPTERUS DOLOMIEU Lacépède.

Small-mouthed Black Bass.

Micropterus dolomieu Lacépède, Histoire Naturelle des Poissons, iv, 325, 1802; locality doubtful. Jordan,
1889b, 130, 152; basins of Neuse and French Broad. Jordan & Evermann, 1896, 1011, pl. clxii, figs.
430, 430a.
Micropterus fasciatus, Cope, 1870b, 450; French Broad River.

DIAGNOSIS.—Depth of body and length of head about .33 total length without caudal,
depth increasing with age; maxillary extending to or in advance of posterior margin of eye;
teeth in villiform bands on jaws, vomer, and palate; eye about .5 length of snout and .16 to
.20 length of head; gill-rakers long, 16 or 17 in number, about 10 on upper portion of arch;
scales small, about 77 in lateral series, about 25 in transverse series; about 17 rows of fine
scales on cheeks; lateral line slightly arched anteriorly; dorsal rays x,13 to x,15, the longest
spine (fifth) about equal to snout and about half longest soft ray; anal rays iii,10 to iii,12,
the first and second spines very short; bases of soft dorsal and anal scaly; pectorals and ventrals
short and rounded; caudal slightly concave behind. Color: body dull green, with golden or
brassy lustre, white below; 3 dark bands radiating posteriorly from eye; caudal yellowish-
green, with blackish margin; young with dark spots, which never form a lateral band but
sometimes collect into vertical bands. (Named in honor of M. Dolomieu, a French naturalist.)

This species was originally found from Vermont through the Great Lakes
basin to Manitoba, and thence southward to South Carolina, Mississippi, and
Arkansas, being confined mostly to the mountainous parts of the southeastern
states. By artificial means, the range has been considerably extended. In

North Carolina the small-mouthed black bass is much less widely distributed than the large-mouthed species. It is known from Neuse River near Raleigh, and Little River at Goldsboro, and from Swannanoa River near Asheville, and Spring Creek at Hot Springs, in all of which places it is common. As its general and local distribution indicates, this species prefers cooler, clearer, and swifter water than its congener, and is a less hardy but more gamy fish. It is one of the best and most sought of American game fishes, and is probably entitled to first rank in this respect, taking the artificial fly, the baited hook, or the troll in a fashion to thrill even the veteran angler.

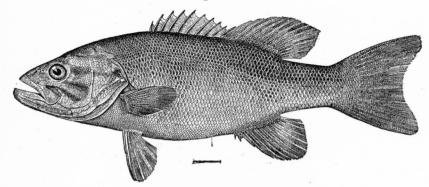

Fig. 106. SMALL-MOUTHED BLACK BASS. *Micropterus dolomieu.*

It is exceeded in size by the other species, and is rarely heavier than 6 pounds, while averaging only 2 or 2½ pounds.

212. MICROPTERUS SALMOIDES (Lacépède).

"Chub"; "Welshman"; "Trout"; "Fresh-water Trout"; Large-mouthed Black Bass.

Labrus salmoides Lacépède, Histoire Naturelle des Poisons, 716, 1802; South Carolina.
Micropterus nigricans, Cope, 1870b, 451; Neuse, Yadkin, Catawba, and French Broad rivers.
Micropterus salmoides, Jordan, 1889b, 130; Neuse and Little rivers. Smith, 1893a, 192, 196, 200; Pasquotank River, Albemarle Sound, Roanoke River at Plymouth and Weldon. Smith, 1893b, 282, pl. lxi; Currituck Sound. Jordan & Evermann, 1896, 1012, pl. clxiii, fig. 431. Evermann & Cox, 1896, 305; Walnut Creek (tributary of Neuse), near Raleigh. Smith, 1901, 134; Lake Mattamuskeet.

DIAGNOSIS.—Greatest depth about .33 length; length of head about equal to depth; mouth large and wide, the maxillary in adults extending beyond eye; bands of villiform teeth on jaws and roof of mouth, teeth sometimes present on tongue; eye .5 to .66 length of snout; gill-rakers on first arch 17 or 18, usually 10 above angle; scales in lateral series about 68, in transverse series 25; scales on cheeks not much smaller than on body, in about 10 rows; dorsal rays x,12 or x,13, the longest spine (fourth) more than half length of longest soft ray; anal rays iii,10 or iii,11, the first spine about .5 length of second, the second about .5 length of third; caudal fin incised posteriorly; pectoral fins rounded, .5 length of head; ventrals rounded, shorter than pectorals. Color: back green, sides silvery green, belly white; a well defined black lateral band in both young and adults, this breaking up and growing fainter with age; a few small irregularly disposed dark spots on sides; 3 dark bands radiating from eye posteriorly; caudal pale near body, black at margin, with a white edge. (*salmoides*, like a salmon or trout; the fish is called "trout" throughout the southern states.)

The large-mouthed black bass is native to a wide expanse of territory, bounded on the north by the Great Lakes and on the south by southern Florida and Mexico. Through the efforts of the general government, as represented by the Bureau of Fisheries, the species has been introduced into nearly every state, and may also be met with in various European countries. While found in the mountain regions of North Carolina, this bass is essentially a fish of the plateau and coastal plain regions, being more numerous in the coastwise waters than elsewhere. It is especially abundant in tributaries of Albemarle Sound and in Currituck Sound, and probably exists there in greater numbers than in any other waters in the country.

The name by which this fish is generally known in North Carolina is "Welsh-man", which is not employed elsewhere. This designation was in use as early as 1709, when Lawson referred to the "brown pearch, or Welshman". Another local name, peculiar to North Carolina and Virginia, is "chub". "Trout" is the name usually applied to the fish in all the southern states, and it was this

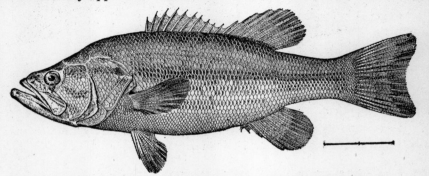

Fig. 107. LARGE-MOUTHED BLACK BASS. *Micropterus salmoides.*

fact that led the Frenchman, Lacépède, to give it the technical name *salmoides* (that is, like a salmon or trout). Among the fishermen of the Wilmington region the fish is known as "chub" and "fresh-water trout".

This is the largest and most important member of the family, and is the equal of the small-mouthed black bass as a food fish and but slightly inferior as a game fish. It inhabits more sluggish and warmer waters than the other species, and thrives under more extreme conditions of environment and temperature; for this reason it is better adapted for transplanting in the country at large. It reaches its maximum weight in Florida, where examples weighing as much as 20 to 25 pounds have been taken in lakes. Relatively large fish of 6 to 8 pounds are also common in the South Central States, while in the north the maximum is about 8 pounds and the average is 2 to 4 pounds.

The fish occasionally enters brackish and salt water. On April 7, 1904, the writer observed several fine examples that had been caught in pound nets in Croatan Sound in water that was quite salt; these had doubtless come out of some of the short rivers about the sound.

PLATE 10

LARGE-MOUTH BLACK BASS; WELSHMAN (MICROPTERUS SALMOIDES)

A HOEN & CO

Both species of black bass are remarkably zealous in the breeding habits. The fish, which have been in schools through the winter, become paired in early spring and begin the preparation of the nest. The nest is located in comparatively shallow water and usually consists of fine gravel, brushed into a circular mass 1.5 to 2 feet in diameter; sometimes the nest is simply a rounded area on a gravel, clay, or mud bottom from which all foreign material is removed by the parent fish. When the eggs are deposited, they become attached to the bottom, and are thenceforth continually guarded by one or both parents, while the water over the nest is kept agitated by a gentle motion of the fins. Fish and other intruders are attacked and driven away from the vicinity of the nest. From 2,000 to upwards of 10,000 eggs are deposited by one fish, and the hatching period is from 1 to 3 weeks. When the young emerge, they remain in the nest for several days while the yolk-sac is being absorbed, and then they rise in a school and hover over the nest for several days more before scattering. During this time the parents continue their guardianship, circling about the nest and keeping all enemies away and at the same time preventing the fry from wandering away. Finally, the young must separate in order to obtain food, and, having been driven among the dense vegetation or in shoal water for protection, they are deserted by their parents.

The food of the young fish consists of minute animals—crustacea, insects, etc. At a very early period, however, they begin to prey on their smaller brothers, and this cannibalism continues after they become adults. The larger fish are very voracious and aggressive feeders, taking all kinds of fish as well as small mammals, frogs, tadpoles, snakes, worms, insects, and also vegetable matter.

Under favorable conditions, the young bass reach a length of 6 to 8 inches in a year, and sexual maturity in reached when 2 years old.

As a market fish the large-mouth black bass is more important in North Carolina than in any other state. In 1890 the catch aggregated 407,530 pounds, valued at $20,492. In 1897 the output increased to 535,340 pounds, worth $33,611; and in 1902 it rose to 632,675 pounds, which sold for $58,013. Currituck Sound produces about three-fourths of the total yield in the state.

Family PERCIDÆ. The Perches.

A numerous family of fresh-water fishes, chiefly represented in eastern North America and Europe; most of them very small species known as darters, which are peculiar to America. The principal family characters are an elongate body, compressed or not; medium sized head; terminal or slightly inferior mouth of small or large size; premaxillaries protractile or not, maxillaries without distinct supplemental bone; villiform teeth in bands on jaws, vomer, and palatines, a few canine teeth in some species, teeth occasionally absent from vomer and palatines; sharp teeth on the lower pharyngeals; branchiostegals 6 or 7; gill-arches 4; gill-rakers long, slender, and dentate; gill-membranes free from isthmus and either connected or separate; pseudobranchiæ small or wanting;

preopercle entire or serrate; opercular margin usually with a flat spine; pyloric cœca few; lateral line present; scales ctenoid, adherent, covering body more or less completely, head naked or partly scaled; dorsal fins 2, nearly always separate, the first with 6 to 15 spines; anal equal to or smaller than second dorsal, with 1 or 2 spines; caudal forked, notched, square or rounded; pectorals of various sizes, sometimes quite large; ventrals well developed, inserted below pectorals, consisting of 1 spine and 5 soft rays.   The family has 12 genera and 22 known species in North Carolina waters.

Key to the North Carolina genera of perches.

i. Pseudobranchiæ and air-bladder well developed; branchiostegals 7; preopercle serrate; species large or medium sized.
   a. Large canine teeth on jaws and palatine bones; ventral fins well separated; pyloric cœca 3 to 7; vertebræ 46...STIZOSTEDION.
   aa. No canine teeth; ventral fins close together; pyloric cœca 3; vertebræ 41 ....PERCA.
ii. Pseudobranchiæ and air-bladder slightly developed or absent; branchiostegals 6; preopercular margin not serrate; species all small, some of them minute.
                    PERCINA, BOLEOSOMA, and other genera of darters.

Genus STIZOSTEDION Rafinesque. Pike Perches.

Large American fresh-water fishes, closely related to the pike perch of Europe, with very elongate, little compressed body; long, conical head; large mouth, with long, sharp canine teeth and villiform teeth in bands; spinous opercles, serrated preopercles; 7 branchiostegals; slender gill-rakers; 3 to 7 pyloric cœca; large air-bladder; small ctenoid scales covering all of body and parts of head; lateral line complete; dorsal fins disconnected, with 12 to 15 spines and 17 to 21 soft rays; 2 slender anal spines; and well-separated ventrals.   Two species, most numerous in the Great Lakes; one found locally.   (*Stizostedion*, pungent throat.)

213. STIZOSTEDION VITREUM (Mitchill).

"Wall-eyed Pike"; "Jack"; "Salmon"; "Pickerel"; "River Trout"; "Brook Trout"; "Golden Trout"; "California Salmon"; Jack Salmon; Pike Perch; Blue Pike; Yellow Pike.

Perca vitrea Mitchill, American Monthly Magazine, ii, 247, 1818; Cayuga Lake, New York.
Stizostedium americanum et salmoneum, Cope, 1870b, 448-449; French Broad and Neuse rivers.
Stizostedion vitreum, Jordan, 1889b, 150; French Broad River. Smith, 1893a, 192, 196, 200; Pasquotank River, Edenton Bay, Roanoke River.   Jordan & Evermann, 1896, 1021, figs. 433, 433a.

DIAGONSIS.—Form rather slender, depth greatest just behind head, somewhat more than .2 length; head .28 to .37 length; mouth large, maxillary reaching beyond middle of orbit; eye somewhat more than .2 head, its diameter shorter than snout; scales small, 110 to 130 in lengthwise series, about 35 in transverse series, a few scales on cheeks and top of head; pyloric cœca 3; dorsal fins separated by a space greater than eye, the rays XII to XVI + 19 to 21, the longest spines .5 head, the bases of the 2 fins of nearly equal length; anal rays II,12 to II,14; caudal deeply concave. Color: variable; general tone dark green, yellow, or blue, more or less blotched or mottled with darker; lower parts and fins pale; a large black spot on posterior part of spinous dorsal; soft dorsal and caudal mottled with yellow and green; pectoral base dusky. (*vitreum*, glassy.)

The pike perch is one of the most important commercial fishes of the United States, and is cultivated on an immense scale by the United States government on Lake Erie and elsewhere.   From the Great Lakes, where it supports fisheries of great extent, it ranges eastward to Vermont and southward to North Carolina, Georgia, and Alabama.   In North Carolina it has a peculiar distribution, involving headwaters of the Mississippi system and also some of the rivers of the Atlantic slope.   Professor Cope gave the following interesting account of his observations of this fish in the French Broad River in 1869:

This is the largest percoid of the western waters, occasionally attaining a weight of 35 pounds; no specimen of more than 10 pounds came under my observation.   It loves the most boisterous and rapid streams, ascendng them to near their sources, having much the manners and haunting the same waters as the trout, but of much less voracious habits.   Its swiftness enables it to take the black perch [=black bass] with ease, though that fish is, after it, much the most powerful swimmer of the river it inhabits.   I took two from the stomach of a lucioperca [= pike perch] of 8 pounds, one of which weighed 2½ pounds.   Suckers are used as bait in taking them by hook; but the mode in which large specimens are most readily taken is by shooting.   When the lucioperca has gorged himself, be seeks some shallow bayou and lies in a slugggish state, digesting his meal.   Then the gun-fisherman, concealed in a tree close by, makes sure of him.   It is the most valued food fish of the French Broad, its flesh being very tender as well as rich.   Without the opercular armature of the Percae, its chief defense is in its numerous and powerful canine teeth, which make serious wounds on the hands of the unwary fisherman.   The common name on the French Broad is "jack".

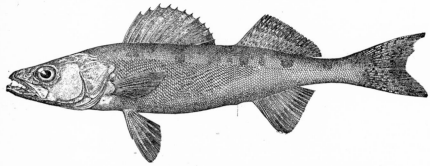

Fig. 108.   WALL-EYED PIKE;   PIKE PERCH.   *Stizostedion vitreum.*

Dr. Jordan in 1888 had this fish reported to him as one of the food fishes of the French Broad under the name of "river trout".   The present writer in 1892 found the fish in various tributaries of Albemarle Sound, where it is known under some extraordinary names.   In Pasquotank River it was noted that numbers of pike perch 12 to 15 inches long were caught by the net fishermen, and, although the fish was not sufficiently abundant to have much commercial importance, it was popular locally and always met with ready sale.   Under the impression that it is a salt-water species which wanders into the sound, some fishermen called it "salt-water pike", to distinguish it from the fresh-water pike (Esox); and the name "California salmon" was also heard in the lower river, this probably based on the belief that it is an introduced species.   In the vicinity of Edenton it is caught in pound nets and dutch nets, and is sometimes called "pickerel".   In the lower Roanoke, where it is not uncommon and goes by the name of "brook trout", it is caught in seines hauled for shad; and in the upper river near Weldon it is rare and known as "salmon".

It has been thought by some persons that this species was not native to the Albemarle region, but Mr. S. G. Worth considers it indigenous to those waters, and the National Museum contains a specimen collected by J. W. Milner at Avoca as long ago as 1878. Salmon Creek is the suggestive name of a small stream between Chowan and Roanoke rivers.

The pike perch spawns in early spring, in shoal waters. The eggs are .08 inch in diameter, and resemble those of the shad in being semibuoyant but differ therefrom in being adhesive. The number laid is about 45,000 for each pound of the female, and the hatching season is a little less than 3 weeks in a water temperature of 45°F. In hatching the eggs artificially the tendency to adhere in masses is overcome by separating them mechanically with starch or muck, which is mixed with the eggs immediately after fertilization.

The species ranks high as a game fish, and is easily lured with artificial fly, trolling spoon, or baited hook. The natural food consists mostly of soft-finned fishes, with a variable proportion of insects and crustaceans.

Its edible qualities are excellent, the flesh being firm, white, and well-flavored; and it stands shipment better than most fishes. In North Carolina the commercial value of the species is small.

Genus PERCA Linnæus. Yellow Perches.

Small fresh-water fishes, of which 3 species are known, 1 from Asia, 1 from Europe, and 1 from North America. Body oblong or elongate, compressed; back elevated; mouth moderate sized, terminal, with protractile premaxillaries and bands of fine teeth on jaws, vomer, and palatines; a spinous process on opercle, and serrations on preopercle and shoulder girdle; gill-membranes not united; scales ctenoid, rather small, completely covering body and part of cheeks and opercles; lateral line present; air bladder present; dorsal fins well separated, the spines high and strong, 12 to 16 in number; 2 weak anal spines; ventral fins close together, with a conspicuous spine. (*Perca*, perch.)

214. PERCA FLAVESCENS (Mitchill).

"Red-fin"; "Englishman"; "Raccoon Perch"; "Yellow Perch".

Morone flavescens Mitchill, Report on Fishes of New York, 18, 1814; near New York City.
Perca flavescens, Cope, 1870b, 448; Neuse River. Smith, 1893a, 192, 196, 200; Pasquotank River, Albemarle Sound, and Roanoke River. Jordan & Evermann, 1896, 1023, pl. clxv, fig. 435. Smith, 1901, 134; Lake Mattamuskeet.

Diagnosis.—Depth greatest under first 4 dorsal spines, less than .33 length; caudal peduncle rather broad, .33 head; head acutely pointed, its length about equal to depth of body; profile concave; mouth slightly oblique, maxillary not extending as far as middle of eye; snout much longer than eye; eye rather small, .16 head; gill-rakers short and stout, about 15 on long arm head of first arch; rows of scales in lateral series 75 to 90, in transverse series about 25; tubes in lateral line 55 to 60; cheeks and upper part of opercles well-scaled; dorsal rays XIII to XV + II,13 to II,15, longest spines less than .5 head; anal rays II,7 or II,8, the spines much shorter than soft rays; caudal slightly concave behind; pectorals .5 head; ventrals somewhat longer. Color:

YELLOW PERCH; REDFIN; ENGLISHMAN (PERCA FLAVESCENS)

above dark olive-green, sides yellow, below pale, back and sides marked by 6 to 8 broad black bands; a black blotch sometimes on spinous dorsal; lower fins red or orange, brightest in males during spawning season. (*flavescens*, yellowish.)

The yellow perch is one of the best known fresh-water fishes of the Atlantic and North Central States. Its range extends from North Carolina to Nova Scotia, throughout the Great Lakes, and in the upper Mississippi basin. The species abounds in Albemarle Sound and tributaries. It is also abundant in Lake Mattamuskeet, but is less numerous than formerly. From Neuse River it was recorded by Cope; McDonald and Milner collected it in the lower course of that stream (Kinston), but Jordan and Evermann & Cox did not record it from that river. In the vicinity of Wilmington, according to Mr. W. H. Yopp, it occurs in Cape Fear River and tributary creeks but is not abundant.

The yellow perch averages less than a foot in length and a pound in weight. The maximum attained, by a specimen recorded from the Delaware River, is

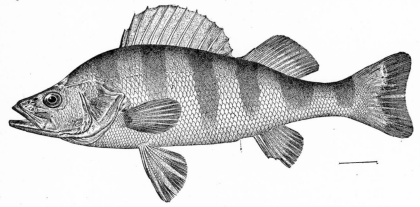

Fig. 109. Yellow Perch. *Perca flavescens.*

4.5 pounds, but examples weighing as much as 2 pounds are very rare. The females average considerably larger than the males.

The paired and anal fins in spring are crimson, whence the local name "red-fin" in use on Pasquotank River, Lake Mattamuskeet, and other waters of the state. The name "raccoon perch", employed at Edenton, Plymouth, and other points, has reference to the vertical markings on the fish, which resemble those on a raccoon's tail. "Englishman", heard at Edenton and elsewhere in the western part of Albemarle Sound, is used in contradistinction to "Welshman", the local name for the large-mouth black bass. The name "English pearch" occurs in Lawson's work.

The perch spawns in early spring—in February in Albemarle Sound. The spawn is very peculiar, in that the eggs are cemented together in a single layer in the form of long hollow strings which, when extruded, are several inches wide and folded or plaited like the bellows of an accordeon, but are capable of being drawn out to the length of 3 to 7 feet. One fish in an aquarium at the Bureau of Fisheries, Washington, D. C., deposited a string 88 inches long, the weight of which after fertilization was 41 ounces, while the weight of the fish before the escape of the eggs was only 24 ounces. The egg masses are not attached to stones, vegetation, or other submerged objects, but are deposited loosely in the water. Spawning takes place at night, in water having a temperature of 44° to 50° F., and the hatching period lasts from 2 to 4 weeks.

The species is usually found in schools, the movements of which in the rivers and larger lakes are influenced by spawning, food, temperature of water, etc.

The yellow perch is fairly good for the table, and is taken for market in large quantities in the Great Lakes and rivers of the Middle Atlantic States. It bites readily at the hooks baited with live minnows, angleworms, etc., and is caught in immense quantities by anglers. The amount taken in the commercial fisheries of North Carolina in 1902 was 105,990 pounds, valued at $5,639. About two-thirds of the catch comes from Currituck County.

<h2 style="text-align:center">Subfamily ETHEOSTOMINÆ. The Darters.</h2>

These diminutive perches are among the most interesting of fresh-water fishes. Their favorite haunts are cold mountain streams, but some few species are found in the lowlands. From the typical perches they differ in having very rudimentary or entirely deficient air-bladder and pseudobranchiæ, an entire preopercular margin, and 6 branchiostegals, and fewer pyloric cœca, in addition to their small size and gay colors. The following interesting account of the group is taken from Jordan & Evermann (1896):

The colors of the Etheostominæ are usually very brilliant, species of the Etheostominæ especially being among the most brilliantly colored fishes known; the sexual differences are often great, the females being as a rule dull in color and more speckled or barred than the males. Most of them prefer clear running water, where they lie on the bottom concealed under stones, darting, when frightened or hungry, with great velocity, for a short distance, by a powerful movement of the fan-shaped pectorals, then stopping as suddenly. They rarely use the caudal fin in swimming, and they are seldom seen moving or floating freely in the water like most fishes. When at rest they support themselves on their expanded ventrals and anal fin. All of them can turn the head from side to side, and they frequently lie with the head in a curved position or partly on one side of the body. The species of *Ammocrypta*, and perhaps some of the others, prefer a sandy bottom, where by a sudden plunge, the fish buries itself in the sand and remains quiescent for hours at a time, with only its eyes and snout visible. The others lurk in stony places, under rocks and weeds. Although more than usually tenacious of vitality, the darters, from their bottom life, are the first to be disturbed by impurities in the water. All of the darters are carnivorous, feeding chiefly on the larvæ of Diptera, and in their way voracious. All are of small size; the largest (*Percina rex*) reaches a length of 10 inches, while the smallest (*Microperca punctulata*) is, next to *Elassoma zonatum*, the smallest spiny-rayed fish known, barely attaining the length of an inch and half.

The different genera are very similar and have not always been recognized by authors, who have sometimes included all the species in the single genus *Etheostoma*; for convenience, however, if for no other reason, about 15 genera may be recognized, and of these the following 10 are known from North Carolina:

Key to the North Carolina genera of darters.

i. Size comparatively large, adults 5 inches or longer; head broad between eyes; premaxillaries free only at sides, not protractile; snout conic, pig-like, projecting; ventral fins separated by a space equal to the width of their base; on median line below a line of large scales which fall off, leaving a naked space; dorsal spines 13 to 15 ....PERCINA.
ii. Size small, rarely more than 5 inches and usually 2.5 to 4 inches; head narrow between eyes; premaxillaries either protractile or not; snout little or not at all projecting.
 a. Parietal region rather depressed, only slightly convex in cross section.
  b. Body more or less completely scaled, not extremely elongate nor hyaline.
   c. Premaxillaries not protractile, a band of skin connecting them in the median with line the forehead; anal fin large, usually larger than second dorsal.
    d. Median line of abdomen usually with more or less enlarged scales which are shed at intervals.....................................HADROPTERUS.
    dd. Median line of abdomen with small scales which are not shed..HYPOHOMUS.
   cc. Premaxillaries protractile, separated by a groove from the skin of the forehead.
    e. Anal spines 2; ventral fins close together.
     f. Maxillary not joined to preorbital except at base; teeth on vomer. ULOCENTRA.
     ff. Maxillary united to preorbital for most of its length; no teeth on vomer. DIPLESION.
    ee. Anal spine single; ventral fins well separated ....BOLEOSOMA.
  bb. Abdominal region naked, body exceedingly elongate and hyaline............IOA.
 aa. Parietal region not depressed, strongly convex or ∩-shaped in cross section; premaxillaries not protractile; belly covered with persistent scales; head naked above; anal fin much smaller than second dorsal; ventral fins inserted close together; lateral line present.
  g. Lateral line straight, sometimes absent posteriorly; dorsal spines 7 to 15. ETHEOSTOMA.
  gg. Lateral line arched anteriorly, incomplete and interrupted.
   h. Top of head naked; dorsal spines 9 or 10.....................BOLEICHTHYS.
   hh. Top of head scaled; dorsal spines 9 to 12.................COPELANDELLUS.

Genus PERCINA Haldeman. Log Perches.

The largest of the darters. Form elongate, somewhat compressed; head depressed; snout tapering, overhanging small mouth; maxillary short; premaxillaries not protractile; teeth on jaws, vomer, and palatines; scales small, those on ventral surface large, plate-like, and deciduous; lateral line not interrupted; air-bladder rudimentary; dorsal fins well separated, the anterior with 13 to 15 spines, the posterior with 12 to 17 rays; anal shorter than second dorsal; ventrals comparatively widely separated; body marked with black vertical bands. Two known species, one peculiar to the Roanoke River, in Virginia, the other widely distributed. (*Percina*, little perch.)

215. PERCINA CAPRODES (Rafinesque).

Log Perch; Hog Molly.

Sciæna caprodes Rafinesque, American Monthly Magazine, 1818, 534; Ohio River.
Percina caprodes, Jordan, 1889*b*, 153; Swannanoa River near Asheville. Jordan & Evermann, 1896, 1026, pl. clxv, fig. 436. Bean, 1903, 914; Cane River.

DIAGONSIS.—Depth contained 5 to 6.5 times in length; head long, contained 4 to 4.75 times in length; mouth small, inferior, maxillary not extending to eye; eye .25 length of head and .6 length of snout; snout rounded, tapering; scales in lateral series 90 to 95, in transverse series 9+15; scales on cheeks, opercles, and nape, but none on chest; dorsal fins low, the rays XIII to XVII + 12 to 17, the commonest formula XV + 15; anal rays II,9 to II,12, the spines feeble; caudal slightly concave behind; pectorals rounded, about length of head. Color: yellowish green, with about 15 blackish bars of unequal size extending from back to below median line, between these bars shorter and narrow ones reaching about to lateral lines; a rounded black spot at base of caudal; fins mostly marked with rows of small black spots. (*caprodes*, pig-like.)

The log perch is the largest of the darters, reaching a length of 8 or 10 inches. It is found from the Great Lakes region to Texas, and along the Atlantic slope as far south as Virginia. In North Carolina it is known only from tributaries of the French Broad. Jordan took one specimen in Swannanoa River near Asheville, and Bean records one fine example from Cane River. The species inhabits clear swift streams, and bites readily at the baited hook.

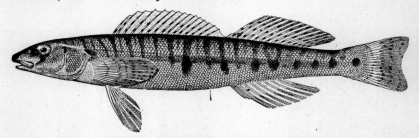

Fig. 110. Log Perch. *Percina caprodes.*

Genus HADROPTERUS Agassiz. Black-sided Darters.

Brightly colored, active, and graceful darters. Body elongate, cylindrical or compressed; head above more or less depressed; mouth wide, terminal; premaxillaries not protractile; teeth on jaws and vomer, and usually on palatines; gill-membranes joined or separate; body scaly, median ventral line with enlarged scales or plates which are shed at intervals; sides of head either scaly or naked; lateral line more or less complete; pyloric cœca 2 to 4; fins rather large; dorsal fins contiguous, the spines 10 to 15, the posterior fin with shorter base than the anterior; anal fin with 2 spines, similar to second dorsal; ventral fins well separated. About a dozen known species, the 3 following recorded from the state, 2 from the Atlantic slope and 1 from the Mississippi drainage basin:

i. Scales in lateral series 52 to 65; gill-membranes separate; eye large, more than .25 length of head; cheeks and throat naked, opercles with large scales; median ventral scales but slightly enlarged; coloration brilliant, the males with black and orange markings. Ohio drainage basin...*evides.*
ii. Scales in lateral series 44 to 56; a few small scales on upper part of opercle; gill-membranes slightly connected. Atlantic drainage system.
  a. First dorsal as high as second; scales 52 to 56; depth much less than .2 length; eye .25 length of head; cheeks usually naked, but sometimes with embedded scales; nape and breast naked; median ventral scales large and few........................*peltatus.*
  aa. First dorsal lower than second; scales 44 to 50; depth much more than .2 length; eye small, less than .25 length of head; cheeks, nape, and breast naked; median ventral scales moderately large, about 8 in number ....*roanoka.*

(*Hadropterus,* strong-finned.)

216. HADROPTERUS EVIDES (Jordan & Copeland).

Darter.

Alvordius evides Jordan & Copeland, Proceedings Academy of Natural Sciences of Philadelphia, 1877, 51; White River, Indiana.
Etheostoma evides, Jordan, 1889b, 153; French Broad River and Spring Creek at Hot Springs, Swannanoa River at Asheville.
Hadropterus evides, Jordan & Evermann, 1896, 1036, pl. clxvii, fig. 440.

DIAGNOSIS (North Carolina specimens).—Depth contained 5.3 times in length; head heavy, contained 4.3 times in length; eye large, contained 3.5 times in head; maxillary extending to front of eye; lower jaw included; throat, cheeks, and neck above without scales; opercles scaly; scales in lateral series 52 to 65, in transverse seies 9+9 to 9+11; dorsal rays XI+10; anal rays II,8 or II,9. Color: Male—olive green, with 8 deep blue-green cross-bars; an orange-brown lateral band forming brownish spaces between the cross-bars; belly, breast, throat, lower jaw, cheeks, opercles and snout orange or orange yellow; a blue-black bar posterior to eye, a golden crescent anterior to this; spinous dorsal rusty orange, last rays black; soft dorsal orange at base and speckled; caudal yellow, with 2 orange spots at base and several dark cross-bars; pectorals and anal yellow, with faint bars. Female—the orange color of male replaced by pale yellow, the markings on side black, dorsal membranes orange at tip and base. (*evides*, handsome.)

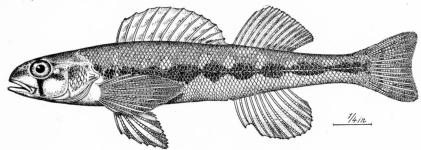

Fig. 111. DARTER. *Hadropterus evides.*

This very brilliantly colored species inhabits the Mississippi basin, and ranges from North Carolina to Indiana, and from Arkansas to Iowa. In North Carolina it is abundant in the French Broad and Swannanoa. Length, 3 inches.

217. HADROPTERUS PELTATUS (Stauffer).

Shielded Darter.

Etheostoma peltatum Stauffer Ms., in Cope, Proceedings Academy of Natural Sciences of Philadelphia, 1864, 233; Conestoga Creek, Pa. Jordan, 1889b, 126, 130, 133, 134, 139; Tar, Neuse, Cape Fear, Yadkin and Catawba rivers and various tributaries. Evermann & Cox, 1896, 305; Neuse River.
Etheostoma nevisense Cope, 1870a, 261; Neuse River near Raleigh. Cope, 1870b, 449; "turbulent waters of Neuse".
Etheostoma maculatum, Cope, 1870b, 449; Buck Creek, tributary of Catawba.
Alvordius crassus, Jordan & Gilbert, 1879, 368; Neuse River at Goldsboro.
Hadropterus peltatus, Jordan & Evermann, 1896, 1034.

DIAGNOSIS.—Body cylindrical, compressed posteriorly, depth contained 5.6 times in length; head rather large, .25 length; maxillary extending slightly beyond anterior margin of eye; lower jaw slightly included; eye .25 length of head, equal to blunt snout; scales in lateral series 52 to 56, in transverse series 6+9; scales on head as stated in key; fins comparatively small; dorsal rays XIII+12; anal rays II,10; caudal slightly concave behind; pectorals shorter than head, extending barely as far backwards as ventral. Color: pale yellow with black markings; cross blotches on back and irregular lengthwise lines above lateral line; 6 large quadrangular spots on sides, with faint bars intervening, the whole sometimes merged into a lateral bar; top of head, a bar below eye, snout, opercle, and axillary band all black; anterior dorsal with black median band and black spots on edge; posterior dorsal and caudal faintly barred; pectorals and ventrals dusky; female paler. (*peltatus*, shielded.)

This darter is found in coastwise streams between Pennsylvania and South Carolina, and is one of the commonest of the North Carolina darters.   Under the name of *Etheostoma nevisense*, Cope described it from the Neuse, and it has since been found in various parts of that river.   It is known from the Tar at Rocky Mount; from South Buffalo Creek and Little Allemance Creek, tributaries of the Cape Fear in Guilford County; from Little Yadkin or South River at Lindsays Mills; and from Catawba River near Marion, Bucks Creek at Pleasant Garden, and Johns River near Morgantown.   Length, 2.5 inches.

218. HADROPTERUS ROANOKA (Jordan & Jenkins).

Roanoke Darter.

Etheostoma roanoka Jordan & Jenkins, in Jordan, 1889*a*, 358, pl. xlv, fig. 10; Roanoke River, Va.   Jordan 1889*b*, 126, 130, pl. xv, fig. 10; Tar and Neuse rivers.
Hadropterus roanoka, Jordan & Evermann, 1896, 1036.
Percina roanoka, Boulenger, Catalogue of Fishes of British Museum, second edition, vol. i, 62, 1895; Neuse River, Raleigh, N. C.

DIAGNOSIS.—Form rather stout, moderately compressed, depth contained 4.30 to 4.75 times in length; head broad, contained 3.75 to 4 times in length; mouth small, low; maxillary reaching beyond front of pupil and more than .25 length of head; premaxillaries not protractile; lower jaw included; snout blunt, equal to eye and contained about 4.5 times in length of head; gill-membranes slightly connected; margin of preopercle smooth; lateral line complete; scales in lateral series 44 to 50, in transverse series 5+9; no scales on cheeks, nape and breast; 2 or 3 large scales on upper part of opercle, these sometimes absent; median ventral surface with a few large plate-like scales; dorsal fins of moderate size, the rays x or xi+11; anal fin rather large, the rays ii,8 or ii,9, the spines strong: caudal slightly concave behind; pectorals as long as head and extending as far as vent, reaching beyond the ventrals.   Color: Male— pale yellow with dark green markings; 10 or 11 vertical green bars on sides which run together into a band, back with dark mottlings; head dark blue above, one black bar below eye and another anterior to eye, under parts of head sulphur yellow; lips orange yellow; a pale spot on nape; fins mostly plain bluish black; on first dorsal a median band of bright yellow; faint bars on second dorsal and anal; orange markings on those fins and also on ventrals; 2 yellow spots at caudal base.   Female—paler; the confluent vertical markings on sides diamond-shaped and black; under parts yellowish; well defined bars on second dorsal and caudal (Named for Roanoke River.)

This species is known only from the Roanoke, Tar, and Neuse basins.   It is stated by Jordan to be very abundant in the Neuse at Milburnie, near Raleigh. Length, 2 inches.

Genus HYPOHOMUS Cope.   Darters.

Comparatively large, showy darters, quite similar to Hadropterus, but the scales on the median ventral surface are small like those of the body and are not shed.   Body elongate, head depressed, premaxillaries not protractile, anal fin rather large, ventrals widely separated, scales very small or moderate, lateral line complete or incomplete.   Five known species, of which the 2 following are recorded from North Carolina:

i. Scales very small, about 100 in lateral series; snout moderately long; gill-membranes slightly connected; general color of body olive green tinged with orange; a lateral band of confluent elongated blotches and a long row of small, discreet brown spots between lateral line and base of dorsal...*aurantiacus.*

ii. Scales larger, about 82 in lateral series; snout long and slender; gill-membranes widely connected across isthmus; general color of body yellowish green, with about 10 broad dusky cross bars and 10 dusky blotches along side; a very distinct black shoulder spot.

squamatus.

(*Hypohomus*, uniform below).

219. HYPOHOMUS AURANTIACUS (Cope).

Orange-colored Darter.

Cottogaster aurantiacus Cope, Journal Academy Natural Sciences of Philadelphia, 1868 (1869), 211; Holston River, Saltville, Va.
Hypohomus aurantiacus, Cope, 1870*b*, 449; French Broad River, Madison County, N. C.   Jordan & Evermann, 1896, 1040, pl. clxviii, fig. 442.
Hadropterus aurantiacus, Bean, Proceedings U. S. National Museum 1885, 165; French Broad River, N. C.

DIAGNOSIS.—Body quite elongate, slightly compressed, the depth contained 6 times in length; head contained 4.25 to 4.5 times in length; mouth very slightly oblique; maxillary reaching to anterior margin of pupil; lower jaw included; snout decurved, rather long, its length contained 3.5 in head; diameter of eye less than snout; interorbital width .2 length of head; gill-membranes slightly joined; scales firm, regular, those in lateral series about 100, in transverse series 14+15, about 85 with pores; cheeks, nape, and opercles covered with fine scales; breast naked; lateral line straight, continuous, beginning opposite upper margin of pupil; dorsal fins long, low, separated by a space equal to half diameter of eye; dorsal rays xv+15, the longest spines less than half length of head, the longest soft rays .33 longer than longest spines; anal fin as high as soft dorsal, the rays II,11; caudal margin nearly straight; pectorals rather long, extending half way to anal.   Color: olive green, with orange tinge; a black lateral band, about width of eye, formed of connected blotches; a row of yellow spots above this band; a row of small brown spots on each side above level of eye, extending from head to a point under soft dorsal; chin and throat orange; head dark above; spinous dorsal orange in front, yellow behind.   (*aurantiacus*, orange colored.)

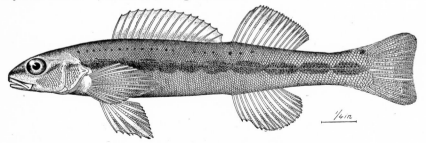

Fig. 112.   ORANGE-COLORED DARTER.   *Hypohomus aurantiacus.*

A very beautiful species, peculiar to the upper tributaries of the Tennessee. Only 2 specimens appear to have been recorded from North Carolina.   One, 4.6 inches long was obtained by Cope (1870); the other, in the National Museum, was collected at Asheville in 1885 by Dr. J. A. Watson and described by Dr. Bean.

220. HYPOHOMUS SQUAMATUS (Gilbert & Swain).

Scaly Darter.

Etheostoma squamatus Gilbert & Swain, Proceedings U. S. National Museum, 1887, 50; French Broad River, Tenn.
Etheostoma squamatum, Jordan, 1889*b*, 153; Spring Creek (tributary to French Broad) at Hot Springs, N. C
Hypohomus squamatus, Jordan & Evermann, 1896,1040.

DIAGNOSIS.—Back elevated, making an angle at nape; depth contained 5.5 times in length; head long, slender, its length contained 3.75 in total length; mouth long, narrow; maxillary extending as far as anterior margin of eye; lower jaw included; jaw teeth in broad band, the outer anterior teeth enlarged; snout long and sharp, equal to maxillary and contained 3.5 in head; eye contained 4.75 times in head, 1.4 times in snout; interorbital space .4 eye; gill-membranes broadly connected; scales in lateral series about 82, in transverse series 10+18; cheeks, breast, and nape covered with finer scales than body; opercles with larger, spiny scales; dorsal rays XIV+13, the longest spine .33 head; anal fin shorter and higher than soft dorsal, the rays II,10; caudal slightly concave, with rounded lobes; pectorals about .8 length of head; ventrals about .6 length of head. Color of North Carolina specimens: body yellowish green, with about 10 dark green cross bars and same number of blotches along lateral line; a black spot on shoulder; a black line through eye; side and top of head dusky; a dusky blotch at base of tail, a round black spot behind it; dorsal yellowish green at base, then a dusky band, then an orange band, and a dusky edge; second dorsal and caudal pale green, spotted, the rays brown; anal dusky, mottled; pectorals dull yellow, mottled; ventrals dusky. (*squamatus*, scaly.)

Known only from the upper part of the Tennessee basin, where it is rare. The only North Carolina specimens, 4 in number, were recorded by Jordan from the French Broad at Hot Springs; the largest of these was 4.6 inches long, which is about the maximum attained by this species.

Genus ULOCENTRA Jordan. Darters.

In this genus the body is moderately elongate and but slightly compressed; head short, thick, with but slightly convex parietal region; mouth small, horizontal, with small vomerine teeth, premaxillaries protractile, occasionally with a bridle extending to the forehead; maxillary not closely joined to preorbital; gill-membranes narrowly or broadly joined; median line of belly without enlarged plate-like scales; lateral line present; 9 to 13 spines in first dorsal; second dorsal larger than anal; anal with 2 prominent spines, the first the longer. Of the half-dozen species known, only one is a member of the local fauna. (*Ulocentra*, complete-spined.)

221. ULOCENTRA SIMOTERA (Cope).

Snub-nosed Darter.

Hyostoma simoterum Cope, Journal Academy of Natural Sciences of Philadelphia, 1868 (1869), 215; Holston River and tributaries. Cope, 1870b, 494; French Broad River, N. C.
Ulocentra simotera, Jordan & Evermann, 1896, 1051, pl. clxx, fig. 448.

DIAGNOSIS.—Form comparatively short, the depth .20 to .25 total length; head about equal to depth; profile from dorsal base to mouth strongly curved; snout short and blunt; maxillary reaching as far as anterior edge of pupil; eye rather longer than snout, .25 length of head; scales in lateral series about 50, in transverse series 6+11; opercles, cheeks, and breast more or less scaly; dorsal rays X+9 to 11, both fins higher than head is long; anal small, beginning under end of first dorsal, the rays II,7; caudal very slightly concave; pectorals longer than head; ventrals as long as head. Color: pale green on back, yellow or orange on belly; some scales on back with reddish centers, surrounded by yellow scales; sides with quadrate dark green blotches; head with dark markings; a dark stripe extending forward from eye, another downward from eye; first dorsal fin with a pale base, then a black bar, then another pale zone, the edge brownish, the membranes with an orange spot on pale part; second dorsal fin with pale yellow rays, a black spot at base of each, membranes brown-spotted;

anal and ventral fins pale yellow; caudal fin yellow, with 3 narrow black bars; pectoral fins pale yellow, with faint bars, (*simotera*, snub-nosed).

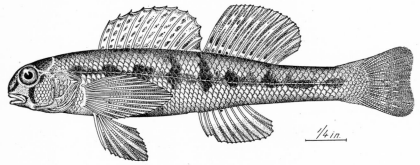

Fig. 113. SNUB-NOSED DARTER. *Ulocentra simotera.*

This species is known from western Virginia to Alabama, being abundant in Holston River and other streams on the western slope of the Alleghanies. It has been recorded from North Carolina only by Cope, from the French Broad, and the National Museum contains a specimen collected there by Cope. Length, 3 inches.

Genus DIPLESION Rafinesque. Darters.

This genus contains only a single species, with body elongate, cylindrical; head short, profile strongly curved; mouth small, somewhat inferior; lower jaw short; premaxillaries protractile, a slight bridle connecting them with forehead; maxillary united to preorbital; jaw teeth strong, no teeth on vomer and palatines; gill-membranes broadly united; gill-rakers short; scales of moderate size, those on ventral surface not enlarged; lateral line complete; anterior dorsal lower and longer than posterior; anal smaller than second dorsal, with 2 strong spines. (*Diplesion*, nearly two, in allusion to the deeply incised dorsal.)

222. DIPLESION BLENNIOIDES (Rafinesque).

Green-sided Darter.

Etheostoma blennioides Rafinesque, Journal de Physique, 1819, 419; Ohio River. Jordan, 1889*b*, 153; Swannanoa River and Spring Creek.
Hyostoma cymatogrammum, Cope, 1870*b*, 450; French Broad River.
Diplesion blennioides, Jordan & Evermann, 1896, 1053, pl. clxx, fig. 449.

DIAGNOSIS.—Depth contained 4.75 to 6 times in length, head 4.3 to 4.6 times; mouth very small, horizontal; upper jaw partly concealed in a groove under snout, maxillary extending about to anterior margin of eye; eye large, contained 3.5 in length of head, rather shorter than snout, the eyes close together and separated by a groove; opercular spine strong; pyloric cœca 4; scales in lateral series 65 to 78, in transverse series 6 + 14, fine scales on cheeks, large scales on opercles; chest naked; dorsal rays XII to XIV + 12 to 15; anal rays II,8 or II,9; caudal slightly concave; pectorals longer than head. Color: olive green, the back tessellated with dark, the sides with about 8 pairs of green vertical bars joined below (sometimes above); orange dots on sides; olive stripes and dark bars on head; first dorsal light brown at base, blue above; second dorsal and anal bluish green; caudal green, with faint bars; females duller. (*blennioides*, blenny-like.)

Inhabits clear brooks from Pennsylvania to South Dakota, and southward to Alabama. Recorded from the French Broad in North Carolina by Cope, and from the Swannanoa at Asheville and Spring Creek at Hot Springs by Jordan, who found it common. It is also known from Richland Creek near Waynesville, where specimens were collected by Mr. P. L. Jouy. This is one of the finest of the darters, having a maximum length of 5 inches.

Genus BOLEOSOMA DeKay.   Tessellated Darters.

Small, active fishes, found among vegetation in mountain and lowland streams. Form elongate, fusiform; head small, contracted anteriorly, the superior profile convex; parietal region slightly convex; mouth small, horizontal, maxillaries protractile, teeth on vomer; gill-membranes connected either narrowly or broadly; pyloric cœca 3 to 6; scales rather large, those on median ventral surface not enlarged or deciduous; lateral line complete, or interrupted behind; dorsal spines 8 to 10, soft dorsal markedly larger than anal; the latter with a single short spine; ventral fins comparatively well separated; coloration rather plain, no red or blue, the males black in spring. About 10 species; 4 known from North Carolina: (*Boleosoma*, arrow-bodied.)

223. BOLEOSOMA OLMSTEDI (Storer).
Tessellated Darter.

Etheostoma olmstedi Storer, Journal Boston Society of Natural History, 1841, 61, pl 5, fig. 2; Hartford, Connecticut.
Etheostoma nigrum olmstedi, Jordan, 1889b, 130; Neuse and Little rivers. Smith, 1893a, 192, 196, 200; Pasquotank and Roanoke rivers, and Albemarle Sound.
Boleosoma nigrum olmstedi, Jordan & Evermann, 1896, 1057, pl. clxxi, fig. 451.

DIAGNOSIS (based on Edenton specimens).—Form slender, rounded, the depth contained 5.5 times in length; head .25 length; eye contained 3.5 times in head; opercles, cheeks, and breast scaly; scales in lateral series 48 to 52, in transverse series 6+8; dorsal fins high, the rays x or xi+13 or 14; anal rays 1,8 or 1,9. Color: olivaceous; back tessellated with darker; sides blotched; head dusky in males, a black stripe below eye and another anterior to eye; dorsal fins irregularly and finely spotted with dark brown or black; caudal with 6 or 8 narrow, dark vertical bars. (Named for Charles Olmstead, an early American fish student.)

This darter occurs from Massachusetts to North Carolina in coastwise streams. It is abundant in Little River at Goldsboro and in Abemarle Sound and tributaries, many examples being collected by the writer among clumps of Myriophyllum in quiet muddy water at Edenton, and in running muddy water at Plymouth; all the fish were under 3 inches in length, the males .25 to .5 inch longer than the females.

224. BOLEOSOMA NIGRUM (Rafinesque).
Johnny Darter; Black Darter.

Etheostoma nigrum Rafinesque, Ichthyologia Ohiensis, 37, 1820; Green River, Ky. Jordan, 1889b, 133, 134, 139; Haw, Yadkin, and Catawba rivers.
Boleosoma nigrum, Jordan & Evermann, 1896, 1056, pl. clxx, fig. 450.

DIAGNOSIS.—Body very long and slender, the depth .16 to .2 length, caudal peduncle longer than head; head about .25 length; eye rather more than .25 head and about equal to snout; mouth small, lower jaw slightly included; opercular spine strong; opercles scaly, space before dorsal fin more or less scaly, cheeks and breast naked; scales in lateral series 44 to 46, in transverse series 5 + 9; vertical fins rather high, spinous dorsal lower than soft dorsal and about .5 head, dorsal rays IX + 12; anal rays I,7 to I,9; caudal fin truncate or slightly concave; pectorals as long as head. Color: pale greenish; back tessellated with brown; sides with brown blotches; head speckled, a black stripe before eye and often one below eye; fins with dark bars, sometimes nearly absent; males in spring anteriorly, and often entirely, black. (*nigrum*, black.)

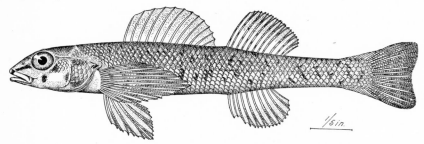

Fig. 114. JOHNNY DARTER. *Boleosoma nigrum.*

The johnny darter is a widely distributed and well known species, and is often the most abundant darter in the streams where it exists; it lives on sandy or gravelly bottom among submerged plants. The male in spring assumes an intense bluish-black color which often covers the entire body and fins. Although it may occur in some of the North Carolina streams west of the mountains, it is as yet recorded only from the upper waters of the Cape Fear, Yadkin, and Catawba, where Jordan found it to be more or less common. Length, 2 to 3 inches.

225. BOLEOSOMA EFFULGENS (Girard).

Effulgent Darter.

Arlina effulgens Girard, Proceedings Academy of Natural Sciences of Philadelphia, 1859, 64; tributaries of Potomac River, D. C.
Boleosoma effulgens, Cope, 1870b, 450; Deep River, Guilford Co., N. C.
Etheostoma nigrum effulgens, Jordan, 1889b, 126; Tar River at Rocky Mount.
Boleosoma nigrum effulgens, Jordan & Evermann, 1896, 1058; Maryland to North Carolina.

DIAGNOSIS.—Body very long, the depth contained more than 6 times in length; head contained 4.2 times in length, snout strongly decurved; eye large, more than .25 head; opercular spine rudimentary; opercles scaly, nape and breast naked, cheeks usually naked; scales in lateral series 40 to 42, in crosswise series 5 + 6; fins well developed; dorsal very high, especially in male, the rays IX,13; anal rays I,9; caudal fin well rounded; pectorals and ventrals extending to or beyond anal origin. Color: lustrous green, with 7 dark cross blotches on back, and 8 faint bars on side; a dark spot at base of caudal; dorsal blackish, with white spots on rays; caudal white spotted. (*effulgens*, brilliant.)

Found coastwise from North Carolina northward as far as Washington, D. C. Jordan records the species as common in Tar River at Rocky Mount, and Cope had specimens from Deep River, a tributary of the Cape Fear in Guilford County. Length, 2.5 inches.

226. BOLEOSOMA MACULATICEPS Cope.

Spotted-head Darter.

Boleosoma maculaticeps Cope, 1870*b*, 269; upper Catawba River, N. C.
Boleosoma nigrum maculaticeps, Jordan & Evermann, 1896, 1058; Catawba River.

DIAGNOSIS.—Body slender, the depth less than .15 length; head .25 length; eye large, contained 3.75 times in head; opercular spine moderate; cheeks scaleless; scales in lateral series 41, in transverse series 5+10; fins large; dorsal rays IX+13; anal rays I,9; caudal fin truncate. Color: pale yellowish, with ill-defined series of dark spots on back and sides, with smaller spots between; nape, top of head, and snout with large brown spots; fins black-barred. (*maculaticeps*, spotted head.)

Known only from the upper waters of Catawba River, where it is reported to be common. No one but Cope appears to have collected the species. Length, 2.2 inches.

Genus IOA Jordan & Brayton. Darters.

Small fishes inhabiting brooks with sandy bottom in the southern pine lands. Body exceedingly elongate, cylindrical, and translucent; head long and pointed; premaxillaries protractile; body only partly scaled; lateral line complete; gill-membranes slightly connected; dorsal spines 7 to 9; anal fin much smaller than second dorsal, with 2 spines. Probably only a single species, peculiar to Virginia and North Carolina. (*Ioa*, arrow or dart.)

227. IOA VITREA (Cope).

Glassy Darter.

Pœcilichthys vitreus Cope, 1870*a*, 263; Walnut Creek, tributary of Neuse River. Cope, 1870*b*, 449; Walnut Creek.
Etheostoma vitreum, Jordan, 1889*b*, 126, 130; Tar and Neuse rivers. Evermann & Cox, 1896, 305; Walnut Creek, tributary of Neuse.
Ioa vitrea, Jordan & Gilbert, 1879, 368; Neuse River at Goldsboro. Jordan & Evermann, 1896, 1064; southeastern Virginia and eastern North Carolina.

DIAGNOSIS.—Form very slender, the depth .14 length; head slender, pointed, contained 4 to 4.5 times in length; maxillary extending to front of eye; eye about equal to snout, contained 3.6 times in head; scales in lateral series 50 to 62; cheeks and opercles covered with large ctenoid scales; breast naked, a naked space on belly anterior to vent, scales on sides very large and rough, back from middle of spinous dorsal forward naked; fins small; dorsal rays VII to IX+11 to 14; anal much smaller than second dorsal, the rays II,6 to II,9; pectorals long and narrow. Color: translucent in life, with 7 green spots on back and 8 or 9 linear green spots on sides; fins plain. (*vitrea*, glassy.)

Cope based this species on a single specimen from Walnut Creek, a tributary of the Neuse in Wake County. Jordan reports the fish as very abundant in Tar River at Rocky Mount, Neuse River at Millburnie, and Little River at Goldsboro. Evermann & Cox (1896) record the fish from Walnut Creek, the type locality. It is also known from Dismal Swamp and from Blackwater River, tributary of the Chowan, in Virginia. Length, 2 inches.

Genus ETHEOSTOMA Rafinesque. Darters.

The most numerous genus of darters, containing some of the most brilliant and interesting species. Their form is varied, and is perhaps susceptible of division in a number of genera.   Body not particularly elongate, and in some species rather stout; mouth terminal or slightly inferior; premaxillaries not protractile; teeth in jaws strong, vomer and palatines usually toothed; parietal region of skull very strongly convex in cross section; gill-membranes either connected or not; body completely scaled, the scales on median ventral surface small and persistent; lateral line nearly straight, sometimes deficient posteriorly; pyloric cœca 3 or 4; fins well developed; first dorsal with 7 to 15 spines, the fin larger than second, which is larger than anal; anal spines 2, the first larger, the second rarely rudimentary; ventral fins close together.   Nearly 40 species known, 7 being recorded from North Carolina, distinguished as follows:

Key to the North Carolina species of Etheostoma.

i. Lateral line complete or practically so, only a few pores being absent.
  a. Gill-membranes rather broadly joined together; ventral fins very close together, the interspace less than width of base of fin.
    b. Head without any scales.
      c. Pectoral fins about length of head; scales in lateral series 48 or less; dorsal spines 9 to 11; head .25 total length or more..............*thalassinum.*
      cc. Pectoral fins .33 longer than head; scales in lateral series 48 or more; dorsal spines 11 or 12; head less than .25 total length................ *swannanoa.*
    bb. Head partly scaled...*zonale.*
  aa. Gill-membranes only slightly joined together; ventral fins still closer together.
    d. Snout abruptly decurved, scales in lateral series 50 to 60.
      e. Dorsal spines 11 or 12......................................*camurum.*
      ee. Dorsal spines 14...*vulneratum.*
    dd. Snout not decurved; scales in lateral series 45 to 48..............*rufilineatum.*
ii. Lateral line incomplete, extending about to end of spinous dorsal; dorsal spines about 8; head naked, scales in lateral series 40 to 65; caudal large, rounded..........*flabellare.*

(*Etheostoma*, various-mouthed.)

228. ETHEOSTOMA THALASSINUM (Jordan & Brayton).

Sea-green Darter.

Nothonotus thalassinus Jordan & Brayton, 1878, 13; Catawba River, Reedy River, Ecoree River; Saluda River and other tributaries of the Santee in North and South Carolina.
Etheostoma thalassinum, Jordan, 1889b, 139; Bucks Creek and Johns River, tributaries of Catawba.   Jordan & Evermann, 1898, 1071.

DIAGNOSIS.—Form rather stout, back arched, depth contained 4.75 to 5 times in length head large, contained 3.6 to 4 times in length; snout blunt, as long as eye, which is contained 3.5 to 4 times in head; upper jaw longer, reaching backward to eye; head, throat, and anterior part of neck without scales; scales in lateral series 40 to 48, in transverse series 6+6; fins large; dorsal rays IX to XI+10 to 12;   anal rays II,7 or II,8; caudal distinctly lunate; pectorals as long as head.   Color: mottled olive green, sides with 6 or 7 bluish green cross-bars;   belly orange;   head grass green, with dark green streaks below eye; spinous dorsal reddish at base, then black, the distal third red; soft dorsal black at base, reddish above;   caudal with 2 orange spots at base, orange on margin, black between; anal brilliant bluish green, with pale tip; ventrals green;   pectorals orange at base with a dark spot;   female duller and more speckled. (*thalassinum,* sea green.)

This species is known only from the Santee basin, in which, according to Jordan, it is much the commonest of the darters.   It is especially abundant in Bucks Creek among weed-grown rocks.   Length, 2.5 inches.

229. ETHEOSTOMA SWANNANOA Jordan & Evermann.

Swanannoa Darter.

Etheostoma swannanoa Jordan & Evermann, in Jordan, 1889*a*, 360, pl. xlv, fig. 13; Holston and Swannanoa
    rivers. Jordan, 1889*b*, 153, pl. xv, fig. 13; south fork of Swannanoa River. Jordan & Evermann,
    1896, 1071.

DIAGNOSIS.—Depth contained 6 times in total length; head rather short and deep, contained 4.3 times in length; superior profile strongly curved; snout short and blunt; mouth
small, horizontal; lower jaw included; premaxillaries not protractile; maxillaries extending
as far as anterior margin of eye; eye high on side of head, large, .25 length of head; branchial
membranes broadly connected across isthmus; scales in lateral series 48 to 58, in transverse
series 6+7 or 8; cheeks, opercles, and breast naked, nape scaly or naked; lateral line complete;
dorsal rays xi or xii+12 to 14, the two fins contiguous; anal rays ii,9; pectorals extending
beyond tips of ventrals, .33 longer than head. Color: Male—dark green on back, light green
below; 6 dark green blotches on back, 8 to 10 more or less connected dark green blotches on
sides; a dark bar below eye; base and edge of spinous dorsal bright brown; soft dorsal and
caudal speckled green; base and lower edge of pectorals saffron; anal and ventrals pale yellow. Female and young—duller, body more spotted, pectorals and caudal with dark bars.
(Named for Swannanoa River.)

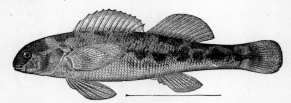

Fig. 115. SWANNANOA DARTER. *Etheostoma swannanoa.*

Known only from the clear cold waters of Holston River in Virginia and
the south fork of Swannanoa River in North Carolina.   Length, 3 inches.

230. ETHEOSTOMA ZONALE (Cope).

Blue-banded Darter.

Pœcilichthys zonalis Cope, Journal Academy of Natural Sciences of Philadelphia, 1868 (1869), 212, pl. xxiv,
    fig. 1; Holston River, Va. Cope, 1870*b*, 450; French Broad River.
Nothonotus zonalis, Jordan & Brayton, 1878, 58; French Broad River (after Cope).
Etheostoma zonale, Jordan, 1889*b*, 153; French Broad River at Hot Springs, Spring Creek at Hot Springs,
    Swannanoa River at Asheville. Jordan & Evermann, 1896, 1075.

DIAGNOSIS.—Body rather slender, the depth .20 to .16 length; head small, short, .25 to
.20 length; mouth small; maxillary extending to anterior margin of orbit; snout short,
decurved, blunt, shorter than eye; eye contained 3.5 to 4 times in head; scales in lateral
series about 50, in transverse series 6+9; cheeks, opercle, and neck scaly, breast rarely so;
dorsal rays x or xi+10 to 12, the posterior fin higher and shorter than the anterior; anal fin
smaller than second dorsal, the rays ii,6 or ii,7; caudal margin slightly concave; pectorals
about length of head. Color: bright green above, golden below; a broad, brown lateral band;
6 dark brown spots on back; 8 turquoise blue stripes extending downward from lateral band
and encircling the belly; back of head, muzzle, a bar below eye, and a spot on opercle black;
anal, caudal, pectoral, and ventral fins golden, with brown spots; central part of spinous dorsal
crimson, base of soft dorsal with a series of round crimson spots; base of pectorals with a
black spot; female speckled and with duller colors. (*zonale*, banded.)

Inhabits Mississippi basin, from northern North Carolina to northern Indiana, westward and southward to Iowa and Louisiana. It is rather common in the French Broad and tributaries in North Carolina. Length, 3 inches.

231. ETHEOSTOMA CAMURUM (Cope).

Blue-breasted Darter.

Pœcilichthys camurum Cope, 1870a, 265; headwaters of Cumberland River in Tennessee.
Etheostoma camurum, Jordan, 1889b, 153; Spring Creek, tributary of French Broad. Jordan & Evermann, 1896, 1076, pl. clxxii, fig. 456.

DIAGNOSIS.—Form stout, the depth contained 4.5 times in total length; caudal peduncle deep; head short, .25 length; maxillary extending beyond anterior margin of eye; eye less than snout, contained 4.5 times in head; snout sharply decurved; scales in lateral series 50 to 58, in transverse series 7 + 8; head naked; dorsal fins high, the rays XI + 13; anal rays II,8; caudal truncate with rounded corners; pectorals much shorter than head. Color: Male—above dark green or blackish, below paler; sides with many crimson dots, which may be arranged in series; fine longitudinal lines along the rows of scales; several dark streaks on side of head; breast and throat deep blue; a black spot in front of spinous dorsal, a crimson spot on margin above this; soft dorsal, anal and caudal red with yellow margin, a narrow edge of the fins being dark blue or black; pectorals and ventrals with broad red border. Female—duller, general color green, with many brown scales on sides; fins mostly yellowish green, the caudal red, all vertical fins black-edged. (*camurum*, blunt-headed.)

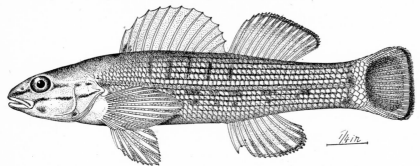

Fig. 116. BLUE-BREASTED DARTER. *Etheostoma camurum.*

This darter, the most beautiful of its kind and perhaps the most ornate of all fresh-water fishes, ranges from Ohio and Indiana to the headwaters of the Tennessee. It is probably rare in North Carolina, and only a single specimen is known from that state; this was collected by Jordan in 1888 in Spring Creek at Hot Springs. Length, 2.5 inches.

232. ETHEOSTOMA VULNERATUM (Cope).

Red-spotted Darter.

Pœcilichthys vulneratus Cope, 1870a, 266; Warm Springs Creek, tributary of French Broad, N. C. Cope, 1870b, 450; Warm Springs Creek.
Etheostoma vulneratum, Jordan & Evermann, 1896, 1077.

DIAGNOSIS.—Form cylindrical, rather robust, depth contained 4.5 times in length; head .25 length of body; caudal peduncle deep; eye equal to snout, .25 length of head; scales in lateral series 53, in transverse series 8+9; dorsal rays xiv+13; anal rays ii,8; caudal rounded. Color: light green, sides with a few small crimson spots and about 8 dark green cross bars which are interrupted above lateral line; first dorsal marked with a median series of red spots, second dorsal with black margin, caudal pale orange, fins otherwise plain. (*vulneratum*, wounded.)

This darter, 2 inches long, was described from Warm Springs Creek, a tributary of the French Broad in Madison County, North Carolina, and is known from no other locality. Warm Springs is now called Hot Springs, and the creek is referred to as Spring Creek in Jordan's report herein frequently cited. This species is possibly the young of *Etheostoma camurum*, but the larger number of dorsal spines suggests that it is distinct.

233. ETHEOSTOMA RUFILINEATUM (Cope).

Red-lined Darter.

Pœcilichthys rufilineatus Cope, 1870a, 267; Warm Springs Creek, Madison County, N. C. Cope, 1870b, 450; Warm Springs Creek.
Etheostoma rufilineatum, Jordan, 1889b, 153; Spring Creek at Hot Springs and Swannanoa River at Asheville. Jordan & Evermann, 1896, 1079.

DIAGNOSIS.—Body rather stout, the depth contained 4.5 to 5 times in length, the back somewhat elevated, the caudal peduncle deep; head .25 length; snout short, conical; eye rather small, equal to snout, contained 4.5 times in head; lateral line complete; scales rather large, those in lateral series 45 to 48, in transverse series 6+7; opercles scaly; cheeks, nape, and breast naked; dorsal fins rather large, the rays x to xii+11 to 13; anal rays ii,8 or ii,9; caudal small, truncate behind; pectorals equal to length of head. Color: Male—body above green, with dark lengthwise stripes and clusters of yellow brown scales; belly orange yellow, breast blue; head with blackish stripe from nape to snout, another below, and 2 spots still lower; side of head with 5 black streaks; sides of lips orange; opercles, cheeks, and branchiostegals with orange spots; fins brilliant, mostly with scarlet borders; dorsal pale yellow, with black dots and reddish edge; anal and ventrals yellow at base, pale and blackish lines on edge, and scarlet between; caudal yellow and orange; pectorals yellow, with black and scarlet base and scarlet bar near edge. Female—body green, with 8 dark, more or less interrupted cross bars; sides with yellow longitudinal streaks; head marked as in male; fins yellow or orange, with blackish spots or bars. (*rufiilneatum*, red-lined.)

A very beautiful species, living in clear brooks in upper waters of Tennessee and Cumberland rivers. Described from Warm Springs Creek by Cope, it was collected in the same locality by Jordan nearly 20 years after and was also found by him in the Swannanoa, being common among river weeds. A specimen in the National Museum from Big Creek, a tributary of the French Broad, was collected by Gilbert & Swain in 1884. Length, 3 inches.

234. ETHEOSTOMA FLABELLARE Rafinesque.

Fan-tailed Darter.

Etheostoma flabellaris Rafinesque, Journal de Physique, 1819, 419; tributaries of Ohio River.
Pœcilichthys flabellatus, Cope, 1870b, 450; Catawba River.
Etheostoma flabellare, Jordan, 1889b, 139, 153; Bucks Creek and Johns River, tributaries of Catawba, and Swannanoa River. Jordan & Evermann, 1896, 1097.

DIAGONSIS.—Body rather slender, depth contained 4.5 to 5.5 times in length; head very long and pointed, contained 3.6 to 4 times in length; mouth oblique, maxillary extending to front of eye, lower jaw projecting; snout straight, .25 length of head; upper lip on level with upper margin of eye; eye rather less than snout; scales in lateral series 40 to 65, in transverse series about 7+7; head naked; lateral line straight, extending about as far as posterior part of spinous dorsal; dorsal rays about VIII+12 to 14, the spinous part in male .3 higher than soft part, the tips with fleshy enlargements; anal similar to soft dorsal, the rays II,7 to II,9; caudal rather large, rounded; pectorals averaging less than head in length. Color: dark greenish brown, dusky above, the sides with dark cross bars or blotches; a dark line along side of head through eye; a black shoulder spot; fins mostly plain; fleshy tips of spinous dorsal reddish; soft dorsal, caudal, and pectorals barred. (*flabellare*, fan-like.)

Ranges from New York to Alabama and Iowa, being found on both slopes of the Alleghanies in North Carolina. It is common in the Catawba, and also in the Swannanoa and its north and south forks, inhabiting cold, clear waters. Length, 2.5 inches. Jordan & Copeland have given the following interesting account of this species:

The darter of darters is the fan-tail (*Etheostoma flabellare*). Hardiest, wiriest, wariest of them all, it is the one which is most expert in catching other creatures, and the one which most surely evades your clutch. You can catch a weasel asleep when you put your finger on one of these. It is a slim, narrow, black, pirate-rigged little fish, with a long pointed head, and a projecting, prow-like lower jaw. It carries no flag, but is colored like the rocks among which it lives. It is dark brown in hue, with a dusky spot on each scale, so that the whole body seems covered with lengthwise stripes, and these are further relieved by cross bands of the same color. Its fins, especially the broad, fan-shaped caudal, are likewise much checkered with spots of black. The spines of the dorsal fin are very low, and each of these in the male ends in a little fleshy pad of rusty-red color, the fish's only attempt at ornamentation. The fan-tailed darter chooses the coldest and swiftest waters, and in these, as befits his form, he leads an active, predatory life. He is the terror of water snails and caddis worms, and the larvæ of mosquitoes. In the aquarium this darter is one of the most interesting of fishes, for, though plainly colored, it is very handsome, and in its movements is the most graceful of all the darters. Its mouth opens wider than that of any of the others, and it is fuller of bristling teeth. Its large, yellow-rimmed black eyes are ever on the watch. The least of a "fish" and the most of a darter, the fan-tailed is worthily left as a type of the genus *Etheostoma*, in which it was first placed by its discoverer, Rafinesque.

Genus BOLEICHTHYS Girard. Darters.

A small genus, similar to some species of Etheostoma, but having the lateral line slightly arched anteriorly and always deficient behind; premaxillaries not protractile; gill-membranes slightly united; top of head naked, opercles scaly, cheeks scaly or not. There are several variable species, inhabiting swampy or lowland waters; one local species. (*Boleichthys*, dart fish.)

235. BOLEICHTHYS FUSIFORMIS (Girard).

Fusiform Darter.

Boleosoma fusiformis Girard, Proceedings Boston Society of Natural History, 1854. 41; Charles River. Mass.
Boleichthys fusiformis, Jordan & Evermann, 1896, 1101. Smith, 1901, 134; Lake Mattamuskeet.

DIAGNOSIS.—Form variable, usually elongate, compressed, the depth .25 to .16 length; caudal peduncle long and slender; head rather long, contained 3.5 to 4 times in length; mouth moderate, maxillary extending beyond anterior margin of eye; snout short, less than eye, .25 length of head; opercular spine strong; lateral line high, more or less interrupted; scales strongly ctenoid, 45 to 60 in lateral series; 3+12 in transverse series; nape, cheeks, opercles, and breast well scaled, rarely naked; fins rather small; dorsal fins well separated, anterior with IX or X low spines, posterior higher, with 9 to 12 rays; anal rays II,6 to II,8; caudal rounded; pectorals about as long as ventrals, shorter than head.   Color: variable, usually dark green above, paler below, the upper parts irregularly blotched or mottled with darker; a dark bar below eye, another anterior to eye; spinous dorsal bright blue, with a median zone of red; soft dorsal, caudal, and pectorals with dark bars or spots; other fins plain.   (*fusiformis*, spindle-shaped.)

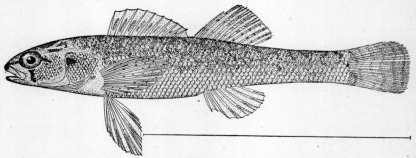

Fig. 117.   FUSIFORM DARTER.   *Boleichthys fusiformis.*

This darter, which inhabits lowland streams, swamps, and lakes from Massachusetts to Texas, and is doubtless to be met with in various parts of North Carolina, is as yet known only from Lake Mattamuskeet, where it was collected by the Bureau of Fisheries in 1900.

Genus COPELANDELLUS Jordan & Evermann.   Darters.

Similar to Boleichthys but differing in having the top of the head closely scaled; body slender, compressed; eye large; gill-membranes not connected; lateral line high, incomplete behind; cheeks, opercles, breast, and nape scaled; snout, jaws and preopercle naked.   One species.   (Named for Herbert Copeland, of Indiana, an early associate of Dr. Jordan and a student of the darters.)

236. COPELANDELLUS QUIESCENS (Jordan).

Copeland's Darter.

Pœcilichthys quiescens Jordan, Proceedings U. S. National Museum, 1884, 478; Allapaha River, Georgia.
Copelandellus quiescens, Jordan & Evermann, 1896, 1100, pl. clxxvi, fig. 468.

DIAGNOSIS.—Depth .2 length; head .27 length; eye more than .25 head and much longer than snout; maxillary reaching to a point under pupil; scales in lateral series 48 to 55, in transverse series 3+10; lateral line on 20 to 28 scales; dorsal rays IX to XII+9 to 12; anal rays II,7; caudal rounded; pectorals long.   Color: dark brown, with bright red and blackish mottlings on back and sides; 3 black bars about eye; a black humeral spot; dorsal, anal, and caudal fins dark-barred; other fins plain.   (*quiescens*, remaining quiet.)

Inhabiting the lowland swamps and sluggish streams of the coastal plain from Virginia to Florida, this species has not heretofore been recorded from North Carolina.   Mr. William P. Seal, of the Aquarium Supply Company, Delair, New Jersey, has collected numbers of specimens in the vicinity of Wilmington, and in January, 1906, forwarded a specimen to the writer with the following interesting note on the species:

I found *Copelandellus* near Wilmington in a cypress pond about 10 miles in circumference, cut off from tide water by a high dam. In this place there are *Centrarchus* and many other kinds of basses and sunfishes, as well as minnows and a great abundance of prawns. This species is also to be found in ditches into which the tide flows to the depth of several inches to a foot and where *Fundulus, Gambusia, Heterandria, Umbra, Chologaster, Elassoma, Aphredoderus*, and sunfishes abound. *Copelandellus* will stand warm and stagnant water better than any other darter I know of. I had specimens to spawn in a small still-water aquarium at Wilmington. The eggs were deposited on the under side of the leaves of lilies and other plants. The fish reaches a length of 2.5 or 3 inches.

Fig. 118. COPELAND'S DARTER. *Copelandellus quiescens.*

This species is known also from Lake Ellis in Craven County, where Mr. C. S. Brimley reports that he collected 15 specimens in June, 1905.

Family APOGONICHTHYIDÆ. The Cardinal-fishes.

A numerous family of small fishes, found chiefly in tropical seas and most abundant in the East Indies and Oceania. Body elongate, usually compressed, back often elevated; mouth rather large, more or less oblique, with villiform teeth on jaws, vomer, and sometimes palatines; lower bones of pharynx with sharp teeth; opercular spine inconspicuous; edge of preopercle entire or slightly serrated; scales rather large, usually ctenoid, completely covering body and more or less of head; lateral line present; dorsal fins separate, the anterior with 6 to 9 spines; soft dorsal short and similar to anal, which has 2 to 4 spines; ventrals thoracic; color in some species bright red. The 9 or 10 American genera are represented by about 20 species, of which only 1 is known from the North Carolina coast, but several others occur as stragglers to the north and south and may sometime be found locally.

Genus HYPOCLYDONIA Goode & Bean.

Very small bottom fishes, completely covered with deciduous, smooth scales, those of head embedded in skin; 2 flat spines on opercle; minute serrations on preopercle; stout gill-rakers in moderate number; 7 branchiostegals; a glandular organ at upper angle of gill-slit; high lateral line; and well-developed fins. One species. (*Hypoclydonia*, below the wave.)

237. HYPOCLYDONIA BELLA Goode & Bean.

Hypoclydonia bella Goode & Bean, Oceanic Ichthyology, 236, fig. 237, 1895; off Cape Fear and other parts of
North Carolina coast, off South Carolina, etc.   Jordan & Evermann, 1896, 1115, pl. clxxix, fig. 475.

DIAGNOSIS.—Depth contained 3.66 times in length; head .33 length; eye large, .28 length
of head and .5 longer than snout; mouth large, maxillary reaching a point under middle of
pupil; minute teeth in bands or patches on jaws, vomer, and palatines, with a few enlarged
canines on upper and lower jaws; scales in lateral series 29, in transverse series 2+7; dorsal
rays IX+1,9; anal rays II,7; caudal long and forked; pectorals and ventrals equal, about .6
head.   Color: plain; head purplish brown above; a dark triangular blotch at apex of spinous
dorsal.   (*bella*, beautiful.)

Known from specimens collected by the steamer Albatross off the coast of
Florida, South Carolina, and North Carolina, in depths of 90 to 259 fathoms,
and from a single example collected by the steamer Fish-Hawk off Cape Lookout
on August 27, 1902.   The length of the species is under 4 inches.

Family SERRANIDÆ.   The Sea Basses, Striped Basses, Groupers, etc.

A large and important family of carnivorous marine and fresh-water fishes,
with numerous representatives in American waters, including some of our most
valuable food-fishes, such as the striped bass, white perch, and sea bass.   The
leading characters of the family are oblong, compressed body covered with persistent scales (usually ctenoid); large or moderate mouth with protractile premaxillary; supplemental maxillary bone either present or absent; pointed teeth,
in bands on jaws, vomerine, and palatines; long or short gill-rakers; 4 gills; large
pseudobranchiae; gill-membranes not connected, and not united to isthmus;
6 or 7 branchiostegals; single lateral line, not reaching caudal fin; scaly cheeks
and opercles; preopercular margin usually serrate; one or two flat points on
posterior margin of opercle; skull without spines; dorsal fin single or double, with
stiff spines 2 to 15 in number, and 10 to 30 soft rays; short anal fin, with 3 spines
(if any) and 7 to 12 soft rays; air bladder present; stomach with few or numerous
pyloric appendages; intestine short.   The North Carolina serranids number 10
and belong in 7 genera.

Key to the North Carolina genera of Serranidæ.
i. Dorsal fins 2.
  a. Dorsal fins not connected; anal rays III,11 or III,12.....................ROCCUS.
  aa. Dorsal fins connected; anal rays III,8 or III,9.........................MORONE.
ii. Dorsal fin single, more or less divided.
  b. Maxillary with supplemental bone.
    c. Anal rays III,7 to III,9; head narrow above; parietal crests not continued forward
       on the frontal bones...EPINEPHELUS.
    cc. Anal rays III, 11 or III,12; head rather broad above; parietal crests continued for-
        ward to middle of orbits...................................MYCTEROPERCA.
  bb. Maxillary without supplemental bone.
    d. Caudal fin rounded or ending in 3 points, with middle rays produced; some of the
       dorsal spines with fleshy filaments.   .........................CENTROPRISTES.
    dd. Caudal fin forked, concave, or square; dorsal spines without fleshy tips.
      e. Branchiostegals 7; caudal fin deeply concave....................DIPLECTRUM.
      ee. Branchiostegals 6; caudal fin truncate................................DULES.

Genus ROCCUS Mitchill.   Striped Basses or Rock-fishes.

American anadromous and fresh-water fishes, with elongate or moderate
body, projecting lower jaw, patches of teeth on base of tongue, unconnnected

dorsal fins, and dark longitudinal stripes along sides.   Two species, one in Great
Lakes and Mississippi basin, the other coastwise.   (*Roccus*, a latinization of the
vernacular name, rock.)

238. ROCCUS LINEATUS (Bloch).

"Rock";   "Rock-fish";   Striped Bass.

Sciæna lineata Bloch, Ichthyologie, ix, 53, pl. 305, 1792; "Mediterranean Sea" (?).
Roccus lineatus, Cope, 1870b, 448; Neuse River.   Yarrow, 1877, 211; Fort Macon, New River, Neuse River,
    Jordan & Gilbert, 1879, 380; New and Neuse rivers.   Smith, 1893a, 192, 196, 200; Pasquotank River,
    Albemarle Sound, Roanoke River at Plymouth and Weldon.   Jordan & Evermann, 1896, 1132, pl.
    clxxx, fig. 478.
Roccus septentrionalis, Jenkins, 1887, 89; Beaufort (after Yarrow.)

DIAGNOSIS.—Body long, slightly compressed, depth contained 3.5 to 4 times in total
length; head less than .33 length; mouth large, maxillary extending nearly to middle of eye,
lower jaw projecting; base of tongue with 2 parallel patches of teeth; eye small, .15 to .20
length of head, .5 to .66 length of snout; preopercle with weak serrations; gill-rakers long and
slender, about 20 in number; scales in lateral series 65 to 70; fins rather small; dorsal rays
XI+1,12, longest spine less than .5 length of head; anal rays III,11; caudal forked.   Color:
above olive, sides and below white; back and sides marked by 7 or 8 black longitudinal stripes,
one along the lateral line; fins pale or dusky.   (*lineatus*, striped.)

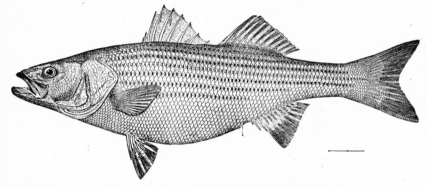

Fig. 119.   STRIPED BASS; ROCK-FISH.   *Roccus lineatus*.

This is the largest and one of the best of American fresh-water or anadromous spiny-rayed fishes.   It ascends streams along the entire Atlantic coast from
New Brunswick to Alabama, being most numerous between Massachusetts and
North Carolina.   It has also been introduced on the Pacific coast, and several
million pounds are now caught for market annually in California.   It ascends all
suitable rivers in North Carolina, and is especially abundant in the Albemarle
region.

Striped bass weighing 60 or 75 pounds are not uncommon, and ocasionally
their weight exceeds 100 pounds.   At Dr. Capehart's shad seine-fishery at Avoca,
North Carolina, fish of 105 pounds have been taken.   Dr. Goode reports one
caught in Massachusetts that weighed 112 pounds, supposed to have been the
largest specimen known.   At Edenton, North Carolina, in April, 1891, the writer
saw several striped bass, from dutch nets in the sound, each of which weighed

125 pounds. Fish weighing from half a pound upward are caught for market, and the average weight is probably 3 to 5 pounds.

In North Carolina striped bass are caught in some numbers throughout the year, just as in the Potomac and other streams to the northward; but the principal run is in spring when the fish are going upstream to spawn.

The spawning season in this state extends from late in April to early in May. Probably the most important striped bass spawning ground in the country at this time is in Roanoke River, in the vicinity of Weldon, where there is a fall of 50 feet in about 6 miles. In these rapids, where the muddy current is exceedingly strong and rendered very erratic by islands, boulders, and rocks, the fish spawns; and it is here that the general government has recently taken up the artificial propagation of the species. The eggs are similar to those of the shad, but average a trifle larger; and the number deposited by a full-sized fish may exceed several millions. In 1903 Mr. S. G. Worth, while conducting hatching operations on the Roanoke, stripped from a 20-pound fish a mass of eggs which after fertilization and immersion in water measured 60 quarts, equivalent to 1,500,000 on a basis of 25,000 to the quart. On April 21, 1897, a female "rock" caught in a shad seine at Avoca weighed 60 pounds, was 4 feet 4 inches long, and had ovaries 16 inches long and 5 inches wide, but the eggs were not nearly ripe. The roe of a fish weighing over 100 pounds taken at the same place in 1896 is said to have weighed 44 pounds. The average egg production of 12 fish stripped at Weldon in 1903 was over 700,000. The eggs may be hatched in shad jars, and the young emerge in 36 hours when the water temperature in 70° F.

Mr. Worth (1903) has given the following very interesting account of the spawning habits of this fish in Roanoke River:

For twenty years and more I have heard of the rock-fish fights at Weldon, and although I had taken eggs there in two seasons about twenty years ago, I never witnessed a rock fight until this year; and this season I saw hundreds of fights, as they term them. When the female fish are in spawning condition the male fish gather around them in great numbers. There will be one big fish, which may weigh five to fifty pounds, as one of them did which I took eggs from, and she will be surrounded by twenty, thirty or fifty small fish, and sometimes the fishermen will run one of their nets under and catch one of these large fish and thirty or more of the small fish; and what seemed to be an interesting point in connection with that is that the small fish appear to be the only male fish that mate with the female. They are known there as perch rock, because they are the size of a perch, and by actual weight they do not weigh as much as two pounds apiece, and yet they seem to represent practically about all there is in the way of male fishes. These rock fights were interesting. The fishes showed themselves on top of the water and flurried the water and made noises that would attract your attention, so that you would turn around to see the water breaking a hundred yards away. I thought before that that there was a good deal of imagination in it, but I know that it is a fact, and any one can witness it, and when that is going on it is the spawning season, which follows right on the heels of the shad spawning.

It is assumed by all the fishermen that operate on the river that the reddening of the water is caused by the gashes made by the fishes finning one another in their attempt to get nearer to the spawning female fish. It causes a bloody stain which I did not myself witness, but I know it has taken place, from the great number of persons who told me about it, and that the water was actually discolored.

A. HOEN & CO.

STRIPED BASS; ROCK-FISH (ROCCUS LINEATUS)

All kinds of fish of suitable size are eaten by the striped bass.   In North Carolina in spring, shad and alewives are the principal food and are consumed in enormous numbers, the bass being gluttonous and becoming very fat.   Crabs, shrimps, lobsters, squid, clams, and other invertebrates are also devoured.

The striped bass is one of the best and most valuable of American fishes, the flesh being white, flaky, well-flavored, and remaining firm when shipped to market.   As a game fish it is a general favorite in both salt and fresh water, and by many anglers it is more highly esteemed than any other species.   A popular method of fishing, practiced mostly in southern New England, is heaving and hauling in the surf with a stout line baited with menhaden or other fish.

In North Carolina the striped bass ranks next in importance to shad and alewives among the anadromous fishes, and the quantity here caught exceeds that in any other state except California.   While considerable quantities are taken with seines, gill nets, lines, and slides, the bulk of the yield, considering the entire state, comes from pound nets; most of the apparatus is operated primarily for shad and alewives.   The fishery is most extensive in Dare County, where about half the total product is obtained.   Other counties in which large quantities are taken are Currituck, Chowan, Bertie, Martin, Halifax, Washington, Beaufort, and Craven.   In the waters about Beaufort and Morehead, striped bass are caught in only small quantities, but they are more numerous at New Bern and other points on the Neuse.   The fishery is more important in Roanoke River than in any other stream, and there the catch is chiefly with sweep seines, the leading seine fishery being near Plymouth.   Other methods of fishing in and near the falls in the upper river are thus described by Mr. Worth (1903):

The fish go up there in March and April, and if there is water enough they distribute themselves over the falls where the current is so strong that it is apparently dangerous to go even when the river is at moderate stages, and when it is high it is really very dangerous; and these fish get up in these numerous channels between the islands, and are inaccessible until the water begins to fall.   When it falls to a certain stage the fishermen use finger traps and begin to take those fishes.   They are swept out by the current on the finger boards and are captured.   As soon as the river falls somewhat lower the fish become uneasy on account of the light covering of water on the falls, and drop below the foot of the falls at Weldon, and from that point down 2 miles there is fishing carried on with dip nets; they are after the manner of the shad skim nets, and are rigged on a bow; one man sits in the bow of the boat and the other in the stern, paddling, and they float down the river one or two miles and then turn back.   There are quite a number of boats engaged in this business, and they catch very considerable numbers of fish there.

Comparative statistics of the North Carolina striped bass catch.

YEARS.	POUNDS.	VALUE.
1880	770,000*	......
1887	499,586	$24,944
1888	560,354	27,981
1889	531,349	30,611
1897	845,123	58,035
1900	568,341	32,138
1902	1,183,400	114,111

*Estimate.

Genus MORONE Mitchill. White Perches.

This genus includes 2 small species, both American, one found in the Mississippi valley, the other on the Atlantic coast, Similar to Roccus, but with no teeth at base of tongue, a shorter anal fin, stouter spines in first dorsal fin, and dorsal fins more or less connected by a membrane. Body rather short and deep; jaws nearly equal; edge of tongue with linear patches of teeth; lower margin of preopercle finely serrate; scales rather large; second anal spine enlarged. (*Morone*, a name of unknown significance.)

239. MORONE AMERICANA (Gmelin).

"Perch"; "Black Perch"; "Silver Perch"; White Perch.

Perca americana Gmelin, Systema Naturæ, iii, 1308, 1788; New York.
Morone americana, Yarrow, 1877, 211; New and Neuse rivers. Jordan & Evermann, 1896, 1133, pl. clxxxi,
   fig. 479. Smith, 1893a, 192, 196, 200; Pasquotank River, Edenton Bay, Roanoke River. Smith,
   1901, 134; Lake Mattamuskeet.

DIAGNOSIS.—Back somewhat elevated, depth .4 to .33 total length; head contained 2.75 to 3.33 times in length; eye .25 head, less than snout; gill-rakers long, 18 to 21 in number; scales in lateral series 50 to 55, in transverse series 20; head scaly as far forward as nostrils; dorsal rays ix+1,12, longest spine .5 head; anal rays iii,8 or iii,9, second spine as long as third and stouter. Color: variable, ranging from almost black in ponds and certain brackish waters to silvery white with faint longitudinal streaks.

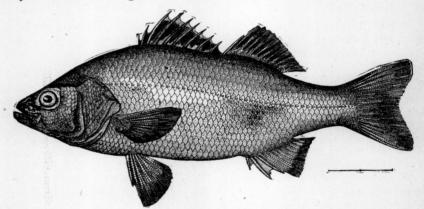

Fig. 120. WHITE PERCH. *Morone americana*.

This excellent little fish of the fresh, brackish, and salt waters of our east coast ranges from South Carolina to the maritime provinces of Canada. While essentially an anadromous species it is often landlocked in fresh water. Its most common and appropriate name is white perch, but in North Carolina it is called "silver perch", "black perch", or simply "perch".

In Albemarle Sound, it is more abundant and more valuable than the yellow perch, although scarcer than formerly; and in Currituck Sound it exists in greater abundance than any other commercial species, The average weight of those marketed is .5 to .75 of a pound, and the maximum weight is about 1.5

pounds.   In Lake Mattamuskeet it is very numerous, attains a large size, and is the most highly prized and important fish there found.   In New, Neuse, and other rivers of the southern part of the state the fish also abounds.

The spawning season in Albemarle Sound begins between April 1 and 10 and continues for about 10 days.   At that time there may be observed in the sound and its tributaries large numbers of white perch 2 to 3 inches long and doubtless a year old, which mix freely with the schools of minnows, silversides, and mullets.

The white perch feeds on minnows, shrimps, and other animals.   It is one of the best of American game fishes, and is a favorite with anglers; it takes the artificial fly readily, and also bites at minnows, worms, etc.   As a pan fish it has few superiors, and is by many persons preferred to any other species.

The annual catch of white perch in North Carolina in recent years has been about a million pounds.   In 1902 the fishermen sold 941,000 pounds and received $62,666 therefor, most of this yield coming from the seine and pound-net fisheries, and nearly half of it being credited to Currituck Sound.

Genus EPINEPHELUS Bloch.   Groupers.

A numerous genus of large marine food-fishes, inhabiting tropical and subtropical waters; some of them of considerable economic value.   Form rather robust, compressed; mouth large, with a few large canine teeth in front of jaws, and with enlarged, depressible inner teeth in each jaw; maxillary large, supplemental bone well developed and scaly; preopercle serrate; opercle with strong spines; gill-rakers short and few; scales small, ctenoid, those of lateral line triangular and cycloid; dorsal fins continuous, with 10 or 11 spines; anal spines 3, the second usually largest; caudal fin concave or rounded; pectorals rounded, short; ventrals close together, with a strong spine.   Of the 12 or more American species, 7 are known from the south Atlantic coast of the United States, and of these the following have been detected in North Carolina:

i. Caudal fin rounded; second dorsal spine shorter than third or fourth; scales in lateral line 110 to 125; body marked by irregular dark cross-bars; vertical fins edged with yellow. *striatus.*
ii. Caudal fin concave; second dorsal spine as long as third or fourth; scales in lateral line 130 to 140; body without cross-bars; vertical fins edged with blue-black..........*morio.*

(*Epinephelus,* clouded over, in allusion to a membrane supposed to cover the eye.)

240. EPINEPHELUS STRIATUS (Bloch).

Nassau Grouper; Hamlet.

Anthias striatus Bloch, Ichthyologie, ix, 109, pl. 324, 1792; Martinique.
Epinephelus striatus, Jordan & Evermann, 1896, 1157, pl. clxxxiii, fig. 483.

DIAGNOSIS.—Form deep, slightly compressed, depth contained 2.8 times in total length; head pointed, contained about 2.5 times in length; mouth moderate, maxillary extending to posterior edge of eye; jaw teeth in bands, with 2 canines in front of each jaw; nostrils close together, of nearly same size; interorbital space contained 8.5 times in length of head; gill-rakers slender, 16 on lower arm of first arch; scales in lateral series 110 to 125, in transverse series 60 to 70; dorsal rays XI,17; anal rays III,8; ventrals short; pectorals long.   Color: above greenish gray, below paler; about 4 dark brown undulating cross-bars extending on dorsal fin; a jet-black blotch on top of caudal peduncle; a dark stripe through eye and snout, another on median line of snout, which divides opposite eyes and extends backward to occiput; lower parts of head orange; a ring of small black spots around eye; edge of dorsals, anal, caudal, and ventrals yellow; pectorals light orange; ventrals blackish.   (*striatus*, striped.)

A specimen 4.25 inches long, taken in Beaufort harbor in the summer of 1903, is probably referable to this species, although it may be one of several other species of which the young are not well known.   This is a large West Indian species, common at Key West, and must occur only as a straggler in North Carolina.

241. EPINEPHELUS MORIO (Cuvier & Valenciennes).

Red Grouper.

Serranus morio Cuvier & Valenciennes, Histoire Naturelle des Poissons, ii, 285, 1828; New York and San Domingo.
Epinephelus morio, Yarrow, 1877, 211; Beaufort.   Jordan, 1886, 27; Beaufort.   Jordan & Evermann, 1896, 1160, pl. clxxxiv, fig. 485.

DIAGNOSIS.—Form comparatively deep, depth contained 2.8 times in length; head large, .4 length of body; mouth large, maxillary extending beyond eye; jaw teeth in narrow bands, 2 small canines in front of each jaw, the lower pair smaller; eye rather large; nostrils small, of equal size; preopercle serrate, teeth at angle slightly enlarged; gill-rakers slender, 15 on lower arm of first arch; scales in lateral series 130 to 140, in transverse series 75 to 80; dorsal rays XI,16 or XI,17, the spines high, second twice length of first; anal rays III,8 or III,9, second spine stronger than third; ventrals short, not extending to vent; pectorals more than .5 length of head, reaching beyond tips of ventrals.   Color: olive gray or brown, with paler clouds; head and breast salmon color; head with numerous small, round, brown dots; vertical fins of same color as body; a broad ridge of black on soft dorsal, anal, and caudal, with narrow white edge; spinous dorsal black-edged; ventrals dusky; pectorals greenish.   (*morio*, Moor.)

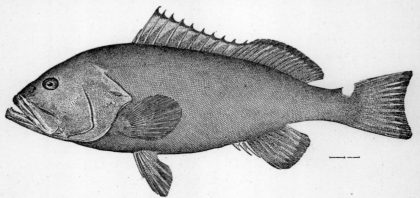

Fig. 121.   RED GROUPER.   *Epinephelus morio.*

This large and excellent grouper is an abundant inhabitant of the American coast from Brazil to Florida, and regularly extends its range for some distance north along the South Atlantic coast.   It occurs as a straggler as far as Massachusetts, where the present writer has found it on several occasions in summer. Although Yarrow saw only one specimen at Beaufort, the species is probably to be found there every year.   One specimen was taken in the laboratory seine in

1902, and fully 150 were collected in the summer of 1903, at Bird Shoal and Uncle Israel Shoal; only the young were noted.

The red grouper is an important food fish at Key West, in the Gulf of Mexico, and southward, attaining a length of 3 feet; but in North Carolina it does not occur in sufficient abundance nor is it of large enough size to have any economic value.

Genus MYCTEROPERCA Gill. Groupers.

This genus contains many species of tropical marine food-fishes, mostly of large size, similar to Epinephelus but differing in cranial characters and in having a longer anal fin, longer body, larger mouth, etc. Head broad and concave between eyes, with strong lateral crests which extend forward to join the supra-ocular crest above eyes; lower jaw strongly projecting; scales chiefly cycloid; gill-rakers various; nostrils small, of equal size or with posterior pair enlarged. More than 20 American species, of which 6 are known from our south Atlantic coast. Three, as follows, occur as stragglers in North Carolina:

i. Angle of preopercle salient, with enlarged teeth; developed gill-rakers on lower arm of first arch about 12; scales in lateral series about 140; caudal margin rather strongly concave... *microlepis.*
ii. Angle of preopercle not salient, the teeth scarcely enlarged.
  a. Developed gill-rakers on lower arm of first arch about 8; scales in lateral series about 125; caudal margin slightly concave ....*venenosa.*
  aa. Developed gill-rakers on lower arm of first arch about 10; scales in lateral series about 110; caudal margin straight ....*bonaci.*

(*Mycteroperca*, nostril perch.)

242. MYCTEROPERCA MICROLEPIS (Goode & Bean).

Gag.

Trisotropis microlepis Goode & Bean, Proceedings U. S. National Museum, 1879, 141; west Florida.
Mycteroperca microlepis, Jenkins, 1885, 11; Beaufort harbor. Jordan, 1886, 27; Beaufort. Jenkins, 1887, 90; Beaufort harbor. Jordan & Evermann, 1896, 1177, pl. clxxxviii, fig. 494.

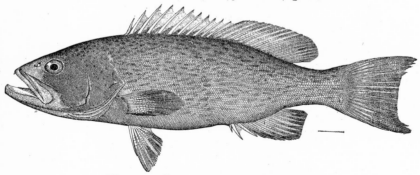

Fig. 122. GAG. *Mycteroperca microlepis.*

DIAGNOSIS.—Body rather long, compressed, depth contained 3.5 times in total length; head long, pointed, contained 2.6 times in length; mouth large, maxillary reaching beyond eye; teeth in narrow bands, 2 canines in front of each jaw, the lower smaller; scales in lateral series 140 to 145, in transverse series 75 to 85; gill-rakers on lower arm of first arch about 12; dorsal rays xi,16 to xi,19, spines slender, third and fourth spines longest; anal rays iii,11;

278 FISHES OF NORTH CAROLINA.

caudal margin concave; pectorals .5 length of head, reaching beyond ends of ventrals. Color: variable; usually brownish gray above, paler below, with faint traces of darker spots; black mustache; dorsal dark green, edge of soft dorsal black; caudal black with bright blue shades, edge white; anal indigo blue with white edge; pectorals green; ventrals black, first ray white-tipped. (*microlepis*, small scaled.)

The gag is found on both coasts of Florida, and ranges northward on the Atlantic coast as far as Beaufort, North Carolina. It reaches a weight of 50 pounds, and is a food-fish of considerable value in Florida, being abundant about the reefs. Dr. Yarrow's collections at Beaufort in 1871 contained a number of specimens of this species now in the National Museum; they were not identified at the time, however, and are not included in Yarrow's list of the fishes of Fort Macon and vicinity. The species was first recognized at Beaufort by Dr. Jenkins in 1885, when one specimen was obtained. Small examples have since been taken in Beaufort Harbor and vicinity on a number of occasions, about 20 being seined at Bird Shoal, Uncle Israel Shoal, and Newport River in July and August, 1902; these were from 2.75 to 8.5 inches long. In June, 1904, Mr. Barton A. Bean, while collecting specimens for the National Museum, obtained the young in Beaufort Harbor, but only in limited numbers.

243. MYCTEROPERCA VENENOSA (Linnæus).
Yellow-finned Grouper; Rock-fish.

Perca venenosa Linnæus, Systema Naturæ, ed. x, 292, 1758; Bahamas.
Mycteroperca venenosa, Jordan & Evermann, 1896, 1173, pl. clxxxvii, fig. 491.

DIAGNOSIS.—Body rather stout and not greatly compressed, depth .33 length; head large, blunt, .4 length of body; mouth large, maxillary extending beyond eye, nearly .5 length of head; jaw teeth in narrow bands, 2 well developed canines in each jaw; eye .14 length of head; interorbital space broad and flat, .2 head; scales small, mostly cycloid, about 125 in lengthwise series; vertical fins rather small; dorsal rays xi,16, second and tenth the same height, longest .33 head; anal rays iii,11; caudal margin slightly concave; pectorals rounded, extending beyond ventrals. Color: dark green above, bluish or pearly below; back and sides reticulated and blotched with light green; body and head covered with round yellowish brown spots; fins variegated. (*venenosa*, venemous or poisonous.)

Known from North Carolina by 2 small specimens seined in Beaufort Harbor in the summer of 1902. The species reaches a length of 3 feet, and is common in southern Forida and the West Indies.

244. MYCTEROPERCA BONACI (Poey).
Black Grouper.

Serranus bonaci Poey, Memorias sobre la Historia Natural de la Isla de Cuba, ii, 129, 1860; Cuba.
Mycteropecra bonaci, Jordan & Evermann, 1896, 1174, pl. clxxxvii, fig. 492 (skull).

DIAGNOSIS.—Form rather long, depth contained 3.25 times in total length; head contained 2.75 times in length; mouth large, maxillary extending beyond eye; in each jaw 2 strong canine teeth directed forward; scales in lateral series 120 to 125, in transverse series about 70; gill-rakers few and long, 10 to 12 on lower arm of first arch; dorsal rays xi,16 to xi,18, the spines weak and slender, third and fourth longest; anal rays iii,11 or iii,12, the fin high and rounded; caudal truncate; pectorals extending beyond tips of ventrals, which are short. Color:

orange brown, olive on back; sides and belly with gray reticulations surrounding round or oblong areas of ground color; reticulations on head bluish, the areas smaller; a line of 6 or 7 spots from eye to preopercle; dorsal and caudal mottled brown; anal with 2 or 3 rows of bluish spots, tip black; pectorals olive brown; ventrals black with blue rays. (*bonaci*, the Cuban name for this fish.)

On the Atlantic coast north of Florida, this species is only a straggler from the West Indies, although it is abundant at Key West. The writer has reported it from Woods Hole, Massachusetts, where it was probably carried in the Gulf Stream. Three small specimens were seined in Beaufort Harbor in the summer of 1902, and several others were taken there in June, 1904. The fish attains a weight of 50 pounds, and is used for food.

Genus CENTROPRISTES Cuvier & Valenciennes. Sea Basses.

Bottom marine fishes, peculiar to the Atlantic coast of America, with robust, slightly compressed body, very large mouth, no supplemental bone, smooth tongue, weak canine teeth, serrate preopercle, long and slender gill-rakers, short dorsal fin, fleshy filaments on tips of dorsal spines, 3–lobed or double concave caudal, ventrals close together and in advance of pectorals. Of the 3 authentic species, 2 occur on the North Carolina coast and may be readily distinguished as follows:

i. Tips of dorsal spines with short fleshy flaps; gill-rakers on lower arm 18; caudal fin rounded, with a produced ray at upper angle; color black or dark blue................*striatus*.
ii. Tips of dorsal spines with long hair-like processes; gill-rakers on lower arm 10; caudal fin deeply double-concave, with central and marginal rays much produced; color, greenish above, with dark cross-bars.......................................*philadelphicus*.

(*Centropristes*, spine-saw.)

245. CENTROPRISTES STRIATUS (Linnæus).

"Black-fish"; "Bass"; Sea Bass; Black Will (Va.).

Labrus striatus Linnæus, Systema Naturæ, ed. x, 285, 1758; "America".
Perca atraria Linnæus, Systema Naturæ, ed. xii, 485, 1766; Carolina.
Centropristis atrarius, Yarrow, 1877, 211; off Shackleford Banks and Cape Lookout. Jordan & Gilbert, 1879, 380; Beaufort.
Serranus atrarius, Jordan, 1886, 27; Beaufort. Jenkins, 1887, 89; Beaufort. Wilson, 1900, 355; Beaufort.
Centropristes striatus, Jordan & Evermann, 1896, 1199, pl. cxc, fig. 500. Linton, 1905, 375; Beaufort.

DIAGNOSIS.—Form robust, back elevated, depth rather more than .33 total length; head large, thick, its length about equal to body depth; mouth oblique, lower jaw longer, maxillary broad, less than .5 length of head; jaw teeth in broad bands, canines small; eye .2 length of head; gill-rakers long, 18 below angle; preopercle finely serrate, angle and lower edge with larger teeth; scales in lateral series 55 to 60, in transverse series 20 to 25, 11 rows of scales on cheeks; dorsal rays x,11, the spines strong, longest .5 length of head; short dermal flaps on some of the spines; anal rays III,7 or III,8; pectorals very long, contained 1.25 times in length of head; ventrals a little shorter; upper caudal ray produced. Color: dark brown, black, or rich blue, more or less mottled and with pale longitudinal streaks; dorsal with lines of white spots, other fins dark. Male in breeding season develops a large nuchal or frontal hump and assumes a bright blue color; fins in male larger. (*striatus*, striped.)

The sea bass, known in North Carolina as "black-fish" and "bass", is a northern species the southern limit of whose range is Florida. It is one of the

best known and more important salt-water fish between Massachusetts and
South Carolina and supports a special fishery in ten states. The largest fish weigh
6 pounds, but the usual weight is under 4 pounds.

The species occurs abundantly off the coast of North Carolina, and is caught
for market in various sections. It is common about jetties and on shelly and
rocky bottoms, attaining the largest size and greatest abundance on the offshore
reefs and banks. Dr. Coker contributes the following notes on the fish in the
Beaufort region:

The "black-fish" has been an undeveloped resource at Beaufort, as the grounds along
the coast were never regularly worked by the fishermen until the winter of 1903-4, when, in
November, the enterprising Mr. George N. Ives, of Newbern, equipped a sharpie with a naphtha motor and began fishing off New River   In December, two Morehead fish dealers began
sending naphtha launches to the "black-fish rocks" off Bear Inlet, about 30 miles below Beaufort.
The boats which carry 4 men, who use hand lines, anchor in the inlet at night and run out to
the "rocks," 10 miles off shore, each suitable day, the trip lasting about a week.   From Beaufort similar fishing is done at Wrightsville and other points further southward.   This fishery
should increase in extent and prove very profitable, as the sea bass is an excellent fish, bearing
shipment well and commanding good prices in the northern markets.

Fig. 123.   SEA BASS; BLACK-FISH.   *Centropristes striatus.*

A special sea-bass ground surveyed by the steamer Fish-Hawk in the summer
of 1902 lies 20.5 miles ssw. ¼ w. from the outer buoy on Beaufort Bar, and is
covered with 13.5 fathoms of water. The bottom is of rough coral, with sea-
fans and other growths such as are found on the coast of Florida, and is rich in
animal life. On September 12 two hours were spent in handline fishing by the
ship's crew, and in that time there were caught about 700 sea bass, together with
a few large grunts, 2 red snappers, and various small fish.

On the ledges and banks lying off Cape Fear the "black-fish" is caught from
July to December, but, according to Mr. W. H. Yopp, of Wilmington, is not very
abundant; the fish in that region run from .5 to 1.5 pounds.

The sea bass feeds on the bottom, eating small fish, squid, crabs, and various
other animals. Its mouth is very large, its teeth are formidable, and it is a
voracious feeder.

Spawning occurs in spring off the North Carolina coast, probably in May. The eggs, which float at the surface, are .04 inch in diameter, and hatch in 5 days in water of 59° or 60°F. The male during the spawning season develops a prominent hump on the nape and assumes a beautiful bright blue color. The young, which are common around the shores, have a broad black longitudinal stripe on the side. Fish 4 to 5 inches long are abundant in Beaufort Harbor in summer.

The catch of sea bass in this state during 3 years was as follows: 1889— 28,900 pounds, $939; 1897—189,225 pounds, $5,564; 1902—57,250 pounds, $1,929. The bulk of the product comes from Carteret and New Hanover counties.

246. CENTROPRISTES PHILADELPHICUS (Linnæus.)

Rock Sea Bass.

Perca philadelphica Linnæus, Systema Naturæ, ed. x, 291, 1758; America.
Perca trifurca Linnæus, Systema Naturæ, ed. xii, 489, 1766; Carolina.
Lutjanus tridens Lacépède, Histoire Naturelle des Poissons, iv, 246, 1802; Carolina.
Serranus philadelphicus, Jenkins, 1887, 89; Beaufort.
Centropristes philadelphicus, Jordan & Evermann, 1896, 1201, pl. cxci, fig. 501.

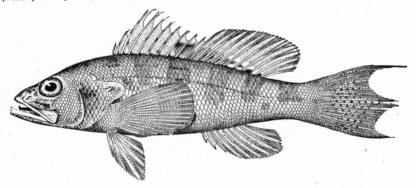

Fig. 124. Rock Sea Bass. *Centropristes philadelphicus.*

DIAGNOSIS.—Form rather elongate, depth contained 3.33 to 3.66 times in total length; head contained 2.75 times in length; maxillary extending to posterior edge of pupil; teeth in bands on jaws, some of them enlarged, a patch of teeth on vomer and on palatines; eye contained 4.75 times in head; preopercular margin serrate, the teeth enlarged on and below angle; subopercle and interopercle finely serrate; gill-rakers .5 length of eye, 10 below angle of first arch; scales strongly ctenoid, those in lateral series 50 to 55, in transverse series 20; scales on opercle of same size as those on body, in 8 or 9 rows; scales on cheeks smaller, in 9 to 11 rows; dorsal rays x,11, the spines with long hair-like processes, third and fourth spines longest and .5 length of head; anal rays iii,7; upper, middle and lower caudal rays elongated; pectoral long and broad, contained 1.3 times in length of head. Color: greenish above, white below; 6 or 7 broad brown bars on back and sides; upper part of head and snout with many brownish red spots and lines; upper lip reddish, tip of lower jaw purple; spinous dorsal translucent, with white and dusky streaks, a large black blotch on membranes between last spines, a few dark spots on spines; filaments on dorsal spines scarlet; soft dorsal with bluish white and reddish spots; caudal translucent, spotted like soft dorsal, with brownish red margin; anal white, with yellow streak and terminal black bar; ventrals whitish or blackish; pectorals plain. (Named after the city of Philadelphia, for no obvious reason.)

This species, which lives on rocky bottom in rather deep water off Charleston, South Carolina, is also known from the North Carolina coast at Beaufort. Dr. Jenkins obtained a few specimens in Beaufort Harbor in 1885. In the summer of 1902, 8 specimens were taken in a trawl by the steamer Fish-Hawk near the sea buoy off Beaufort Inlet; and 2 others, 4 inches long, were seined on Bird Shoal in Beaufort Harbor in 1903. The maximum size is about 1 foot.

Genus DIPLECTRUM Holbrook. Squirrel-fishes.

Small American marine species, with preopercle armed with 2 clusters of strong spines; low dorsal fin, without elongated rays; deeply concave caudal fin; rounded pectorals; small scales, and top of head with a large bare area. Five known species, 1 found on the South Atlantic Coast. (*Diplectrum*, double spur.)

247. DIPLECTRUM FORMOSUM (Linnæus).

Squirrel-fish.

Perca formosa Linnæus, Systema Naturæ, ed. xii, 488, 1766; Carolina.
Diplectrum formosum, Jordan & Evermann, 1896, 1207, pl. cxci, fig. 502.

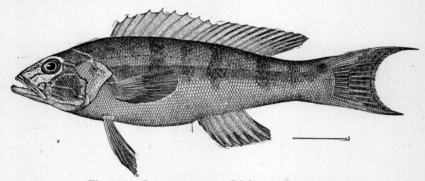

Fig. 125. SQUIRREL-FISH. *Diplectrum formosum.*

DIAGNOSIS.—Body elongate, depth contained 3.4 times in total length; head contained 3.33 times in length; mouth large, maxillary extending to pupil, lower jaw the longer; eye .2 length of head, shorter than snout; preopercle with finely serrate upper margin and 2 patches of divergent spines; gill-rakers 14 or 15 below angle of first arch; scales in lateral series 80 to 90, in transverse series 30; numerous rows of scales on cheeks and opercles; dorsal rays x,12, all low, the longest .5 head; anal rays iii,7, soft rays of uniform length, the spines shorter and weak; caudal concave. Color: dull, light brownish above, white below; 7 or 8 rather broad dark cross-bands, 3 or 4 dark longitudinal stripes, 8 narrow blue longitudinal stripes; head yellow, with 5 or 6 wavy blue stripes below eye; 5 narrow blue cross-bars between eyes; dark spot at base of caudal; dorsal yellowish green with 2 median blue cross-lines which form ocelli posteriorly; caudal like dorsal; other fins white. (*formosum*, handsome.)

This beautiful little serranid, which ranges as far south as Uruguay, has not heretofore been recorded north of Charleston, South Carolina. In the summer of 1903, 4 young specimens were caught in the laboratory seine in Beaufort Harbor. The species is usually found on sandy shores, takes the baited hook readily, reaches a length of a foot, and is a good food fish.

Genus DULES Cuvier.

In this genus the body is deep and compressed, the caudal fin is square; and the branchiostegals number only 6. Three species are known, 1 South American, 1 West Indian, and the following. (*Dules*, slave, "the fish being under the lash of the long dorsal spine".)

248. DULES SUBLIGARIUS (Cope).

Centropristes subligarius Cope, Proceedings Academy of Sciences of Philadelphia, 1870, 120; Pensacola.
Serranus dispilurus, Jordan, 1886, 27; Beaufort.
Serranus subligarius, Jenkins, 1887, 89; Beaufort.
Dules subligarius, Jordan & Evermann, 1896, 1218; Beaufort, etc.

DIAGNOSIS.—Depth contained 2.66 times in total length; head long, low, .4 length; mouth small, maxillary extending to posterior edge of pupil; teeth small canines, not well developed; eye .25 length of head; preopercle sharply serrate; gill-rakers 6 or 8, short; scales in lateral series about 42, in transverse series 23; 10 series of scales on cheeks; no scales on jaws, preorbital, and front of head; dorsal rays x,13; anal rays III,7, second spine longer and stouter than third; caudal truncate. Color: olivaceous, tinged with brown, pale below; scales on sides with black margin; 5 very distinct dark cross-bars posteriorly; a large cream-colored blotch on side anterior to vent; a black ring around peduncle; a large black blotch on soft dorsal; cheeks yellow; head brown below; a net-work of wavy blue lines on branchiostegals, lower jaw, and interopercle; dorsals mottled; ventrals faintly barred; other fins grayish with blackish bars. (*subligarius*, truss-wearing, in allusion to the light blotch on each side near vent.)

This small fish is known from the coasts of North Carolina, South Carolina, and Florida, and has usualy been taken in deep water. Dr. Jenkins, in 1885, took several young specimens in Beaufort Harbor in eel-grass. The Fish-Hawk dredged 3 specimens 20.5 miles from the sea buoy off Beaufort Inlet in 13.5 fathoms on September 12, 1902 (station 7344).

Family LOBOTIDÆ. Triple-tails.

This family, which contains only one species, a large, widely distributed marine fish, is related to the sea basses (Serranidæ). Body oblong, compressed; dorsal fin continuous, the spinous part longer than the soft; anal spines 3, the soft part opposite and similar to the soft dorsal; skull broad anteriorly, the eyes placed far forward, the snout short.

Genus LOBOTES Cuvier. Triple-tails or Flashers.

Back elevated; caudal peduncle short and deep; upper profile of head slightly concave; mouth of moderate size, lips thick, upper jaw protractile, lower jaw projecting; bands of conical teeth in jaws, a row of larger conical teeth in front, vomer and palatines toothless; preopercle serrate; air-bladder present; pyloric cœca 3; body and head covered with ctenoid scales, which extend on the fleshy bases of the soft dorsal and anal fins; soft rays of the dorsal and anal elongated, extending backward, and producing with the rounded caudal a three-lobed effect. (*Lobotes*, lobed.)

249. LOBOTES SURINAMENSIS (Bloch).

"Steamboat"; Triple-tail; Flasher; Sea Perch (S. O.); Black Perch (S. O.).

Holocentrus surinamensis Bloch, Ichthyologie, pl. 243, 1790; Surinam.
Lobotes surinamensis, Jordan & Evermann, 1896, 1235, pl. exciv, fig. 510.

DIAGNOSIS.—Depth variable, averaging .5 length; head .3 length; maxillary heavy, extending to pupil; eye about equal to snout and contained 6 times in head; scales in lateral series about 55, those about eye very fine, those on opercle large; dorsal rays xii,15 or xii,16, the fifth spine longest; anal rays iii,11, the third spine longest; pectorals short, rounded, .5 length of head; ventrals longer than pectorals. Color: dull black above, silvery gray on sides and below; fins dusky; sides and fins sometimes with small yellowish blotches. (*surinamensis*, inhabiting Surinam.)

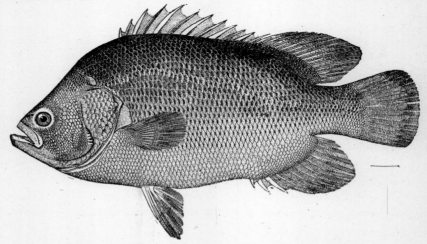

Fig. 126. TRIPLE-TAIL; FLASHER. *Lobotes surinamensis*.

This large, easily recognized species, which inhabits all warm seas, is found on the Atlantic coast of the United States as far north as Massachusetts, but is not common anywhere. It attains a length of 3 feet.

There appear to be no published North Carolina records, and the specimens known to have been taken in the state are few. One 25 inches long, now in the State Museum at Raleigh, was collected in Carteret County in 1892 by Mr. H. H. Brimley, who reports that the species is called "steamboat" by the fishermen of Wilmington. Another specimen, 23 inches long, now in the laboratory, was taken in Beaufort Harbor in September, 1903. Mr. S. G. Worth states that he had an 11-pound fish from Beaufort several years ago which was served on his table; the meat was firm, white, and flaky like that of a sheepshead, and was well-flavored.

A laboratory specimen 3.5 inches long taken in Beaufort Harbor in the summer of 1902 has a broad white margin on the caudal fin and white pectorals.

Family PRIACANTHIDÆ.   The Catalufas.

A sharply defined family of tropical, carnivorous fishes, with compressed, oblong or ovate body; deep head; large, oblique mouth, having minute teeth on jaws, vomer, and palatines; protractile premaxillaries, broad maxillary without supplemental bone; large eye, with diameter nearly .5 length of head; post-orbital part of head much shortened, opercle with 2 or 3 pointed flaps; preopercle serrate; gills 4, gill-rakers long, gill-membranes separate, and not joined to isthmus; pseudobranchiæ very well developed; entire body, head, snout, and maxillary covered with small rough scales; lateral line present, continuous; air-bladder large; pyloric cœca few; dorsal fin continuous, with 10 spines and 9 to 15 soft rays; anal fin with 3 spines and 9 to 15 soft rays; pectorals rather small; ventrals large, thoracic, inserted anterior to pectorals and joined to abdomen by a membrane.   Two genera, both represented in American waters but only 1 in North Carolina, although the other (Priacanthus) may be looked for, as 1 species has been taken as a straggler as far north as Massachusetts and Rhode Island.

Genus PSEUDOPRIACANTHUS Bleeker.   Big-eyes.

Small deep-water fishes with very deep body; very rough scales; strongly arched lateral line; 2 small spines at angle of preopercle; dorsal and anal fins with strong rough spines.   (*Pseudopriacanthus*, false Priacanthus.)

250. PSEUDOPRIACANTHUS ALTUS (Gill).

Short Big-eye.

Priacanthus altus Gill, Proceedings Academy of Natural Sciences, Philadelphia, 1862, 132; Narragansett Bay,
    R. I.
Pseudopriacanthus altus, Jordan & Evermann, 1896, 1239, pl. cxcv, fig. 512.

DIAGNOSIS.—Depth about .5 length, least depth of caudal peduncle .25 depth of body; head very short, less than .3 length; mouth nearly vertical, the broad maxillary extending to middle of pupil; eye very large, .5 length of head and more than twice length of snout; scales ctenoid, number in lateral series 42; dorsal fin high, the rays x,11, the longest spine .66 length of head; anal rays iii,11, the longest spine (third) .5 head; caudal margin square; pectorals .6 head; ventrals as long as head and extending to first anal spine. Color: lustrous crimson, the back dark; fins black-edged except pectorals. (*altus*, high.)

The short big-eye is a beautiful West Indian species which sometimes strays northward and is occasionally taken in considerable numbers as far as southern Massachusetts.   The largest recorded specimen, 11 inches long, was taken at Charleston, S. C.   The only North Carolina example thus far known was .5 inch long and was obtained by the steamer Fish-Hawk off Beaufort on August 14, 1902.

Family LUTIANIDÆ.   The Snappers.

The snappers constitute a very numerous family of warm-water shore fishes, nearly all of them being food fishes and some of great economic importance in the United States and other countries.   Form mostly oblong, compressed; head large, with conspicuous crests on skull; mouth usually large, terminal, low, well supplied with teeth on jaws and usually on vomer and palatines; premaxillaries moderately protractile; maxillaries long, slipping under a sheath formed by the preorbital; supplemental bone absent; opercles without spines, preopercles serrate or entire; gill-arches 4; gill-rakers short, moderate, or long; gill-membranes separate and not joined to isthmus; pseudobranchiæ conspicuous; air-bladder present; intestines short; pyloric cœca few; lateral line present; scales ctenoid, of moderate size, adherent, and completely covering body and usually sides of head; dorsal fin single or double, with 10 or 12 rather strong spines; anal similar to posterior dorsal, with 3 spines; caudal concave or forked; pectorals long and pointed; ventrals thoracic, the rays 1,5, with modified scales at base.

Of the 15 American genera only one, Lutianus (or Neomænis) is represented in the state, although several others, which occur on the coast of South Carolina and Florida, may be looked for.

Genus LUTIANUS Bloch. Snappers.

A numerous genus of cosmopolitan distribution, characterized by an oblong, compressed body with moderately elevated back; a long, pointed head; a large mouth, well supplied with bands of villiform teeth in jaws, 2 to 4 canine teeth in front of upper jaw, and bands or patches of teeth on vomer, palatines, and tongue (in adult); preopercle finely serrate; gill-rakers few and moderately long; scales deficient on top of head except for an oblique band on nape; lateral line concurrent with dorsal outline; dorsal fin single, the spines 10 or 11; anal rays 7 to 9. Upwards of 20 American species, of which 4 have thus far been detected in North Carolina.

Key to North Carolina snappers.*

i. No black spot on side, young with dark cross bands; anal fin rounded, its middle rays less than .5 length of head; caudal with concave margin.
 a. Depth contained 2.75 to 3 times in length; mouth large, maxillary .4 length of head; scales in lateral series about 50; 7 oblique series of scales between dorsal and lateral line; pectoral short, less than .66 length of head; soft dorsal, anal, and caudal blackish.
                          griseus.
 aa. Depth contained 2.5 times in length; mouth smaller, maxillary .33 length of head; scales in lateral series about 43; 5 or 6 oblique series of scales between dorsal and lateral line; pectorals longer, more than .66 length of head; soft dorsal, anal, and caudal orange or yellow . . . . *apodus.*
ii. A black blotch on side, either permanent or growing fainter with age, young without dark cross bands; anal fin angulated, the middle rays much more than .5 length of head; caudal fin forked.
 b. Lingual teeth well developed, in a broad patch; color nearly uniform rose red.
                           blackfordi.
 bb. Lingual teeth few, in a narrow patch; color greenish above, with dark cross bands, numerous oblique streaks, and a persistent black spot on side . . . . *analis.*

(*Lutianus*, a latinization of a Malayan name for one of the snappers.)

251. LUTIANUS GRISEUS (Linnæus).

Gray Snapper; Mangrove Snapper.

Labrus griseus Linnæus, Systema Naturæ, ed. x, 283, 1758.
Neomænis griseus, Jordan & Evermann, 1898, 1255.

 * The key is based on adult characters

DIAGNOSIS.—Body rather elongate, depth contained about 3 times in length; length of head somewhat greater than depth; maxillary extending as far as pupil; snout pointed, contained 3 times in length of head; eye small, a little more than .2 length of head; gill-rakers short and thick, about 8 on lower arm of first arch; scales large, about 50 in lateral series, 7 + 12 in transverse series, 7 rows on cheek, 7 rows on opercle, and 3 rows on temporal region; dorsal rays x,14, the fourth spine largest; anal rays III,8; caudal slightly concave; pectorals short, contained about 1.6 times in head; ventrals shorter than pectorals. Color: dark green above, coppery red below, with dark lengthwise streaks corresponding with rows of scales; spinous dorsal blackish with red edge; soft dorsal dusky, with white edge anteriorly; anal reddish, with white margin: caudal reddish black; pectorals and ventrals pale. (*griseus*, gray.)

The gray snapper is abundant in Florida and the West Indies, often being seen on sandy shores and on the edges of mangrove swamps; it also ascends fresh-water streams. Stragglers, usually young, have been found in Chesapeake Bay, on the New Jersey coast, at Woods Hole, Mass., and at other points on the Atlantic seaboard. Four small examples were seined at Beaufort in the summer of 1902. The species reaches a weight of 15 to 18 pounds, but averages less than 5 pounds; and is a food fish of considerable value in Florida.

252. LUTIANUS APODUS (Walbaum).

Schoolmaster.

Perca apoda Walbaum, Artedi Genera Piscium, 351, 1792.
Neomœnis apodus, Jordan & Evermann, 1898, 1258, pl. cxcvii, fig. 515.

DIAGNOSIS.—Body rather deep, the depth .4 length; length of head equal to depth; maxillary extending to front of orbit; 4 canine teeth in front of upper jaw; snout very long and pointed, more than .3 length of head; gill-rakers short and thick, about 9 on long arm of first arch; scales rather large, 42 to 45 in lateral series, 6 + 13 in transverse series, 7 rows on cheeks and 7 on opercles; dorsal rays x,14; anal rays III,8; caudal slightly forked; pectorals .75 length of head; ventrals .5 lengths of head. Color: dark greenish above, orange on sides and below, with 8 or 9 narrow pale bluish vertical bars; head greenish above, bright orange on sides; all fins orange, the dorsal with blue spots; young with a distinct blue stripe below eye, usually lacking in adult. (*apodus*, without feet, the species having been based on a drawing in which the pectoral fins were omitted.)

This snapper, whose regular range is from Florida to Brazil, occasionally strays to the northeast coast, young examples having been taken at Woods Hole, Mass., by the writer. In the summer of 1902 one small specimen was seined in Beaufort Harbor, and on September 25, 1905, another 2 inches long was taken at the wharf on Pivers Island, Beaufort, these being the only North Carolina records. The maximum weight of this species is 7 or 8 pounds and the average 2 or 3 pounds.

253. LUTIANUS BLACKFORDI Goode & Bean.

"Red Snapper".

Lutjanus blackfordi Goode & Bean, Proceedings U. S. National Museum, 1876, 176; Pensacola, Fla.
? *Bodianus aya* Bloch, Ichthyologie, 227, 1790; Brazil.
Neomœnis aya, Jordan & Evermann, 1898, 1264, pl. cxcvii, fig. 516.

DIAGNOSIS.—Body rather deep, depth contained 2.6 times in length, back elevated; head large, its length equal to body depth, superior profile straight from snout to nape; mouth large, maxillary not extending beyond front of orbit; a broad patch of teeth on tongue, in addition to the usual teeth in jaws; snout contained 2.8 times in head; eye less than .2 length of head; gill-rakers .5 diameter of eye, 8 on lower arm of first arch; scales in lateral series 60, in transverse series 8+15, 6 rows on cheek, 7 on opercle; dorsal rays x,14, the fourth and fifth spines longest; anal rays iii,9, the middle rays very long; caudal slightly forked; pectorals pointed, .8 length of head, extending to or beyond front of anal fin; ventrals .5 to .6 length of head. Color: rich rose red, paler below; a black spot, disappearing with age, above lateral line under anterior rays of soft dorsal; fins mostly brick red.   (Named for the late Eugene G. Blackford, of New York City.)

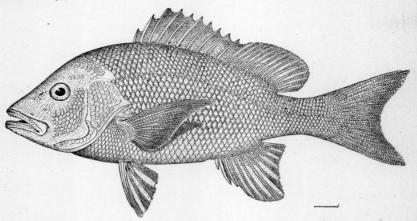

Fig. 127. RED SNAPPER. *Lutianus blackfordi.*

This important food fish of the Gulf of Mexico and the West Indies has occasionally been found as far north as Woods Hole, in southern Massachusetts. The fish caught for market are from 1 to 3 feet long, and several million pounds are taken annually with lines in the Gulf of Mexico and sent all over the United States.   The Fish-Hawk took several specimens of this species while line-fishing on the black-fish grounds off Beaufort in September, 1902, and at least 5 young examples were seined on the beach at Cape Lookout and in Beaufort Harbor in the summers of 1902 and 1903.   The species, however, will probably not be found in sufficient numbers on the grounds lying off North Carolina to make it a product of any economic value, although in the extensive seine fisheries formerly conducted in the ocean at Cape Lookout examples were sometimes caught.   The State Museum at Raleigh contains a specimen from Cape Lookout presented by Mr. George N. Ives.   The species becomes more common toward the southern part of the coast, and is said to be taken in considerable numbers on the "snapper banks" lying off Cape Fear.

254. LUTIANUS ANALIS (Cuvier & Valenciennes).

Mutton-fish. ·

Mesoprion analis Cuvier & Valenciennes, Histoire Naturelle des Poissons, ii, 452, 1828; San Domingo.
Neomænis analis, Jordan & Evermann, 1898, 1265, pl. cxcviii, fig. 517.

DIAGNOSIS.—Depth of body .37 length, back somewhat elevated; length of head equal to depth; a small narrow patch of teeth on middle of tongue, usual teeth in jaws; maxillary not extending to front of eye; snout long and pointed, contained 2.6 in head; eye small, contained 3 times in snout and 6 times in length of head; interorbital space equal to diameter of eye; gill-rakers .5 length of eye, 8 on long arm of first arch; scales in lateral series about 67, in transverse series 10+17, 7 rows on cheeks and about 9 on opercles; dorsal fin low, the rays x,14, fourth spine longest, ninth and tenth soft rays longest; anal fin angulated, the rays III,8; caudal broad, forked; pectorals extending about to anal   Color: above lateral line dark green with oblique lines of blue spots; sides bluish; belly white tinged with red; back and sides with 6 to 8 dark narrow vertical stripes wider than spaces between them; head bronze green, darker above, a pearly streak under eye from snout to gill-opening; a blue streak from eye to nostrils; iris bright red; a small, persistent lateral blotch immediately above lateral line under first dorsal soft rays, anal, caudal, pectorals, and ventrals brick red, the caudal with a narrow black margin; dorsal yellowish with reddish markings. (*analis*, relating to anal fin, which has long rays.)

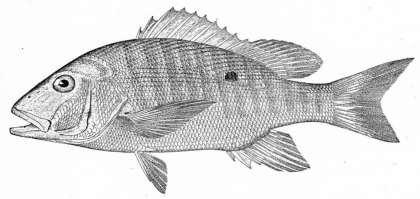

Fig. 128. MUTTON-FISH. *Lutianus analis.*

This snapper is common from the east coast of Florida to Brazil, and is a food fish of some importance, reaching a weight of 25 pounds. Stragglers have been found at Woods Hole, Mass., and may be looked for at all intervening points. It has been taken on the North Carolina coast at Beaufort, where 10 small specimens were seined at Bird Shoal and Uncle Israel Island in the summer of 1902.

Family HÆMULIDÆ. The Grunts.

A numerous family of small or moderate-sized carnivorous fishes inhabiting temperate and tropical shores, important as food in Florida, West Indies, and elsewhere. They are related to the snappers on one hand and the porgies on the other. Body outline varying from oblong to ovate; head large, the skull with conspicuous crests; mouth variable, terminal, low, horizontal; premaxillaries protractile; maxillary slipping under margin of preorbital, no supplemental bone; jaw teeth pointed, none canine, no teeth on tongue, vomer, or palatines; opercle destitute of spines, preopercle entire or serrate; gill-arches 4; gill-membranes not united, free from isthmus; gill-rakers in moderate number; branchiostegals 6 or 7; body covered with adherent ctenoid or cycloid scales; sides of head scaly;

lateral line continuous, concurrent with dorsal outline; air-bladder present; pyloric cœca few; intestinal canal short; dorsal fin usually continuous, sometimes divided into 2 separate parts, the spines 10 to 12; anal similar to soft dorsal, the spines 3; caudal margin more or less concave; pectorals well developed; ventrals thoracic, the rays 1,5, a scaly appendage at base. All the species make a grunting noise by means of the air-bladder, whence the names grunt, pig-fish, and hog-fish, by which these fish are commonly known. There are about 15 American genera, of which 3 are represented on the North Carolina coast by a single representative each.

Key to the North Carolina genera of grunts.

i. Anal fin long, the rays iii,10 to iii,13; mouth small, its inside not scarlet; vertical soft fins either naked or scaled only at base...ORTHOPRISTIS.
ii. Anal fin shorter, the rays iii,7 or iii,8; mouth large, its inside scarlet; vertical soft fins densely scaled from base to margin.
　　a. Dorsal spines 12; 10 to 14 gill-rakers on lower limb of first arch; second anal spine much longer than third...HÆMULON.
　　aa. Dorsal spines 13; 12 to 18 gill-rakers on lower limb of first arch; second anal spine scarcely longer than third...BATHYSTOMA.

Genus ORTHOPRISTIS Girard. Pig-fishes.

Rather small fishes with oblong, compressed body, elevated back, compressed head, small mouth, teeth in bands in jaws, rather small scales, single dorsal fin with a slight notch, 12 or 13 slender dorsal spines, 15 or 16 short soft rays, rather long anal fin with 3 small spines and 10 to 13 soft rays, and naked or partly scaled vertical fins. About half a dozen known species from Atlantic and Pacific coasts of America. (*Orthopristis*, straight saw, in allusion to the evenly serrated preopercle.)

255. ORTHOPRISTIS CHRYSOPTERUS (Linnæus).

"Pig-fish"; "Hog-fish"; Sailor's Choice (S. C.).

Perca chrysoptera Linnæus, Systema Naturæ, ed. xii, 485, 1766; Charleston.
Orthopristis fulvomaculatus, Yarrow, 1877, 211; Beaufort. Jordan & Gilbert, 1879, 379; Beaufort.
Orthopristis chrysopterus, Jordan, 1886, 27; Beaufort. Jenkins, 1887, 90; Beaufort. Jordan & Evermann.
　　1898, 1338, pl. ccx, fig. 541. Wilson, 1900, 355; Beaufort. Linton, 1905, 376; Beaufort.
Pomadasys fulvomaculatus, Goode, 1884, 398; Beaufort. Earll, 1887, 493; banks off Wilmington.

DIAGNOSIS.—Form ovate, compressed, the back strongly arched, depth 4 length; head contained 3 times in length; mouth small, low, with a narrow band of slender teeth in each jaw; maxillary short, a little more than half length of head; vertical limb of preopercle straight and nearly entire; gill-rakers short, 7 + 12 on first arch; scales in lateral series 60, in transverse series 10 + 20, those above lateral line in oblique rows, those below in horizontal rows; top of head, opercles, and cheeks scaled; snout and jaws naked; a scaly sheath at base of dorsal and anal spines; dorsal fin continuous, with scarcely any notch separating the two parts, the rays xii,16 or xiii,16, longest spines (third and fourth) .4 length of head, longest rays shorter than longest spines; anal rays iii,12 or iii,13, the length of rays similar to those in soft dorsal; caudal forked, upper lobe longer; pectorals pointed, .8 length of head; ventrals .66 length of head. Color: dull light blue, becoming silvery below; edges of scales orange-brown, this color forming narrow stripes which are oblique above lateral line and horizontal below; snout and part of upper lip sky-blue; various bronze spots on snout and side of head; inside of mouth pale; dorsal clear, with bronze spots; anal whitish, with bronze base and dusky edge; caudal yellow, with dusky margin; other fins yellow; peritoneum black. (*Chrysopterus* golden-finned.)

PLATE 13

PIG-FISH OR HOG-FISH (ORTHOPRISTIS CHRYSOPTERUS)

From Chesapeake Bay to Mexico this species is more or less abundant on sandy shores; the young are found in numbers as far north as New York.

The "pig-fish" or "hog-fish" is one of the commonest food fishes of the North Carolina coast, occurring in all the sounds and salt-water estuaries, and also on the outlying banks. At Beaufort it is abundant, and is present throughout the year. The spawning season is May and June. While the fish reaches a length of 15 inches, those caught in North Carolina do not average more than 8 or 10 inches.

The stomachs of 42 adult hog-fish examined by Dr. Coker between June 15 and July 19, 1904, contained for the most part annelids of various kinds (Axiothea, Diopatra, Cerebratulus, and mutilated parts resembling Rhyncobolus and Arenicola; also pectinarian sand-tubes). Solenomya shells were very commonly present, and in one case a part of the body of the mollusk. Amphipods of various species were also often found to constitute an article of diet. The forms

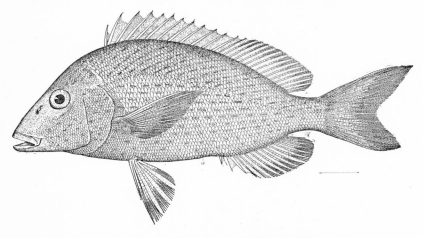

Fig. 129. PIG-FISH; HOG-FISH. *Orthopristis chrysopterus.*

found only 2 or 3 times were (Gebia large and small), parts of young common blue crabs, and fragments of ophiurans. In single fishes there were nematode worms, small ascidians, eggs and young of the horse-shoe crab, abdomen of hermit crab, an isopod, and fragments of grass. The stomachs of six hog-fish 2 to 4 inches long seined at Town Marsh were full of small shrimps.

The "hog-fish" is one of the leading food fishes of the state, and is caught for market with hand-lines and seines, the most extensive fishing being carried on in the Beaufort region, in Pamlico Sound in Hyde County, and on the coast of New Hanover County. At Beaufort it is one of the most important fishes, finding a ready market in North Carolina and at Norfolk, Petersburg, and other points. The entire catch for sale is now disposed of fresh, but at one time the fish were mostly salted and sold in Baltimore. Many are still salted in fall for local consumption. The fish is considered of much finer quality in fall—in

October and later—than earlier; and a striking difference in quality is said to be noticed in fish from different localities—the Bogue Sound fish being distinctly superior to those from Harker Island in Cove Sound, and those from Neuse River still better.   The hog-fish catch of North Carolina in 1902 was 191,670 pounds, for which the fishermen received $6,677, an average of 3.4 cents per pound; in 1890 it amounted to 256,520 pounds, worth $7,971, an average of 3.1 cents per pound.   The largest catch is made in New Hanover County.

Genus HÆMULON Cuvier. Grunts.

Small American shore fishes, some of them highly colored; some very important as food fishes in southern Florida.   Body oblong, compressed, back more or less elevated, mouth large; maxillary long and extending to below eye; lower jaw included; preopercle finely serrate; rows of scales not parallel with lateral line; junction of spinous and soft parts of dorsal fin marked by a notch; dorsal spines 11 or 12; second anal spine very large; caudal forked; caudal fin and soft parts of dorsal and anal fins densely scaled from base to tip; lips and inside of mouth bright red.   About 12 species, of which only 1 ranges northward to the North Carolina coast.   (*Hœmulon*, bloody gum.)

256. HÆMULON PLUMIERI (Lacépède).
"Snapper"; "Grunt"; Black Grunt (S. C.).

Labrus plumieri Lacépède, Histoire Naturelle des Poissons, iii, 480, pl. 2, fig. 2, 1802; Martinique.
Hœmulon arcuatum, Yarrow, 1877, 211; Beaufort (identification doubtful).
Diabasis formosus, Earll, 1887, 493; black-fish banks off Wilmington.
Hœmulon plumieri, Jordan & Evermann, 1898, 1305, pl. ccv, fig. 532; Cape Hatteras to Rio Janeiro.

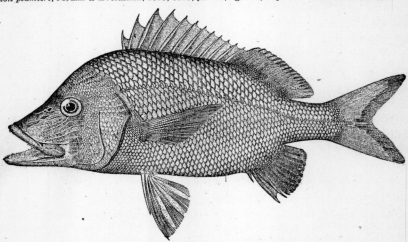

Fig. 130. GRUNT. *Hœmulon plumieri.*

DIAGNOSIS.—Body somewhat elongate, elevated at shoulders, depth about .4 length; head large, about equal to depth, upper profile slightly concave; mouth large, maxillary extending as far as pupil, .5 length of head; teeth strong, in rather broad bands; snout long, about 2.5 times diameter of eye; eye small, .16 to 20 length of head; gill-rakers short, about 12 + 15 on first arch; scales in lateral series 50, in transverse series 8+17, those above lateral line larger and in irregular and oblique rows; those below in oblique rows; dorsal rays xII,16, the spinous part much higher than soft, the longest spine (third or fourth) equal to snout; anal rays III,8, the second spine twice diameter of eye, the soft rays longer than those in soft dorsal; caudal rather deeply forked; pectorals pointed, .66 length of head; ventrals .6 head. Color: bluish gray, bases of scales with greenish bronze spots forming oblique lines; head golden with numerous sharply defined narrow sky-blue stripes mostly horizontal, 3 or 4 of the stripes extending to anterior part of back; inside of mouth bright orange; fins all grayish, spinous part of dorsal with yellow margin; anal tinged with yellow, ventrals with blue luster. (Named for Father Plumier, who more than 200 years ago sent drawings of Martinique fishes to Europe.)

This grunt is found from North Carolina to Brazil, and is abundant on the lower part of the South Atlantic coast. At Key West it is more abundant than all other grunts combined, and it is also quite common on the coast of South Carolina. The largest fish are 18 inches long, but the average is under 1 foot. This species doubtless occurs regularly on the various banks lying off the North Carolina coast, and Mr. Earll noted the species as one of those caught in the summer line-fishing off Wilmington. Yarrow said of this fish at Beaufort: "Very abundant in early spring and summer, generally found in marshy creeks inside of inlet; size 4 to 8 inches." There is considerable doubt, however, as to the species Yarrow had in mind, and Jordan & Gilbert believed that his remarks referred to the pig-fish (Orthopristis).

Mr. W. H. Yopp, of Wilmington, in November, 1905, forwarded to the writer 2 grunts of this species that had recently been caught on the "snapper banks" off Cape Fear; the specimens were 11.5 and 12.5 inches long. The fish is known as "snapper" in the Wilmington market and among the local fishermen, and is caught in considerable quantities from May to October. The market fish weigh from half a pound to 1.5 pounds, and bring the fishermen about 2.5 cents a pound.

Genus BATHYSTOMA Scudder. Tom-tates.

Similar to Hæmulon and perhaps scarcely separable therefrom, but with the dorsal spines definitely 13. Body rather elongate, back very little elevated, mouth large and low, eye large, gill-rakers on first arch rather numerous (12 to 18 on lower limb), preopercle not serrate, inside of mouth red. Three known species, with center of abundance in the West Indies, one found as far north as Cape Hatteras. (*Bathystoma*, low mouth.)

257. BATHYSTOMA RIMATOR (Jordan & Swain).

"Grunt"; Tom-tate; Red-mouthed Grunt.

Hæmulon rimator Jordan & Swain, Proceedings U. S. National Museum, 1884, 308; Charleston, Key West, and Pensacola. Jordan & Fesler, Review of the Sparoid Fishes of America and Europe, 477, 1893; refers to specimens from North Carolina.
Diabasis chrysopterus, Earll, 1887, 493; black-fish banks off Wilmington.
Bathystoma rimator, Jordan & Evermann, 1898, 1308, pl. ccvi, fig. 534.

DIAGNOSIS.—Form moderately elongate, back slightly elevated, depth about one-third length; head about equal to depth; mouth large, maxillary extending to middle of eye, .5 length of head; teeth in bands, rather weak; snout somewhat more than .33 length of head; eye large,

.25 length of head; vertical limb of preopercle straight, entire; gill-rakers short, about 11+16 on first arch: scales in lateral series about 50, in transverse series 7+13; scales above lateral line in oblique rows, those below in horizontal series; top of head, opercles, and cheeks scaly; dorsal fin notched, the rays XIII,14, the longest spine (fourth) .5 length of head; anal rays III,8, the second spine but slightly longer than third and contained 2.6 times in head; caudal widely forked, upper lobe longer; depth of caudal peduncle less than length of snout; pectorals .66 length of head; ventrals .8 length of pectorals. Color: generally silvery, back bluish; scales with yellow edges, these spots forming longitudinal lines oblique above, horizontal below; a narrow yellow stripe from a point over eye to posterior base of dorsal fin; another broader yellow stripe from snout to base of caudal; a round black spot at base of caudal; head yellowish above; mouth red inside; fins colorless or slightly yellow; young with a number of bronze longitudinal stripes on sides and head, the caudal spot more distinct.   (*rimator*, an inquirer.)

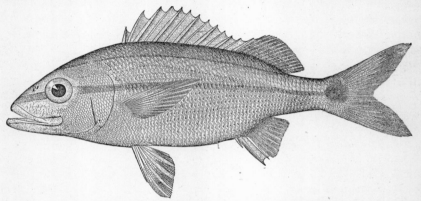

Fig. 131. GRUNT; TOM-TATE. *Bathystoma rimator.*

The tom-tate or red-mouth grunt, which reaches a length of 1 foot, is abundant at Charleston, South Carolina, and ranges thence through the West Indies. It will doubtless prove to be common on the southern part of the North Carolina coast, but as yet there are few definite records of its occurrence in this state. A specimen said to have come from North Carolina was obtained by Dr. S. E. Meek in the New York market (Jordan & Fesler, l.c.) some years ago. Mr. Earll, in his report on the North Carolina fisheries in 1880, notes that in the summer line-fishing on the "black-fish" banks off Wilmington, grunts of this species are caught; and the State Museum at Raleigh contains an example 1 foot long obtained at Wilmington in 1884 by Mr. H. H. Brimley. One specimen was collected for the Beaufort laboratory at Bird Shoal in the summer of 1902, and in June, 1904, Mr. Barton A. Bean, of the National Museum, found the young very common in the harbor. On the "black-fish" grounds lying off Beaufort the steamer Fish-Hawk secured several specimens in September, 1902.

Family SPARIDÆ.   The Scups, Pin-fishes, and Sheepsheads.

The members of this family are mostly small or moderate sized shore fishes of temperate and tropical waters, feeding chiefly on crabs, mollusks, and small fish. The family, which is closely related to the grunts (Hæmulidæ), has the following characters: Body usually compressed and rather deep; head large, with prominent ridges on skull; mouth small, terminal, and low, with strong teeth in jaws, no teeth on vomer and palatines; maxillary short, overlapped by a broad preorbital, no supplemental bone; gill-membranes not united, free from isthmus; preopercle little if at all serrate; no spines on opercle; scales on body large, adherent, head more or less scaly; lateral line prominent, concurrent with back; dorsal fin long and continuous, spines strong and usually fitting in a groove when flexed; anal fin about length of soft part of dorsal, with 3 spines; caudal fin forked or deeply concave; air bladder present. Of the 7 genera represented on the eastern coast of the United States, 6, with 7 species, are known from North Carolina. Two of the local sparids are among the best known food-fishes of the Atlantic coast. The common porgy of southern Europe (*Pagrus pagrus*), known also from Charleston, S. C., to Uruguay, may be looked for on the lower part of the North Carolina coast.

Key to the North Carolina genera of sparids.

i. Bone (interhemal) supporting second anal spine large, partly hollow, and receiving posterior end of swim-bladder; teeth in front of jaws either narrow incisors or canines.
   a. Front teeth very narrow incisors; first dorsal spine rudimentary and directed forward.
      b. Anterior dorsal spines not noticeably long, the third one-half to two-thirds length of head..STENOTOMUS.
      bb. Anterior dorsal spines very long and filamentous, the third longer than head. OTRYNTER.
   aa. Front teeth canine; first dorsal spine not rudimentary and not directed forward.
                                                    CALAMUS.
ii. Bone supporting second anal spine normal; teeth in front of jaws broad incisors.
   c. Body marked by dark cross bands.
      d. Incisor teeth deeply notched; size small .... LAGODON.
      dd. Incisor teeth entire or slightly notched; size large.................ARCHOSARGUS.
   cc. No dark cross-bands; black blotch on caudal peduncle..................DIPLODUS.

Genus STENOTOMUS Gill. Scuppaugs.

Small fishes of our Atlantic coast, very abundant and furnishing much food in the New England and Middle States. The Indian name "scuppaug" has been corrupted into "scup" and "porgy", by which names these fishes are generally known. Body rather deep; back elevated; head pointed, incisor teeth long and flat; eye small and placed high; gill-rakers small, about 16 on first arch; top of head, snout, and orbital region naked, opercle and cheek scaly; dorsal spines 12, the first less than half length of second and the longest much shorter than head; antrorse dorsal spine attached to interneural bone by a long process. The 2 known species, both found in North Carolina, are very similar but may be distinguished by following characters:

i. Body with about same depth from first to tenth dorsal spines; depth more than half length of body; head .28 length of body; snout less than .5 length of head..........*chrysops.*
ii. Depth of body decreasing rapidly backward from anterior dorsal spines; depth less than half length of body; head .33 length of body; snout .5 length of head........*aculeatus.*

(*Stenotomus*, narrow cutting, in reference to the incisor teeth.)

258. STENOTOMUS CHRYSOPS (Linnæus).

"Pin-fish"; Scuppaug; Porgy (S. C.); Scup; Fair Maid (Va.).

Sparus chrysops Linnæus, Systema Naturæ, ed. xii, 471, 1766; Charleston.
Stenotomus argyrops, Yarrow, 1877, 210; Beaufort.   Jordan & Gilbert, 1879, 379; Beaufort.
Stenotomus chrysops, Jordan, 1886, 27; Beaufort.   Jenkins, 1887, 90; Beaufort.   Jordan & Evermann, 1898,
    1346, pl. ccxi, fig. 544.

DIAGNOSIS.—Back arched, depth about .5 length; profile steep, nape convex, a depression over eyes; head contained 3.5 times in total length; eye less than .25 length of head; snout 4 length of head; incisors very narrow, lateral teeth (molars) in two rows in upper jaw; scales in lateral series 50, in transverse series 25; dorsal rays XII,12, first spine about equal to eye, third spine longest and half length of head; anal rays III,11, third spine longest; pectoral fin 1.5 times length of head; caudal fin forked.   Color: silvery, often with irregular dark brown cross bands under certain conditions; the young with well defined blackish cross bands.   (*chrysops*, golden-eyed.)

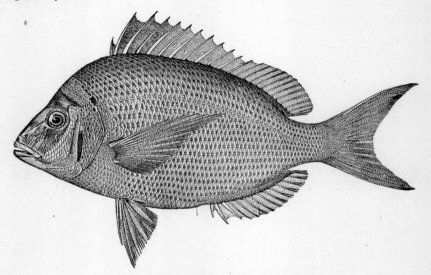

Fig. 132. SCUP; PIN-FISH. *Stenotomus chrysops.*

This scup is found coastwise from Massachusetts to South Carolina and is an abundant and important food fish in the northern part of its range, but on the North Carolina coast is not particularly numerous and has no economic value, being "hardly noticed by the fishermen" and at Beaufort not distinguished from the southern scup, *Stenotomus aculeatus*.   The species is known as "pin-fish", which seems to be the only local name.   The maximum weight is about 4 pounds, but the usual weight is a pound or less.   The scup feeds on shrimp, small crabs, and other crustaceans, mollusks, worms and small fish.   It bites readily at the hook baited with fish or crab, and is often a nuisance when a fisherman is seeking other fish.   The flesh is of excellent flavor.

259. STENOTOMUS ACULEATUS (Cuvier & Valenciennes).

"Pin-fish"; Southern Scup or Porgy.

Chrysophrys aculeatus Cuvier & Valenciennes, Histoire Naturelle des Poissons, vi, 137, 1830; Charleston, S. C.
Stenotomus aculeatus, Jordan & Evermann, 1898, 1347, pl. ccxii. fig. 545; Cape Hatteras to Texas.

DIAGNOSIS.—Very similar to *Stenotomus chrysops*, the depth somewhat less than .5 length; profile less steep than in the other species; head contained about 3.25 times in length; eye larger, contained 3.75 to 4 times in head; snout long, .5 length of head; scales in lateral series about 55, in transverse series 23; dorsal rays XII,12, the first spine shortest, the third longest; anal rays III,11. Color: dull silvery. (*aculeatus*, spiny.)

This species replaces the common scup southward, and is reported to be common from Cape Hatteras to Texas. It is very similar to other species, and is not distinguished therefrom by fishermen. There appear to be no definite North Carolina records, but the species may undoubtedly be found at Cape Fear, Beaufort, and other points.

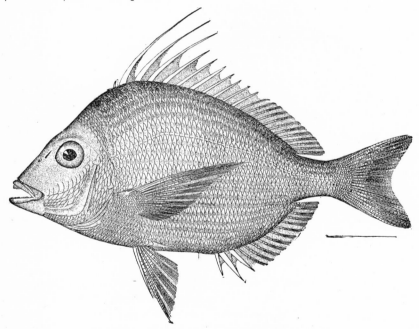

Fig. 133. LONG-SPINED PORGY. *Otrynter caprinus.*

Genus OTRYNTER Jordan & Evermann. Long-spined Porgies.

Very similar to Stenotomus, but with differences in the structure of the skull and dorsal spines. The antrorse dorsal spine is attached directly to the interneural bone; the third, fourth, and fifth spines are long and filamentous, the third being longer than head. One species. (*Otrynter*, one who whips, in allusion to the long dorsal spines.)

260. OTRYNTER CAPRINUS (Bean).

Long-spined Porgy.

Stenotomus caprinus Bean, Proceedings U. S. National Museum, 1882, 426; snapper banks off Pensacola, Fla.
Otrynter caprinus, Jordan & Evermann, 1898, 1345, pl. ccxi, fig. 543.

DIAGNOSIS.—Body ovate, back elevated, depth more than .5 length; profile from mouth to dorsal fin nearly straight; head .33 length; eye large, .33 head, .66 snout; mouth rather large, maxillary longer than eye, incisor teeth in front of jaws small, in a compact group, molars in 2 rows; scales in lateral series 50, in transverse series 5+15; first row of scales on cheek enlarged; a well-developed scaly sheath at base of soft dorsal and anal fins; dorsal rays XII,12, the first 2 spines very short, the third long and filamentous, the fourth and fifth similar, soft dorsal low; anal rays III,12, the spines large and strong; caudal slightly concave; pectorals long, pointed, longer than head; ventrals long, reaching to anal fin. Color: back light green, sides and belly silvery; body under certain conditions marked by irregular dark bars; young with indistinct, narrow dark bars. (*caprinus*, goat-like.)

A rare species, hitherto known only from specimens taken from the stomachs of snappers and groupers caught on the west coast of Florida. In the summer of 1904, 9 specimens, the largest 7 inches long, were taken in Beaufort Harbor, 2 in a seine and 7 in a pound net. The larger fish are plainly colored, but a small example is marked by irregular dark cross bands.

Genus CALAMUS Swainson. Porgies.

A numerous genus of small, well-flavored, American shore fishes, inhabiting both coasts, only a single species as yet known from the Atlantic coast north of Florida. The genus closely resembles Stenotomus, but the front teeth are canine, the dorsal spines are lower, there is no antrorse spine on the first spine-bearing interneural bone, the caudal fin is more deeply forked, etc. Body ovate or oblong, back much elevated, head large and very deep, eye placed high on side of head, snout long, mouth small or moderate, dorsal and anal fins low, pectoral fin pointed and longer than head, second interhemal bone as in Stenotomus. (*Calamus*, a reed or quill, in allusion to the quill-like interhemal bone.)

261. CALAMUS LEUCOSTEUS Jordan & Gilbert.

White-bone porgy.

Calamus leucosteus Jordan & Gilbert, in Jordan, Catalogue of Fishes of North America, 1885, 91; Charleston, S. C. Jordan & Evermann, 1898, 1353.

DIAGNOSIS.—Body short and deep, back elevated, depth a little less than .5 length; head deeper than long, its length contained slightly more than 3 times in total length; profile straight from snout to eyes, convex posteriorly; eyes large, about .28 length of head; maxillary .4 length of head; about 10 rather large canine teeth in each jaw; gill-rakers short, 12 to 14 on first arch; scales in lateral series 50, in transverse series 7+15; scales on cheek in 5 rows; dorsal rays XI,12, the highest spine less than half length of head; anal rays III,10; caudal fin well forked; pectorals very long, reaching as far back as base of third anal spine, and nearly .4 total length; ventrals more than .5 as long as head. Color: dull silvery, with indefinite dark cross-bars; dorsal and anal fins dark blotched. (*leucosteus*, white-boned.)

The habitat of this porgy is quite circumscribed. It has heretofore been recorded only from the Charleston (S. C.) market, where it is called "white-bone porgy", a name of unknown application. The species is entitled to be listed in the North Carolina fauna because of a specimen, 12 inches long, obtained by Mr. H. H. Brimley at Wilmington in 1884 and now preserved in the State Museum at Raleigh. This specimen was caught by a market fisherman off the mouth of Cape Fear River, and the species may doubtless be looked for regularly in that region. Like other members of the genus, it is a good food fish.

Genus LAGODON Holbrook. Sailor's Choice.

This genus contains a single species, and is distinguished from related genera chiefly by the form of the cranial bones; other characters are noted in the key. (*Lagodon*, hare-tooth.)

262. LAGODON RHOMBOIDES (Linnæus).

"Robin"; "Pin-fish"; "Thorny-back"; Bream; Sailor's Choice; Salt-water Bream (S. C.); Fair Maid (Va.).

Sparus rhomboides Linnæus, Systema Naturæ, ed. xii, 470, 1766; Charleston.
Lagodon rhomboides, Yarrow, 1877, 210; Beaufort. Jordan & Gilbert, 1879, 378; Beaufort. Goode, 1884, 393; Cape Hatteras, Beaufort. Jordan & Evermann, 1898, 1358, pl. ccxv, fig. 552. Linton, 1905, 380; Beaufort.
Diplodus rhomboides, Jordan, 1886, 28; Beaufort. Jenkins, 1887, 90; Beaufort. Wilson, 1900, 355; Beaufort.

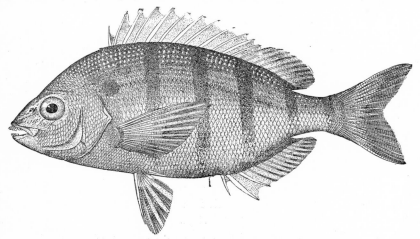

Fig. 134. SAILOR'S CHOICE; ROBIN. *Lagodon rhomboides*.

DIAGNOSIS.—Form elliptical, the depth about .4 length; head rather pointed, profile not steep, contained 3.25 times in total length; mouth small, maxillary not extending beyond anterior margin of eye; 4 deeply notched incisors and 2 rows of molars in each jaw; eye less than snout, .25 length of head, equal to interorbital space; gill-rakers 18 to 20; scales in lateral series 65 to 70, in transverse series 28; dorsal rays xii,11, the first spine short and directed forward, the longest spine about half length of head; anal rays iii,11, the second spine largest; pectorals extending about to anal origin; caudal fin moderately forked. Life colors: dark green above, silvery below; a round dark spot on shoulder about size of eye; 4 to 6 dark cross bars about width of eye; numerous golden longitudinal stripes; dorsal spines purplish or bluish silvery, the membrane pale yellow, free edge of fin bright yellow; anal fin yellow, with a broad light-blue margin; caudal and pectorals pale yellow; ventrals bluish white, with 2 middle membranes pale yellow. (*rhomboides*, rhomb-like.)

This attractive little sparid abounds in the bays and estuaries from New York to Cuba, and has on several occasions been taken in southern Massachusetts (at Woods Hole). Owing to an evident error in identification, Yarrow listed this species as "not abundant", whereas it is an exceedingly abundant fish at Beaufort and elsewhere on the North Carolina coast, where its local name are "pin-fish" and "robin." ·The name "pin-fish" refers to the dorsal spines, which are exceedingly sharp and resemble ordinary pins in size and metallic color. The name "thorny-back", applied to this fish in Topsail and Myrtle Grove sounds, refers to the same thing.

The maximum length is about 10 inches and the usual length only 6 inches. Fish of all sizes may be taken in Beaufort Harbor throughout the year, and in the laboratory fine-meshed seines many thousands are caught yearly, in company with spot, mullet, silversides, killi-fish, etc.

The food is quite varied, comprising small fish, worms, crustaceans, mollusks and seaweed.

Fish opened at the laboratory in June and July (1899) had no obvious reproductive organs, but ovarian eggs were noted on August 6 (1903). A large male examined by Mr. Worth on November 20 (1903) was fully ripe, and it is evident that the species breeds in winter.

Until very recently the species was not marketable in North Carolina and when caught incidentally was thrown away; but it is now shipped from Beaufort and other points, ranking among the lowest grade of fishes, although it is by many persons considered a superior pan fish. The principal catch is made in New Hanover County, and in the Wilmington market the fish is regularly sold from April to October, the fishermen receiving about 1 cent per pound. The quantity sold in the entire state probably falls below 40,000 pounds yearly.

Genus ARCHOSARGUS Gill. Sheepsheads.

In this genus of American shore fishes, the body is stout, deep, compressed; the rather small mouth has conspicuous, broad incisor teeth in front and strong molars laterally; the posterior nostril is a mere slit in front of the eye; the spinous dorsal is about twice length of soft part and the spines are strong, the first spine being short and procumbent; the anal fin is comparatively short; the caudal is slightly forked or deeply concave; and in the North Carolina species the body is marked by broad black transverse bands. Five species, the 1 represented in local waters being the largest and most valuable of all. (*Archosargus*, chief *Sargus*, the latter being an ancient name for fishes of this group.)

263. ARCHOSARGUS PROBATOCEPHALUS (Walbaum).

"Sheepshead".

Sparus probatocephalus Walbaum, Artedi Genera Piscium, 295, 1792; New York.
Archosargus probatocephalus, Yarrow, 1877, 210; Cape Lookout and Beaufort. Jordan & Gilbert, 1879, 379; Beaufort. Jordan & Evermann, 1898, 1361, pl. ccxvi, fig. 554. Linton, 1905, 382; Beaufort.
Diplodus probatocephalus, Jordan, 1886, 27; Beaufort. Jenkins, 1887, 90; Beaufort.

PLATE 14

SHEEPSHEAD (ARCHOSARGUS PROBATOCEPHALUS)

A. HOEN & CO.

DIAGNOSIS.—Body very stout, deep, moderately compressed, the depth .4 to .5 length; head large, heavy, deep, less than .33 length; bony area between eyes honeycombed; mouth horizontal, maxillary .33 length of head; 3 broad incisors in upper jaw, 4 in lower jaw, these nearly entire in adult but serrate in young; molar teeth in 3 rows in upper jaw and 2 series in lower jaw; eye .20 to .25 length of head, less than interorbital space; gill-rakers 9 or 10; scales in lateral series 45 to 50, in transverse series 22 to 24; dorsal rays XII,10 to XII,12, the fifth spine longest, the first equal to eye; anal rays III,10 or III,11, the second spine very strong and more than twice length of first; caudal slightly forked; pectorals longer than head, extending beyond origin of anal; ventrals large. Color: grayish, with 6 to 8 broad, black, nearly vertical bands on body, these very distinct in young; dorsal fin dusky, anal and ventrals blackish, pectorals dark at base. (*probatocephalus*, sheep-head.)

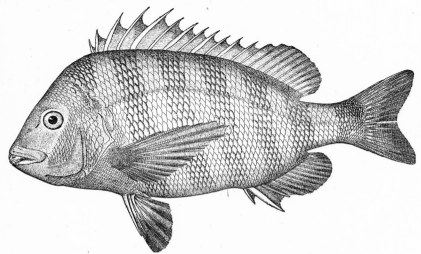

Fig. 135. SHEEPSHEAD. *Archosargus probatocephalus.*

The sheepshead is a well-known and valuable food fish, found from Massachusetts to Texas. It reaches a weight of 20 pounds, and is often taken about wharves, breakwaters, and sunken wrecks where food abounds. It feeds chiefly on mollusks and crabs, which it is easily able to crush between its strong teeth.

The species occurs in all the bays and estuaries of the North Carolina coast from spring to fall, but nowhere in great abundance. Writing about the sheepshead at Beaufort about 35 years ago, Yarrow said:

Abundant in early spring; will not take the hook until later in season. In 1871, large numbers were taken in the bight of Cape Lookout in nets. Size, 8 to 24 inches. A small specimen was taken January 30, 1872, an early arrival.

At the spawning season, which is in spring, the sheepshead swim in schools, and appear to prefer sandy shores. The eggs are about .03 inch in diameter, and more than 1,500,000 are in a fluid quart. They float at the surface, and hatch rapidly, only 40 hours being required in water of 76° or 77° F. The young are active and hardy. At Beaufort young fish from 1.5 to 7 inches long are found in the harbor in summer, and the variations in size suggest either a prolonged spawning season or an irregular rate of growth; thus, during one year, in the third week in August specimens only 1.5 inches long were seined, while in the first week of the same month the young averaged 4 inches long, and in the last week in July the average length was 5 inches. A specimens 2.75 inches over all (2.25 inches to base of caudal), taken by the writer at Beaufort October 25, 1904, had the following colors in life: Body marked by 7 broad shining black cross bands, separated by silvery spaces; dorsal dusky, the membrane of spinous part with black edge; anal black; pectorals white; ventrals blue-black; tail white; a round black humeral spot, larger than pupil, partly in second cross band and partly in first interspace, on level with upper half of eye.

An old wrecked bark in the Beaufort Harbor was for a long time one of the best places for hook and line fishing; this was blown up and removed by the government in November, 1903. After the first explosion of dynamite 15 small sheepshead 6 to 8 inches long were collected at the surface, and after the second discharge 2 days later a number of others were found. Six days later, a small trap at the laboratory wharf, which had been set a year and had caught no sheepshead during that time, was found to contain 20 sheepshead of the same size as those killed at the wreck; the following day, the 20 not having been removed, the trap contained about 40.

The sheepshead is a much sought fish, and the comparatively small catch indicates that it is not numerous at this time in North Carolina. It is taken for market with lines, gill nets, seines, and pound nets, but the line catch is insignificant except in Dare County. Carteret County ranks first in the amount of the catch, followed by Dare, Beaufort, and Pamlico counties. The yield in 1890 was 146,345 pounds, valued at $5,981; in 1897 it was 271,205 pounds, valued at $9,243; and in 1902 it was 154,930 pounds, valued at $7,303.

The sheepshead is deservedly regarded as one of the best of salt-water fishes. The meat is white, flaky, juicy, and well flavored, and is usually prepared for the table by boiling or baking.

Genus DIPLODUS Rafinesque. Sargoes, or Spot-tailed Pin-fishes.

This is essentially an old world genus, with a few American representatives. Similar to Archosargus, but with bony interorbital region more cavernous; body ovate, compressed, back elevated; incisor teeth broad, not notched; molar teeth in several rows; gill-rakers short; dorsal spines about 12; color silvery, with dark area on caudal peduncle. One species in local fauna. (Diplodus, double tooth.)

264. DIPLODUS HOLBROOKII (Bean).

"Spot-tailed Pin-fish"; "Pin-fish"; Ring-tailed Bream (S. C.); Salt-water Bream (S. C.); Sailor's Choice.

Sargus holdrookii Bean, Forest and Stream, June 13, 1878; Charleston, S. C. Jordan & Gilbert, 1879, 379; Beaufort.

Diplodus holbrookii, Goode, 1884, 386; Beaufort. Jenkins, 1887, 90; Beaufort. Jordan & Evermann, 1898, 1362, pl. ccxvii, figs. 555 and 555a. Linton, 1905, 383; Beaufort.

DIAGNOSIS.—Dorsal and ventral outlines similar, depth .5 length; head short, a little less than .25 length, longer and more pointed in young; 4 incisors in each jaw, directed obliquely forward, 3 series of molars in upper jaw, 2 in lower jaw; eye .25 head, behind posterior end of maxillary; gill-rakers on first arch about 20, very short, less than .25 diameter of eye; scales in lateral series 55 to 57, in transverse series 20 to 22; dorsal rays XII,14, third to fifth spines longest, less than half length of head; anal rays III,13, second spine largest; caudal rather deeply forked; pectorals pointed, reaching about as far as anal origin. Color: back dull blue, sides and below silvery; a conspicuous black blotch or band on each side of anterior part of caudal peduncle; opercular margin black; base of pectoral black; back and side of young with about 5 very narrow vertical dark stripes, with about same number of short intermediate stripes on back. (Named for John Edwards Holbrook, author of Ichthyology of South Carolina.)

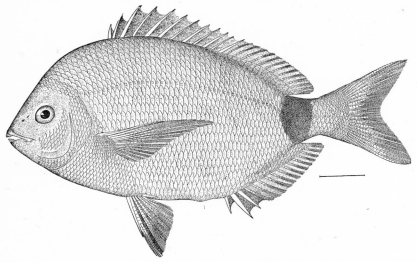

Fig. 136. SPOT-TAILED PIN-FISH. *Diplodus holbrookii.*

This species is known from the coast between Cape Hatteras and Cedar Keys. Jordan & Gilbert, writing of it in 1879, said:

Extremely abundant everywhere along the Beaufort shore. This species was first described by Dr. Bean during the past year. That so strongly marked and so abundant a species should have so long escaped notice is very remarkable. Its color is bright silvery, with a large black blotch on the upper part of the caudal peduncle, which is very conspicuous while the fish is in the water. It reaches but a small size, and is not at Beaufort used as food. The fishermen call it pin-fish, and as such it is beneath their notice. Most of the fishermen, indeed, did not distinguish it from *Lagodon rhomboides.*

The vernacular names for this fish in the Beaufort region and about Bogue Inlet are "pin-fish" and "spot-tailed pin-fish". The maximum length of the species is 10 about inches. In 1871 Dr. Coues collected at Beaufort a specimen of this species now in the U. S. National Museum, but failed to recognize it as distinct from Stenotomus; and the species is not mentioned in Yarrow's list.

Family GERRIDÆ.   The Mojarras.

Small marine fishes, chiefly tropical, most readily distinguishable by their small, very protractile mouth, which, when protruded, is turned downward. Body more or less elongate, compressed, and covered with rather large scales; a deep groove in top of head to receive premaxillary; no supplemental maxillary bone; villiform teeth in jaws, no teeth on vomer or palatine bones; nostrils round and double; gill-rakers short and broad; gill-membranes not united, free from isthmus; lateral line continuous, more or less parallel with outline of back; branchiostegals 6; air-bladder present; spinous and soft dorsal rays united into one fin, with scaly sheath at base; dorsal spines 9 or 10; anal fin with 2 or 3 spines and fewer soft rays than in dorsal; ventral fins thoracic, close together.   These fishes are carnivorous, and the larger ones are used as food, but they have no economic value in the United States, although abundant in Florida and other southern states.   Four genera are represented in American waters; of these only 1 is as yet known from North Carolina.

Genus EUCINOSTOMUS Baird & Girard.   Mojarras, or Irish Pompanoes.

This genus embraces numerous small species, several of which are found along the south Atlantic and Gulf coasts and in the West Indies.   Body elongate; dorsal fin deeply notched; anal spines 3; interhemal bone connected with second anal spine expanded into a hollow cylinder into which the posterior end of air-bladder is inserted.   Two species found on North Carolina coast:

i. Premaxillary groove not scaled; anal rays III,7; second anal spine contained 4.5 times in length of head; depth of body contained 3.25 times in length . . . . *pseudogula.*
ii. Premaxillary groove scaled in front, the scales leaving a naked pit behind; anal rays III,8; second anal spine contained 3.33 times in length of head; depth of body contained 2.4 times in length. . . . . *gula.*

(*Eucinostomus*, freely movable mouth.)

265. EUCINOSTOMUS PSEUDOGULA Poey.

Irish Pompano.

Eucinostomus pseudogula Poey, Enumeratio Piscium Cubensium, 53, pl. 1, 1875; Havana.   Jordan & Evermann, 1898, 1368.

DIAGNOSIS.—Body elliptical, not greatly compressed; head contained 3.25 to 3.50 times in length; mouth small, maxillary extending a little beyond front of eye, its length contained 3.25 times in head; snout conical, contained 3.25 times in head; diameter of eye slightly greater than length of snout; scales in lateral series 49, in transverse series 14; 3 rows of scales on cheek; gill-rakers on lower arm of first arch 7; dorsal rays IX,10 to IX,12, the spines weak and flexible; anal rays III,6 or III,7, the second spine stoutest, its length .22 head.   Color: greenish above, silvery below; snout and tips of spinous dorsal black; caudal reddish; other fins pale.   (*pseudogula*, false throat.)

This species, which has heretofore been known from Cuba, West Indies, Bermuda, and Brazil, was taken at Beaufort in the summer of 1902, and several additional specimens were taken there in September, 1905, which are preserved in the laboratory collection.   The maximum length of the species is about 7 inches.

266. EUCINOSTOMUS GULA (Cuvier & Valenciennes.)

Silver Jenny; Irish Pompano.

Gerres gula Cuvier & Valenciennes, Histoire Naturelle des Poissons, vi, 464, 1830; Martinique.
Eucinostomus argenteus, Jordan & Gilbert, 1879, 378; Beaufort.
Gerres gula, Jordan, 1886, 28; Beaufort. Jenkins, 1887, 91; Beaufort.
Eucinostomus gula, Jordan & Evermann, 1898, 1370. Linton, 1905, 383; Beaufort.

DIAGNOSIS.—Body elliptical, back moderately elevated; length of head contained 3.33 times in total length; mouth small, maxillary reaching somewhat beyond front of eye; eye .33 length of head; snout .28 length of head; gill-rakers small, 7 below angle of first arch; scales in lateral series 42, in transverse series 14; dorsal rays ix,10, the longest spine .66 length of head; anal rays iii,8, the second spine shorter and stouter than third, and contained 3.33 times in length of head. Color: beautiful uniform silvery, the back dark greenish in certain lights; upper margin of spinous dorsal black; soft dorsal and anal plain or dusky; other fins pale. (*gula*, throat.)

The species ranges from North Carolina to Brazil, stragglers ascending the coast in summer to New Jersey, New York, and southern Massachusetts. In Beaufort Harbor the fish was abundant in 1902, more than a thousand specimens 1.5 to 2 inches long being seined incidentally; in the following year it was scarcer, less than 100 being noticed. On October 24 and 25, 1905, the writer took numerous specimens 2 to 4.25 inches long in Beaufort Harbor in company with spots, silversides, and may-fish. The species is small (maximum length 5 inches) and no use is made of it. Examples examined at Beaufort in August had been feeding chiefly on worms, but contained also crustaceans, diatoms, and fragments of vegetable tissue.

Family KYPHOSIDÆ. The Rudder-fishes.

In this family the body is elongate or deep, compressed; mouth of moderate size, with incisor teeth in front of each jaw, the vomer and palatines with or without teeth; maxillary more or less sheathed by the preorbital; premaxillaries moderately protractile; gill-membranes not united, free from isthmus; pseudo-branchiæ well developed; opercular margin entire; scales of varied size and form; intestine long; air-bladder with 2 posterior horns; dorsal fin single or divided, the spines strong, 10 to 15 in number, the soft part rather long and either scaly or naked; anal fin with 3 spines and 10 to 19 soft rays; caudal lunate or forked; ventrals with accessory scale at base. A rather numerous family of shore fishes, which feed largely on green algæ, some of them important food species in America and Europe. Six American genera, only 1 represented on the east coast of the United States.

Genus KYPHOSUS Lacépède. Chubs or Chopas.

Body elongate-ovate, compressed; head short; snout blunt; mouth small, horizontal, with a row of incisors in each jaw, a band of villiform teeth behind them and small teeth on tongue, vomer, and palatines; gill-rakers long; scales small, ctenoid, completely covering body, most of head, soft parts of vertical fins and base of paired fins; lateral line continuous; pyloric cœca numerous;

dorsal fin continuous, a notch between the two parts; dorsal spines 11, depressible in a scaly groove; anal similar to soft dorsal; caudal forked; pectorals small; ventrals posterior to pectorals. Five species are American. (*Kyphosus*, humped.)

267. KYPHOSUS SECTATRIX (Linnæus).

Rudder-fish; Chub.

Perca sectatrix Linnæus, Systema Naturæ, ed. x, 293, 1758; Carolina.
Pimelepterus bosci, Jordan & Gilbert, 1879, 379; Beaufort.
Kyphosus sectatrix, Jordan, 1886, 28; Beaufort. Jenkins, 1887, 90; Beaufort. Jordan & Evermann, 1898, 1387, pl. ccxix, fig. 559. Linton, 1905, 383; Beaufort.

DIAGNOSIS.—Body ovate, much compressed, depth slightly less than half length; length of head contained 3.75 times in length of body; mouth quite small, maxillary barely extending to eye; snout .25 head; eye equal to snout; interorbital area swollen; preopercle with weak serrations; gill-rakers long, about 16 on long arm of first arch; scales in lateral series 55, in transverse series 10+16; dorsal rays xi,12, the longest spine .2 depth of body; anal rays iii,11, second spine longest; soft dorsal and anal very low; lower caudal lobe longer. Color: bluish gray, edges of scales on back and sides brassy, this color forming faint longitudinal streaks; a pale stripe below eye, with a yellow one above and below; ventrals and anal fins blackish; fins otherwise grayish. (*sectatrix*, a follower.)

The rudder-fish is abundant in the West Indies, the Bermudas, and at Key West, but is not common on our east coast and in Massachusetts occurs only as a rare straggler. It is found occasionally in Beaufort Harbor, and is doubtless uncommon outside. During 1906, 6 specimens were seined in the harbor, at Bird Shoal and Town Marsh. On October 26, 1903, a Beaufort fisherman caught one near Cape Lookout which was 14.5 inches long and weighed 1.75 pounds.

The rudder-fish, named from its habit of following vessels, has very marked game qualities, and is an excellent food fish. Considerable numbers are caught at Key West, and in the Bermudas it is one of the leading economic species. The maximum length is 18 inches. Four specimens examined at Beaufort by Prof. Edwin Linton in August, 1902, contained crabs, small bivalve shells, vegetable debris, and sand.

Family SCIÆNIDÆ. The Drums, Croakers, etc.

The drums are a numerous and important family found in temperate and tropical waters in all parts of the world, and well represented in America by many valuable food species. The name drum is strictly applicable only to certain members which have the power of producing a loud drumming or croaking sound, and only a few of these bear popular names which relate to this function. The manner in which the drumming sound is made has been the subject of much speculation, and is still not generally appreciated. From a recent discussion[*] of this subject by the present writer, the following observations are extracted:

It is rather remarkable that so common a function as the drumming of fishes should have remained so long misunderstood; that so much speculation should have been indulged in

[*] The drumming of the drum-fishes (Sciænidæ). Science, New York, Sept. 22, 1905, pp. 376–378.

regarding a phenomenon so easily investigated in most parts of the world; and that a conspicuous specialized drumming muscle should have been either overlooked or ignored by ichthyologists.

For several years, as opportunity was afforded, I have been studying the peculiar drumming sounds made by those fishes in which this function is so strikingly developed that it has determined the family name, the inquiries being in continuation of some observations and experiments on the squeteague (*Cynoscion regalis*) carried on by Professor R. W. Tower, at Woods Hole, in 1901 and 1902, and noted by me in the Report of the U. S. Fish Commissioner for 1902 (page 137).

The drumming act has been more thoroughly studied in the squeteague than in any other sciænid species; and the facts regarding it, as determined by Professor Tower, may here be repeated substantially as stated by me in 1902 (*l. c.*), but in somewhat greater detail:

1. There is in the squeteague a special drumming muscle, lying between the abdominal muscles and the peritoneum and extending the entire length of the abdomen on either side of the median line, the muscles of the two sides being united dorsally by a strong aponeurosis. The muscle is of a decided red color, in sharp contrast to the pale muscles of the abdominal parietes, and the fibers are very short, running at right angles to the long axis of the muscle.

2. The muscle, with the aponeurosis, is in close relation with the large air-bladder, and by its rapid contractions produces a drumming sound, with the aid of the tense air-bladder, which acts as a resonator. Experimentally, the removal of the air-bladder or the section of the nerves supplying the muscle abolishes the sound; if a removed air-bladder is restored to its place the drumming is resumed; and the substitution for a removed air-bladder of any hollow, thin-walled vessel of suitable size permits the resumption of drumming when the special muscle is stimulated.

3. The muscle exists only in the males, and only the males are able to make a drumming sound.

It is probable the drumming mechanism and function as existing in the squeteagues are typical of a majority of the genera of Sciænidæ; but there are some interesting variations in the limited number of genera which I have been able to examine in the field and laboratory. Thus in the croaker (*Micropogon undulatus*) the special drumming muscle is present in both male and female, and both sexes make the drumming sound; while in the so-called king-fishes or whitings (*Menticirrhus*) the drumming muscle and air-bladder are absent in both sexes and no drumming sounds are made. The seven commonest genera of drum-fishes found along the Atlantic coast may be thus classified with reference to the drumming function:

i. Drumming muscle present in both male and female, and drumming sound made by both sexes . . . . *Micropogon.*
ii. Drumming muscle present only in male, and drumming sound produced only by the male. *Pogonias, Sciænops, Cynoscion, Leiostomus, Bairdiella.*
iii. Drumming muscle absent in both male and female, and no drumming sound produced by either sex . . . . *Menticirrhus.*

The fishes of this family in North Carolina are in the aggregate more valuable than all the other salt-water fishes combined. The annual catch exceeds 7,000,000 pounds and is worth over $225,000.

The most important anatomical characters of this family are as follows: Body elongate, variously compressed, covered with scales which are usually thin ctenoid; head large, scaly, bones cavernous; mouth large or small, teeth in one or more series on jaws, no teeth on vomer, palatals, pterygoids or tongue; barbels sometimes present on chin; maxillary bone without supplemental bone, slipping under edge of usually broad preorbital; premaxillaries protractile; gill-membranes not united; and free from isthmus, branchiostegals 7; pseudobranchiæ usually present and large; posterior margin of opercle with 2 flat points; lateral line continuous, curved, and extending on caudal fin; dorsal fins continuous or separate, the soft portion longer; anal fin with 1 or 2 spines and comparatively few soft rays; caudal fin usually square or emarginate; ear bones or otoliths ("lucky stones") large; air-bladder (absent in 1 genus) usually large. Of 28 genera and about 110 species found in American waters, 10 genera and 14 species are represented in the North Carolina fauna.

Key to North Carolina genera of Sciænidæ.

i. Dorsal spines well separated; dorsal rays 17 to 32.
   a. No barbels on lower jaw.
     b. Body elongate, fusiform; back not elevated; mouth large, lower jaw projecting; 2 canine teeth at tip of upper jaw; none at tip of lower jaw.............CYNOSCION.
     bb. Body less elongate, compressed, back elevated; no canine teeth in jaws.
       c. Teeth well developed, permanent in both jaws.
         d. Gill-rakers long and slender; no black spot at base of tail.
           e. Head not very broad, interorbital space not spongy or cavernous; lower jaw projecting.
             f. Snout very short, less than diameter of eye; mouth large, very oblique; no bony teeth on margin of preopercle.....................LARIMUS.
             ff. Snout moderate, equal to or greater than diameter of eye; mouth moderate, slightly oblique; margin of preopercle serrate ....BAIRDIELLA.
           ee. Head very broad above, the interorbital space flat, cavernous, the septa very thin; lower jaw equal to or shorter than upper ....STELLIFER.
         dd. Gill-rakers short and thick; one (sometimes several) black spot at base of tail.
                                          SCIÆNOPS.
       cc. Teeth very small, those in lower jaw wanting or deciduous; mouth small, inferior.
                                      LEIOSTOMUS.
   aa. Barbels on lower jaw.
     g. A row of minute barbels on each side of lower jaw; air bladder with long horns.
                                   MICROPOGON.
     gg. A single thick barbel at tip of lower jaw; air-bladder absent......MENTICIRRHUS.
     ggg. Numerous large barbels along inner edge of each side of lower jaw; air-bladder very large, thick, and with fringed appendages..........................POGONIAS.
ii. Dorsal spines close together; dorsal rays 36 to 55.............................EQUES.

Genus CYNOSCION Gill.   Squeteagues or "Sea Trouts".

Large coastal fishes, some of them of great economic importance, found on both coasts of America and also in the old world. Body long, graceful, very slightly compressed; head pointed; mouth large, terminal, maxillary broad; teeth in narrow bands, 2 canines at tip of upper jaw (1 sometimes obsolete); gill-rakers long and rather stout; pseudobranchiæ present; dorsal fins very close together, the spines slender, soft dorsal long and low; anal spines 1 or 2, feeble, soft rays 7 to 13; caudal fin slightly concave or slightly rounded; air-bladder large, 2-horned. Of the 20 or more American species, the following 3 occur regularly on the east coast of the United States.

i. Soft rays of dorsal and anal fins more or less closely scaled; gill-rakers long and slender, 9 to 12 on lower arm of first arch.
   a. Coloration nearly uniform silvery...*nothus.*
   aa. Body marked by numerous irregular dark blotches, some of which form wavy oblique lines running forward and downward ....*regalis.*
ii. Soft rays of dorsal and anal fins scaleless; gill-rakers comparatively short and thick, 6 to 8 on lower arm of first arch; body covered with round black spots...........*nebulosus.*

The catch of squeteagues or "sea trouts" in this state during the past 25 years has ranged from 1,000,000 to 4,000,000 pounds annually, and in that time has aggregated over 60,000,000 pounds, valued at not less than $1,800,000.   The quantity taken and sold in each of 4 widely separated years beginning in 1880 was as follows:

Year.	Pounds.	Value.
1880	1,120,000	$25,550
1890	1,885,680	48,856
1897	3,090,255	95,219
1902	3,781,455	156,247

(*Cynoscion,* dog drum.)

268. CYNOSCION NOTHUS (Holbrook).

Silver Squeteague; Bastard Trout (S. C.).

Otolithus nothus Holbrook, Ichthyology of South Carolina, 134, pl. 19, fig. 1, 1860; South Carolina.
Cynoscion nothus, Jordan & Evermann, 1898, 1406, pl. ccxx, fig. 561.

DIAGNOSIS.—Body rather deep and more compressed than in other species; head contained 3.5 times in total length; mouth rather small, maxillary extending to posterior margin of pupil; snout short, contained 4.5 times in length of head; eye large, .25 length of head; gillrakers about 13, 9 being on lower arm of arch, the longest .5 diameter of eye; scales in lateral series 58 to 62, in transverse series 13; lateral line curved anteriorly, straight posteriorly to 7th dorsal spine; dorsal rays x+1,27 (to 29), the soft dorsal scaled throughout; anal rays II,9 or II,10; caudal fin well rounded. Color: silvery gray above, very finely spotted on back and on sides to level of pectorals, silvery below; snout and tip of lower jaw blackish; inside of mouth white; upper fins dusky, lower fins white. (*nothus,* bastard.)

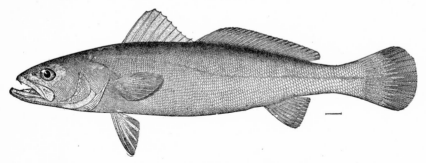

Fig. 137. SILVER SQUETEAGUE. *Cynoscion nothus.*

This is the least abundant and least known of the squeteagues of the east coast of the United States. It has been found in Chesapeake Bay, South Carolina, and Florida, but has not heretofore been recorded from North Carolina. On September 1, 1899, a small specimen, now in the Beaufort laboratory, was taken in a beam trawl, in 9 fathoms of water, 2 miles southeast of Beaufort Inlet.

269. CYNOSCION REGALIS (Bloch & Schneider).

"Trout"; "Sea Trout"; "Gray Trout"; "Summer Trout"; Weak-fish; Squeteague;
Yellow-finned Trout (S. C.); Shad Trout; Sun Trout.

Johnius regalis Bloch & Schneider, Systema Ichthyologiæ, 75, 1801; New York.
Cynoscion regalis, Yarrow, 1877, 209; Beaufort. Jordan & Gilbert, 1879, 377; Beaufort. Earll, 1887, 493;
coast near Wilmington. Jenkins, 1887, 91; Beaufort. Jordan & Evermann, 1898, 1407, pl. ccxx, fig.
562. Wilson, 1900, 355; Beaufort. Linton, 1905, 384; Beaufort.   •

DIAGNOSIS.—Body elongate, very slightly compressed, depth contained 4 to 4.25 times
in total length; head large, contained 3.33 times in length; mouth large, maxillary extending
beyond pupil and contained 2.16 times in length of head; teeth sharp, canines large; snout
contained 4 to 4.33 times in head; eye .14 to .20 head, .75 snout; gill-rakers long and sharp, 16
in number, 11 on lower arm of arch; scales in lateral series about 56, in transverse series about
17; dorsal rays x+1,26 (to 29); anal rays II,11 to II,13; caudal very slightly concave; pectorals
short, .5 head. Color: silvery purple and other reflections; head, back and sides marked by
numerous small irregular blackish blotches, mostly arranged in wavy oblique lines; dorsal and
caudal fins dusky; ventral, anal, and lower margin of caudal yellow. (*regalis*, royal.)

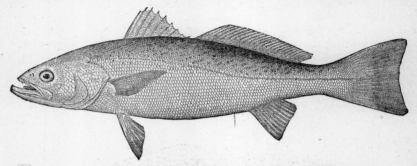

Fig. 138. SQUETEAGUE; WEAK-FISH. *Cynoscion regalis.*

This species is found along our coast from southern New England to the Gulf
States, and is very abundant from North Carolina northward, being caught for
market in large quantities and being the most valuable member of the drum
family in United States waters. It goes in schools, which may contain many
thousands of individuals, and the fish composing a given school are ordinarily
of the same size. The usual weight is about 2 pounds, but many fish weigh 4 to 6
pounds, and examples weighing 10 to 12 pounds are occasionally met with, the
maximum known weight being 30 pounds.

The common names of this species are numerous, and some of them are very
improper. Weak-fish and squeteague are those most frequently employed on
the northern part of the east coast; but in the Southern States "trout" and its
compounds are in general use. The names applied in North Carolina are "trout",
"sea trout", "summer trout", and "gray trout".

In North Carolina this species is much less abundant than the "spotted
trout", although it is by no means uncommon. Like the other species, it is
present almost throughout the year. It is taken in "sink nets" in winter, and with
drag nets, drift nets, and hook and line in spring and fall. The catch is smaller
than formerly, and the market value of the fish is less than that of the "spotted
trout".

PLATE 15

SQUETEAGUE; WEAKFISH (CYNOSCION REGALIS)

Mr. S. G. Worth reports that a "trout numb" occurred at Beaufort during the last week in November, 1903; on the 27th the weather became cold very suddenly, and on the 28th many gray trout were picked up by numerous fishermen, the fish floating or on the shores and just able to move their fins. One boat with 2 men secured 900 pounds.

Menhaden and small school fishes generally are preyed on by the weak-fish, which is an extremely voracious species. Crabs, shrimps, annelids, and various other invertebrates are also eaten.

The spawning season is in late spring or early summer. The eggs are buoyant, very numerous, and about .036 inch in diameter, and hatch in 2 days in water of 60° F.

270. CYNOSCION NEBULOSUS (Cuvier & Valenciennes).

"Trout"; "Speckled Trout"; "Sea Trout"; "Salmon Trout"; "Black Trout"; "Salmon"; Spotted Weak-fish; Spotted Squeteague; Southern Squeteague.

Otolithus nebulosus Cuvier & Valenciennes, Histoire Naturelle des Poissons, v, 79, 1830.
Cynoscion carolinensis, Yarrow, 1877, 209; Beaufort. Jordan & Gilbert, 1879, 377; Beaufort.
Cynoscion maculatum, Goode, 1884, 365: North Carolina. Jordan, 1886, 28; Beaufort. Earll, 1887, 486, 493; Beaufort, Morehead, and coast near Wilmington. Jenkins, 1887, 91; Beaufort. Wilson, 1900, 355; Beaufort.
Cynoscion nebulosus, Jordan & Evermann, 1898, 1409, pl. ccxxi, fig. 563. Linton, 1905, 385; Beaufort.

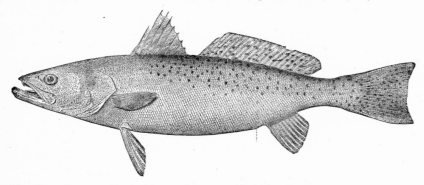

Fig. 139. SPOTTED SQUETEAGUE; SOUTHERN SQUETEAGUE. *Cynoscion nebulosus.*

DIAGNOSIS.—Body elongate, somewhat compressed, depth contained 4.5 times in length; head large, contained 3.5 times in length; maxillary extending to posterior border of orbit; snout long, sharp, contained 3.75 times in head; eye .14 to .16 head; gill-rakers short and thick, longest not longer than pupil, 11 in number, 7 on arm of arch; scales in lateral series 70 to 75, in transverse series 20; dorsal rays x+1,25 (to 27), longest spines less than .5 head; caudal slightly concave. Color: silvery, back darker and marked posteriorly by numerous round black spots; caudal and dorsal fins similarly spotted. (*nebulosus*, clouded.)

While the spotted weak-fish is found from New York to Texas, it is rare north of Chesapeake Bay, from which region southward it begins to replace the other species, *Cynoscion regalis*. It swims in schools, and preys on all kinds of small fishes, and is itself eaten by blue-fish, drum, and northern squeteague. The average weight is 3 to 4 pounds, but larger fish are common and a weight of 10 pounds is not infrequently attained.   One of the largest examples of the spotted squeteague ever caught and possibly the largest ever recorded was taken in Neuse River in the winter of 1903–4 and exhibited in New Bern by Mr. George N. Ives, who reports that the fish weighed 16.5 pounds.

The local names applied to the species are indefensible, but will probably never be supplanted by appropriate ones.   Besides "trout" and "sea trout", which are shared by its congener, the northern squeteague, it is known as the "speckled trout", "salmon trout", and "salmon".   Mr. W. H. Yopp reports the name "black trout" as in use among the Wilmington fishermen, by whom the other species is called "summer trout".   Spotted weak-fish and spotted squeteague are the best names, and their use should be encouraged.

The fish is very abundant in North Carolina, and it is the principal member of the drum family in that state from the economic standpoint.   Yarrow's notes on the fish as observed at Beaufort in 1871–2 are interesting because of the changes that have occurred; he wrote:

Very abundant from February to June, April being considered the best month; are taken at this time in nets only as they will not take the hook until September, upon their return from the northward.   The roe in female specimens was found to be quite large in April.   Size from 6 to 36 inches; one specimen, taken in September, 1871, with hook, measured 24 inches in length and weighed 3¾ pounds.   In 1872 the species first appeared January 9, which was considered unusually early.

The susceptibility of the squeteagues to cold, as was illustrated in the case of the preceding species, is shown also for the spotted squeteague in the following account of N. E. Armstrong, of Onslow County:

When we have extremely cold and cloudy weather, and I believe also windy weather for three or four days, the trout at the mouth of New River are benumbed, and on the first sunny day, rise to the surface, and after a day or two die and sink to the bottom or are washed ashore. As soon as they rise, there are generally hundreds of men ready with nets, dip nets, gigs, and in some instances nothing but their hands and boats, to pick them up.   They are sometimes washed ashore in long heaps, two and three feet deep, for a considerable distance.   When these "numbs" occur it is generally known throughout this and adjoining counties, and carts and wagons come for the fish by hundreds, sometimes from a distance of fifty or sixty miles. There was a "numb" in January, 1877, and another in the winter of 1879, about the same time, but they do not occur frequently.*

It is interesting to observe that in the note on this species in Lawson's work (1709) reference is made to the same phenomenon:

Trouts of the salt water are exactly shaped like the trouts in Europe, having blackish, not red spots.   They are in the Salts, and are not red within, but white, yet a very good fish.   They are so tender that if they are in or near fresh water, and a sudden frost come, they are benum'd and float on the surface of the water, as if dead; and then they take up canoe-loads of them.   If you put them into warm water, they perfectly recover.

The egg of this species is somewhat smaller than that of the northern squeteague, and hatches in 40 hours in water of 77°F.   The spawning grounds are the bays and sounds.

*American Fishes. By G. Brown Goode. New York, 1888. P. 119.

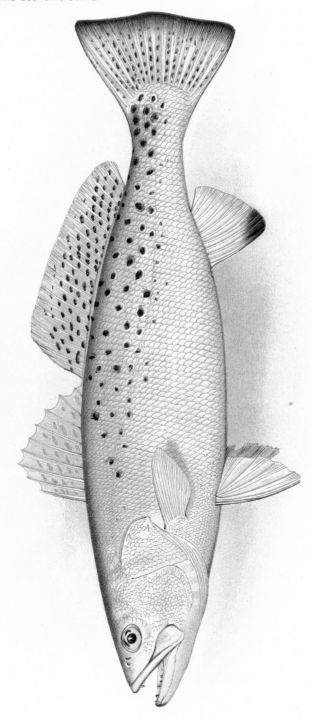

SPOTTED SQUETEAGUE; SPOTTED WEAKFISH (CYNOSCION NEBULOSUS)

No recent statistics have been gathered to show the relative catch of "spotted trout" and "gray trout" in this state. In 1880 the yield of the former was 950,000 pounds as against only 170,000 pounds of the latter. Dr. Coker contributes the following data pertaining to the year 1903 and the seasons immediately preceding in the Beaufort region:

The spotted trout is taken now in spring and fall as it was formerly, but not in such quantities as in winter. The special value of this fish to the fisherman at present is that it is caught during the winter when other fish are scarce. The winter fishing is of recent development, and large schools of spotted trout are now found. It is hardly to be supposed that fishermen who sail up and down the sounds and bays, and whose daily experience trains their eyes to detect schools of fish, have for years overlooked such schools as now appear in frequented or easily accessible places. Presumably, the presence of these schools in winter presents something new and unexplained. Possibly the explanation could be found in changed conditions at some other originally frequented place. Sometimes a school of trout is found in some creek where it is possible to hem them in and hold them. Then by some device the law against placing an obstruction entirely across such creeks is evaded or disregarded, and the entire school of possibly ten or fifteen thousand pounds is taken out at once, or in installments. Two years ago an immense catch was made in this way; the figures cannot be given, but one dealer states that he received 60,000 pounds from this one school and estimates that it contained over 100,000 pounds.

Spotted trout, formerly classed with the gray trout, are now in better and growing demand and are regarded as less deserving of the name weak-fish, as the flesh is firmer and keeps better. To the fishermen they are worth 2 cents a pound more than the squeteague, which means about double the price of the latter. Formerly there was a good demand for the sounds of trout, the price ranging from 75 cents to $1.25 per pound. A unique instrument was devised by means of which the sounds could be extracted through the throat and gill cleft, without other injury to the fish, which were afterwards strung or boxed and sold. The essential part of this instrument was the "hook", a piece of stiff wire hooked at the end and filed sharp. The hook might or might not have a "gouger" of wood attached. Now only one dealer ships the sounds, receiving 25 to 30 cents per pound.

In the Cape Fear region this fish is caught mostly from September to May; it weighs 2 to 10 pounds and brings twice as much per pound as the "gray trout".

Genus LARIMUS Cuvier & Valenciennes.

Small American shore fishes, with elongate, compressed body; large, terminal mouth, which is vertical or very oblique; short snout; projecting lower jaw; very small teeth; no bony teeth on preopercle; well developed pseudobranchiæ; long and slender gill-rakers. Six known species, 1 found on coast of United States. (*Larimus*, a name whose significance has not been stated.)

271. LARIMUS FASCIATUS Holbrook.

Bullhead (S. C.); Chub (S. C.); Banded Drum.

Larimus fasciatus Holbrook, Ichthyology of South Carolina, 153, pl. 22, fig. 1, 1860; Charleston. Jordan & Evermann, 1898, 1424.

DIAGNOSIS.—Body much compressed, back elevated, depth .33 length; head contained 3.5 times in total length; length of snout contained 5.5 times in head; maxillary .5 length of head, extending as far as posterior third of eye; teeth small, in single series in each jaw; eye .25 head; minute cilia on preopercle; gill-rakers as long as eye, 36 in number, 24 being below angle; scales large, ctenoid, about 50 in lateral series, 14 to 16 in transverse series; dorsal rays x+1,24 to 26, third and fourth spines contained 2¼ times in head; anal rays II,5 or II,6, second spine .33 length of head.   Color: grayish olive above, silvery white below; 7 to 9 dark vertical bars extending from back to middle of sides; anal, ventrals, and lower rays of caudal yellow; cheeks, opercles, inside of mouth, and gill-cavity light yellow.   (*fasciatus*, banded.)

The regular range of this species is Chesapeake Bay to Texas, but stragglers have been found as far north as Massachusetts (Woods Hole).   It is not common anywhere, and has not heretofore been recorded from North Carolina.   Within the past few years several specimens have been collected at Beaufort, and 3 about 3 inches long, obtained in 1902, are now in the laboratory at that place. The species probably does not exceed 1 foot in length.

Genus BAIRDIELLA Gill.   Mademoiselles.

Small American shore fishes, mostly of a plain silvery color, with moderately elongate, compressed body;   elevated back;   somewhat oblique mouth, with small teeth in several rows; slender gill-rakers; toothed margin of preopercle; and continuous dorsal fin.   The species are mostly subtropical, only 1 being known from the United States.   (Named for Spencer Fullerton Baird, late U. S. Commissioner of Fisheries and Secretary of the Smithsonian Institution.)

272. BAIRDIELLA CHRYSURA (Lacépède).

"Perch"; "White Perch"; "Sand Perch"; "Yellow-finned Perch"; "Silver Perch"; Yellow-tail.

Dipterodon chrysurus Lacépède, Histoire Naturelle des Poissons, iii, 64, 1802; South Carolina.
Bairdiella punctata, Yarrow, 1877, 210; Beaufort.   Jordan & Gilbert, 1879, 377; Beaufort.
Sciæna chrysura, Jordan, 1886, 28; Beaufort.   Jenkins, 1887, 90; Beaufort,
Bairdiella chrysura, Goode, 1884, 375; Beaufort.   Jordan & Evermann, 1898, 1433, pl. ccxxii, fig. 566.   Linton, 1905, 387; Beaufort.

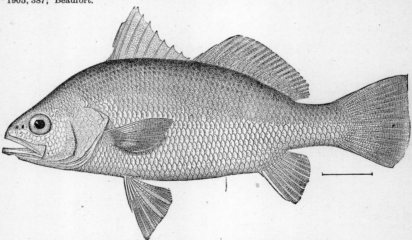

Fig. 140.   YELLOW-TAIL.   *Bairdiella chrysura.*

DIAGNOSIS.—Body oblong, compressed, the depth .33 total length; head contained 3.33 to 3.50 times in length; snout short and blunt, as long as eye; maxillary extending beyond pupil; teeth in lower jaw in a close-set series, with a few smaller teeth in front, teeth in upper jaw in a villiform band, with a series of small canines outside; preopercle serrate; gill-rakers long and slender, 24 in number, 16 on lower arm; scales in lateral series about 50, in transverse series 20; dorsal rays XI+1,22; anal rays II,10; caudal, double truncate; soft dorsal and anal scaled for about half their height. Color: dull greenish above, silvery below; upper parts with minute dark specks which form streaks along sides; fins mostly yellow; peritoneum white. (*chrysura*, golden-tailed.)

The yellow-tail, which is known as "perch", "silver perch", "white perch", "yellow finned perch", and "sand perch" in North Carolina, frequents the shore of the Middle Atlantic, South Atlantic, and Gulf States. It abounds in the North Carolina sounds, estuaries, and salt waters generally from early spring to late fall, and may be present in winter on the southern part of the coast. Its maximum length is only about 8 inches, and it is therefore too small to be of great economic value, but it is an excellent pan fish, comparable with the spot. The male yellow-tails make a faint drumming sound, which usually lasts 5 to 10 seconds; while the sound continues the abdomen is flattened, and the sides rise slightly. The air-bladder is similar to that of the squeteagues, consisting of a long cylindrical body, a head, and two short horns. The drumming muscles are connected by a stout tendon or aponeurosis.

Spawning of the yellow-tails at Beaufort occurs during late April and early May. By June the young of the year are about an inch long, and during summer specimens of all sizes from 1 to 7 inches long are observed.

Genus STELLIFER Oken.

Small American fishes, allied to Bairdiella, chiefly distinguished by the spongy and cavernous structure of the skull, which is broad and flattened between the eyes. Of the numerous species, only 1 is known from the United States coasts. (*Stellifer*, star-bearing, in allusion to the radiating lines on the suborbital.)

273. STELLIFER LANCEOLATUS (Holbrook).

Homoprion lanceolatus Holbrook, Ichthyology of South Carolina, ed. i, 168, pl. 23, 1856: Port Royal Sound, Beaufort, S. C.
Stellifer lanceolatus, Jordan & Evermann, 1898, 1443.

DIAGNOSIS.—Body elongate, compressed, depth contained about 3.33 times in length; head short, deep, equal to depth; mouth moderate, maxillary extending to pupil; snout short, about .25 length of head; eye .2 length of head; 6 to 8 spines on preopercle; teeth in upper jaw in broad bands; interorbital space .33 length of head; gill-rakers .75 diameter of eye, 35 in number, 22 on lower arm of first arch; scales in lateral series 47 to 50, in transverse series 13; dorsal fins continuous; dorsal rays XI+1,20 (to 23), the spines slender, the soft rays low and of uniform length; anal rays II,7 or II,8; caudal fin with its central rays longest; first ventral ray filiform. Color: bluish gray above, silvery white below; a series of small black spots at base of dorsal fin; fins more or less yellow. (*lanceolatus*, lanceolate, in allusion to the shape of the caudal.)

This small, rare drum, heretofore known from South Carolina to Texas in rather deep water, was found at Beaufort in the summer of 1903, and 2 specimens about 3 inches long are now in the laboratory museum. The maximum length appears to be only 6 inches.

Genus LEIOSTOMUS Lacépède. Spots.

This genus, which contains only 1 known species, is characterized by a comparatively short, elevated, compressed body, with short, obtuse head, small mouth, rounded snout, toothless lower jaw, entire preopercular margin, continuous dorsal fins, the anterior high and with 10 spines, and short gill-rakers. (*Leiostomus*, smooth mouth.)

274. LEIOSTOMUS XANTHURUS Lacépède.

"Spot"; "Jimmy"; Chub (S. C.); Roach (Va.); Goody; Lafayette.

Leiostomus xanthurus Lacépède, Histoire Naturelle des Poissons, iv, 439, pl. 10, fig. 1, 1802; Carolina. Yarrow, 1877, 210; Beaufort. Jordan & Gilbert, 1879, 377; Beaufort. Jordan, 1886, 28; Beaufort. Earll, 1887, 486, 493; Beaufort region and coast near Wilmington Jenkins, 1887, 90; Beaufort. Jordan & Evermann, 1898, 1458, pl. ccxxiii, fig. 569. Linton, 1905, 391; Beaufort.
Leiostomus obliquus, Yarrow, 1877, 210; Beaufort. Jordan & Gilbert, 1879, 377; Beaufort.

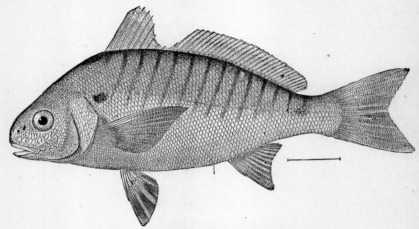

Fig. 141. SPOT. *Leiostomus xanthurus.*

DIAGNOSIS.—Back elevated, much compressed in front of dorsal, depth .33 length; head contained about 3.5 times in total length; snout blunt, contained about 3.5 times in head; mouth small, horizontal, slightly inferior, maxillary extending to pupil; eye shorter than snout, about .25 length of head; gill-rakers short and slender, about 30 in number, 22 below angle; scales strongly ctenoid, number in lateral series 60 to 70, in transverse series about 20; dorsal rays x+ 1,30 (to 32), the longest spine (third) .66 length of head; soft dorsal with a sheath of scales along its base; anal rays ii,12; pectorals as long as head; ventrals .33 shorter; caudal slightly forked. Color: bluish gray above, silvery below; back and sides with 12 to 15 narrow bronze or yellow bands extending obliquely downward and forward; a round bronze or yellow spot on shoulder; fins pale yellow, the soft dorsal with a row of pale blue spots involving only the membranes, the caudal margin black. (*xanthurus*, yellow-tailed.)

The spot, which gets its name from the round mark on its shoulder, inhabits the east coast of the United States from Massachusetts to Texas, and is one of the most abundant and best known of our food fishes. It abounds in the sounds and other coastal waters of North Carolina, and often enters water that is perfectly fresh. In spring, during the shad fishery, it is found throughout

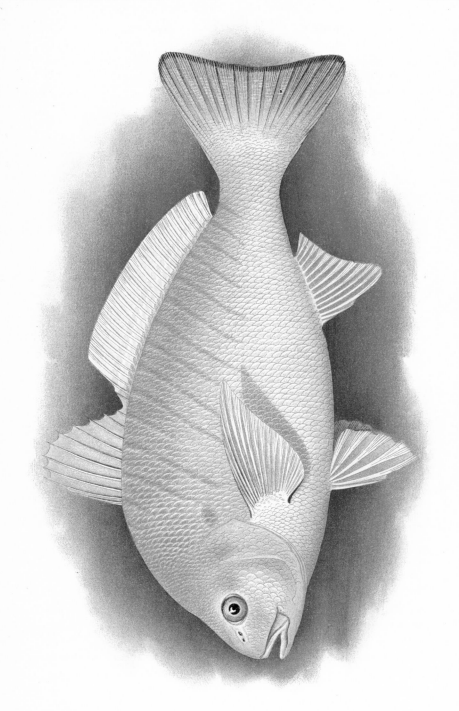

SPOT (LEIOSTOMUS XANTHURUS)

Albemarle Sound, being frequently taken in the shad seines and pound nets of the Avoca section. In the Beaufort region the spot is exceedingly abundant, being exceeded in numbers only by mullet among the staple food fishes. The fish is known almost everywhere in the state as "spot", but the name "jimmy" is also in quite general use.

The species seldom exceeds 10 inches in length and averages only 6 or 7 inches. One of the largest specimens of which a record has been made was collected by Mr. Worth at Cape Lookout in November, 1903; it was a ripe male 13 inches long over all, 11 inches to base of tail, and 4 inches deep.

The mouth of the spot is small and weak, and the foot consists chiefly of little invertebrates (mollusks, crustaceans, annelids, sea-urchins, etc.) and young or small fishes. Sea-weeds are not infrequently found in the stomach, but whether they are taken intentionally is not known.

The male spots makes a drumming sound which is not nearly so loud as that produced by the croaker, the air-bladder being very thin and the special drumming muscle only slightly developed.

Spawning occurs in North Carolina in late fall or early winter in the salt-water sounds and inlets, but no special observations on the eggs have been made. The very young may be found in great abundance at Beaufort in late winter, and from that time until maturity the growth of the fish may be observed in all the local waters south of Cape Hatteras. In the early part of March the young are about 1 inch long, but some examples only .5 inch long are noted at Beaufort as late as April 1. By the middle of April they have attained a length of 1.6 to 1.75 inches, and by the middle of May they average 2 to 2.25 inches. By June 15 fish 3 to 3.5 inches long are met with, and by the end of that month specimens 4 inches long may be taken. Through the summer the growth continues rapid, and it would seem that spawning size may be reached within a year after hatching. The very young are marked with vague oblique bars, but the characteristic color pattern and the shoulder spot do not appear till the fish are about 2 inches long.

The spot does not support a special fishery in this state, but is taken incidently in seines, gill nets, and pound nets in all the coastal counties, the bulk of the catch being credited to Dare, Carteret, Hyde, and New Hanover counties in the order given. In 1890 the quantity sold was 408,260 pounds, worth $10,862. By 1897 the product had increased to 849,980 pounds, valued at $14,197. The yield in 1902 was 872,695 pounds, for which the fishermen received $20,116; of this quantity 208,800 pounds, worth $7,384, were salted.

In North Carolina, as elsewhere, the spot ranks high as a food and is by many persons regarded as the best of the salt-water pan fishes. There is a good demand for North Carolina spots in Baltimore, Washington, and other markets of the Chesapeake region, and the fish is also rated high as a salt fish for local consumption.

Genus MICROPOGON Cuvier & Valenciennes.   Croakers.

Moderate sized American shore fishes, with somewhat elongate body; large rounded snout; strongly serrate preopercle; teeth in villiform bands; a row of short, slender barbels on each side of chin; short gill-rakers; bitruncate caudal fin; and air-bladder with long, slender lateral horns.   Of the 5 or 6 known species, only 1 inhabits the waters of the United States.   (*Micropogon*, small beard.)

275. MICROPOGON UNDULATUS (Linnæus).

"Croaker"; "Crocus"; "Hard-head".

Perca undulata Linnæus, Systema Naturæ, ed. xii, 483, 1766; South Carolina.
Micropogon undulatus, Yarrow, 1877, 210; Beaufort.   Jordan & Gilbert, 1879, 378; Beaufort.   Goode, 1884, 378; Beaufort.   Earll, 1887, 493; coast near Wilmington.   Jenkins, 1887, 90; Beaufort.   Jordan & Evermann, 1898, 1461, pl. ccxxiv, fig. 570.   Linton, 1905, 394; Beaufort.

DIAGNOSIS.—Form stout, back moderately elevated and compressed, depth contained 3.3 times in total length; head large, equal to depth, snout prominent, twice length of eye; mouth small, horizontal, the maxillary barely reaching front of eye; eye .2 length of head or less; gill-rakers about 23, 16 below angle; scales in lateral series about 55, in transverse series 28; dorsal rays x+1,28 (or 29), the spinous part high, the longest spine a little less than .5 length of head; anal rays ii,7, the longest ray equal to longest dorsal spine; pectorals pointed, .6 head.   Color: brassy or grayish silvery above, silvery white below; back profusely spotted with dark brown, the spots smaller than scales and irregularly arranged; sides marked with numerous wavy, dark brown oblique stripes, longest anteriorly and becoming very short under posterior end of soft dorsal fin where they terminate; both dorsal fins with numerous small dark spots; caudal dusky greenish; other fins pale yellow.   (*undulatus*, wavy.)

Fig. 142.   CROAKER.   *Micropogon undulatus.*

This fish, known as croaker throughout its range, is one of the commonest food fishes on the South Atlantic and Gulf coasts.   While it is occasionally taken as far north as Massachusetts, it is not ordinarily numerous north of Chesapeake Bay.   It is one of the most abundant food fishes of the North Carolina coast, being found in the sounds, estuaries, and inlets, and on the outer shores from early spring; and in Beaufort Harbor is said to be exceeded in abundance only by the mullet and the spot among the staple market fishes.

The croaker gets its name from the peculiar grunting or croaking noise it emits, through the joint action of a tense air-bladder and a rapidly contracting pair of special muscles.   This sound may be heard for a considerable distance below the surface when a fish is caught on the hook, and is also produced after the fish is landed.   Both sexes croak, in which respect this species differs from all other local sciænids.   The croaker's air-bladder is of a very peculiar shape. The body is oblong; from each side arises a slender process or horn which extends forward beyond the anterior end of the bladder and then curves backward, the two horns approaching close together near the anterior pole; extending backward from the posterior end of the bladder is a slender tail-like appendage.

On parts of Pamlico Sound this fish is known as "hard-head", and "crocus" is in quite general use.   The latter name, which has by some persons been regarded as a modern corruption of croaker, was applied to the fish in North Carolina at least as early as 1709, when John Lawson wrote:

The crocus is a fish, in shape like a pearch, and in taste like a whiting.   They croke and make a noise in your hand, when taken with hook or net.   They are very good.

The croaker does not usually exceed 10 or 12 inches in length but may reach 18 inches.   It feeds largely on crustaceans, and bites readily at crab bait, but it also eats fish.   The stomach contents of 17 adults examined by Dr. Coker at Beaufort in June and July consisted chiefly of razor clams, annelids, and amphipods.   Twelve young croakers, 2 to 3.5 inches long, contained large numbers of young and adult copepods and amphipods, young barnacles (cypris stage), ostracods, and nematode worms.

The spawning time of the croaker is late fall or early winter, and the spawning grounds are the sounds, estuaries, and inside waters generally.   By the first of August the young have attained an average length of 5 inches in Beaufort Harbor, and by the time the spawning period arrives the largest yearlings may be 7 or 8 inches long.

Among the salt-water fishes of the state the croaker is exceeded in importance by only the mullets and squeteagues.   At Beaufort and other points it was for a long time regarded with little favor and often discarded, but it has now become a very salable species, being a good pan fish and keeping well when shipped to the markets.   It is caught along the entire coast in seines, gill nets, and pound nets, and is taken also in considerable quantities with hand lines, especially in Craven County.   From 285,775 pounds, worth $7,172, marketed in 1889 the yield arose to 1,279,000 pounds, worth $18,936, in 1897, and by 1902 the catch had increased to 1,928,635 pounds, valued at $38,320.   A small proportion of the product is salted.

Genus SCIÆNOPS Gill.   Red Drums.

This genus includes a single species, and is distinguished by a rather elongate, slightly compressed body; arched back; well developed teeth in jaws; short, thick gill-rakers; serrations on preopercle disappearing with age; absence of scales on soft dorsal fin, and other characters indicated in the foregoing key. (Sciænops, having the appearance of Sciæna, an ancient name of one of the Mediterranean drums.)

276. SCIÆNOPS OCELLATUS (Linnæus).

"Drum"; "Red Drum"; "Puppy Drum" (young); "Spotted Bass"; Channel Bass; Red-fish; Branded Drum (S. C.).

Perca ocellata Linnæus, Systema Naturæ, ed. xii, 483, 1766; South Carolina.
Sciænops ocellatus, Yarrow, 1877, 210; Beaufort. Jordan & Gilbert, 1879, 378; Beaufort. Jordan & Evermann, 1898, 1453, pl. ccxxii, fig. 567. Linton, 1905, 390; Beaufort.
Sciæna ocellata, Jordan, 1886, 28; Beaufort. Jenkins, 1887, 90; Beaufort. Earll, 1887, 486; Beaufort.

DIAGNOSIS.—Form rather robust, depth contained 3.5 times in length; head long, equal to depth, profile rather steep; snout blunt, .25 length of head; eye .14 length of head; mouth large, horizontal, maxillary extending nearly to posterior edge of eye; jaw teeth in villiform bands, the outer teeth in upper jaw enlarged; gill-rakers very short, less than diameter of pupil, 12 in number, of which 7 are below angle; scales in lateral series 45 to 50, in transverse series 16, those on breast deeply imbedded; dorsal fins scarcely separate, rays x + 1,24; anal fin long, rays II,8; caudal margin square or slightly concave. Color: silvery red; each scale with a dark center, these marks forming obscure lateral stripes; a jet black spot at base of caudal fin above; sometimes several such spots, and occasionally a line of them along the sides. (*ocellatus*, having eye-like spots.)

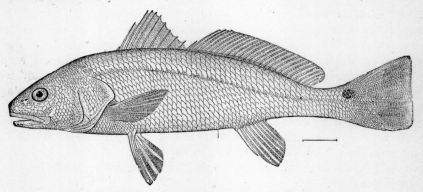

Fig. 143. RED DRUM; RED-FISH. *Sciænops ocellatus.*

The red drum is one of the largest and most valuable fishes of the South Atlantic and Gulf coasts; it occurs as a straggler as far north as Massachusetts, but is not regularly taken in any numbers north of Chesapeake Bay. It reaches a length of 5 feet and a weight of 75 pounds; the average weight, however, is about 10 pounds. The food consists of small fish and crustaceans.

In North Carolina, where this fish is called "drum", "red drum", and "spotted bass", it is abundant and is a food fish of moderate importance, being caught with nets and lines in the spring, fall and winter. The fishery is most extensive in Carteret County. In the Cape Fear region the fish is taken chiefly from September to March. Mr. George N. Ives states that it is found in Neuse River throughout the year. It is abundant about Roanoke Island in spring, especially in May, going in large schools. There is a record of a 59-pound fish caught with a line at Manteo.

The value of the red drum varies much in accordance with the size. At Beaufort four grades are recognized by fishermen and dealers: "Puppy drums",

RED DRUM; RED-FISH (SCIAENOPS OCELLATUS)

"yearling drums", "two-foot drums", and "old drums". The most valued is the yearling, but the two-foot drum is of nearly the same value; these are shipped to the northern markets. The puppy drums are shipped only in boxes of assorted fish. The old drums, while highly prized as game fish, are of little value as food when eaten fresh, but are very acceptable when salted and dried, the viscera being removed, the back-bone taken out, and the sides cut off, salted, and laid out to dry, often on the roof of the fisherman's house. The dried fish are rather coarse, but with proper cooking are reported to be very good. The catch of this species in North Carolina in 1902 was about 200,000 pounds, valued at about $3,000.

The characteristic caudal spot normally lies between the lateral line and the upper edge of the tail, and is about the size of the eye. Supernumerary spots are often met with, these being in advance of the other spot above, on, or below the lateral line or occasionally immediately below the regular mark; the extra spots are nearly always smaller, and usually absent from one side.

Genus MENTICIRRHUS Gill. Whitings.

Small American shore fishes, most frequently found on sandy bottom; characterized by elongate, little compressed body; long conical head with overhanging snout; small, horizontal mouth, with teeth in bands in both jaws; a single barbel on chin; short gill-rakers; 10 or 11 rather high, slender dorsal spines; anal fin with a single sharp spine; asymmetrical caudal fin, the upper lobe sharp, the lower rounded; and absent air-bladder. Three of the 9 or 10 known species are found on the North Carolina coast, and are not often distinguished, all being known there as "sea mullet".

Key to the North Carolina species of Menticirrhus.

i. Gill-rakers on first arch mere tubercular projections, covered with teeth; scales on breast large; some of outer teeth in upper jaw enlarged; body with more or less distinct dark markings.
  a. Soft rays of dorsal fin 25 or 26; spinous dorsal little elevated, the longest spine not reaching soft dorsal when flexed; color silvery gray with obscure dusky bars on back and sides; pectorals yellowish...*americanus.*
  aa. Soft rays of dorsal fin 26 or 27; spinous dorsal elevated, the longest spine reaching beyond front of soft dorsal when flexed; color dusky gray, with well defined black irregular bars on back and sides; color sometimes almost entirely black; pectorals dark......*saxatilis.*
ii. Gill-rakers on first arch short and slender; scales on breast small; outer teeth in upper jaw scarcely enlarged; body silvery, without any dark markings whatever.........*littoralis.*

(*Menticirrhus,* chin barbel.)

277. MENTICIRRHUS AMERICANUS (Linnæus).

"Sea Mullet"; "Whiting"; "Round-head"; "Sea-mink"; "King-fish"; "Virginia Mullet"; Carolina Whiting.

Cyprinus americanus Linnæus, Systema Naturæ, ed. x, 321, 1758; Carolina.
Menticirrus alburnus, Yarrow, 1877, 210; Beaufort. Goode, 1884, 376; Cape Fear River, N. C., to Rio Grande, Texas. Earll, 1887, 486; Beaufort. Jenkins, 1887, 90; Beaufort. Kendall & Smith, 1894, 24; Hatteras Inlet.
Menticirrhus americanus, Jordan & Evermann. 1898, 1474, pl. ccxxv, fig. 572. Linton, 1905, 398; Beaufort.

DIAGNOSIS.—Depth .20 to .25 length; head .28 length; maxillary reaching as far as pupil; outer teeth in upper jaw much enlarged; eye small, .14 length of head, .5 length of snout; scales in lateral series 55; dorsal rays xi+ 1,24 (or 25): anal rays 1,7; lower caudal lobe longer than upper.   Color: silvery gray, with obscure dusky bars on back and sides; a dark bar at nape; pectoral fins yellow, with dusky tip.

This is a common species from Chesapeake Bay to Texas on sandy shores, and is the principal member of the genus at Beaufort and other points on the North Carolina coast.   The prevailing local name is "sea mink," but "whiting" is also in use, and of late the name "king-fish" has come into vogue through transfer from the New York market.   Another name that is quite local is "Virginia mullet", which is heard from Beaufort to Wilmington.

About Roanoke Island, where this fish is known as "king-fish", "sea mullet", and "round-head", it is abundant and bites freely at the hook from May to September; the average weight of line-caught fish in that section is reported to be 1.5 pounds, but some fish are said to weigh 3 pounds.   In Pamlico Sound, during the winter of 1901-2, 2 kingfishes each 7 inches long, and laterally connected so as to constitute twins, were caught with hook and line by Joseph H. Kemp, of Baltimore, Maryland.

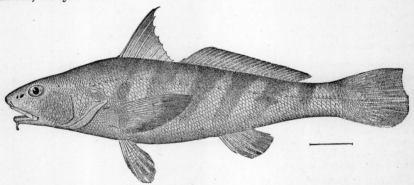

Fig. 144. KING-FISH; CAROLINA WHITING. *Menticirrhus americanus.*

In the Cape Lookout fisheries, the "sea mullet" is common; it there usually runs .5 pound, but examples weighing 1 pound or more are often taken.   According to Mr. W. H. Yopp, this fish is supplied to the Wilmington market from July to December, being known there as "Virginia mullet"; it weighs from .5 pound to 1.5 pounds, and brings the fishermen 3.5 cents a pound on an average.

In the Beaufort region the laboratory seines take this species everywhere, but not in great numbers at any one time, and no large specimens have been obtained in this way.   The species is most abundant in spring, but is also present in numbers in fall, when it is found in schools on the outer beaches.   During summer the fish is almost entirely absent from the Beaufort waters.

The species is a bottom feeder, and subsists chiefly on small mollusks and crustaceans, although it will sometimes bite readily at a hook baited with fish.   The spawning season is early June, and ripe fish of both sexes have been noted at Beaufort during the first week of that month.

The whiting is of exceptionally good quality. In New York there is steady but limited demand for it, and only there does it command a fancy price; but while it has been known to bring 75 cents a pound, the market is easily over-stocked, and frequently only 3 cents a pound is obtained. It is not uncommon for the price to drop from 30 cents a pound one day to 5 cents a pound the next. Dr. Coker gives this account of the whiting fishery at Beaufort:

King-fish are caught in small numbers when fishing with hook and line for gray trout, and are taken more abundantly in the drag nets; but the most remunerative method is with the sink net, employed near Cape Lookout. A gill net of 1.37-inch bar and 75 to 100 yards in length, or shorter, is weighted and lowered to the bottom with its ends buoyed. The next morning the net is taken up, sometimes with a king-fish seemingly in every mesh. It is remarkable that thousands of king-fish may be caught, and not a single other fish; but some-times, instead, gray trout are taken or immense hauls of croakers. Occasionally the weight of the fish taken is so great that it is necessary to cut the net in pieces to get it in. It is stated that in the last few years this fishery has not been so successful.

278. MENTICIRRHUS SAXATILIS (Bloch & Schneider).

"Sea Mullet"; Sea-mink"; "King-fish"; "Whiting"; Barb; Hake

Johnius saxatilis Bloch & Schneider, Systema Ichthyologiæ, 75, 1801; New York.
Menticirrus nebulosus, Yarrow, 1877, 210; Beaufort. Goode, 1884, 375; North Carolina.
Menticirrhus saxatilis, Jordan & Evermann, 1898, 1475.

DIAGNOSIS.—Depth contained about 4.5 times in length; head contained 3.75 to 4 times in length; mouth large, maxillary extending to pupil; snout long, more than .25 length of head; eye small, .14 length of head and .4 length of snout; scales in lateral series 53; dorsal rays x+1,26 (or 27); anal rays 1,8. Color: dusky above, with distinct, irregular, oblique, blackish bands extending downward and forward on back and sides; pale below, bounded by a dark lateral streak extending to lower caudal lobe; pectorals dark; entire body except abdomen sometimes black. (*saxatilis*, pertaining to rocks.)

Although this fish ranges from Massachusetts as far south as western Florida, it is most common north of Chesapeake Bay. This is the species to which the name "king-fish" properly belongs. In North Carolina it is not usually dis-tinguished from *Menticirrhus americanus* and bears the same names, and, accord-ing to Goode, it is also called "sea mink" there. A weight of 2 pounds is attained. Spawning takes place in June in southern Massachusetts; by October, when they have withdrawn from those waters, the young have attained a length of 4 or 5 inches; many of the young and half-grown fish are almost jet black, while others exhibit the normal markings of the adult.

The king-fish is one of the choicest food fishes of our east coast, and is espe-cially esteemed in New York and New Jersey. In North Carolina it is sent to market with the preceding species, and the two, as has been stated, bring a good price.

279. MENTICIRRHUS LITTORALIS (Holbrook).

"Sea Mullet"; "Whiting"; Surf Whiting; Silver Whiting.

Umbrina littoralis Holbrook, Ichthyology of South Carolina, 1st ed., 142, pl. 20, fig. 1, 1856; South Carolina.
Menticirrus littoralis, Yarrow, 1877, 210; Beaufort. Jordan & Gilbert, 1879, 378; Beaufort. Jenkins, 1887, 90; Beaufort. Jordan & Evermann, 1898, 1477; North Carolina to Texas.

DIAGNOSIS.—Depth contained about 4 5 times in length; head contained 3.5 times in length; snout overhanging, .28 length of head; maxillary extending about to pupil; eye contained 6.5 times in head; scales in lateral series 53; dorsal rays x+ 1,23 (to 25); anal rays 1,7; caudal fin with concave margin, upper lobe not longer than lower.   Color: above silvery gray without markings, below white; dorsal fins light brown, spinous part with black tip; caudal pale, with black tip.   (*littoralis*, pertaining to the shores.)

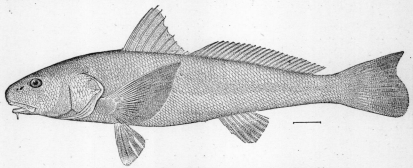

Fig. 145.   SURF WHITING.   *Menticirrhus littoralis.*

The surf whiting or silver whiting abounds on the South Atlantic and Gulf coasts, rarely if ever straying north of North Carolina.   In size and habits it is like the other species, from which it is not always distinguished by fishermen. Jordan & Gilbert reported the fish as rather common at Beaufort in summer, and found the young abundant in the surf on the outer beach, in company with pompano.   At Cape Lookout spawning fish were found by the writer in June, and at Beaufort ripe eggs have been taken on several occasions between June 1 and 10.

Genus POGONIAS Lacépède.   Black Drums.

Large marine drums, with rather short, deep, elevated body; moderate sized mouth with teeth in bands in both jaws; numerous barbels on lower jaw; entire preopercular margin; short and blunt gill-rakers; large pesudobranchiæ; large, thick, complicated air-bladder; continuous dorsal fins, the anterior high and with slender spines; caudal fin square; and greatly enlarged second anal spine.   One species South American, 1 North American.   (*Pogonias*, bearded.)

280. POGONIAS CROMIS (Linnæus).

"Black Drum"; "Sea Drum".

Labrus cromis Linnæus. Systema Naturæ, ed. xii, 479, 1766; Carolina.
Pogonias cromis, Yarrow, 1877, 209; Beaufort.   Jordan & Gilbert, 1879, 377; Beaufort.   Jenkins, 1887, 90; Beaufort.   Jordan & Evermann, 1898, 1482, pl. ccxxv, fig. 573.

DIAGNOSIS.—Form robust, back much elevated, ventral outline straight, depth .37 to .40 total length; head contained 3.3 times in length; lower jaw shorter than upper, with numerous short barbels mostly on chin; maxillary not extending as far as pupil; snout blunt, longer than eye; eye .20 to .25 head; gill-rakers 16, 12 below angle of first arch; scales large, 47 in lateral series, 16 in transverse series; dorsal rays x+ 1,20; anal rays II,5 or II,6, the second spine very broad and .4 to .6 length of head; caudal fin long and truncate; pectorals long, reaching fourth ray of soft dorsal.   Color: silvery gray; young with 4 or 5 broad vertical dark bands,

3 of which extend on dorsal fins, these bands disappearing in adult; fins dark.   (*cromis*, an ancient name for some similar fish, meaning a croaker or grunter.)

The black drum is found on the coasts of the Middle Atlantic, South Atlantic, and Gulf States, and is a common species, well known on account of its large size, which probably exceeds that of any other drum.   The largest specimen known, taken in Florida, weighed 146 pounds.   Examples weighing 40 to 60 pounds are common.

The drum is a bottom feeder, and is aided in its feeding by the sensitive filaments which depend from the chin.   It consumes all kinds of crustaceans and mollusks; and its teeth are so strong and its jaws so powerful that oysters and other thick-shelled mollusks are easily crushed.   Schools of drum sometimes do great damage to oyster beds, and have been known to destroy in a single night practically every oyster on a planted ground.

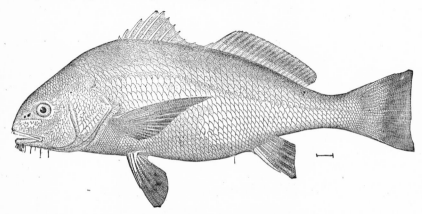

Fig. 146. BLACK DRUM. *Pogonias cromis.* Adult.

At Beaufort the black drum is found along with the red drum, but is less abundant.   Writing of the species at Beaufort in 1871, Yarrow said:

Exceedingly abundant, resident, and is taken both within and outside of the inlet.   This species runs in schools in early spring, but in the fall is generally found alone, and will take the hook.   Size 10 inches to 5 feet.

The black drum is now less abundant at Beaufort than the red drum (which Yarrow reported as not abundant), and is much less valuable, the flesh being coarse and stringy; and, according to the fishermen, it is a very wormy fish, being infested with parasites.   It is never shipped, but is eaten locally by some people.

Genus EQUES Bloch. Ribbon-fishes.

Small fishes of striking form and coloration, with elongate body tapering rapidly backward from the anterior dorsal fin; rather small mouth; included lower jaw; teeth in broad bands; fringed preopercular margin without bony teeth; short, slender gill-rakers; anterior dorsal fin placed far forward, very high, composed of weak, close-set spines; posterior dorsal low, with numerous soft rays. About 5 American species, 3 of which are found on our southern coast. (*Eques*, a horseman.)

281. EQUES ACUMINATUS (Bloch & Schneider).
Ribbon-fish.

Grammistes acuminatus Bloch & Schneider, Systema Ichthyologiæ, 184, 1801; no locality given.
Eques acuminatus, Jordan & Evermann, 1898, 1487.

DIAGNOSIS.—Form elongate, compressed, with steep profile, the greatest depth contained 2.6 times in length; maxillary extending beyond center of pupil and contained 3 times in length of head; eye less than snout, .25 head; interorbital space less than eye; gill-rakers short and slender, 6+9 on first arch; scales rather large, about 50 in lateral series; dorsal rays x+1,38 (to 40), the spines not much elevated, the longest .22 length of body and .62 head; anal rays II,7, the second spine .42 head; caudal margin straight; pectorals .63 head. Color: adults dark brown, with about 7 lengthwise whitish stripes on body and head; fins dusky. (*acuminatus*, ending in a sharp point.)

The recorded range of this species is from Charleston, through the West Indies, to Brazil. It has not heretofore been noted from North Carolina, and may occur there only as a straggler, although more likely it occurs regularly south of Cape Hatteras in suitable haunts. One specimen was taken in Beaufort Harbor in September, 1903; another was caught in a trap at the laboratory wharf in October of the same year; a third specimen was brought to notice by the explosion of a charge of dynamite in a wrecked bark in Beaufort Harbor on Nov. 23, 1903; and another was obtained sometime during the summer of that year. In the summer of 1904 still another specimen was collected at Beaufort by Dr. E. W. Gudger. These specimens were from 3 to 5 inches long, and all were of a light color, with about 7 dark brown lengthwise stripes. Apparently, as the fish grows the width of the dark stripes increases and encroaches on the original light ground-color, so that finally the general color becomes dark brown, with pale longitudinal stripes (so-called variety *umbrosus*).

Family LABRIDÆ. The Labrids, or Lipped Fishes.

A very numerous and important family, found mostly in tropical waters but also represented in temperate regions. The family takes its name from the presence of conspicuous thick, longitudinally-folded lips in each jaw, which character, together with protractile premaxillaries, maxillaries without supplemental bone, and strong, prominent jaw teeth, gives to the mouth a peculiar appearance. Body moderately elongate, in some species greatly compressed, and covered with persistent cycloid scales; mouth terminal and usually of small or moderate size, with no vomerine or palatine teeth; jaw teeth separate or else fused at their base; lower pharyngeal bones firmly united and surmounted with conical or tubercular teeth; nostrils round, without flaps, and double on each side; branchiostegals 5 or 6, pseudobranchiæ well developed, and gill-arches 3.5; pyloric cœca absent; air-bladder present; dorsal fin continuous and usually long, the spines varying from 3 to 20; anal fin with 2 to 6 spines and similar to soft dorsal; ventrals thoracic, with 1 weak spine and 5 soft rays. About 20 American genera, of which the following 5 are now known from the coast of North Carolina:

Key to the North Carolina genera of labrids.

i. Dorsal spines 16; caudal fin truncate; lateral line complete; jaw teeth in two series in each jaw, the 4 anterior canines; vertebræ 36 .... TAUTOGA.
ii. Dorsal spines 9 to 14; caudal fin either forked or rounded; lateral line interrupted or complete; jaw teeth in a single series in each jaw; vertebræ 22 to 29.
  a. Dorsal spines 14; the anterior spines greatly elongated; scales in lateral series 40; caudal fin deeply forked... LACHNOLAIMUS.
  aa. Dorsal spines 9, none greatly elongated; scales in lateral series 30 or less; caudal fin rounded.
    b. Lateral line complete, uninterrupted; cheeks and opercles naked; anterior canines 2 in upper jaw, 4 in lower .... IRIDIO.
    bb. Lateral line interrupted posteriorly; cheeks and opercles scaly; anterior canines 2 in each jaw.
      c. Posterior canines present; 3 anterior dorsal spines with a filamentous appendage; cheeks and opercles scaly................................. DORATONOTUS.
      cc. Posterior canines absent; no dorsal spines filamentous; head naked except a few scales below eye..................................... XYRICHTHYS.

Genus TAUTOGA Mitchill. Tautogs.

This genus, which contains a single species, has the following characters: Body oblong, robust, not greatly compressed; head large, superior profile rather strongly but evenly convex; caudal peduncle deep; mouth small, but jaws powerful and teeth strong; teeth conical, in two series in each jaw, the anterior teeth larger and canine; gill-membranes free from isthmus; gill-rakers short and weak; body fully covered with small scales; head unscaled, except a small space posterior to and below eye, and another on upper part of opercle; vertical fins scaly; lateral line complete; dorsal fin very long but not high, the spinous part much longer than the soft, the 16 spines nearly equal and each with a soft appendage at tip; anal similar to but larger than soft dorsal; caudal short, square, with rounded tips; pectorals broad and short; ventrals placed well behind pectorals. The generic name has been formed from the most appropriate of the common names of the fish, which, in turn, was the name applied to the species by the Mohegan or Narragansett Indians.

282. TAUTOGA ONITIS (Linnæus).

"Oyster-fish"; Tautog.

Labrus onitis Linnæus, Systema Naturæ, ed. x, 286, 1758.
Labrus hiatula Linnæus, Systema Naturæ, ed. xii, 475, 1766; Carolina.
Tautoga onitis, Yarrow, 1877, 207; Beaufort. Jordan & Gilbert, 1879, 374; Beaufort. Jordan & Evermann, 1898, 1578, pl. ccxxxvii, fig. 596.
Hiatula onitis, Jordan, 1886, 28; Beaufort. Jenkins, 1887, 91; Beaufort.

DIAGNOSIS.—Depth contained 2.6 to 3 times in length; caudal peduncle .5 depth of body; head contained 3.25 to 3.5 times in length; mouth small, the maxillary extending not nearly to anterior margin of eye; jaws equal; snout blunt, .33 length of head; eye small, about .5 length of snout; gill-rakers on first arch 3+ 6, all short and blunt; scales in lateral series about 60, in transverse series about 14+ 25; 5 or 6 rows of minute scales on cheeks; lateral line arched anteriorly, straight on caudal peduncle; dorsal rays XVI,10, the soft rays somewhat higher than the spinous; the longest spine .33 length of head; anal rays III,8, the third spine longest; caudal very short and broad; pectorals .75 length of head; ventrals .5 length of head.   Color: dull blackish, blackish green, or blackish blue, often with irregular darker blotches or bands; lips, chin, throat, and belly lighter, sometimes white; eye green; young green or brown, more or less mottled with darker, or with dark, connected cross bands.   (*onitis*, a kind of plant; application of name not known.)

The tautog or "oyster-fish" reaches the southern limit of its range about Charleston, S. C., whence it is found as far north as New Brunswick; in the southern New England and Middle States it is abundant, and is a food fish of considerable importance, being caught mostly with hand lines.   It is strictly a bottom species, preferring rocky or broken shores, where, sheltered in a crevice or by an overhanging rock, it often lies on its side or with its head or tail turned upward.   The eyes are very movable, and the fish keeps a sharp lookout for food or enemies, rotating its eyes in a peculiar manner.   Its strong teeth enable it to crush crustaceans and mollusks, which constitute its chief food; in New England it is especially fond of lobsters and crabs, which it attacks and dispatches very skilfully.

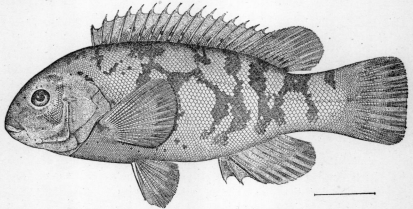

Fig. 147. TAUTOG. *Tautoga onitis.*

The flesh is white, flaky, and well flavored.   The maximum length is 3 feet, but the average is 12 to 15 inches and fish 2 feet long are not common. Spawning occurs in early summer.   The eggs are numerous; a fish weighing less than 10 pounds has been known to yield more than 1,000,000 eggs.   The eggs are buoyant, 1mm. in diameter, float at the surface, and hatch in 2 or 3 days when the water temperature is 70° F.

In North Carolina, where the species is called "oyster-fish", it is not abundant and supports no special fishery.   The fish referred to by Lawson (1709) as the "sea tench" is identified by Dr. Gill (1903) as the tautog.   At Beaufort it is not uncommon, and the young have at times been reported as "abundant about the wharves".   On March 27, 1906, a specimen was caught with hook and line from the pier on Pivers Island in Beaufort Harbor.   In 1897 a catch of 14,125 pounds of tautog was reported, but in 1902 the quantity taken was only 2,650 pounds, all in Carteret County. The average price received by the fishermen is 2 cents a pound.

Genus LACHNOLAIMUS Cuvier & Valenciennes. Hog-fishes.

Body much compressed; back elevated and compressed to a sharp edge; snout sharp; profile steep; mouth terminal, horizontal, and low; premaxillary mostly concealed by broad preorbital; jaw teeth prominent, canine, in a single row; scales of moderate size; cheeks and opercles partly scaled; lateral line complete; dorsal fins continuous but distinct, the first with 14 spines of which the 3 anterior are very long and curved backward over the other spines; soft dorsal elongate; anal larger than soft dorsal, with 3 spines; caudal deeply concave, the lobes filamentous; pectorals and ventrals short. The genus contains a single species. (*Lachnolaimus*, velvet throat.)

285. LACHNOLAIMUS MAXIMUS (Walbaum).

Hog-fish; Capitaine.

Labrus maximus Walbaum, Artedi Genera Piscium, 261, 1792; Bahamas (after Catesby).
Lachnolaimus maximus, Jordan & Evermann, 1898, 1579, pl. ccxxxvii, fig. 597.

DIAGNOSIS.—Back elevated, greatest body depth about .4 total length; head .33 length; mouth large, the gape wider in male, maxillary extending to a point under middle of eye; 4 prominent canine teeth in front of upper jaw, 2 in lower jaw with 2 small conical teeth between and a row of blunt teeth on sides of each jaw; snout .4 head; eye .20 head; scales in lateral series 36 to 39, in transverse series 21 to 25, 6 rows of scales on cheeks, 5 rows on opercles; dorsal rays, XIV,11 or 12, the longest spines much longer than head, the longest soft rays about equal to head; anal rays III,11, the third spine longest. Color: varying from dull red to orange red, lighter below; cheeks greenish; a wavy blue line below eye; a black bar from snout to back of head; a large black spot at base of soft dorsal; dorsal greenish at base, with reddish edge; anal and caudal with rows of green spots; pectorals orange; ventrals reddish; in adult males the vertical fins usually black at base. (*maximus*, largest.)

This hog-fish should not be confounded with the hog-fish or pig-fish, Orthopristis, which is abundant on this coast, whereas Lachnolaimus is an exceedingly rare straggler. It is a well known and abundant species in the West Indies, southern Florida, and Bermuda, but does not appear to have been previously noted at any point on our Atlantic coast north of Florida, and the present record is based on a single young specimen 3.75 inches long seined at Beaufort in the summer of 1902. The fish reaches a weight of 20 pounds and is highly esteemed as food.

Genus IRIDIO Jordan & Evermann. Slippery Dicks; Doncellas.

A rather numerous genus of highly colored American fishes, usually found among the kelp in tropical waters. Form elongate, compressed; head conic; mouth small, terminal, with 2 enlarged canine teeth in front of upper jaw and 4 in front of lower jaw, together with a large canine tooth on each side of upper jaw near angle of mouth and small intervening teeth; gill-membranes attached to isthmus; gill-rakers short; preopercular margin entire; scales rather large on body, none on head; lateral line abruptly decurved posteriorly; dorsal fins low, continuous, spines 9; anal similar to soft dorsal, with 3 spines; caudal slightly rounded; pectorals and ventrals small, the latter attached under base of former. One species certainly and another possibly are known from the North Carolina coast; these may be thus distinguished:

i. Depth of body .25 length; a black spot on opercle; a dark band extending from snout through eye to base of caudal, with a narrower band below; spinous dorsal plain or with small black spot between fifth and seventh spines......................*bivittatus.*
ii. Depth of body rather more than .25 length; no black spot on opercle; a dark band extending from snout through eye to body, and thence nearly to tip of caudal, without another band below; a prominent black spot on spinous dorsal between fifth and seventh spines.
maculipinna.

(*Iridio*, from iris, the rainbow.)

284. IRIDIO BIVITTATUS (Bloch).

Slippery Dick.

Labrus bivittatus Bloch, Ichthyologie, pl. 284, fig. 1, 1792; Martinique.
Chœrojulis grandisquamis Gill, Proceedings Academy Natural Sciences, Philadelphia, 1863, 206; Beaufort.
    Gill, Catalogue of Fishes of East Coast of North America, 1873, 23; North Carolina. Yarrow, 1877,
    207; Beaufort.
Pusa grandisquamis, Jordan & Gilbert, 1879, 374; Beaufort.
Platyglossus bivittatus, Jordan, 1886, 28; Beaufort.
Iridio bivittatus, Jordan & Evermann, 1898, 1595, pl. ccxxxix, figs. 600, 601; north to Charleston and Beaufort,
    N. C.

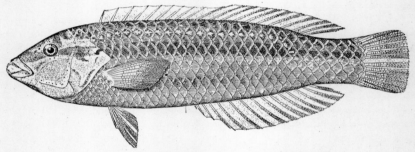

Fig. 148. SLIPPERY DICK. *Iridio bivittatus.*

DIAGNOSIS.—Form slender, the depth .25 total length; head small, its length slightly greater than body depth; maxillary extending half-way from end of snout to pupil; snout .3 length of head; eye small, .16 to .20 length of head; scales in lateral series 27 or 28, in transverse series 2+8 or 9; dorsal rays IX,11; anal rays III,11 or 12; caudal fin very slightly convex posteriorly; pectorals and ventrals short.   Color: pale greenish above, purplish on sides; a dark brown lateral stripe from snout, through eye, to base of caudal fin and a similar fainter band from pectoral base backward, these two becoming fainter with age and sometimes fading completely; many of the body scales with a dark blue spot; head variously marked with bands or stripes of red, green, blue, and violet; a dark spot on opercle; dorsal and anal fins marked, from base outward, with blue, red, yellow, red, and pale; caudal red, with oblique yellow and blue lines; pectorals plain; ventrals red; in young a small jet-black spot on back at base of last dorsal ray. (*bivittatus*, two-banded.)

The range of this abundant species extends from Brazil to North Carolina. Its length is only 6 inches, but it is well known on the shores of Florida and the West Indies, and is caught often by youthful anglers.   A specimen 6 inches long collected at Beaufort July 11, 1860, and sent to the National Museum (no. 4318) by Sergeant Wm. Alexander, U. S. Army, was described by Dr. Theodore Gill in 1863 as a new species under the name of *Chærojulis grandisquamis.* Another specimen was obtained there by Dr. Yarrow in 1870; but later collectors did not find the fish, and it was not until 1902 that the species was again recorded. In that year, on September 12, the steamer Fish-Hawk dredged 8 or 10 specimens 1 to 3.5 inches long off Beaufort (at station 7344), at a depth of 13 fathoms. All of these show a distinct dark lateral stripe from snout to base of caudal and a paler stripe below, a black spot at base of last dorsal ray, and a round dark spot at base of caudal rays; the two largest specimens have a black spot on opercle, and the larger of them has a black triangular spot on the tip of each caudal lobe; while in the smallest specimens (1 to 2.67 inches long) there is a very distinct black spot on dorsal fin between fifth and seventh spines, and the terminal caudal spots are faint or absent.

285. IRIDIO MACULIPINNA (Müller & Troschel).

Spotted-finned Doncella.

Julis maculipinna Müller & Troschel, in Schomburgk, History of Barbados, 674, 1848; Barbados.
Pusa (?) *radiata,* Jordan & Gilbert. 1879, 374; Beaufort.
Platyglossus maculipinna, Jordan, 1886, 38; Beaufort. Yarrow, 1887, 91; Beaufort.
Iridio maculipinna, Jordan & Evermann, 1898, 1594, north to Beaufort, N. C.

DIAGNOSIS.—Very similar to *Iridio bivittatus,* but the depth a little greater, eye larger (contained 4.5 times in head), and snout shorter (3.5 times in head). Color: a dark lateral band extending from snout nearly to tip of tail; no second band below this; no dark spot on opercle; a small black spot in axil of pectorals; a large black spot on dorsal fin, usually between fifth and seventh spines but often extending further forward. (*maculipinna,* spotted-finned.)

The claims of this West Indian species to a place in the North Carolina fauna rest on a specimen 1.5 inches long taken at Beaufort in 1878 by Jordan & Gilbert. The specimen was lost before a final identification was made, and it is possible that the little fish was *Iridio bivittatus.* The principal mark of distinction is the black spot on the spinous dorsal fin, but, as has been shown, this is sometimes present on small, deep-water examples of *bivittatus.*

Genus DORATONOTUS Günther.

Small fishes of beautiful coloration peculiar to the West Indies and the South Atlantic coast. Form compressed, head not sharp anteriorly, the profile straight or concave; mouth wide; jaw teeth in a single series, with 2 enlarged canines in front of each jaw and a posterior canine present on each side of upper jaw; lateral line interrupted posteriorly; scales large; opercles and cheeks scaly; gill-membranes connected, not attached to isthmus; dorsal spines strong, 9 in number, anterior ones elevated; soft part of dorsal similar to anal. Two known species, 1 recently described from Porto Rico, and the following. (*Doratonotus,* spear back.)

286. DORATONOTUS MEGALEPIS Günther.

Doratonotus megalepis Günther, Catalogue of Fishes in British Museum, iv, 1862; St. Kitts.   Jordan & Ever-
      mann, 1898, 1611.

DIAGNOSIS.—Body much compressed, rather deep, depth .37 length; caudal peduncle
short and deep; length of head a little less than depth; top of head depressed; mouth wide,
maxillary .25 length of head; snout long, slender, compressed, .3 length of head; eye .2 length
of head; gill-membranes broadly united; lateral line following line of back to beyond dorsal
fin, there broken and continues horizontally on peduncle; scales in lateral series 20; a single
row of 4 large scales on cheeks, 5 or 6 similar scales on opercles; dorsal rays ix,10, the first 3
spines with filamentous appendages; anal rays iii, 9; caudal rounded; pectorals extending beyond
ventrals; ventrals short, .5 head.   Color: uniformly bright grass-green, head a little lighter;
the green of the dorsal, anal, caudal, and ventral fins mottled with orange; pectorals light yellow.   (*megalepis*, large-scaled.)

An example of this rare and beautiful species, of which 6 specimens are
known, from the West Indies and Florida, was taken by the steamer Fish-Hawk
(station 7344) off Cape Lookout, at a depth of 13 fathoms, September 12, 1902.
The fish was 1.75 inches long.   The maximum size attained by the species is
2.75 or 3 inches.

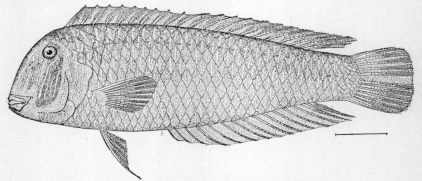

Fig. 149.   RAZOR-FISH.   *Xyrichthys psittacus.*

Genus XYRICHTHYS Cuvier.   Razor-fishes.

The razor-fishes are brilliantly colored tropical species, so named because
of their extremely compressed oblong bodies, the upper and anterior edges being
sharp.   Body deepest immediately behind head, whence it tapers gradually to
the rather broad caudal peduncle; head very short, deeper than long; profile from
eye to mouth nearly vertical; eyes small, near top of head; mouth small, low,
terminal, with 2 anterior canines in each jaw; scales rather large, head practically
naked; lateral line high, interrupted posteriorly and beginning again on a lower
row of scales; dorsal fin beginning close behind eye, long, low, and continuous,
with 9 spines.   Several American species.   (*Xyrichthys*, razor-fish.)

287. XYRICHTHYS PSITTACUS (Linnæus).

Razor-fish.

Coryphæna psittacus Linnæus, Systema Naturæ, ed. xii, 448, 1766; Charleston, S. C
Xyrichthys psittacus, Jordan & Evermann, 1898, 1618, pl. ccxlii, fig. 607.

DIAGNOSIS.—Body strongly compressed, the depth a little less than .33 length; head .25 length; eye placed high, near superior profile, .16 length of head and about .5 length of maxillary; scales in lateral series 26 or 27, in transverse series 2+ 8; lateral line on second row of scales, dropping to fourth row on peduncle; dorsal rays IX,12, the longest spine 2 times diameter of eye, the posterior rays slightly produced; anal rays III,11, the soft rays longer than in dorsal; caudal rounded, shorter than head; pectorals shorter and ventrals slightly longer than caudal, the first ventral ray produced. Color: reddish, each scale with a vertical blue streak; similar streaks on head; a silvery area behind and below pectorals; a dark red shade across pectorals in male; dorsal plain; anal streaked obliquely with green; caudal with 6 to 8 dark vertical lines. (*psittacus*, a parrot.)

The range heretofore ascribed to the razor-fish has been from the West Indies to Pensacola and Charleston. It is now recorded for the first time from the North Carolina coast. Three specimens 4.25 inches long were collected by the steamer Fish-Hawk off Beaufort in August, 1902, and another specimen is reported to have been taken at the Mullet Pond on Shackleford Bank during the same summer. An example 7 inches long now in the State Museum was obtained in the Wilmington market in the summer of 1884. The species reaches a length of 15 inches.

Family SCARIDÆ. The Parrot-fishes.

Several hundred parrot-fishes are known from the warmer waters of the world; they are for the most part gaily-colored, large scaled, herbivorous fishes, particularly numerous among coral reefs, and having but little food value, the flesh being soft. The shape of the head, the size and position of the eye, the character of the teeth, and the coloration strongly suggest the parrots. Body more or less elongate, rather stout; mouth terminal, of rather small size, the jaw teeth fused so as to form a strong beak, the lower pharyngeal teeth arranged in a mosaic; scales cycloid, completely covering body and part of head; lateral line present; dorsal fins continuous, with about 9 spines and 10 soft rays; anal fin similar to soft dorsal, preceded by 2 spines. Only 1 species has as yet been recorded from the waters of the state, but representatives of several other genera occur as stragglers on the Middle Atlantic and Southern New England coast, and 1 appears to range regularly as far north as Charleston, so others may in time be met with in North Carolina.

Genus SPARISOMA Swainson. Oldwives.

A numerous genus of small fishes, practically confined to American waters, distinguished by having the gill-membranes broadly united to isthmus; the jaw teeth for the most coalesced in adult, with a median suture, sometimes a supplementary row of canine teeth in upper jaw; lower pharyngeal bones broader than long; few scales on head, a single row on cheeks; a continuous lateral line, with tubes much branched; sharp dorsal spines; and color plain or showy. (*Sparisoma*, having the body of Sparus, which is an ancient name for some sparoid fish.)

288. SPARISOMA NIPHOBLES Jordan & Bollman.

White-spotted Parrot-fish.

Sparisoma niphobles Jordan & Bollman, Proceedings U. S. National Museum, 1888, 551; Bahama Islands.
    Jordan and Evermann, 1898, 1633.

DIAGNOSIS.—Body oblong, depth .33 length; length of head somewhat greater than depth
of body; eye contained 4.5 times in head; snout obtuse, contained 2.8 times in head; upper lip
large, covering most of jaw; 2 canine teeth in front of upper jaw, and 1 on each near angle of
mouth; scales in lateral series 24, in crosswise series 2+ 6; a row of 5 large scales on cheek; 4
median scales anterior to dorsal fin; tubes of lateral line with 3 to 5 branches; dorsal rays IX,10;
anal rays II,11; caudal fin truncate.   Color: brownish green, thickly covered with white specks
and mottlings; head speckled with blue and black; chin with silvery spots; 5 bluish white
lengthwise stripes along row of scales; a black spot on shoulder; spinous dorsal with dark
mottlings; soft dorsal with rows of brown spots; anal similar to soft dorsal; caudal marked by
4 or 5 wavy, white vertical bars; pectorals yellowish; ventrals with indistinct white spots.
(*niphobles*, snowed upon.)

Two specimens about 3.5 inches long taken at Beaufort in the summer of
1902 are referable to this species, which has heretofore been known from Florida,
Porto Rico, and the Bahamas.   The maximum length is about 6 inches.

Family EPHIPPIDÆ.   The Spade-fishes.

Body much compressed, very deep, back strongly arched, ventral outline
less so; mouth small, terminal; bands of slender, sharp, movable teeth in jaws;
maxillary short, with no supplemental bone; premaxillary slightly protractile;
nostril double; gill-rakers short; gill-membranes broadly united to isthmus;
branchiostegals 6 or 7; pseudobranchiæ present; preopercle either finely serrated
or entire; scales ctenoid, of small or moderate size; lateral line present, strongly
arched; pyloric cœca few; air-bladder present; dorsal fins 2, anterior with 8 to 11
spines depressible in a groove, posterior much larger, with anterior rays elongated;
anal spines 3 or 4, the soft rays similar to posterior dorsal, both with fleshy
scaled base; caudal broad, with posterior margin square or concave; pectorals
short, the rays branched; ventrals thoracic.   A rather small family, with a single
representative on the east coast of the United States.

Genus CHÆTODIPTERUS Lacépède.   Spade-fishes.

In this genus the much compressed body is nearly as deep as long; vomer
and palatines toothless; preopercle finely serrate; branchiostegals 6; scales small,
60 to 70 in lateral series; lateral line concurrent with back; pyloric cœca 4 to 6;
dorsal fins disconnected, the first with 8 spines, the third longest; anal spines 3,
the second longest; a large accessory scale at base of ventrals.   Two American
species, 1 on the Pacific coast, and the following. (*Chætodipterus*, two-finned
chætodon, in allusion to the divided dorsal.)

289. CHÆTODIPTERUS FABER (Broussonet).

"Porgee"; "Pogy"; Angel-fish (S. C.); Spade-fish; Moon-fish.

Chætodon faber Broussonet, Ichthyologia, 1782; Jamaica and Carolina.
Parephippus faber, Yarrow, 1877, 211; Beaufort.   Jordan & Gilbert, 1879, 380; Beaufort.
Chætodipterus faber, Jordan, 1886, 28; Beaufort.   Goode, 1884, 445; Beaufort.   Jenkins, 1887, 91; Beaufort.
    Jordan & Evermann, 1898, 1668, pl. ccxlvii, fig. 619.   Linton, 1905, 400; Beaufort.

DIAGNOSIS.—Body short and deep, the depth contained 1 to 1.5 times in length, depending on age; head contained 3 to 3.5 times in length, the anterior profile very steep; mouth small, maxillary extending barely as far as anterior margin of eye; snout .4 length of head; eye .3 length of head; scales in lateral series about 60; cheeks and opercles densely scaled; lateral line arched like back, straight on the short caudal peduncle; vertical fins high and falcate; dorsal rays VIII+ I,20, the third spine more than .5 length of head; anal rays III,18, the second spine longest; caudal deeply concave; pectorals less than twice diameter of eye; ventrals much longer than pectorals, with first soft ray produced as a filament; young with vertical fins lower. Color: gray, with 5 dark vertical bands of different widths on head and body, becoming obscure in old specimens; ventrals black. (*faber*, a blacksmith.)

Fig. 150. SPADE-FISH; PORGEE. *Chœtodipterus faber.*

Under the name of "porgee" or "pogy" the North Carolina fishermen recognize this well-marked fish, which is known in South Carolina as angel-fish, and elsewhere as moon-fish and spade-fish. Its range extends from Massachusetts to South America, and it is particularly abundant on the southeastern coast of the United States.

The fish sometimes reaches a length of 3 feet, but does not average to exceed a foot. It frequents rocky patches, wrecks, and piling in search of food, which consists of small crustaceans, worms, etc. It is found on the North Carolina coast only in summer, leaving as soon as the weather becomes cool. At Beaufort, ripe male and female fish have been found early in June. The eggs are quite small, being less than 1 mm. in diameter. In the latter part of August fish about 3 inches long, the young of the year, may be seined in Beaufort Harbor.

The spade-fish is of excellent quality as food, and in the New York and Washington markets is highly regarded. In Pamlico Sound it is sometimes taken abundantly in pound nets, and on other parts of the coast it is caught incidentally in seines and other appliances. Of late it has not been numerous in the Beaufort region. The quantity taken and sold in 1897 was 39,910 pounds, valued at $472, and in 1902 was 16,800 pounds, valued at $269. The bulk of the catch comes from Craven, Dare, and Pamlico counties.

Family CHÆTODONTIDÆ. The Butterfly-fishes.

A rather numerous family of mostly small, active, highly colored fishes of tropical waters in all parts of the world. Form short, deep, and greatly compressed; mouth small, terminal, and projecting; teeth long, fine, in dense narrow bands in jaws, no teeth on vomer or palatines; eye lateral, of moderate size; gill-membranes connected with isthmus; gill-rakers minute; branchiostegals 6 or 7; pseudobranchiæ large; preopercle either unarmed or with a strong spine; scales ciliated or smooth, moderate or rather small, covering body, more or less of head, and soft parts of vertical fins; lateral line present; air-bladder present; dorsal fin single with rather numerous spines and soft rays; anal fin similar to soft dorsal, with 3 or 4 spines; caudal rounded or truncate; ventrals thoracic, with rays 1,5. There are about 6 American genera, but only 1 is represented on the North Carolina coast.

Genus CHÆTODON Linnæus. Butterfly-fishes.

This, the most numerous genus of the family, contains many strikingly beautiful little fishes, with short, deep body much compressed, especially above; short, pointed, scaly head; small mouth, with numerous long, flexible teeth in bands; preopercle without spine; narrow gill-openings; ctenoid, moderate-sized scales; lateral line strongly arched; about 13 spines in dorsal fin, the spinous part longer than the soft; 3 stout anal spines; caudal margin straight or rounded; ventral spine strong. Of the 8 or 10 American species, only 1 has yet been noted in North Carolina. (*Chætodon*, bristle tooth.)

290. CHÆTODON OCELLATUS Bloch.

Butterfly-fish.

Chætodon ocellatus Bloch, Ichthyologie, pl. 211, fig. 2, 1787. Jordan & Evermann, 1898, 1674, pl. ccxlix, fig. 621.

DIAGNOSIS.—Depth equals length of body posterior to head or about .7 total length; head .4 length of body; snout produced, about length of eye, and somewhat less than .33 head; scales in lateral series about 34, in transverse series 21; lateral line terminating near end of dorsal fin; dorsal rays xii,20, the longest spines (third and fourth) twice length of eye; anal rays iii,16; ventrals more than .8 length of head. Color: yellowish gray; a black band extends from front of dorsal fin through eye and thence downward to throat; a black spot on opercle; a large black spot on soft dorsal; a black vertical band from this spot to base of anal. (*ocellatus*, having eye-like spot.)

A common West Indian species, occurring as a straggler along the Atlantic coast as far as New England; sometimes, however, taken in large numbers as far north as Massachusetts.* This species was not heretofore recorded from North Carolina, but has recently been taken on several occasions at Beaufort, as follows: In the summer of 1902 one 1.5 inches long at Bird Shoal; in 1903 one 1.75 inches long near the laboratory; and on July 21, 1904, two 2.25 inches long in the harbor. The species rarely exceeds 3 inches in length.

Family HEPATIDÆ. The Surgeon-fishes or Tangs.

The fishes of this family may easily be recognized by the presence of 1 or 2 spinous processes on each side of the narrow caudal peduncle, together with an oblong, much compressed body, with elevated back; short head; small, low, terminal mouth, armed with a single row of narrow teeth in jaws; short maxillary closely united with premaxillary; small, high eye; double nostrils; 4 gill-arches, with rudimentary rakers; gill-membranes attached to isthmus; large pseudo-branchiæ; small scales completely covering body and head; complete lateral line; long, narrow, connected pelvic bones; few pyloric cœca; large air-bladder; a single greatly elongated dorsal fin, with spinous part shorter than soft part; anal fin similar to but shorter than dorsal; broad caudal fin with concave margin; and thoracic ventrals with about 5 soft rays preceded by a spine. The family has about 100 members in the warmer regions of the world, most of them belonging in the only genus found on the eastern coast of North America.

Genus HEPATUS Gronow. Surgeon-fishes; Tangs.

In this genus the armature of the caudal peduncle consists of a single sharp, movable spine on each side which fits in a groove and is capable of being extended like the blade of a lancet, whence the various common names of these fishes; as the species are herbivorous, it is evident the spines, which can inflict a painful wound, are employed only for protection. Lateral line arched; scales very fine and numerous; dorsal spines 9, anal spines 3; teeth strong and immovable. About 6 species known from American waters. Of the 3 species found regularly in Florida and as stragglers as far north as Massachusetts, 2 were recently detected in North Carolina waters which may thus be distinguished:

i. Caudal fin slightly concave behind; caudal lobes about equal; about 12 dark vertical bars on sides.. ....*hepatus.*
ii. Caudal fin deeply concave behind; upper caudal lobe terminating in a produced filament; no vertical bars on sides...*bahianus.*

(*Hepatus,* an old name for some European fish.)

291. HEPATUS HEPATUS (Linnæus).

Surgeon-fish; Tang; Lancet-fish; Doctor-Fish.

Teuthis hepatus Linnæus, Systema Naturæ, ed. xii, 507, 1766; Carolina. Jordan & Evermann, 1898, 1691.

DIAGNOSIS.—Body ovate, the depth .4 to .5 length; head contained 3.5 times in total length; superior profile very steep, making an angle of 45° with long axis of body; snout about .6 head; eye .5 snout; dorsal fin of nearly uniform height throughout, the rays ix,25 or 26; anal rays iii, 22 to 24; caudal somewhat shorter than head, the lobes of nearly equal length. Color:

* In a small bay on Marthas Vineyard more than 100 were collected by the writer in the summer and fall of 1900.

dark greenish brown, paler on sides; about 12 narrow, vertical blackish bars on sides; fins generally dark; dorsal with brown stripe at base, spinous part with blue and green stripes, soft rays bluish anteriorly.

Up to this time only 2 specimens of this fish have been recorded from North Carolina waters. The first, 6 inches long, was captured in a mullet net near Beaufort Inlet in the fall of 1904 and presented to the Bureau of Fisheries by Mr. Joseph Lewis, of the Mullet Pond Fishery, who states that during his 30 years' fishing experience near Beaufort he has seen only 1 other fish of this kind. The second specimen was obtained near Pivers Island, Beaufort Harbor, July 15, 1905, by Prof. Howard E. Enders, and is now in the laboratory collection. The species is abundant in Florida and the West Indies, and is eaten in considerable quantities. The maximum length is about 1 foot.

292. HEPATUS BAHIANUS (Castelnau).

Surgeon-fish; Tang; Lancet-fish; Doctor-fish; Barber.

Acanthurus bahianus Castelnau, Animaux Nouvelles ou Rares de l'Amerique du Sud, p. 24, pl. 11, fig. 1, 1855; Bahia.
Teuthis bahianus, Jordan & Evermann, 1898, 1693, pls. cclvi and cclvii, figs. 629, 630.

DIAGNOSIS.—Form as in *Hepatus hepatus*; dorsal rays ix,24, longest less than .5 length of head; anal rays iii,22; caudal deeply incised, the upper lobe longer and often filamentous. Color: dark brown, with paler blotches below; sides with brown wavy lengthwise streaks; dorsal fin with 8 dark longitudinal lines and a black edge; caudal with light blue or whitish margin. (*bahianus*, relating to Bahia.)

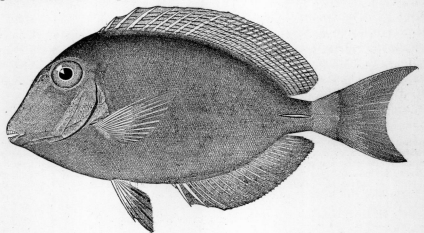

Fig. 151. SURGEON-FISH; TANG. *Hepatus bahianus.*

This surgeon-fish is common at Key West and thence throughout the West Indies. It is now recorded for the first time from North Carolina. On October 11, 1905, Mr. S. G. Worth obtained from a local fisherman at Beaufort a specimen 5.5 inches long which is now in the laboratory at that place. This species reaches somewhat over a foot in length, and in Florida, Porto Rico, and the Danish West Indies is of considerable importance as food.

Family BALISTIDÆ.   The Trigger-fishes.

Rather large-sized shore fishes of tropical waters, feeding on small animals or on algæ; protected by their tough, rough skin; rarely eaten by man, the flesh of some reputed to be exceedingly poisonous.   Body ovate or elongate, considerably compressed; mouth very small, terminal; jaws short but strong, a single row of incisor teeth in each; premaxillaries fused with maxillaries; eye small, high; preorbital region very wide; gill-openings short slits at base of pectorals; opercular bones not evident externally; head and body covered with rough scales or plates; lateral line absent or rudimentary; air-bladder present; vertebræ few in number (17); 2 dorsal fins, the anterior with 2 or 3 spines, the first spine largest, the second firmly locking it when extended, whence the name triggerfishes, applied to the family; posterior dorsal with numerous soft rays; anal similar to second dorsal; caudal rounded, forked, or concave; pectorals short and broad; ventrals represented by a stout spine at the end of a long pelvic bone. About 6 American genera, only 1 regularly represented on our Atlantic coast.

Genus BALISTES Linnæus.   Trigger-fishes.

This genus contains the typical trigger-fishes, with 3 dorsal spines, of which the first is much the largest, the second in close relation thereto, the third remote; by depressing the second spine the firmly locked first spine may be bent backward.   Body compressed, rather deep; irregular teeth in each jaw; scales rather small, rough, implanted in a tough, leathery skin; lateral line very small and exceedingly irregular, extending on cheeks, sometimes incomplete; a groove in front of eye below nostrils; enlarged bony plates behind gill-openings; pelvic flap large, movable, with numerous sharp spines; anal and second dorsal fins long, falcate or filamentous in adult; caudal lobes produced in old specimens; colors often brilliant and in remarkable patterns.   Two species occur on our east coast, straggling as far north as Massachusetts; only 1 of these thus far recorded from North Carolina, but the other likely to be found any season.   These 2 may be thus distinguished:

i. Lateral line complete, extending from cheek upward to near dorsal, thence abruptly downward to near anal, again upward, and then straight along caudal peduncle; color olive gray, with a dark cross-bar under anterior part of soft dorsal and violet or blue spots on back, head, and fins. . . . .*carolinensis.*
ii. Lateral line incomplete, only on cheeks, nape, and peduncle; color brownish yellow, with bright blue streaks on head, fins, and peduncle. . . . .*vetula.*

(*Balistes,* cross-bow.)

293. BALISTES CAROLINENSIS Gmelin.

Leather-jacket; Trigger-fish.

Balistes carolinensis Gmelin, Systema Naturæ, i, 1468, 1788; Carolina.   Jordan & Evermann, 1898, 1701, pl. cclviii, fig. 632.

DIAGNOSIS.—Depth .5 total length to end of tail; peduncle narrow, about .16 depth of body; head .25 total length to end of tail; snout very long, .8 length of head; eye very small, less than .25 snout; scales in lateral series 55 to 65; lateral line undulating, very irregular (as described in key), the lines of two sides united by a branch over nape; dorsal rays III+ 27, the anterior soft rays elongated but not so long as head; anal rays 25; caudal lobes produced in adult. Color: in general grayish olive; 2 dark cross-bars under soft dorsal fin; small purplish spots on back and purplish marks on snout; eye surrounded by a ring of blue spots and green streaks; first dorsal with blue spots; second dorsal and anal yellow, with rows of light blue spots and a green network; pectorals green, with blue base and green spots. (*carolinensis*, inhabiting Carolina.)

Fig. 152. TRIGGER-FISH. *Balistes carolinensis.*

A widely distributed species, very common in the West Indies and the Mediterranean Sea, sometimes carried northward in the Gulf Stream to New York and Massachusetts. It attains a length of more than a foot, and at Key West, where it is called turbot, it is extensively eaten. There are no published records of the fish's occurrence in North Carolina, but it must have been observed on many occasions and at various points. The only specimens known from state waters have been taken at Beaufort—1 in the summer of 1903; another caught on a hook in August, 1905; and a third obtained at Pivers Island on October 9, 1905.

Family MONACANTHIDÆ. The File-fishes.

Shore fishes of warmer regions, feeding chiefly on algæ; species mostly small, of no food value, the flesh bitter; similar to the trigger-fishes but having only a single dorsal spine. Body much compressed, rather deep; mouth small, terminal; incisor teeth in upper jaw in a double series; in lower jaw in a single series; gill-openings mere slits; lateral line absent; scales small, spine-bearing; dorsal spine barbed or smooth, sometimes a rudimentary spine behind; second dorsal long, widely separated from the spine; anal similar; caudal peduncle long or short, the fin broad or elongate; pectorals very short; ventrals either absent or represented by a long spine surmounting the pelvic bone. Four American genera, 2 represented in the local fauna.

i. Dorsal spine comparatively stout, its posterior surface with retrorse barbs; pelvic bone surmounted with a spine projecting through skin of abdomen; gill-openings short, and more or less vertical; caudal fin broad...Monacanthus.

ii. Dorsal spine rather slender, without barbs; no spine on pelvic bone; gill-openings long and very oblique; caudal fin elongate.................................Ceratacanthus.

Genus MONACANTHUS Cuvier.   File-fishes.

A very numerous genus of small fishes with short, deep, much compressed body; very small mouth; about 6 teeth in outer row and 4 in inner row in upper jaw, and about 6 in lower jaw; gill-slit shorter than eye, slightly oblique, and under posterior part of eye; minute scales, individually rough, but giving to the skin a velvety feel; ventral flap and sometimes caudal peduncle spinous; large dorsal spine, with 2 series of retrorse spines; second dorsal and anal fins with 25 or more rays; broad, rounded caudal; blunt, movable ventral spine; pelvic bone united with abdomen by a broad flap of skin.   Several American species, 1 common along our Atlantic coast.   (*Monacanthus*, one spine.)

294. MONACANTHUS HISPIDUS (Linnæus).

"Fool-fish"; File-fish.

Balistes hispidus Linnæus, Systema Naturæ, ed. xii, 405, 1766; Carolina.
Stephanolepis setifer, Yarrow, 1877, 204; Beaufort.   Jordan & Gilbert, 1879, 367; Beaufort.
Monacanthus hispidus, Jordan, 1886, 30; Beaufort.   Jenkins, 1887, 93; Beaufort.   Jordan & Evermann, 1898, 1715, pl. cclix, fig. 635.   Linton, 1905, 401; Beaufort.

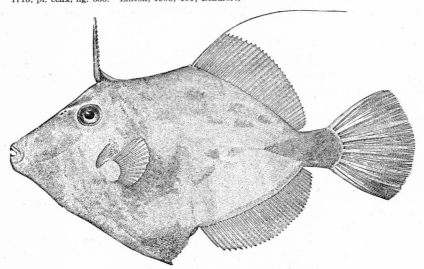

Fig. 153.   File-fish.   *Monacanthus hispidus.*

Diagnosis.—Depth contained 1.75 times in length in adults; head about .5 depth; profile from dorsal spine to end of snout nearly straight; snout very long, about 3 times diameter of eye; gill-slits length of eye; margin of abdominal flap not extending beyond ventral spine; body completely scaly, each scale with 3 prickles; dorsal spine straight, above posterior part of eye, shorter than snout, posterior surface with 2 rows of barbs; dorsal soft rays about 32, the first ray often filamentous, the others becoming gradually shorter from before backward; anal rays about 32; caudal fan-shaped, the margin rounded; pectorals less than twice diameter of eye. Color: nearly uniform green, the shade varying from grass green to olive; irregular faint whitish spots on back and sides; fins transparent greenish. (*hispidus*, bristly.)

This species is found from southern Massachusetts to Brazil, and is common throughout its range. It is extremely abundant on the North Carolina coast, where it is known as "fool-fish". In July, 1903, during a period of 5 days, over 600 were seined in Beaufort Harbor, mostly on Bird Shoal; these were 1 to 3 inches long. A series of young collected in sargassum-weed in the Gulf Stream off Beaufort July 27, 1901, had individuals .38 to 1.75 inches long. The maximum length of the species is 10 inches. Numerous specimens examined at Beaufort by Professor Linton were found to have eaten bryozoans, small crustaceans and mollusks, gastropod eggs, annelids, small sea-urchins, and algæ.

Genus CERATACANTHUS Gill. File-fishes; Fool-fishes.

Moderate-sized shore fishes, with somewhat elongate, strongly compressed body; projecting lower jaw; very oblique gill-openings much longer than eye and extending in advance of eye; a long, curved pelvic bone without a spinous extremity; single small, slender, barbless dorsal spine inserted over middle of eye; soft dorsal widely separated from the spine, its rays numerous (35 to 50); anal fin similar to soft dorsal; caudal fin more or less elongate; pectoral fins very small. Numerous species, in all warmer parts of the world; 4 American species, 2 of which are here noted.*

i. Color variable—dusky olive, orange yellow, or whitish—without definite spots; anterior profile convex; depth of body in adult .5 length..............................*schœpfii.*
ii. Color light brown, with numerous dark brown round spots half diameter of pupil; anterior profile concave; depth of body in adult .4 length........................*punctatus.*

(*Ceratacanthus*, horn spine.)

295. CERATACANTHUS SCHŒPFII (Walbaum).

File-fish; Fool-fish; Devil-fish.

Balistes schœpfii Walbaum, Artedi Genera Piscium, 461, 1792; Long Island, N. Y.
Alutera cuspicauda, Yarrow, 1877, 204; Beaufort. Jordan & Gilbert, 1879, 367; Beaufort.
Ceratacanthus aurantiacus, Yarrow, 1877, 204; Beaufort.
Alutera aurantiaca, Jordan & Gilbert, 1879, 367; Beaufort.
Alutera schœpfii, Jordan, 1886, 30; Beaufort. Jordan & Evermann, 1898, 1718, pl. xxlx, fig. 636. Linton, 1905, 401; Beaufort.
Ceratacanthus schœpfii, Jordan & Evermann, 1898, 2860.

DIAGNOSIS.—Depth about .5 length in adult, less in young; caudal peduncle slender, 2 times diameter of eye; head .33 length; profile from mouth to dorsal spine slightly convex; lower jaw somewhat the longer, chin projecting; snout nearly as long as head and 4 times diameter of eye; eye under dorsal spine and over posterior part of gill opening; gill-opening twice diameter of eye; scales minute, rough, completely covering body and head; dorsal spine slender, its length varying with age, about 2 times length of eye in adults; soft dorsal rays about 36, anal rays 38, the fins low; caudal long, slender, becoming shorter in old specimens; pectorals short, about twice diameter of eye. Color: adults dirty gray, orange, or whitish; young dirty white, mottled or blotched with reddish brown or sometimes showing dark and light longitu-

---

* A third species, *Ceratacanthus scriptus*, has occasionally been taken as far north as South Carolina.

dinal bands; caudal usually yellowish.   (Named for Dr. Schöpf, a surgeon with the Hessian troops on Long Island during American Revolution.)

Along the coast of the United States from Massachusetts to Texas, the fool-fish or file-fish is well known, being caught in the nets of the commercial fishermen.   It is called fool-fish because of its peculiar appearance and the general stupidity shown in captivity; it will often remain in a pound net or other trap when every other fish will have escaped through a rent in the netting.   Its rough, sandpaper-like skin has given rise to its other common name.

The fish attains a length of 2 feet, and older examples exhibit 3 distinct color phases: a dull, dirty, greenish-gray, a rich orange-yellow, and a milky white, the yellow and white often being partly replaced by irregular areas of blackish-gray.   These colors appear to be independent of sex or environment, and fishes representing each, as well as intermediate phases, may be taken together.

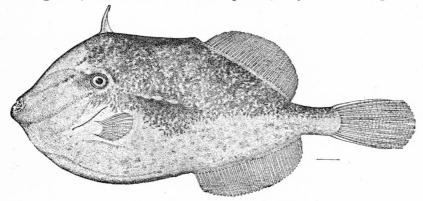

Fig. 154. FILE-FISH; FOOL-FISH. *Ceratacanthus schœpfii.*

When the fish is swimming the head is lower than the tail, and the movements and appearance are singularly awkward.   In captivity the fish eat succulent algæ, the branches of which are bitten off and swallowed rapidly.

The species is common on the shores of North Carolina.   Specimens have been taken for the Beaufort laboratory.   Small examples examined by Professor Linton at Beaufort in July and August contained bryozoans, shrimp, amphipods, and sea lettuce.

296. CERATACANTHUS PUNCTATUS (Agassiz).

Spotted File-fish; Long Mingo.

Alutera punctata Agassiz, Pisces Brasilienses, 137, pl. 76, 1829; Brazil. Jordan & Evermann, 1898, 1719.
Ceratacanthus punctatus, Jordan & Evermann, 1898, 2860.

DIAGNOSIS (based on North Carolina specimens).—Depth slightly less than .5 length; width of peduncle 1.5 times diameter of eye; head contained 3.12 times in length; profile concave; lower jaw projecting; teeth in a single series in each jaw; eye .25 length of snout and somewhat less than supraorbital space; gill-slit .33 length of head, its posterior end under pupil and over base of pectoral; dorsal spine over posterior third of eye, short, slender, its length 2.5

times diameter of eye; rays in soft dorsal 36, origin of the fin same distance from pupil as pupil is from tip of lower jaw; anal rays 38; caudal long, posterior margin rounded; pectorals short, 1.5 times diameter of eye.   Color: grayish brown, with numerous small, round dark brown spots; back and snout dark; caudal black.   (*punctatus*, spotted.)

The spotted file-fish, which ranges from the West Indies to Brazil, is now recorded for the first time from the east coast of the United States on the strength of 2 specimens taken at Bird Shoal, Beaufort Harbor, in the summer of 1902. The fish, 6.75 inches long over all, were profusely marked with discreet, round, brown spots somewhat smaller than the pupil; the dorsal, anal, and pectoral fins were plain; and the caudal was black.

Family OSTRACIIDÆ.   The Trunk-fishes.

The trunk-fishes are among the most curious fishes in our waters, and are at once recognizable by the hard 3-, 4-, or 5-angled shell or box in which the body is encased.   Body rather short and deep; caudal peduncle rather long and narrow; shell formed of numerous large, more or less regular, polygonal bony plates which are deficient only about jaws, at bases of fins, and on caudal peduncle; mouth small, terminal, with a single row of slender teeth in each jaw; maxillary and premaxillary closely united; eye large, high, protruding; gill-opening a short narrow, nearly vertical slit below and posterior to eye; vertebræ 14; dorsal fin inserted far backward, single, short, composed wholly of soft rays; anal fin similar to and opposite dorsal; caudal fin of 10 rays, the posterior margin square or rounded; pectoral fins short, inserted close to lower end of gill-openings; ventral fins absent.   There are 25 or 30 known species, representing several genera, inhabiting tropical waters; all the American species fall into 1 genus.

Genus LACTOPHRYS Swainson.   Three-angled Trunk-fishes.

In this genus the shell or box present 3 well-marked angles, the ventral surface being broad and either flat or convex, and the sides inclining inward to make a more or less acute angle at the back; the shell is continuous across the median line behind the anal fin; the characters by which the species are separated are the presence or absence of horns on the frontal and ventral regions, the existence of a complete or imperfect shell posterior to dorsal fin, and the coloration.   Four American species, 2 known from North Carolina.*   The trunk-fishes are sometimes baked in the shell and regarded with favor in Florida and the West Indies.   Owing to the ease with which they may be preserved, all the American species became known in Europe upwards of 200 years ago; and as a matter of local interest it may be mentioned that Peter Artedi, the "father of ichthyology", in his notes on this group of fishes published in 1738, mentions his having seen several of our species at "The Nagg's Head" tavern in London.

---

*Another species of trunk-fish, *Lactophrys tricornis*, common on the South Atlantic coast and throughout the West Indies, is known from Charleston, S. C., and Chesapeake Bay, and will no doubt in time be detected on the North Carolina coast.   It reaches a length of 18 inches, and may easily be distinguished by a projecting horizontal horn in front of each eye.

i. Shell or carapace with a large spine at end of each ventral ridge; carapace deficient behind
    dorsal fin; color olive gray, nearly every plate with a small pale blue spot at its center.
                                                             trigonus.
ii. Shell or carapace without spines; carapace continuous behind dorsal fin; color dark brown,
    with numerous small, circular, yellow-white spots......................*triqueter.*

(*Lactophrys*, milk-cow eyebrow, in allusion to the horns in one species.)

297. LACTOPHRYS TRIGONUS (Linnæus).

Camel-fish; Box-fish; Trunk-fish; Shell-fish.

Ostracium trigonus Linnæus, Systema Naturæ, ed. x, 330, 1758; "India".
Ostracion trigonum, Jordan, 1886, 30; Beaufort. Jenkins, 1887, 93; Beaufort.
Lactophrys trigonus, Yarrow, 1877, 204; Fort Macon. Jordan & Gilbert, 1879, 367; Beaufort. Jordan & Ever-
    mann, 1898, 1723, pl. cclxiii, fig. 641.

DIAGNOSIS.—Body sharply 3-angled, the back elevated into a well marked, strongly compressed hump; depth .5 length; head .25 length, the profile straight; peduncle long and slender,
its depth less than diameter of eye; each ventral ridge terminating in a long spine which extends
beyond origin of anal fin; shell open behind dorsal fin; a conspicuous ridge over each eye; dorsal rays 10; anal rays 10; caudal with rounded corners. Color: olive gray above, light green on
ventral surface; most of the side plates with a light blue spot in the center; outlines of upper
plates black, of lower ones blue; several dusky areas on side; fins pale green; vent, iris, nostrils,
and base of pectorals yellow. (*trigonus*, three-angled.)

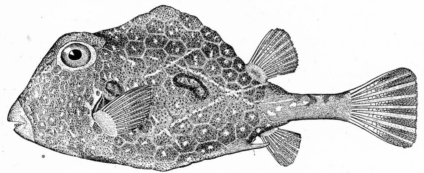

Fig. 155. CAMEL-FISH; TRUNK-FISH. *Lactophrys trigonus*.

    A common West Indian species, well known in Florida and sometimes found
as far north as Massachusetts.* It has occasionally been reported from Beaufort,
N. C. Yarrow recorded 2 specimens from the beach at Fort Macon; a specimen
in the State Museum at Raleigh came from Beaufort; and Jenkins states, on the
authority of Prof. W. K. Brooks, that small examples are often taken in tow nets
outside Beaufort Inlet. There appear to have been no recent captures at
Beaufort. Maximum length about 1 foot.

    * At Woods Hole the writer has found the very young not uncommon in summer; and on quiet days they
have been seen, singly or in small bunches, in eel grass about the wharves. Several dozen have been taken at
one haul of a small seine.

298. LACTOPHRYS TRIQUETER (Linnæus).

Trunk-fish.

Ostracion triqueter Linnæus, Systema Naturæ, ed. x, 330, 1758; India.
Lactophrys triqueter, Jordan & Evermann, 1898, 1722, pl. cclxi, fig. 638.

DIAGNOSIS.—Form ovate, back evenly arched, depth .5 length; sides making an angle of about 30 degrees at back; ventral surface convex; depth of caudal peduncle greater than diameter of eye; head .25 length; profile concave; eye about .33 length of head and .8 length of gill-slit; shell without spines, continuous behind dorsal fin; 9 plates along median line posterior to eye; dorsal rays 10; anal rays 10; caudal fin rounded. Color: dark brown above, lighter on belly; each scale except on ventral surface with 1 or more round whitish spots somewhat smaller than pupil; lips, bases of fins, and tip of caudal dark brown or blackish; caudal peduncle marked like sides; caudal margin black, other fins plain; young light green, with numerous round dark greenish blue spots on sides and below. (*triqueter*, three-angled.)

The occurrence of this trunk-fish on the United States coast north of Florida does not appear to have been previously noted. There are 3 North Carolina records. In July, 1900, several young examples were taken in Beaufort Harbor, and in July, 1904, a number of others were obtained in the same locality. The only adult specimen was collected at Perry Island, Beaufort Harbor, in the summer of 1902.

Family TETRAODONTIDÆ. The Swell-fishes.

The fishes of this family have the faculty of inflating themselves with air or water, which is pumped into a special sac, lying external to the peritoneal cavity, its duct opening into the mouth or esophagus. The amount of the inflation is extreme in some genera, the fishes being converted into veritable balloons. Body oblong or elongate, little if at all compressed; mouth small, terminal, the teeth in each jaw fused into a kind of beak with a median suture; lips conspicuous; gill-slits small, situated immediately in front of pectorals; scales absent, the skin usually covered with small, weak, movable prickles or spines; lateral line conspicuous or not; air-bladder present; vertebræ few (16 to 21); spinous dorsal and ventral fins absent; dorsal fin placed near the caudal, composed of a few soft rays; anal fin similar to and opposite dorsal; caudal fin well developed, of various shapes; pectoral fins short and broad, the upper rays longest. These fishes are for the most part found in warmer coastal waters, and have only feeble swimming powers. While some of them attain a considerable size, none are food fishes, the flesh being rank and sometimes poisonous. About 10 genera and 60 species; 4 genera American, 2 represented in North Carolina fauna.

i. Body oblong; skin prickly or with soft appendages above and below, sometimes smooth; dorsal and anal fins short, with 6 to 8 rays; caudal more or less rounded; lower surface of body without a prominent longitudinal fold or keel; size moderate or small....SPHEROIDES.
ii. Body elongate; skin of abdomen very prickly, back and sides smooth; dorsal and anal fins falcate, with 12 to 15 rays; caudal fin strongly concave behind; a prominent longitudinal fold or keel on each side of belly and peduncle; size large..............LAGOCEPHALUS.

Genus SPHEROIDES Duméril. Puffers; Swell-fishes.

Typical puffers, with oblong, plump body; short nasal canal on each side, with 2 openings near its tip; skin either smooth, prickly, or with cirri (prickly in local species); mucous canals inconspicuous; dorsal and anal fins small, of 6 to 8 rays; caudal fin rather short, broad, its posterior margin rounded or nearly square; abdomen exceedingly dilatable with either air or water. Numerous species, most of them American, 4 known from east coast of United States, but only 2 as yet recorded from North Carolina.

i. Head and body prickly, the prickles small, stiff, 3-rooted; no cirri present; about 12 irregular black blotches on back and sides...................................... *maculatus.*
ii. Sides of head and of body smooth, except an area behind pectorals, the prickles on back and belly larger and wider apart than in *maculatus* and sometimes lacking; small cirri or flaps on sides; numerous small black spots above, and a single series of 12 to 16 small, round black spots along junction of sides and abdomen, these most distinct in young... *spengleri.*

299. SPHEROIDES MACULATUS (Bloch & Schneider).

"Swell-toad"; Puffer; Swell-fish; Balloon-fish.

Tetrodon hispidus, var. *maculatus* Bloch & Schneider, Systema Ichthyologiæ, 504, 1801; Long Island, N. Y.
Chilichthys turgidus, Yarrow, 1877, 204; Beaufort.
Cirrisomus turgidus, Jordan & Gilbert, 1879, 366; Beaufort.
Tetrodon turgidus, Jordan, 1886, 30; Beaufort. Jenkins, 1887, 93; Beaufort. Wilson, 1900, 355; Beaufort.
Spheroides maculatus, Jordan & Evermann, 1898, 1733, pl. cclxiv, fig. 645. Linton, 1905, 402; Beaufort.

DIAGNOSIS.—Depth (uninflated) about equal to width, .33 total length; length of head greater than depth of body; snout more than .5 head; eye small, .25 snout; interorbital space concave, 2.6 times diameter of eye; skin prickles small, 3-rooted, stiff, and of uniform size; prickles absent posterior to dorsal fin and vent; fins small; dorsal rays 7, the longest one-third head; anal rays 6, of same size as dorsal; caudal margin slightly convex, the central rays .4 length of head; pectorals rather broad. Color: upper parts rich dark green with black mottlings; below white or pale yellow; sides marked with about 12 short black bars, of unequal size and mostly oblique, the 2 or 3 immediately behind pectorals most distinct; fins plain, caudal dark-edged. (*maculatus,* spotted.)

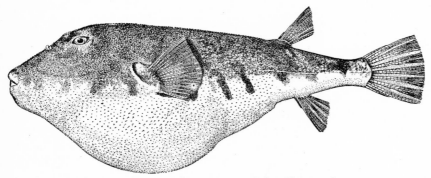

Fig. 156. PUFFER; SWELL-FISH. *Spheroides maculatus.*

"Swell-toad" is the name applied to this and the related species by the North Carolina fishermen. The fish is common as far north as Cape Ann, and is abundant during the warmer months on the coast and in the bays and sounds of this state. Its maximum length is about 10 inches. Specimens examined at Beaufort in July and August by Professor Linton were found to contain a very great variety of animal food, including fragments of oysters, scallops, mussels, razor-clams, gastropods, barnacles, crabs, shrimp, sea-urchins, worms, ascidians, bryozoans, together with seaweeds and watermelon seed. The fish is often caught in nets, and will also take the hook, but has no food value and is regarded as useless.

300. SPHEROIDES SPENGLERI (Bloch).

"Swell-toad"; Puffer; Balloon-fish; Swell-fish.

Tetrodon spengleri Bloch, Ichthyologie, i, 135, pl. 144, 1782; West Indies.
Spheroides spengleri, Jordan & Evermann, 1898, 1732, pl. cclxiv, fig. 644.

DIAGNOSIS.—Shape as in *Spheroides maculatus;* head contained 2.4 times in length; eye rather large, .5 snout and nearly .25 head; interorbital space narrow, slightly concave or flat; skin of body prickly, sometimes smooth; usually a patch of small prickles on middle of back; belly spinous from anterior to vent to chin; head, sides, and tail mostly smooth; small dermal flaps or cirri on sides; young more prickly and with more conspicuous flaps than adult; dorsal rays 7, short, less than twice diameter of eye; anal rays 6, similar to dorsal; caudal less than .5 length of head, the margin rounded. Color: above greenish brown, thickly marked with small light green spots; small black spots on back, and a row of 12 to 16 along middle of side from chin to caudal, these becoming less distinct in adult; belly flesh color; caudal with two dark bars; pectorals yellow. (Named for a Mr. Spengler, who sent the type specimen to Bloch.)

A very widely distributed species, known from the West Indies, Brazil, Canary and Madeira Islands, the Gulf coast of the United States, and recently recorded by the writer from Massachusetts, where it occurs as a straggler in summer. The fish is now reported from North Carolina for the first time, a small specimen having been taken at Beaufort in the summer of 1900. A length of 1 foot is attained by the species.

Genus LAGOCEPHALUS Swainson.   Rabbit-fishes, or Puffers.

Similar to Spheroides, but the dorsal and anal fins longer and falcate, each with 12 to 15 rays; the caudal concave behind; the skin prickles in American species confined to the inflatable abdomen, the skin otherwise smooth and tense; the under side of caudal peduncle with a fold. Size rather large. Two American species. The rabbit-fishes are so called from the resemblance of the snout, mouth, and teeth to those of a rabbit. (*Lagocephalus*, hare head.)

301. LAGOCEPHALUS LÆVIGATUS (Linnæus).

Puffer; Rabbit-fish.

Tetrodon lævigatus Linnæus, Systema Naturæ, ed. xii, 411, 1766; Charleston, S. C.   Yarrow, 1877, 204; Beaufort.
Lagocephalus lævigatus, Jordan & Gilbert, 1879, 366; Beaufort (after Yarrow).   Jordan & Evermann, 1898, 1728, pl. cclxiii, fig. 642; "rare north of Cape Hatteras".   Wilson, 1900, 355; Beaufort.

DIAGNOSIS.—Body elongate, greatest depth .25 length; caudal peduncle slender, its least depth equal to diameter of eye; head contained 3.7 times in length; eye rather large, contained 5.5 times in head, 3 times in snout, and 2.5 times in interorbital space; mouth very small; gill-openings somewhat wider than base of pectorals; skin of belly beset with large, sharp, 3-rooted spines, skin elsewhere very smooth; dorsal rays 13, the anterior much longer than posterior, so that fin is pointed or falcate, its height contained 1.5 times in head, origin of fin midway posterior between edge of eye and base of central caudal rays; anal fin opposite and similar to dorsal, its rays 12, the longest contained 1.75 times in head; caudal fin with deeply concave margin, the longest rays nearly .7 length of head; pectorals broad, .5 length of head. Color: above blackish green, sides and belly silvery white. (*lævigatus*, smoothed.)

This, the largest of the American puffers or swell-fishes, occurs coastwise from Massachusetts to Brazil, but is not common north of Cape Hatteras. The type came from Charleston. There are but few records of the fish in North Carolina waters, owing chiefly to the fact that it has no economic value. Yarrow's note on the species in the Beaufort region in 1871 was as follows:

Found in small streams running through salt marshes; but few seen. Found in nets, and is taken with the hook. Never eaten, being considered poisonous. Size, from 3 to 6 inches.

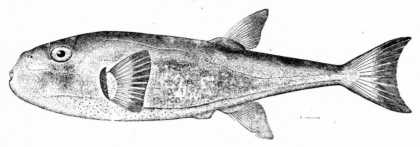

Fig. 157. PUFFER; RABBIT-FISH. *Lagocephalus lævigatus.*

Subsequent collectors recorded the species from that locality only on the authority of Yarrow until 1899, when a specimen 16 inches long was taken in June on Bird Shoal. Another specimen, representing the maximum length attained by the species, was caught on Bird Shoal October 31, 1904, and is now in the Beaufort laboratory; its length is 25.75 inches over all, 21.25 inches long to base of caudal, head 5.75 inches, depth 5.37 inches. The foregoing diagnosis is based on this example. Recently a specimen only 2.25 inches long has been added to the laboratory collection.

Family DIODONTIDÆ. The Porcupine-fishes and Bur-fishes.

Similar to the puffers (Tetraodontidæ), but with the scaleless body thickly beset with conspicuous spines and with the teeth represented by a single bony, beak-like plate in each jaw. Body short, rounded; abdomen inflatable with air or water, but to a less degree than in the puffers; mouth small, terminal, the jaws strong; nostrils tubular, each with 2 openings; gill-opening restricted; spinous processes with 2 or 3 roots, inserted on all parts of the body except about mouth and caudal peduncle; fins small, the pectorals largest; a single dorsal fin, placed posteriorly, opposite anal; caudal rounded; ventrals absent. A rather small family, with weak swimming powers, living mostly on the bottom in warmer seas; of no food value, but often sold as curiosities, the dried distended skins being met with in all parts of the world. Three American genera, 2 with members in North Carolina.

i. Skin prickles long, slender, erectile, and mostly 2-rooted.......................DIODON.
ii. Skin prickles short, blunt, immovable, and mostly 3-rooted ...........CHILOMYCTERUS.

Genus DIODON Linnæus.   Porcupine-fishes.

These are the porcupine-fishes proper, the dermal spines being long, slender, and capable of being erected like those of a porcupine.   Form stout; caudal peduncle rather long and slender; nasal tube simple, with 2 lateral openings; pectorals short, very broad, upper lobe longer.   Probably only 1 American species, occurring on both coasts.   (*Diodon*, double tooth.)

302. DIODON HYSTRIX Linnæus.

Porcupine-fish.

Diodon hystrix Linnæus, Systema Naturæ, ed. x, 335, 1758.   Jordan & Evermann, 1898, 1745, pl. cclxvi, fig. 648.

DIAGNOSIS.—Depth about .4 length; head contained 3 times in length; eye rather small, about .16 length of head; lips thick; skin thickly beset with strong, sharp spines, longest on top of head, back, and sides; the spines posterior to pectorals longest; spines on back anteriorly and on peduncle 3-rooted and immovable, other spines 2-rooted and capable of being depressed and elevated; dorsal rays 13 to 15, height of fin .5 length of head; anal rays 13 to 15; caudal short, rounded; pectorals very broad, rather less than .5 length of head.   Color: dusky above, white below, entire body and fins marked by small round black spots.   (*hystrix*, the porcupine.)

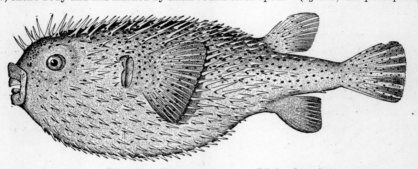

Fig. 158.   PORCUPINE-FISH.   *Diodon hystrix*.

Although the porcupine-fish has been taken at various points on the east coast of the United States as far north as Massachusetts, it occurs only as a straggler north of Florida.   The fish has doubtless been found from time to time by the coast fishermen of North Carolina, but the only specimen known from that state is one 2.5 inches long obtained at Beaufort in the summer of 1902 and now in the fishery laboratory at that place.   The species attains a length of 3 feet.

Genus CHILOMYCTERUS Bibron.   Bur-fishes.

Small marine fishes, with broad, slightly depressed body, covered with short, firmly fixed, 3-rooted spines; short caudal peduncle; 2 nasal tentacles each with 2 lateral openings; small fins, as in Diodon; a few cirri variously placed on head and body.   About 6 American species, 2 represented in the local fauna:

i. Back marked with parallel longitudinal black stripes; under parts pale (sometimes black in
　　young)...*spinosus*.
ii. Entire body marked with black stripes which form hexagonal reticulations, the stripes
　　broader on the under parts...*antillarum*.

303. CHILOMYCTERUS SPINOSUS (Linnæus).

"Swell-toad"; "Lemon-toad"; "Spiny Toad-fish"; Bur-fish.

Diodon spinosus Linnæus, Systema Naturæ, ed. x, 335, 1758; India.*
Diodon schœpfi Walbaum, Artedi Genera Piscium, 601, 1792; Long Island, N. Y.
Chilomycterus geometricus, Yarrow, 1877, 203; Beaufort. Jordan & Gilbert, 1879, 366; Beaufort. Jenkins, 1877, 93; Beaufort. Wilson, 1900, 355; Beaufort.
Chilomycterus schœpfi Jordan, 1886, 30; Beaufort. Jordan & Evermann, 1898, 1748, pl. cclxvi, fig. 649. Linton, 1905, 403; Beaufort.

DIAGNOSIS.—Body short and broad, the depth somewhat less than breadth and .33 total length; depth of caudal peduncle at junction with fin equal to diameter of eye; head less than depth; nasal tentacle as long as pupil; eye large, lateral, about equal to snout; interorbital space concave; gill-slit equal to diameter of eye, opposite upper half of pectoral base; dermal spines broad-based, far apart, and short, their height averaging diameter of pupil; a series of about 9 spines between eye and caudal; 2 supraorbital spines, 1 spine on middle of forehead; spines on abdomen smallest and partly imbedded; a short cirrus above each eye; a fleshy tip on some of the posterior spines; cirri on chin; dorsal rays 12, their tips reaching caudal; anal rays 10; caudal small, lanceolate; pectorals much broader than long, the upper rays longer. Color: greenish above, whitish or pale yellow below (sometimes black in young); back and sides with 10 to 16 black longitudinal stripes about width of interspaces, those on sides becoming oblique; similar narrower stripes on head extending crosswise; a black ocellated spot about size of eye above each pectoral, a larger black spot behind each pectoral, another black spot on each side of back at base of dorsal, and a smaller black spot below it; a narrow dark bar across dorsal fin near its base; fins otherwise plain; iris blue. (*spinosus*, full of spines.)

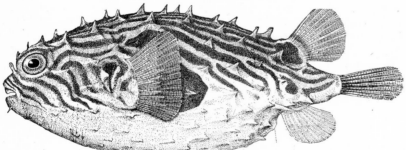

Fig. 159. BUR-FISH; SPINY TOAD-FISH. *Chilomycterus spinosus.*

The fishermen of North Carolina know this species under the names "swell-toad", "lemon-toad", "spiny toad-fish", etc. The fish occurs in the West Indies and along the entire Atlantic coast as far north as Massachusetts, reaching its greatest abundance from Chesapeake Bay to Florida. It is more or less abundant on the shores of North Carolina in summer, and at Beaufort examples are then taken varying in size from 1.5 to 6 inches. The fish reaches Beaufort early in April and remains at least as late as the latter part of October, and probably does not withdraw from the shoal coast waters until the advent of cold weather. A length of 10 inches is sometimes attained. The strong, bony beak enables the fish to crush and eat mollusks and crustaceans, which are its principal food.

* It is more than probable that the bur-fish thus designated by Linnæus is identical with the one called *schœpfi* by Walbaum 34 years later, as suggested by Jordan & Evermann (1898). Linnæus' species is said to differ from Walbaum's only in the absence of lines on the back—a character of too uncertain value in a preserved specimen.

304. CHILOMYCTERUS ANTILLARUM Jordan & Rutter.

Chilomycterus antillarum Jordan & Rutter, Proceedings Academy Natural Sciences, Philadelphia, 1897, 131; Jamaica. Jordan & Evermann, 1898, 1749.

DIAGNOSIS.—Form similar to *spinosus*; a transverse row of short cirri on chin; cirri on nearly all the spines along margin of belly, no cirri above eyes; a spine below and in front of each eye. Color: brown above, yellow below, entire body marked with small hexagonal areas formed by black lines, the lines on abdomen wider; black spots as in *spinosus*, together with black blotches on chin in front of and at each end of the row of cirri. (*antillarum*, of the Antilles.)

A straggler from the West Indies to the east coast of the United States, where it has been observed only at Woods Hole, Mass., and Beaufort, N. C. From the former place the writer recorded 1 specimen in 1898; at Beaufort 1 was taken in a trawl net in the harbor in the summer of 1902, according to Dr. R. E. Coker, and another was caught in the summer of 1904, according to Dr. E. W. Gudger.

Family MOLIDÆ. The Head-fishes.

Large fishes of remarkable appearance, with feeble swimming powers, inhabiting the open sea but frequently seen along the coasts or stranded on the shores. The compressed ovate body is covered with a very thick leathery skin; the posterior part of the body is truncate; the small terminal mouth is armed with a single bony plate in each jaw; the single high dorsal fin is placed far back, and the anal fin is similar to it in shape and position, the caudal fin extending between their posterior margins; the pectoral fins are small and are placed immediately posterior to the very short branchial opening; ventral fins are lacking; and the air-bladder is absent. The young differ much from the adults in form, and have frequently been described under other names. There are several genera and half a dozen known species, but only 1 is recorded from the coasts of the United States.

Genus MOLA Cuvier. Ocean Sun-fishes.

Very large fishes with ovate body and compressed sides; tough, leathery skin without scales; a projecting nose; dorsal and anal fins high, with short base; pectorals short. (*Mola*, a millstone.)

305. MOLA MOLA (Linnæus).

Sun-fish; Head-fish; Moon-fish; Mola.

Tetrodon mola Linnæus, Systema Naturæ, ed. x, 334, 1758; Mediterranean.
Mola mola, Jordan & Evermann, 1898, 1753, pl. cclxviii, fig. 651.

DIAGNOSIS.—Head in adult about .25 total length , depth more than .5 length, the body becoming longer in older examples; eye small, about .16 head; gill-opening about diameter of eye; dorsal and anal fins more than .5 length of body, the rays 16 or 17 in each; caudal fin short and wavy. Color: dark gray or slaty, sides and belly lighter; a more or less distinct dark band extending along bases of posterior fins.

The ocean sunfish is a lazy, clumsy species, with limited swimming powers, and seems content to be borne about listlessly by currents and tides. It occurs regularly as far north as Massachusetts and on the Pacific coast to San Francisco. It also inhabits the Mediterranean, and along the shores of western Europe is not uncommon, the writer having seen stranded specimens in Norway beyond the Arctic Circle.   The species is usually seen floating or swimming at the surface with the dorsal fin out of the water; and it may be easily approached and harpooned.   The fish is probably more common off the east coast of Florida than elsewhere, but is not rare in southern Massachusetts; in Vineyard Sound 8 or 10 large ones have sometimes been observed in a single summer.

Fig. 160.   Sun-fish.   *Mola mola.*

The North Carolina records are few, as follows: A specimen now in the National Museum (no. 41002) was taken at Cape Lookout in 1889 by William H. Gaskill, of the life-saving station at that place.   Another specimen, 24 inches long and 15 inches wide, was found dead on the beach at Cape Lookout about March 15, 1904, by James Willis and was presented by him to the laboratory at Beaufort.   The third example likewise was taken at Cape Lookout, and was one of the largest recorded; it was harpooned by fishermen in May, 1904, and taken ashore in the "bight" of the cape; it was 8 feet long, and was estimated by the fishermen to weigh 1,000 pounds.

The sun-fish attains a weight of 1,500 pounds, and one is recorded from the California coast which is reported to have weighed 1,800 pounds. The powerful turtle-like jaws suggest that the species feeds on hard-shelled creatures, but as a matter of fact jellyfish have proved to be the only food found in a number of specimens examined at Woods Hole, Mass. The fish has no economic value at the present time, although it has been suggested that glue may be made from the abundant subdermal elastic tissue.

Family SCORPÆNIDÆ. The Scorpion-fishes and Rock-fishes.

A numerous and important marine family represented in all parts of the world, but most abundant in the temperate portions of the Pacific Ocean; most of the American species occur on the Pacific coast, where they enter largely into the fisheries. These fishes are of small to moderate size, inhabit rocky bottom, and many produce their young alive. The leading family characters are an oblong, compressed body; a large head with more or less prominent bony ridges terminating in spines; a large terminal mouth with small teeth on jaws and vomer; protractile premaxillary; broad maxillary; wide gill-slits; gill-membranes not united and free from the isthmus; large pseudobranchiæ; opercle and pre-opercle usually spinous; small, usually ctenoid scales completely covering body; a simple lateral line; rather few pyloric cœca; air-bladder present or absent; 2 continuous dorsal fins, the anterior with 8 to 16 spines and longer than soft portion; short anal with 3 spines; caudal well developed, of various shapes; broad pectorals; thoracic ventrals with the rays 1,5. There are about 8 American genera, 5 represented on the Atlantic coast but only 2 in shoal water. Only 1 genus as yet detected in North Carolina waters, but fishes belonging in several other genera occur off that coast.*

Genus SCORPÆNA Linnæus. Scorpion-fishes.

A numerous genus of warm-water fishes with rather elongate, somewhat compressed body; large, rough head; large mouth, with bands of villiform teeth on jaws, vomer, and palatines; 2 pairs of spines on occiput, 2 spines on opercle, and 4 or 5 on preopercle; gill-rakers few in number; ctenoid scales, the top of head more or less naked; body and head more or less thickly beset with short dermal flaps or filaments; air-bladder absent; 12 dorsal spines; rounded caudal; large, broad pectorals, usually with procurrent base; and ventrals arising posterior to pectorals. Rather small fishes of peculiar form and variegated coloration, having little food value; about a dozen American species, some of which stray northward along the Atlantic coast of the United States. The strong dorsal spines can inflict a painful wound, which fact, together with the repulsive appearance, makes these fishes unpopular or even dreaded among fishermen. Besides the 2 following species, several others may be looked for as stragglers:

---

* *Pontinus rathbuni* is known only from off Cape Hatteras in 80 fathoms; *Setarches parmatus* has been taken in the Gulf Stream off North Carolina and other states; and *Helicolenus maderensis* occurs offshore from Cape Hatteras to New York.

i. Lower jaw included; cranial spines and ridges more prominent; a deep pit under anterior margin of orbit; axil jet black, with large white spots; general body color pale, often scarlet, the fins with much red...*plumieri.*
ii. Jaws equal; cranial spines and ridges less prominent; no pit under anterior edge of orbit; axil pale, with a few black spots; general color greenish or brownish, the body and fins never red ....*brasiliensis.*

(*Scorpæna,* a scorpion, in allusion to the sting-like wound inflicted by the spines.)

306. SCORPÆNA PLUMIERI Bloch.

Scorpion-fish.

Scorpæna plumieri Bloch, Kongliga svenska vetenskaps akademien, nya handlingar, Stockholm, x, 234, 1789; Martinique. Jordan & Evermann, 1898, 1848.

DIAGNOSIS.—Body short, the depth contained 3 times in total length; head .4 total length, the surface very irregular, with strong spines and many grooves and pits; a conspicuous pit below eye; lower jaw included; maxillary extending beyond eye, .5 length of head; eye .2 head; gill-rakers very short and broad; scales in lateral line about 40, a few scales on opercle and preopercle but none on other parts of head; numerous fleshy flaps on body and head, a large one over eye and on other parts of head; dorsal rays xii,10, the longest spine but little more than .33 head; anal rays iii,5, the second spine very robust and longer than third; pectorals broad, procurrent, reaching as far as anal origin, the lower 10 or 11 rays simple and exserted. Color: variable; usually sand color or bright red above, purplish below; the body and head marked by several broad black bands; back covered with light specks and white filaments; axil jet black, with large round, white spots; lower part of head finely spotted with blue; angles of mouth yellow; radiating dark spots about eye; fins variegated like body; the dorsal with white spots, the anal and ventrals white with red and black shades, the caudal with 3 black and 3 light vertical bars, the pectorals with tip scarlet and inner surface yellow, black, and red. (Named for Plumier, a priest who collected fishes in Martinique.)

A common species from Florida to Brazil, straggling as far north as Massachusetts, where it has been found by the writer. Six specimens, all about 2 inches long, in the collection of the Beaufort laboratory, were obtained in July and August, 1903, on Bird Shoal and Uncle Israel Shoal.

307. SCORPÆNA BRASILIENSIS Cuvier & Valenciennes.

Scorpion-fish.

Scorpæna brasiliensis Cuvier & Valenciennes, Histoire Naturelle des Poissons, iv, 305, 1829: Brazil. Jordan & Evermann, 1898, 1842, pl. cclxxvii, fig. 670.

DIAGNOSIS.—Body short, the depth .4 length; head compressed, its length equal to greatest depth of body; jaws equal; maxillary extending opposite posterior edge of eye, rather less than .5 head; eye large, equal to snout and more than .25 in head; interorbital space deep, .5 diameter of eye; 2 sharp spines on preorbital, 2 or 3 on suborbital stay, upper preopercular spine long, opercular spines small; scales in lateral line about 55, a few scales on opercles, preopercles, and cheeks; small dermal flaps present on many scales of body, on cheeks, before eyes, at bases of cranial spines, on membrane of spinous dorsal, etc.; a long and slender flap above eye; dorsal rays xii,10, a deep notch between the two parts; anal rays iii,6; caudal rounded; pectorals long, about length of head, extending beyond first anal spine; ventrals .5 length of head, reaching to vent, the last ray attached to abdomen by a membrane. Color: grayish brown, with regular and obscure blackish blotches, one across base of peduncle; white below, axil of pectorals pale, with a few round black spots, similar spots also on sides of body; a fringed white flap on anterior nostril; dorsal and anal fins irregularly marbled; caudal white, with a broad median and a narrow terminal vertical black bar; pectorals obscurely barred; ventrals blackish blue. (*brasiliensis*, inhabiting Brazil.)

Fig. 161. Scorpion-fish. *Scorpæna brasiliensis.*

The foregoing description is based on several specimens, under 2 inches long, taken on Uncle Israel Shoal, Beaufort Harbor, July 20, 1904. The species ranges from Brazil northward, probably occurring regularly as far as Cape Hatteras, although not previously recorded north of South Carolina.

Family COTTIDÆ.   The Sculpins.

The sculpins constitute an exceedingly numerous and varied family, found chiefly along the shores of northern regions; some, however, occur at great depths and some are confined to streams and lakes. The principal characters of the family are a usually broad and depressed head, from which the elongate fusiform or compressed trunk tapers backward to a rather slender peduncle; head either smooth or spiniferous; large mouth, with teeth in bands on jaws; protractile premaxillaries; large eyes, placed high on the head and usually separated by a narrow space; spinous processes usually present on preopercle; suborbital connected with preopercle by a bony stay; united gill-membranes, which are joined to or free from isthmus; 3.5 or 4 gill-arches with short or rudimentary gill-rakers; body naked, partly scaled, or partly covered with prickles or plates; lateral line present; air-bladder usually lacking; pyloric cœca few; dorsal fins either separate or connected, with 6 to 18 usually weak spines and rather numerous soft rays; anal fin without spines; caudal fin truncate or rounded; large pectoral fins with broad base; thoracic ventral fins (rarely absent), with 1 spine and 3 to 5 soft rays. The sculpins have little value as food, but are sometimes eaten and also used as bait; they must, however, be of considerable importance, owing to their wide distribution, and some of them are known to be very destructive to fish eggs. Of the 50 or more American genera only 1 is represented in the state.

Genus COTTUS Linnæus.   Fresh-water Sculpins; Miller's Thumbs; Blobs.

Small, numerous, and variable sculpins of the colder fresh waters of North America, Asia, and Europe; often abundant in trout streams and feeding largely on trout eggs in season.   Form elongate, little if at all compressed, head with few spines; teeth on jaws, vomer, and (sometimes) palatines; isthmus very wide, the gill-membranes not passing across it; a simple spine at angle of preopercle, usually several spines below and a single concave spine on subopercle; skin smooth, sometimes with feeble prickles; lateral line sometimes deficient; pyloric cœca about 4; dorsal fins separated or joined, the spines slender, 6 to 9 in number; ventrals with 4 soft rays and a concealed spine.   Of the numerous American species, only 1 is recognized as inhabiting any of the waters of North Carolina. (*Cottus*, an old name for the miller's thumb of Europe.)

308. COTTUS ICTALOPS (Rafinesque).

Blob; Miller's Thumb; Mull-head (Va.).

Pegedictis ictalops Rafinesque, Ichthyologia Ohiensis, 85, 1820; Kentucky.
Potamocottus carolinæ Gill, Proceedings Boston Society of Natural History, 1861, 40; Carolina.
Cottus ictalops, Jordan & Evermann, 1898, 1950.   Bean, 1903, 914; Bollings Creek, N. C.
Cottus bairdi, Jordan, 1889*b*, 154; South Fork of Swannanoa River and Spring Creek at Hot Springs, N. C.
Uranidea carolinæ, Cope, 1870*b*, 455; French Broad River, Madison County, N. C.

DIAGNOSIS.—Form robust; depth about .25 length; head .33 length; palatine teeth well developed; isthmus very broad; skin smooth, no axillary prickles; lateral line continuous or interrupted; dorsal rays VI,16 to VIII,17, the spinous rays low and weak; anal rays 12; pectorals large, nearly as long as head, and reaching to or beyond origin of soft dorsal.   Color: olivaceous, with dark bars and spots; fins dark barred or mottled.   (*ictalops*, having an eye like a cat-fish.)

A species of wide distribution and great variability; ranging from New York to the Dakotas and along the Alleghanies to Alabama.   Known only from tributaries of the French Broad River in North Carolina, but doubtless occurring also in the headwaters of the Holston and other streams on the western slope of the mountains.   Reaches a length of 6 inches, and is a very undesirable inhabitant of the trout streams.

Family TRIGLIDÆ.   The Sea-robins or Gurnards.

The sea-robins are found in the tropical and temperate regions of both hemispheres, and some forms occur in great abundance in America, Europe, and Asia.   The most striking family features are the head completely enclosed in strong bony plates, the wing-like pectoral fins, and the conversion of the 3 lowermost pectoral rays into long, slender, detached feelers.   Body elongate, fusiform, deepest at junction with head; head large and more or less spiny; mouth large, mostly terminal, with bands of small teeth on jaws and sometimes on vomer and palatines; premaxillaries protractile; maxillary slipping under preorbital; no supplementary maxillary; gill-arches 4, gill-rakers various, gill-membranes not attached to isthmus; lateral line present; body covered with scales or bony plates; air-bladder and usually pyloric cœca present; 2 dorsal fins, the spinous short and beginning far forward; anal fin without spines, similar to second dorsal; caudal rather long; ventral fins thoracic, wide apart, their rays 1,5. The genera are few, and only 1 genus is represented on the shores of the United States.

Genus PRIONOTUS Lacépède. Sea-robins; American Gurnards.

The sea-robins are among the most numerous and best known of the shore fishes of the east coast. Their principal anatomical characters are: Body more or less round in section, tapering regularly backward from shoulder to slender caudal peduncle; head entirely covered with bony plates, which have granulations, ridges, and spines; snout broad, depressed, and much longer than eye; mouth broad, terminal, with bands of small teeth on jaws, vomer, and palatines; the spines on head definitely placed, 1 on opercle, 1 or 2 at angle of preopercle, 2 on nape, and 1 on shoulder girdle; gill-membranes free from isthmus; gill-rakers rather long and numerous; lateral line continuous; small, regularly arranged rough scales completely covering body, only a few on head; pyloric cœca present in moderate number; air-bladder rather large, with a specialized muscle attached to its external surface; vertebræ about 25; dorsal fins separate, the first with 8 to 10 strong spines, the second longer and similar to anal; caudal rather long; pectorals broad, wing-like, the 3 anterior rays separated from others, long, thickened, free from each other, and developed as flexible tactile organs.

The species are of small size, rarely exceeding a foot in length. They live mostly on the bottom, using their finger-like pectoral rays very dexterously in finding food. They are able to make a grunting sound by the action of the air-bladder, and are hence called pig-fish in some localities.

The flesh is white and of good flavor, but these fishes are rarely eaten, although the closely related gurnards of Europe (Trigla) are food fishes of some importance. Immense quantities of sea-robins are caught in pound nets, seines, and other nets along the entire Atlantic coast from Massachusetts southward, but no use is made of them except as compost. More than 20 species are known from our coasts; 9 from the eastern seaboard of the United States; and 4 from North Carolina, all the local species being known as "flying-fish" or "flying-toad" among the fishermen.

Key to the North Carolina species of sea-robins.

i. Head large, more than .3 total length; mouth relatively large, the maxillary at least .4 length head; pectoral at least .5 length of body; free rays of pectoral tapering, not expanded at tip.
    a. No distinct spine on cheek bone at center of radiation nor on edge of preorbital; head of moderate width, the spines except those on nape not prominent; gill-rakers long and slender, 18 to 20 developed on lower arm of first arch; depth of body more than .2 total length; pectorals dark green......................................*evolans.*
    aa. A distinct spine on cheek bone at center of radiation, and a preorbital spine with a smaller one at base; head very broad, with high, knife-like spines; gill-rakers shorter and thicker, about 10 developed on lower arm of first arch; depth of body .2 total length; pectorals light green...*tribulus.*
ii. Head smaller, its length less than .3 total length; mouth relatively small, the maxillary less than .4 length of head; pectoral less than .5 total length of body; free rays of pectoral expanded.
    b. Body very slender, the depth about .16 total length; dorsal spines high, the third contained 1.6 times in head; caudal fin square behind; general color olive, with numerous round bronze or reddish spots on back and sides, a black spot on spinous dorsal, soft dorsal and caudal sometimes black or dark brown....................*scitulus.*

bb. Body less slender, the depth about .22 total length; dorsal spines low, the third less than .5 length of head; caudal fin moderately forked; general color dark olive, without well defined spots, some dark mottling on back and 4 obscure dark blotches, the fins plain except for a black spot on first dorsal, pectorals reddish...............*carolinus.*

(*Prionotus,* saw back.)

309. PRIONOTUS EVOLANS (Linnæus).

"Flying-fish"; "Flying-toad"; "Striped Flying-toad"; Sea-robin.

Trigla evolans Linnæus, Systema Naturæ, ed. xii, 498, 1766; Carolina.
Prionotus evolans, Jordan & Gilbert, 1879, 373; Beaufort. Jordan, 1886, 28; Beaufort. Jenkins, 1887, 91; Beaufort. Jordan & Evermann, 1898, 2168, pl. cccxx, fig. 772; North and South Carolina.

DIAGNOSIS.—Depth of body contained about 4.5 to 4.75 times in total length; narrowest part of caudal peduncle less than diameter of eye; head contained 2.6 times in total length; maxillary .4 length of head; eye large, rather less than .5 snout; interorbital space less than diameter of eye; pores in lateral line about 53; scales in transverse series from last dorsal spine to vent about 30; dorsal rays x + 12, the first spine only weakly serrate, the longest spines and soft rays about equal and same length as maxillary; anal rays 11; caudal .5 length of head; the posterior margin nearly straight; pectorals more than .5 total length of body (occasionally in North Carolina specimens nearly .66 total length). Color: back greenish brown, sides light green, usually with small irregular whitish spots; back with 3 brownish crossbars, the third extending to base of posterior soft rays; sides and head marked by narrow lengthwise brown stripes along lateral line, from shoulder spine to opposite end of anal fin, with a fainter one above, and from angle of mouth to preopercular spine; belly white; branchiostegal membrane yellow; opercle brown; anterior dorsal dusky, with a black spot between fourth and sixth spines; anal reddish; caudal mostly orange, with transverse lines of white and brown toward base; pectorals lustrous green on inner surface with upper rays white and lower red, olive on outer surface with a narrow blue edge; ventrals pale red. (*evolans,* flying out.)

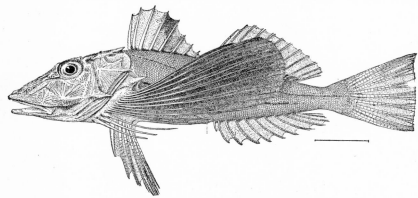

Fig. 162. STRIPED SEA-ROBIN. *Prionotus evolans.*

Known only from the coast of North and South Carolina, where it is abundant in places. For the Beaufort region it was not listed by Yarrow, was recorded as abundant by Jordan and Gilbert and common by Jenkins, but has not recently been reported and no specimens appear to have reached the Beaufort laboratory.

310. PRIONOTUS TRIBULUS (Cuvier).

"Flying-fish"; "Flying-toad"; Big-headed Gurnard; Sea-robin.

Trigla tribulus Cuvier, Regne Animal, ed. 2, vol, 2, 161, 1829; America.
Prionotus tribulus, Jordan & Gilbert, 1879, 373; Beaufort. Jordan, 1886, 28; Beaufort. Jenkins, 1887, 91; Beaufort. Kendall & Smith, 1894, 21; Hatteras Inlet. Jordan & Evermann, 1898, 2171; Beaufort, etc. Linton, 1905, 404; Beaufort.

DIAGNOSIS.—Depth .2 total length of body; head broad, .4 total length; spines and striations on head very strong; maxillary rather less than .5 length of head; pores on lateral line about 50; dorsal rays ix or x + 12 or 13; anal rays 11; pectorals .5 length of body, shorter in young. Color: back light green with dark green reticulations; sides with a bright orange lateral band; under parts white; 2 dark bands below spinous dorsal; anterior dorsal with obscure dark bars and a large black spot between fifth and sixth spines; posterior dorsal dull reddish, with dark spots; anal similar to soft dorsal; caudal reddish brown, with 3 dark cross-bars; inner surface of pectorals grayish, outer surface light green, with 4 or 5 dark crossbands; free pectorals rays red, barred with dark; ventrals light red. (*tribulus*, scraping.)

The big-headed gurnard ranges from New York to Texas, and is common at Beaufort and on other parts of the North Carolina coast. It is distinguishable from the other local species by the very broad and spinous head, the spines being longer and sharper in the young. The diet is varied, and embraces all kinds of living animals of suitable size; examples examined by Professor Linton at Beaufort in July and August had eaten fish, worms, crabs, fiddler crabs, shrimp, amphipods, copepods, horse-shoe crabs, bivalve mollusks, and sea urchins.

311. PRIONOTUS SCITULUS Jordan & Gilbert.

"Flying-fish"; "Flying-toad"; "Slim Flying-toad"; Sea-robin.

Prionotus scitulus Jordan & Gilbert, Proceedings U. S. National Museum, 1882, 288; Beaufort, N. C. Jordan, 1886, 28; Beaufort. Jordan & Evermann, 1898, 2157, pl. cccxix, fig. 769; Beaufort to St. Augustine, Linton, 1905, 404; Beaufort.
Prionotus punctatus, Yarrow, 1877, 207; Beaufort. Jordan & Gilbert, 1879, 373; Beaufort.

Fig. 163. SLENDER SEA-ROBIN. *Prionotus scitulus.*

DIAGNOSIS.—Form very slender, the depth much less than .2 total length; caudal peduncle much wider than eye; head small, contained 2.75 to 3.6 in total length; mouth small, maxillary short, less than .3 length of head; snout long, .5 head; eye small, .3 snout; interorbital area concave, narrower than eye; spines on top of head short, sharp; gill-rakers long, slender; pores in lateral line 52: dorsal rays x + 13, the spines high, the longest (third) equal to distance from pupil to end of snout, the soft rays low and of uniform length; anal rays 12; caudal square behind; pectorals in male .4 to .5 length of body, in female .33. Color: Male—above light greenish brown, with 4 dark blotches on back; sides spotted with reddish brown; opercle reddish brown, branchiostegal membrane black; dorsal fins greenish brown, a black spot on membrane between fourth and fifth spines, both fins with translucent streaks; anal dark, the base and edge white; caudal reddish, with narrow white longitudinal streaks; pectorals dark brown, with irregular light brown and green markings; free rays of pectorals and ventrals orange-tinged. Female—above dark green, back and sides thickly spotted with bronze; branchiostegal membranes pink; spinous dorsal dusky with light streaks, a black ocellated spot between fourth and fifth spines, a similar spot on upper part of first spine and membrane; second dorsal and caudal spotted with black; anal black; ventrals pale. (*scitulus*, slender.)

This small species, although reported as tolerably abundant at Beaufort by Yarrow, was represented by only 2 specimens in the collections of Jordan and Jenkins. Recently it has been found in great abundance in the Beaufort region in summer. Upwards of a dozen fish examined by Professor Linton in August (1901 and 1902) contained fish, crustaceans, and bivalve and univalve mollusks. The species attains a length of only 6 inches, and is the smallest of the local sea-robins. Jordan & Gilbert record the local vernacular name of "slim flying-toad" in allusion to its very slender form.

312. PRIONOTUS CAROLINUS (Linnæus).

"Flying-fish"; "Flying-toad"; Sea-robin.

Trigla carolina Linnæus, Mantissa Plantarum, ii, 528, 1771; Carolina.
Prionotus carolinus, Yarrow, 1877, 207; Beaufort. Jordan & Evermann, 1898, 2153, pl. cccxviii, fig. 768; Maine to South Carolina.

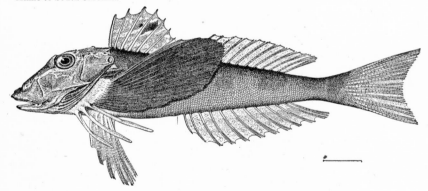

Fig. 164. CAROLINA SEA-ROBIN. *Prionotus carolinus*.

DIAGNOSIS.—Form slender, but much less so than in *Prionotus scitulus*, the depth less than .2 total length; depth of caudal peduncle equal to eye; bones of head comparatively smooth, the spines low; head contained 3 times in total length; mouth small, maxillary less than .33 length of head; snout .5 head; eye rather large, .4 snout; gill-rakers of moderate length, about 10 on lower arm of first arch; pores in lateral line about 58; dorsal rays x + 13, the spines low, the longest (third) not .5 length of head; anal rays 12; caudal slightly forked; pectorals short, rounded, not as much as .5 length of body. Color: brownish above, with dark mottlings and about 4 obscure dark crossbars; white below; throat and branchiostegal membranes blackish; a black ocellus between fourth and fifth dorsal spines, and several pale streaks below the spot; whitish oblique streaks on second dorsal; pectorals reddish brown.

Jordan & Gilbert (1879) regarded the species called *Prionotus carolinus* by Yarrow as probably not that species but *Prionotus tribulus;* they, as well as Jenkins, failed to find the fish at Beaufort.   In the summer of 1903 about 25 specimens were taken on Bird Shoal and elsewhere in Beaufort Harbor, and in Bogue Sound; and in 1904 the fish was frequently taken in June, July, and August in the vicinity of the laboratory.   One foot is about the maximum length of the species; but the Beaufort specimens have not averaged nearly so large.   The spawning season is spring, and the eggs are bright orange in color.   The young are abundant in summer.

Family CEPHALACANTHIDÆ.   The Flying Gurnards.

This family is related to the Triglidæ, differing in the shape of the pectoral fin, the absence of "feelers", the broad union of the gill-membranes with the isthmus, the closeness together of the ventral fins, the ventral rays being 1,4, as well as in numerous bony characters.   Body elongate, rather broad, sides flattened; head blunt, quadrangular, nearly the entire surface bony; mouth small, lower jaw included, granular teeth in jaws, no teeth on roof of mouth; bones about eye united into a shield; a long bony process ending in a sharp spine extending backward from the nape on each side beyond origin of dorsal fin; preorbital projecting beyond the jaws; preopercle extending backward as a long, round spine beyond ventrals; opercle small; gill-slits narrow, gill-rakers small, pseudobranchiæ large; body covered with small, keeled, bony scales, which occur also on opercles and cheeks; 2 serrated spines at base of tail; pyloric cœca numerous; air-bladder divided into 2 lateral halves; dorsal fins separated, the anterior with 7 flexible spines, the posterior and anal with a few slender rays; caudal rather broad; pectorals large, divided into 2 lengthwise sections, the posterior part much the longer; ventrals long and pointed.   The family contains 1 genus, with a single representative in American waters.

Genus CEPHALACANTHUS Lacépède.   Flying Gurnards.

The generic characters are indicated in the family diagnosis.   In the adults the pectoral fins are much longer than in the young, and reach nearly to base of caudal; the anterior part of the fin contains a few closely connected rays as long as head; the posterior part is made up of numerous slender, unbranched rays. The flying gurnards possess the power of flight like the true flying-fishes, but to a much less degree.   (*Cephalacanthus*, head spine.)

313. CEPHALACANTHUS VOLITANS (Linnæus).

"Flying-fish"; Flying-robin.

Trigla volitans Linnæus, Systema Naturæ, ed, x. 1, 302, 1753; Mediterranean Sea and ocean within the tropics.
Dactylopterus volitans, Jordan & Gilbert, 1879, 372; Beaufort Harbor.
Cephalacanthus volitans, Jordan, 1886, 28; Beaufort. Jenkins, 1887, 91; Beaufort. Jordan & Evermann, 1898, 2183, pl. cccxxiii, fig. 778.

DIAGNOSIS.—Depth somewhat less than .2 total length; caudal peduncle slender, its depth less than diameter of eye; head short, contained about 4.5 in total length, the profile steep and straight; maxillary extending as far as anterior margin of orbit; eye large, about .75 snout; preopercular spine nearly as long as head, not reaching beyond nuchal spine; dorsal rays VII+8, the 2 anterior spines separated from the others and connected at their bases by membrane, the last spine very short; both dorsal fins rather high, the posterior higher, its longest rays about equal to depth of body; anal rays 6, the fin similar to soft dorsal; caudal concave behind; pectoral rays about 34, the upper section with 6 rays; ventrals about length of head. Color: variable; above irregularly marked with different shades of green and brown; pale below, with blotches of red and yellow; spinous dorsal with several dark bars; caudal with 3 vertical reddish bars; pectorals marked with blue streaks, bars, and spots, their under surface glistening blue. (*volitans*, flying.)

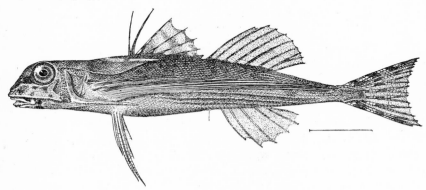

Fig. 165. FLYING GURNARD. *Cephalacanthus volitans.*

Although Jordan & Gilbert found this species rather common at Beaufort in 1878 and Jenkins reported it as common in 1885, it had not recently been met with in that region until the summer of 1904, when 1 was collected by Dr. E. W. Gudger. Another was seined on Bird Shoal August 5, 1905, by Mr. C. B. Wilson. It occurs regularly, but in limited numbers, as far north as Massachusetts, and ranges thence southward along the entire coast, being most numerous on the shores of the South Atlantic and Gulf States. The North Carolina fishermen call this species "flying-fish". It reaches a length of a foot, and is very singular in appearance and interesting in habits.

Family GOBIIDÆ. The Gobies.

The gobies form an exceedingly large and diversified family of carnivorous fishes, found in the warmer waters of all parts of the world. They are for the most part small and live upon the bottom, in both fresh and salt water. Some species are blind. A few are of economic importance. The American genera number more than 30 and the species nearly 100. The family characters are: Rather elongate body; mouth small, moderate or large with protractile premaxillaries and teeth of various kinds; gills 4, gill-membranes united to the isthmus; opercle without spines, preopercle with a short spine or none; pseudobranchiæ present; pyloric cœca absent; air-bladder usually lacking; skin either naked or scaly, the scales cycloid or ctenoid; lateral line absent; fins of a great variety of shapes; 2 dorsal fins, which are either separate or connected, the spinous part less developed than the other, the spines 2 to 8 (rarely absent); anal similar to soft dorsal, usually with a weak spine; caudal rounded or pointed, not concave or forked; pectorals large or small; ventrals thoracic, the rays 1,5, the fins either close together or united, if the latter a fold of skin across base forms a kind of sucking cup. The species now known in the state fall in 4 genera, as follows:

Key to the North Carolina genera of gobies.

i. Ventral fins not united; body covered with large scales................DORMITATOR.
ii. Ventral fins united; scales if present small or moderate.
   a. Dorsal spines 6...CTENOGOBIUS.
  aa. Dorsal spines 7 or 8.
     b. Body more or less scaly, head naked; soft dorsal and anal rays 15 to 17; size minute.
                                                 MICROGOBIUS.
    bb. Body and head without scales; soft dorsal and anal rays 10 to 14; size small.
                                                GOBIOSOMA.

Genus DORMITATOR Gill. Puñecas.

Form rather stout; head broad and flat; mouth small, oblique; no vomerine teeth; preopercle without spine; scales on body and opercles large, ctenoid, those on cheeks small; all fins large, the second dorsal high. Apparently only a single, variable species. (*Dormitator*, a sleeper.)

314. DORMITATOR MACULATUS (Bloch).

Guavina; Spotted Goby.

Sciæna maculata, Bloch Ichthyologie, pl. 299, fig. 2, 1790; West Indies.
Dormitator maculatus, Jordan & Evermann, 1898, p. 2196, pl. cccxxiv, fig. 782.

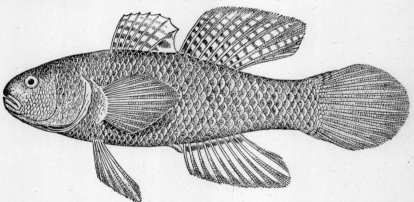

Fig. 166. SPOTTED GOBY. *Dormitator maculatus.*

DIAGNOSIS.—Body stout, the depth about .33 length; head short and broad, a little more than .25 total length; lower jaw very slightly longer than upper; maxillary extending about to anterior edge of eye; snout blunt, rounded, longer than diameter of the small eye; scales in lateral series about 33, in transverse series 12; dorsal rays VII+1,8 or 9, the posterior soft rays longer than head; anal rays 1,9 or 10, the fin somewhat smaller than soft dorsal; caudal broad and rounded; pectorals broad, their length less than head; ventrals reaching to vent. Color: dark gray or brown, with lighter spots; a large black spot above base of pectoral; a dark streak along side; dark streaks on head; branchiostegal membrane black; dorsal fins with several series of dark spots; anal with bluish bars and a white margin. (*maculatus*, spotted.)

Mr. William P. Seal collected a number of small specimens of this species in fresh water near Wilmington in the winter of 1905–6, and thus extended its known range, South Carolina heretofore being the most northern state from which it was recorded. The fish is found in fresh and brackish waters as far south as Brazil, and is also known from the west coast of Mexico and Central America. It reaches a length of several feet, and is eaten in some countries.

Genus CTENOGOBIUS Gill. Gobies.

A very numerous genus of small fishes found in both salt and fresh waters in all parts of the world. The body is elongate and compressed; the head is rather long and more or less depressed; the mouth is of moderate size, with several series of conical teeth in jaws; the eye is anterior to middle of head; the scales are of moderate or rather small size, ctenoid, not deciduous, sometimes absent from nape, breast, and cheeks; dorsal fins separate, the anterior with 6 weak spines; soft dorsal and anal long; caudal pointed; pectorals well developed; ventrals united, not adnate to abdomen. Besides the following species known from the shore waters of North Carolina, several others range as far northward as Charleston, S. C., and may in time be detected in this state. (*Ctenogobius*, comb goby; in allusion to the ctenoid scales.)

315. CTENOGOBIUS STIGMATICUS (Poey).

"Scallop-fish"; Goby.

Smaragdus stigmaticus Poey, Memorias, ii, 281, 1861; Cuba.
Gobius stigmaticus, Jordan & Evermann, 1898, 2224, pl. cccxxvi, fig. 787; North Carolina to Brazil.
Gobius encæomus Jordan & Gilbert, Proceedings U. S. National Museum, 1882, 611; Charleston, S. C. Jenkins, 1885; Beaufort. Jordan & Eigenmann, Proceedings U. S. National Museum, 1886, 496; Beaufort. Jenkins, 1887, 91; Beaufort. Jordan & Evermann, 1898, 2223.
Gobionellus encæomus, Jordan, 1886, 28; Beaufort.

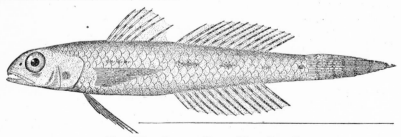

Fig. 167. GOBY. *Ctenogobius stigmaticus*.

DIAGNOSIS.—Form very elongate, the depth .16 length; head slightly compressed, .25 length; mouth low, horizontal, comparatively large, the maxillary .4 length of head and extending to a point under pupil; height of cheeks less than eye; eye high, less than .3 length of head; interorbital space less than .3 diameter of eye; snout short, obtuse, its length less than eye; scales large, strongly ctenoid, 27 to 33 in lengthwise series; nape, head, and breast naked; dorsal fins contiguous, the rays VI + 11 or 12, the spines high (longest .6 head); soft dorsal and anal long and high, reaching the base of caudal when depressed; anal rays 12 or 13; caudal lanceolate, the middle rays longer than head; pectorals about as long as head; ventrals somewhat shorter. Color: Male—light green, with dark mottlings above; sides with 4 to 6 dark blotches; a large, distinct bluish-black spot on each side of nape; several rows of brown spots on each dorsal; 4 to 6 irregular brown vertical bars on caudal; lower fins dusky. Female —duller; sides with a row of elongated dark spots, the light bars absent or faint. (*stigmaticus*, spotty.)

This little species inhabits sandy bays from North Carolina to Florida, and is apparently common about Beaufort. Jenkins reports that he "obtained about 30 specimens with considerable difficulty", and notes the local name of "scallop-fish". Numerous specimens about 1.25 inches long were seined on Uncle Israel Shoal in January, 1905. The maximum length is 2 inches. The species is subject to considerable variation in form and color, depending on size, sex, and locality. The form called *encæomus* does not appear to be distinct from *stigmaticus*.

Genus MICROGOBIUS Poey. Gobies.

Very small shore fishes, with elongate, more or less compressed body; large and very oblique mouth, the lower jaw prominent; strong teeth; small cycloid or weakly ctenoid scales; 7 or 8 dorsal spines; and 15 to 18 soft dorsal and anal rays. Four species are now known from the coast between Virginia and Texas, and several others occur in the West Indies; therefore, in addition to the 2 following, several other species may be looked for in North Carolina:

i. Body strongly compressed; depth contained 5 times in length; caudal fin much longer than head; color green; anal fin with a row of distinct black spots on margin; no distinct black spot on spinous dorsal...*holmesi.*
ii. Body slightly compressed; depth contained 5.5 times in length; caudal fin equal to head; color yellow or light brown; no black spots on anal fin; a distinct black spot on spinous dorsal...*eulepis.*

(*Microgobius*, small goby.)

317. MICROGOBIUS HOLMESI Smith, new species.

Holmes' Goby.

DIAGNOSIS.—Form elongate, the body greatly compressed, the depth greatest over base of pectorals where it is .2 length; caudal peduncle very short, broad, its greatest depth equal to its length and more than .5 body depth; head comparatively large, contained 3.6 times in length of body, slightly compressed, its width somewhat less than its depth, which is .66 its length; eye placed high and directed upward and outward, contained 3.4 times in head; eyes separated by a deep narrow groove; interorbital space very narrow, .3 width of pupil; snout about .7 eye and less than .25 head; mouth large, strong, very oblique; lower jaw projecting, its tip nearly on level with lower edge of pupil; maxillary extending to point under anterior margin of pupil, its length nearly .5 head; teeth in a narrow band in each jaw; cheek large, its height greater than diameter of eye and about .3 length of head; scales cycloid, non-deciduous, rather small, largest on posterior part of body and gradually becoming smaller anteriorly; head, nape, and breast naked; scales, in lateral line about 48, in transverse line between the origin of second dorsal and anal 11 or 12; dorsal fins distinct, the rays VII + 16, the first and last soft rays unbranched; spinous dorsal begins behind posterior margin of opercle a distance equal to diameter of pupil, all the rays slender and high, the longest more than .8 head; origin of soft dorsal directly over vent, the rays of nearly uniform height, .5 head, the base of the fin more than .5 trunk, the last rays reaching beyond base of outer caudal rays; anal fin directly under soft dorsal and of same length, but the rays 18 in number and somewhat shorter; caudal large, broad, and pointed, its length greater than head; pectorals very broad, their insertion slightly in advance of dorsal, their broad base equal to .5 length of head, their length about equal to head and extending beyond origin of anal; ventrals large, nearly as long as head, reaching to anus, the basal membrane very well developed and nearly .33 length of fin.   Color: body and head uniformly pale clear green, each scale with a fine dark edge; anterior half of body marked by 5 or 6 pale, narrow, vertical crossbars, widest anteriorly, placed at irregular intervals; a similar bar at base of caudal; spinous dorsal with 4 oblique rows of dark spots on membranes; soft dorsal with 5 or 6 similar rows of spots; anal dusky, the distal margin of each membrane except the first, sixteenth, and seventeenth having a vertically elongated distinct black spot in a clear area, these spots forming a regular row; caudal, pectorals, and ventrals dusky.

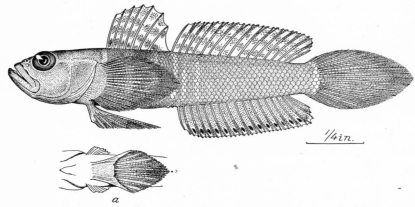

Fig. 168. HOLMES' GOBY. *Microgobius holmesi.* *a.* Ventrals fins viewed from below.

Type, a specimen 1.75 inches long taken on Uncle Israel Shoal, Beaufort Harbor, July 20, 1904, by Dr. E. W. Gudger.

Named for Prof. J. A. Holmes, former state geologist of North Carolina, now associated with the U. S. Geological Survey.

This species resembles *Microgobius thalassinus* Jordan & Gilbert, from Charleston, S. C., but differs in having a much deeper caudal peduncle, a projecting lower jaw, shorter maxillary, smaller eye, no filamentous dorsal spines, shorter caudal fin, more numerous anal rays, shorter ventrals, persistent scales, and in color of dorsal, caudal, and anal fins, body, and head.

From *Microgobius eulepis* Eigenmann & Eigenmann, from Fortress Monroe, Va., this species may be distinguished by its rather larger head, deeper and much more compressed body, longer snout, longer caudal fin, absence of a sharply defined black spot on spinous dorsal fin, and various other characters of form and color.

Only a single specimen is as yet known, but other examples will no doubt be collected at Beaufort and other points.

317. MICROGOBIUS EULEPIS Eigenmann & Eigenmann.
Goby.

Microgobius eulepis Eigenmann & Eigenmann, Proceedings California Academy of Science, 1888, 69; Fortress
     Monroe, Va.   Jordan & Evermann, 1898, 2244.

DIAGNOSIS.—Body scarcely compressed, depth contained 5.5 times in length; head .25
length, its depth .75 length; eye large, .28 length of head; interorbital as wide as pupil; snout
short, broad, .2 length of head; preorbital narrower than pupil; mouth oblique, maxillary not
reaching to anterior margin of pupil; teeth in both jaws in a narrow band, some of them
enlarged; scales rather large, crowded anteriorly, the breast, nape, and spinous dorsal region
naked, number in lateral series 50, in transverse series 14; dorsal rays VII + 15 to VII + 17, the
longest spine .66 length of head; anal rays 16 or 17; caudal .25 length of body; pectorals and
ventrals about as long as head.   Color; yellow or very light brown without bars or stripes, the
scales on back with dark margin; a light vertical bar on preopercle; a sharply defined black
spot on upper part of spinous dorsal between fourth and fifth spines; other fins plain. (*eulepis*,
well scaled.)

Up to this time this species has been known only from the type specimen,
1.87 inches long, collected at Fortress Monroe, Virginia.   During 1905 a number
of specimens were seined by Charles Hatsel on sandy shoals in Beaufort Harbor;
4 were taken in February on Uncle Israel Shoal, and another on May 18.   The
last, 1.5 inches long, is a female distended with nearly ripe eggs; the mouth is
much more vertical than in the preceding species and the snout is shorter; and
the black spot on spinous dorsal is very distinct.

Genus GOBIOSOMA Girard.   Naked Gobies.

These gobies reach a length of only 2 or 3 inches, and are easily recognizable
by the entire absence of scales, combined with a rather elongate body, small to
large mouth with jaw teeth in several rows, the outer teeth larger, normally 7
dorsal spines, and united ventral fins.   Several species in West Indies and on
our southern coasts, but only 1 ranging as far northward as North Carolina.
(*Gobiosoma*, having the body of *Gobius*.)

318. GOBIOSOMA BOSCI (Lacépède).
Naked Goby.

Gobius bosci Lacépède, Histoire Naturelle des Poissons, ii, 555, pl. 16, fig. 1, 1798; Charleston, S. C.
Gobiosoma bosci, Jenkins, 1885, Beaufort.   Jordan, 1886, 28; Beaufort.   Jenkins, 1887, 91; Beaufort.   Jordan
     and Evermann, 1898, 2259.

DIAGNOSIS.—Depth .16 to .20 total length; head broad, flat, .33 total length; mouth
large, jaws equal; teeth in a few rows, some of them enlarged and canine, teeth smaller in
female; maxillary extending to posterior third of eye; cheeks tumid; eye .2 head and wider
than snout; dorsal rays vii + 14, the spines slender; anal rays 10; caudal rounded; ventrals
forming a sucking disk.   Color: greenish, with 7 or 8 pale transverse bars and dark shades; fins
barred. (Named for M. Bosc, French consul at Charleston.)

This fish ranges from Cape Cod to Florida and is common in suitable localities on the coast of North Carolina; it was first recorded from Beaufort by Jenkins (1885), and has recently been obtained at the same place, specimens being
preserved in the government laboratory there.   The fish lives on the bottom in
shallow bays, and is often found in empty oyster shells.   Its length is 2.5 inches.

Family ECHENEIDIÆ.   The Remoras.

These fishes are instantly recognized by the presence of a large, oval disk on the top of the head by means of which they adhere firmly to sharks and other fishes as well as to turtles, boats, and other objects.   The disk, which is a modified spinous dorsal fin, is divided by numerous crosswise partitions, or laminæ, and by a single lengthwise septum, and is of a leathery consistency.   Other characters of the family are elongate or slender body; wide mouth; projecting lower jaw; bands of fine teeth on jaws, vomer, and palatines; no opercular armature; 4 gill-arches, with short gill-rakers; gill-membranes not connected and free from isthmus; 7 branchiostegals; body covered with minute cycloid scales; no air-bladder; a few pyloric cœca; long and low dorsal and anal fins, rather large caudal of variable shape; upper edge of pectoral base near the back; and thoracic ventrals.   Four genera are represented in American waters, all occurring on the east coast of the United States, but only 2, as follows, are as yet known from North Carolina:

i. Form stouter; lower jaw not produced as a flap; laminæ 13 to 18; soft dorsal and anal rays 22 to 32; pectorals rounded; ventrals broadly attached to abdomen .... ECHENEIS.
ii. Form very slender; lower jaw produced as a flap; laminæ 20 to 28; soft dorsal and anal rays 31 to 40; pectorals sharp-pointed; ventrals narrowly attached to abdomen.
LEPTECHENEIS.

Genus ECHENEIS Linnæus.   Remoras; Shark-suckers.

Body comparatively stout; disk relatively short, with 13 to 18 laminæ; soft dorsal with 22 to 32 rays; anal rays 22 to 30; caudal margin square or slightly concave; pectorals short, rounded; ventrals rather short, and broadly adnate to abdomen.   Three widely distributed species, 2 known from the east coast as far north as Cape Cod, but only 1 recorded from the state.   (*Echeneis*, one that holds back a ship.)

319. ECHENEIS REMORA Linnæus.

"Sucker"; Remora.

Echeneis remora Linnæus, Systema Naturæ, ed. x, 260, 1758; Indian Ocean.   Yarrow, 1877, 212;   Shackleford Banks.
Remora jacobœa, Jordan & Gilbert, 1879, 381; Beaufort (after Yarrow).
Remora remora, Jordan, 1886, 27; Beaufort.   Jenkins, 1887, 87; Beaufort (after Yarrow).   Jordan & Evermann, 1898, 2271.

DIAGNOSIS.—Depth about .15 total length; head broad, .25 length; lower jaw not produced as a flexible tip; maxillary extending to anterior margin of eye; disk .35 length of body, the laminæ about 18; soft dorsal rays 23; anal rays 25; caudal fin rather broad, concave behind; pectorals short, broad, rounded, .6 length of head; ventrals joined to abdomen by more than .5 length of inner rays.   Color: nearly uniform dark brown   (*remora*, holding back.)

This remora is usually observed attached to large sharks; its frequents all warm seas, and is found on the east coast of the United States as far north as Woods Hole.   Its maximum length is about 1.25 feet.   No one but Yarrow has recorded the species in North Carolina waters; his note reads:

Uncommon; a few specimens seen, which were taken by the fishermen on Shackleford Banks.   They stated that these fish were found in the mouths of sharks.   Size of specimen six inches.

Genus LEPTECHENEIS Gill.   Shark-suckers; Remoras.

Body slender, fusiform; disk long, with 20 to 28 laminæ; soft dorsal with numerous short rays; anal similar, the anterior rays somewhat elongate; caudal slightly concave behind; pectorals pointed, the rays soft and flexible; ventrals long, narrowly adnate to abdomen.   A single species of world wide distribution. (*Leptecheneis*, slender *Echeneis*.)

320. LEPTECHENEIS NAUCRATES (Linnæus).

"Pilot"; "Shark's Pilot"; Shark-sucker; Remora.

Echeneis naucrates Linnæus, Systema Naturæ, ed. x, 261, 1758; Indian Ocean.   Jordan & Gilbert, 1879, 381;
   Beaufort.   Jenkins, 1887, 87; Beaufort.   Jordan & Evermann, 1898, 2269, pl. cccxxix, fig. 796.
   Wilson, 1900, 355; Beaufort.
Leptecheneis naucrates, Yarrow, 1877, 212; Beaufort.
?*Echeneis naucrateoides* Zuiew, Nova Acta Academiæ Scientiarum Imperialis Petropolitanæ, iv, 1789, 279.
   Jordan & Evermann, 1898, 2270.
Echeneis lineata Holbrook, Ichthyology of South Carolina, 102, 1860; Charleston.

DIAGNOSIS.—Depth contained 9 to 12 times in total length; the caudal peduncle very slender; head about .2 length; strongly projecting lower jaw with flexible tip; maxillary not reaching anterior margin of eye, .33 length of head; snout more than .4 length of head; eye small, .2 head; gill-rakers very short and slender, the longest equal to diameter of pupil; length of disk .2 to .3 length of body, its width .4 its length, the laminæ 20 to 28; soft dorsal very low, the rays 32 to 40; anal rays 31 to 38; caudal rather long, the edge concave in adults, the middle rays longer than in young; pectorals .66 length of head; ventrals slightly longer than pectorals, the inner rays narrowly joined to abdomen by a membrane.   Color: slaty brown; a broad blackish stripe, widest anteriorly, extending from pectoral base to caudal fin, margined with white; the same stripe extending across opercle, through eye, to snout; dorsal and anal fins with white margins; caudal black, the angles white; pectorals and ventrals black, with pale edges.   (*naucrates*, a pilot.)

Fig. 169.   SHARK-SUCKER; REMORA.   *Leptecheneis naucrates.*

This is the best known remora of the Atlantic coast, most frequently found attached to large fishes.   It attains a length of nearly 3 feet.   At Beaufort it is not uncommon, usually attached to sharks, but also swimming independently and sometimes caught with hook and line from the wharves.   The local names are "pilot" and "shark's pilot".   In July, 1905, a number were taken in a pound net operated in connection with the laboratory.

The nominal species *naucrateoides* is said to differ from *naucrates* in having 20 or 21 laminæ in the sucking disk and the disk contained less than 4 times in total length of fish; but it seems to the present writer that this distinction can not be maintained.   Examples from Beaufort have 23 laminæ and the disk contained 3.5 times in total length of fish, thus partaking of the character of both forms.

Family URANOSCOPIDÆ.   The Star-gazers.

The star-gazers are strongly marked, carnivorous marine fishes, living on the bottom in shallow waters.   Body elongate, very broad, slightly compressed; head large, broad, with bony plates; mouth vertical, lower jaw strong and prominent, premaxillaries protractile, maxillary broad; small teeth on jaws, vomer, and palatines, eyes very small, on upper surface of head and directed upward; gill-slits wide, gill-membranes not joined to isthmus; pseudobranchiæ present; branchiostegals 6; pyloric cœca present; air-bladder usually lacking; skin either naked or covered with small, smooth scales in oblique rows; lateral line high; spinous dorsal fin either short or wanting; soft dorsal and anal rather long; caudal truncate or rounded; pectorals with broad base, the lower rays very short; ventrals jugular, the rays 1,5, inner ray longest.   Two American genera and 5 species, only 1 species known from the south Atlantic coast.

Genus ASTROSCOPUS Brevoort.   Electric Star-gazers.

Body stout; upper part of head covered with bony plates in young, not fully covered in adult; a Y-shaped bony process on top of head, between eyes; a naked area on each side of the Y; a fringed groove or furrow extending forward from behind and on inner side of eyes; head destitute of spines; nostrils and lips fringed; back and sides covered with small, densely set scales, head naked and abdomen more or less so; first dorsal composed of 4 or 5 low, stout spines with connecting membrane; caudal margin square or slightly rounded; pectorals and ventrals rather large.   The naked areas on the head give an electric shock when touched.   (*Astroscopus*, star gazer.)

321. ASTROSCOPUS Y-GRÆCUM (Cuvier & Valenciennes).

"Electric-toad"; Star-gazer.

Uranoscopus y-græcum Cuvier & Valenciennes, Histoire Naturelle des Poissons, iii, 308, 1829.
Upsilonphorus y-græcum, Jordan, 1886, 28; Beaufort.   Jenkins, 1887, 92; Beaufort.
Astroscopus anoplus, Yarrow, 1877, 207; Beaufort.   Jordan & Gilbert, 1879, 372; Beaufort.
Astroscopus y-græcum, Jordan & Evermann, 1898, 2307, pl. cccxxxiv, fig. 808; Beaufort, etc.

DIAGNOSIS.—Body compressed behind, robust forward, the depth .25 length; head (to end of snout) .33 length; mouth large, turned upward, a fringe of stiff barbels on each jaw: small, conical teeth in numerous bands in each jaw, teeth also on vomer and palatines; tongue large and fleshy; maxillary .4 head; eyes protruding, very small, .08 head and .25 interorbital space; bones of head with granular surface; on either side of Y-shaped bony ridge is a naked area , and between the forks of the Y is another; nostrils with branched fringe; each posterior nostril extends backward as a curved, fringed groove terminating behind eye; body scaled except on belly, scales very small, about 80 in lateral series; head naked; a slight median keel from ventral fins to vent; dorsal rays IV+1,12; anal rays 13; caudal margin nearly straight; pectorals long and pointed, their broad base .5 length of head; ventral rays thick and fleshy. Color: variegated and variable; upper parts dark brown, with numerous small, round, white spots with a black edge; top of head not so dark as back, the spots elongated and interspersed with irregular black lines; eyes, chin, and whiskers spotted; lower parts pale; fins with black and white bands or stripes.   (*y-græcum*, Greek Y, in allusion to the bony process on top of head.)

Under the name of "electric toad" this fish is known to all the fishermen of the Beaufort region. The species ranges from Cape Hatteras to the West Indies, but is nowhere abundant. It frequents sandy shores, and buries itself with the exception of the eyes and lips while lying in wait for its prey. A specimen in the Beaufort laboratory is 10.75 inches long, but the species reaches a length of 15 inches or more.* A star-gazer 2.5 inches long taken on Bird Shoal, Beaufort Harbor, July 14, 1904, had the following colors: Back, sides, and head black without spots; under parts white; opercle brownish; lower jaw, chin, and throat jet black; fins as in adult.

Fig. 170. STAR-GAZER. *Astroscopus y-græcum.*

The electric organ in this species is of a peculiar structure not found in any other fishes, and in proportion to its size is said to be the most powerful known in animals.

Family BATRACHOIDIDÆ.   The Toad-fishes.

A small family of marine, bottom fishes, with robust form, compressed posteriorly and depressed anteriorly; large mouth with strong teeth; reduced gill-openings, 3 gills, gill-membranes united to isthmus; no pyloric cœca; air-bladder present; scaled or scaleless body; 2 dorsal fins, the anterior with 2 or 3 low spines, the posterior very long and similar to anal; caudal rounded, free from dorsal and anal; pectorals broad; ventrals large and jugular.   About 5 American genera, of which 2 are represented on the east coast of the United States, although 1 of these (Porichthys) is recorded only as far north as South Carolina.

Genus OPSANUS Rafinesque.   Toad-fishes.

Rather small carnivorous shore fishes, found mostly in warmer waters; body stout, scaleless, with loose, wrinkled skin and obscure lateral line; numerous flaps or cirri on head; mouth very wide, with fleshy lips and with a single row of blunt teeth on jaws, vomer, and palatines; opercle with 2 concealed spines; a large foramen in axil of pectorals; dorsal spines 3.   Two American species, 1 in the Gulf of Mexico and the following.   (*Opsanus,* eye upward.)

---

* Jenkins (1887) states that Dr. Coues obtained one specimen of *Astroscopus guttatus* at Beaufort; but the specimen referred to is listed by Yarrow (1877) as *anoplus,* a synonym of *y-græcum.*   There is no record of the occurrence of *guttatus* south of Virginia, but it may be looked for on the shores north of Cape Hatteras, which locality is given by Jordan & Evermann (1898) as the southern limit of its range.

322. OPSANUS TAU (Linnæus).

"Toad-fish"; "Toad"; "Rock-toad"; Oyster-fish.

Gadus tau Linnæus, Systema Naturæ, ed. xii, 440, 1766; Carolina.
Batrachus tau, Yarrow, 1877, 206; Beaufort. Jordan & Gilbert, 1879, 372; Beaufort, Jordan, 1886, 28; Beaufort. Jenkins, 1887, 91; Beaufort. Wilson, 1900, 355; Beaufort.
Opsanus tau, Jordan & Evermann, 1898, 2315. Linton, 1905, 406; Beaufort.

DIAGNOSIS.—Depth somewhat more than .2 length; head broad, .37 length: jaws very strong, the teeth smaller anteriorly; end of upper jaw and under side of lower jaw with large flaps; smaller flaps on preopercle; diameter of eye equal to length of snout and interorbital space; dorsal rays III + 24; anal rays 24. Color: back, sides, and head dull greenish or brownish, with profuse black markings which run together on sides and form irregular bars; belly and under sides of head dirty yellowish, sometimes dark spotted; numerous small, pale yellow or whitish spots on sides; soft dorsal and anal fins with 5 to 9 oblique irregular black bands; caudal, pectorals, and ventrals with 5 to 7 similar but more sharply-defined cross bands. (*tau,* the Greek letter τ; in allusion to the shape of bones on top of head when dried.)

Fig. 171. TOAD-FISH. *Opsanus tau.*

The toad-fish is one of the best known and least liked fishes along the coast from Cape Cod to Florida. Its sluggish habits, repulsive appearance, ability to inflict a painful wound with its powerful jaws, and its uselessness are sufficient to condemn it in the estimation of most people. It is abundant along the shores of North Carolina, and is called "toad", "toad-fish", and "rock-toad" by the fishermen. It is frequently caught in nets and is also taken with hook-and-line in still-fishing, especially on oysters bars or broken bottoms. The maximum length is 15 inches, but the species reaches sexual maturity when 6 or 7 inches long. On March 26, 1904, a specimen 1.37 inches long was seined at Beaufort. Owing to its extreme ugliness, the toad-fish is rarely eaten; the flesh is well flavored, however.

The breeding habits of the species are very interesting. The eggs are laid in summer, and are attached in a single layer to the under side of rocks or the inside of tin cans, oyster shells, etc. For some time after hatching the young remain attached by means of a special sucking disk. Yarrow (1877) notes that at Beaufort "in April, 1871, a female was discovered watching her eggs, which had been deposited in an old boot-leg; the tide had receded, leaving her in about 4 inches of water, and, although attempts were made to drive her away, she preferred to remain and was consequently captured".

All kinds of animal food are eaten by this fish. Numerous examples examined at Beaufort by Professor Linton in July and August were found to have been feeding on fish, blue crabs, spider crabs, stone crabs, fiddler crabs, hermit crabs, shrimp, various bivalve and univalve mollusks, and sea urchins.

Family GOBIESOCIDÆ. The Cling-fishes.

The cling-fishes are small, carnivorous, and easily recognizable by the existence of a large sucking disk between and behind the ventral fins. The disk is rounded in outline, is in part formed by the ventral fins, and its surface is covered with thick skin; by means of it these fishes are able to attach themselves tightly to stones, rocks, and other objects. Other characters of the family are elongate body, depressed anteriorly; moderate-sized mouth with well developed jaw teeth; greatly reduced opercle; $2\frac{1}{2}$ or 3 gill-arches; broadly connected gill-membranes; skin without scales; deficient air-bladder; no spinous dorsal fin, the soft dorsal placed posteriorly, similar to and opposite anal; pectoral fins well developed; and ventral fins widely separated, the rays 1,4 or 1,5.

These fishes are found mostly in shoal, warm waters among rocks or stones. The largest species are under 8 inches long, and the family has no direct economic importance. There are 5 or 6 American genera, but only the typical genus, Gobiesox, is known from the east coast of the United States.

Genus GOBIESOX Lacépède. Cling-fishes.

A numerous American genus, having the body very broad anteriorly and slender posteriorly; the head large; the mouth terminal, with strong teeth in jaws and no teeth on vomer or palatines; a strong spine on the opercle; 3 gills; broadly connected gill-membranes free from the isthmus; dorsal and anal rays in moderate number (6 to 12); and the posterior section of the sucking disk without a free anterior margin. (*Gobiesox*, goby pike.)

323. GOBIESOX VIRGATULUS Jordan & Gilbert.

Cling-fish.

Gobiesox virgatulus Jordan & Gilbert, Proceedings U. S. National Museum, 1882, 293; Pensacola. Jordan & Evermann, 1898, 2333.

DIAGNOSIS.—Depth of body .16 total length; head low, broadly rounded anteriorly, its length .35, its width .3 total length; posterior angle of mouth below front of eye; lower jaw the shorter; 2 series of teeth in upper jaw, 4 teeth in outer series somewhat enlarged; eye small, about .2 head and .4 broad interorbital space; cheeks bulging; opercle ending in a sharp spine; dorsal rays 10; anal rays 8 or 9; sucking disk shorter than head; pectorals short, less than .5 head. Color: olive green, with pale spots, broad dark cross-bars, and faint, wavy longitudinal yellowish brown lines; the dorsal and anal crossed by the dark bars of the body; caudal dusky, with yellow tip. (*virgatulus*, narrowly striped.)

The first North Carolina record for this little species was August 19, 1899, when it was found at the wharf of an oyster cannery in Beaufort Harbor. It has since been found abundantly among the rocks of the Fort Macon jetties, and doubtless occurs elsewhere in suitable situations. It has heretofore been known only as far north as Charleston, whence it ranges to Pensacola. Its maximum length is 4 inches.

Family BLENNIIDÆ. The Blennies.

The blennies are small or medium sized carnivorous marine and fresh-water fishes, found in all latitudes, the number of known species being about 400, divided into nearly 100 genera. They are particularly abundant on rocky shores and among seaweeds and, while some of them are viviparous, most of them are oviparous The body is moderately or greatly elongated, and more or less compressed; the head large or small; the mouth usually small, sometimes large, never vertical, variously provided with teeth; no spines on head; gill-membranes either free from isthmus or joined to it; skin naked or covered with small or moderate sized cycloid or ctenoid scales; lateral line simple, double, or absent; dorsal fin very long, the anterior part, the posterior part, or the entire fin with spines; anal similar to dorsal; caudal sometimes united with dorsal and anal, sometimes distinct, usually rounded; pectorals varying in size, from large to rudimentary; ventrals small or wanting, if present far forward, with 1 spine and 1 to 3 soft rays. Of the many American genera, 3 closely related are known from North Carolina.

Key to the North Carolina genera of blennies.

i. No fang-like canine teeth in posterior part of either jaw; maxillary extending to or beyond posterior border of eye; a cirrus or filament present or absent over each eye.
   a. Upper profile of head gently curved, the snout sharp; orbital cirrus small or wanting.
                           CHASMODES.
   aa. Upper profile very abruptly curved, the snout blunt; orbital cirrus well developed.
                           HYPSOBLENNIUS.
ii. Fang-like canine teeth in posterior part of both jaws; maxillary reaching as far as pupil; large cirrus or filament over each eye, with 4 smaller ones at base (the cirrus shorter in female) ....HYPLEUROCHILUS.

Genus CHASMODES Cuvier & Valenciennes. Blennies.

Body oblong, compressed; head pointed; mouth large, maxillary extending as far as or beyond posterior margin of eye, premaxillaries not protractile; teeth long and slender, in one series and only in front of jaws, no canines; gill-slits very short and above upper half of the base of pectoral fins; lateral line incomplete; skin without scales; a small cirrus over each eye, often wanting; dorsal fin with anterior rays spinous; anal fin similar to soft dorsal; caudal rounded, either united to or free from dorsal; pectorals large; ventrals well developed, jugular, the rays ɪ,3. (*Chasmodes*, yawning.)

324. CHASMODES BOSQUIANUS (Lacépède).
Banded Blenny.

Blennius bosquianus Lacépède, Histoire Naturelle des Poissons, ii, 493, 1800; South Carolina.
Chasmodes bosquianus, Jordan & Gilbert, 1879, 372; Beaufort. Jordan, 1886, 28; Beaufort. Jenkins, 1887, 92; Beaufort. Jordan & Evermann, 1898, 2394.

DIAGNOSIS.—Depth more than .25 length; head equal to depth; maxillary reaching to or beyond posterior edge of eye; interorbital space very narrow; tentacle over eye minute or absent; dorsal fin continuous, arising anterior to ventrals and extending to caudal, the rays

XI,19; anal rays II,19: caudal fin joined to dorsal. Color: Male olive green, with about 9 narrow longitudinal blue lines; opercular margin orange yellow; spinous dorsal with a broad median orange yellow stripe; anal dark, with white tip; a dusky spot at base of caudal. Female darker, with narrow wavy pale green lines and several broad dark bars; head with black dots; a dusky spot at base of caudal. (Named for Bosc, the French consul who collected for Lacépède at Charleston.)

A well known and rather abundant blenny of the east coast from New York to Florida. It is common in Beaufort Harbor on the shoals. The sexes are quite dissimilar in color, and have several times been described as different species. Maximum length 4 inches.

Genus HYPSOBLENNIUS Gill. Blennies.

Form oblong, compressed; head short, profile steep, snout blunt; mouth small, horizontal; maxillary extending to middle of eye or to posterior border; teeth long, slender, in a single series in each jaw, none of them canine; gill-openings very much reduced, owing to the junction of the gill-membranes with the isthmus as far upward as base of pectorals; skin naked; lateral line deficient posteriorly; well developed tentacles over eyes; dorsal fin long, anterior part spinous and separated from posterior by a slight notch; anal similar to posterior dorsal; caudal rounded, free from dorsal and anal; pectorals well developed; ventrals jugular, with 1 strong spine and 3 unbranched jointed rays. Small American shore fishes, found on both coasts; 2 Atlantic species, 1 ranging from Texas to South Carolina (*ionthas*), and the following. (*Hypsoblennius*, high blenny.)

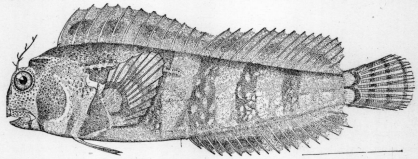

Fig. 172. BLENNY. *Hypsoblennius hentz.*

325. HYPSOBLENNIUS HENTZ (LeSueur).

Blenny; Spotted Seaweed-fish.

Blennius hent LeSueur, Journal Academy Natural Sciences, Philadelphia, iv, 1825, 363; Charleston, S. C.
Hypleurochilus punctatus, Yarrow, 1877, 206; Beaufort. Jordan & Gilbert, 1879, 372; Beaufort. Jenkins, 1887, 92; Beaufort.
Isesthes punctatus, Jordan, 1886, 28; Beaufort.
Hypsoblennius hentz, Jordan & Evermann, 1898, 2390, pl. cccxxxix, fig. 823; North and South Carolina, etc. Linton, 1905, 410; Beaufort.

DIAGNOSIS.—Body rather deep, depth .33 length; head short, .3 length; snout very short and nearly vertical; mouth low, horizontal, maxillary extending to or beyond posterior margin of eye; eye large, more than .2 length of head; interorbital space concave, .5 diameter of eye;

gill-opening less than .5 length of head; a branched tentacle, as long as first dorsal spine, over each eye, and a minute cirrus over each nostril; dorsal fin rather high, the 2 parts separated by a slight notch, the rays xi,14 to xii,15, the soft rays higher than spines; anal rays 16 to 18: caudal rounded; pectorals broad; ventrals more than .5 head. Color: light bluish ash mixed with brownish red, with numerous irregular black and reddish spots; 3 narrow dark bars on lower side of head; cheeks dark, spinous dorsal black, with light spots; soft dorsal and caudal with dark bands; anal dusky; pectorals greenish, with brown spots; ventrals blackish with pale bands. (Named for the collector, Dr. Nicholas Hentz.)

This species is abundant on sandy shores and among seaweeds, from North Carolina to Florida. It has often been found in the Beaufort region in company with other blennies, and is recorded in all the lists of Beaufort fishes. Length, 4 inches.

Genus HYPLEUROCHILUS Gill. Blennies.

Body oblong, compressed; head short; mouth low, horizontal, with strong posterior canine teeth in both jaws, in addition to smaller teeth in front; gill-openings much restricted, the membranes being broadly joined to isthmus; lateral line present on anterior part of body; skin naked; a large tentacle over eye in male, a smaller one in female; dorsal fin long, low, and continuous, without notch. The genus contains a single American species. (*Hypleurochilus*, having v-shaped side-lips.)

326. HYPLEUROCHILUS GEMINATUS (Wood).

Blenny; Seaweed-fish.

Blennius geminatus Wood, Journal Academy Natural Sciences, Philadelphia, iv, 1824, 278; Charleston, S. C. Jordan & Gilbert, 1879, 371; Beaufort.
Blennius fucorum, Yarrow, 1877, 206; Beaufort.
Hypleurochilus geminatus, Jordan, 1886, 28; Beaufort. Jenkins, 1887, 92; Beaufort. Jordan & Evermann, 1898, 2385.
Hypleurochilus multifilis, Wilson, 1900, 355; Beaufort.

DIAGNOSIS.—Depth .25 to .28 length; head not very blunt, its length rather greater than depth of body, anterior profile straight and oblique; besides the single row of long, slender teeth in each jaw, there are strong, hooked canines, those in lower jaw the larger; gill-slits short, extending downward to lower edge of pectoral base; interorbital space concave, less than .5 diameter of eye; a large tentacle over each eye in male, with 4 smaller ones at its base; tentacle in female shorter than eye; dorsal rays xi,15 to xiii,14, the spines slender and shorter than soft rays; anal rays ii,18; caudal rounded. Color: brownish green, with indistinct dark bars; sides with a double row of reddish brown spots; anal and other vertical fins with black margins. (*geminatus*, twin.)

This appears to be the most abundant blenny on the North Carolina coast, whence it ranges to Texas. The maximum length is about 2.5 inches. Dr. Coker contributes the following note on the species at Beaufort:

Adults very common about piles of wharves (at the Morehead railroad pier), living amongst ascidians, sponges, etc.; very abundant among the rocks of the Fort Macon jetties. In captivity the fish seek to hide under shells, etc.; specimens were once kept in the laboratory in an earthenware jar for weeks without change of water, the water meanwhile evaporating nearly one half. The eggs are laid [in August] in a single layer, attached to the rocks, ascidians, shells, etc., among which the adults live. All stages, from .5 inch up to adults, can be gotten in such a locality, but the early stages (except the young just from the egg) have not been obtained, though a careful search has been made with different methods; evidently the species has a different habitat in very early life.

Family ZOARCIDÆ.   The Eel-pouts.

Marine fishes of moderate size abounding in cold water and living on the bottom, sometimes at considerable depths; some of the species viviparous. Body elongate, eel-shaped in some genera; head and mouth large; conical teeth in jaws, teeth sometimes present on vomer and palatines; gill-opening a vertical slit; gills 4, gill-rakers small, gill-membranes united to the isthmus; skin naked or covered with small, imbedded cycloid scales; lateral line present but inconspicuous; pyloric cœca rudimentary; dorsal fin long, low, continuous, the rays usually soft but sometimes spinous posteriorly; anal long, low, of soft rays only; dorsal and anal usually confluent around tail; pectorals short and broad; ventrals if present jugular and very small.   About 15 American genera.

Genus ZOARCES Cuvier.   Mutton-fishes; Eel-pouts.

Form elongate, somewhat compressed, tapering posteriorly; head moderately long, contracted above; mouth large, provided with strong, blunt jaw teeth in several rows; lateral line present; scales small and imbedded; dorsal fin beginning at head, long, low, and continuous, free from caudal, some of the posterior rays spinous; anal fin similar to dorsal but shorter and continuous with caudal; pectoral fins broad; ventrals fins very small, jugular.   A small genus of marine, viviparous fishes, inhabiting the northern part of the northern hemisphere; 1 American species.   (*Zoarces*, viviparous.)

327. ZOARCES ANGUILLARIS (Peck).

Eel-pout; Mutton-fish.

Blennius anguillaris Peck, Memoirs American Academy of Sciences, ii, 1804, 46; New Hampshire.
Zoarces anguillaris, Yarrow, 1877, 206; Fort Macon.   Jordan & Gilbert, 1879, 371; Fort Macon (after Yarrow).
      Goode, 1884, 247; Fort Macon (after Yarrow).   Jordan, 1886, 29; Beaufort (after Yarrow).   Jordan
      & Evermann, 1898, 2457, pl. cccxlviii, fig. 850.

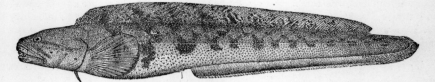

Fig. 173.   EEL-POUT.   *Zoarces anguillaris.*

DIAGNOSIS.—Depth .14 length; head .17 length; maxillary extending well behind eye; lower jaw included; eye small, about .5 length of snout; dorsal rays 95, XVIII,17, the first ray over ventrals, the longest rays less than .5 head, the posterior rays very short and spinous; anal rays about 105; pectorals broad, about .66 length of head; ventrals very small, their length less than snout.   Color: reddish brown, with dark green mottlings on sides and back extending on dorsal fin; a dark stripe behind eye and another below eye.   (*anguillaris*, eel-like.)

The claim of this fish to a place in the North Carolina fauna is based on 2 small specimens said to have been caught by Dr. Yarrow with hook and line from the wharf at Fort Macon in May, 1871. The species has been observed by no one else, and must be regarded as a rare straggler so far south, assuming there has been no error in identification. Jordan & Evermann (1898) give the range as extending from Labrador to Delaware. The eel-pout reaches a length of 3 feet and a weight of 7 pounds, and is a common fish in the northern part of its range, and is often caught incidentally by fishermen; although its flesh is of good flavor, it is rarely eaten. The young are brought forth alive.

Family OPHIDIIDÆ. The Cusk-eels.

Eel-shaped marine fishes with compressed body; large head; villiform teeth in jaws, usually in roof of mouth; protractile premaxillaries; wide gill-openings, the membranes attached to isthmus posterior to ventral fins; scales small, in oblique rows; pyloric cœca and air-bladder present; vent posterior; dorsal and anal fins destitute of spines, low, and confluent around tail; ventral fins jugular, consisting of a long, forked filament. Five or 6 American genera, only 1 represented on the east coast of the United States.

Genus RISSOLA Jordan & Evermann. Cusk-eels.

Form moderately elongate; lower jaw included; jaw teeth villiform, vomer and palatine teeth blunt; vent posterior to pectorals; no spine on opercle; scales much as in the common eel (Anguilla), head naked; air-bladder short, broad, with a posterior foramen. One American species. (Named for Risso, a French ichthyologist.)

328. RISSOLA MARGINATA (DeKay).

Cusk-eel.

Ophidium marginatum DeKay, New York Fauna, Fishes, 315, 1842; New York Harbor. Yarrow, 1877, 206; Beaufort. Jordan & Gilbert, 1879, 371; Beaufort (after Yarrow). Jordan, 1886, 29; Beaufort.
Rissola marginata, Jordan & Evermann, 2489, pl. cccliii, fig. 868. Gudger, 1905*b*; Beaufort.

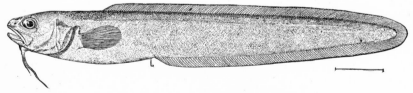

Fig. 174. CUSK-EEL. *Rissola marginata.*

DIAGNOSIS (based on North Carolina specimen).—Depth .14 total length; head contained 5.3 times in length; mouth rather large, maxillary extending to or beyond posterior margin of orbit; snout .25 head; eye somewhat longer than snout; gill-rakers short, papillose, 2 on upper arm and 4 on lower arm of first arch; air-bladder tapering behind; dorsal fin beginning close behind head and about length of head anterior to anal; pectorals .75 length of head; longest ventrals ray .8 length of head and twice length of shorter. Color: back and sides golden yellow, darker above; belly milk white; a dark lateral stripe from gill-opening to end of tail; a dark stripe at base of dorsal fin; preopercle spotted; dorsal fin edged with white anteriorly, with black posteriorly; pectorals transparent, edged with white; ventrals white. (*marginata*, margined.)

A rather uncommon fish along the coast from New York to Texas. A single specimen, observed by Dr. Coues at Beaufort in 1871, remained the only North Carolina record until 1904, when Dr. E. W. Gudger obtained a specimen 4.5 inches long on a sandy shoal near the laboratory at Beaufort. Very little has been published regarding the habits of Rissola or other members of the family, and Dr. Gudger's observations on the behavior of this specimen cover practically all that is known:*

On July 13, 1904, while walking on a sand spit, exposed at low water and lying northwest of the island on which is situated the laboratory of the United States Bureau of Fisheries at Beaufort, N. C., I noticed thrust out of the wet sand, a conically pointed head which instantly disappeared. Throwing myself down, I immediately began with my bare hands to dig the wet sand where I had seen the head. The animal went down tail first, and so rapidly that I began to despair of capturing it. Presently, however, when I had dug below water level, this little fish was brought out in a great double handful of sand. When taken into the laboratory and put into an aquarium of running salt water, after a few struggles it turned on its side and so remained, seemingly in considerable distress, being unable to maintain itself in the normal position by its delicate filament-like ventral fins which are inframandibular in position. I then filled a tall glass jar some eight inches deep with fine sand, introduced into it the little fish and placed it under a salt water jet. At first the fish lay quiescent on the sand, but when I returned some hours later, it had burrowed into and was never again seen on top of the sand. Frequently, however, the little fish could be seen with its body half outlined against the glass side of the aquarium. There could then be seen slow undulation of the long dorsal and anal fins together with slight bendings of the body, both motions beginning at the head and progressing towards the tail. Evidently by this means a current of water was maintained through the gill-chambers. On the surface of the sand, small conical half-filled depressions could be found. These seemed to have been formed by the fish either in burrowing into the sand or in drawing water over the gills. However, I did not notice any distinct currents through these depressions and can not positively say that they were excurrent and incurrent openings.

Family GADIDÆ. The Cods.

The fishes of this numerous and important family are found chiefly in cold waters, and support extensive fisheries in the north temperate and arctic regions. Body moderately or considerably elongated, mouth large, terminal, and well provided with small teeth in bands; chin with a barbel; gill-arches 4, gill-openings wide, gill-membranes usually free from isthmus; pseudobranchiæ absent; scales very small, cycloid; pyloric cœca numerous in most genera; air-bladder well developed; no spines in fins, dorsal fin long and either single or divided into 2 or 3 separate parts; anal fin long, and either single or double; caudal fin prominent, sometimes distinct, sometimes joined to dorsal and anal; ventral fins jugular and consisting of 1 to 8 rays. There are about 25 genera and several hundred species; the American members of the family include such well known fish as the cod, the pollock, the hake, the cusk, and the fresh-water ling. The family is only sparingly represented in North Carolina, although 1 of the species

*Dr. Theodore Gill, in a note prefatory to Dr. Gudger's, quotes a brief observation on this species by Professor Verrill, who "dug two specimens out of the sand near low-water mark, where they burrowed to the depth of a foot or more. When placed upon moist sand, they burrowed into it *tail foremost* with surprising rapidity, disappearing in an instant".

there found, the cod, is the most valuable of the entire family.   The 2 following genera are in the local fauna:

i. Dorsal fin divided into 3 separate parts; anal fin divided into 2 parts; ventral fins large, expanded, with 7 rays.. GADUS.
ii. Dorsal fin divided into 2 separate parts; anal fin long, undivided; ventral fins filamentous, with 2 rays.. UROPHYCIS.

Genus GADUS Linnaeus.   Cods.

This genus contains the true cods, with moderately elongate body which is compressed posteriorly and tapers to the rather narrow peduncle; large head, contracted anteriorly; large mouth, with teeth on jaws and vomer; barbel on chin; pale lateral line; very small scales; large air-bladder; 3 dorsal fins, 2 anal fins, ventral fins with 7 rays.   Important food fishes of northern waters; only 1 species on east coast of the United States.   (*Gadus*, a Latin name, equivalent to the English word cod.)

329. GADUS CALLARIAS Linnæus.

"Cod".

Gadus callarias Linnæus, Systema Naturæ, ed. x, 252, 1758; European seas.   Jordan & Evermann, 1898, 2541
    pl. ccclxi, fig. 891.
Gadus morrhua, Goode, 1886, 202; south to Cape Hatteras and Ocracoke Inlet.

DIAGNOSIS.—Greatest depth about .25 length;   head large, its length about equal to depth; maxillary extending as far as pupil; jaw teeth sharp, in narrow bands; snout .33 length of head, eye small, .5 length of snout;   scales minute; lateral line curved anteriorly, straight posteriorly;   dorsal rays 14+21+19;   height of first dorsal about .5 length of head;   anal rays 20+18;   caudal square or slightly concave; pectorals broad, .5 length of head; ventrals small, much shorter than pectorals.   Color: variable; body yellowish, reddish, brownish, or greenish above, whitish below; back and sides with numerous round brown spots; lateral line always pale; fins plain.   (*callarias*, an old name for the cod.)

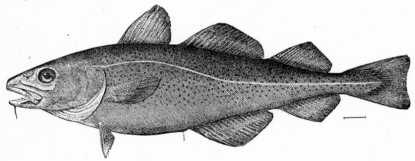

Fig. 175.   COD.   *Gadus callarias.*

This well known species, which supports very important fisheries in the North Atlantic Ocean, on the coasts and "banks" of America and Europe, in the United States is more valuable than any other single marine species, the annual catch being worth several millions of dollars.   There is a special cod fishery in all the states from New Jersey northward, but the great bulk of the fishing is carried on from Maine and Massachusetts ports.

The cod goes in schools when feeding, spawning, or migrating.   Although sometimes found in shoal water or even at the surface, it is essentially a deep-water fish, preferring depths of 20 to 70 fathoms and even occurring at a depth of 300 fathoms.

The largest cod recorded from New England waters weighed 211 pounds and was more than 6 feet long.   The average weight of the large run of fish caught on the New England shore is about 35 pounds, while on the far distant Grand Banks the average is only 20 pounds; the small run of fish on all the grounds is about 12 pounds.

The cod eats almost any kind of animal food of proper size, and takes it anywhere between surface and bottom.   Favorite articles are mollusks, crabs, lobsters, and various kinds of fish, especially herring, menhaden, alewives, mackerel, capelin, and lant.

The spawning season on our coast extends from October to June.   The eggs float at the surface, are about .055 inch in diameter, and several millions may be laid by a full sized fish.   Several hundred millions of cod are hatched each year by the United States Bureau of Fisheries at its stations in Massachusetts and Maine.   The eggs hatch in 20 to 23 days in water of a temperature of 38° F., and in 11 days at a temperature of 47° F.   The young reach a length of 3 inches in 6 months, 9 to 12 inches in 18 months, 22 inches in 42 months.

The cod is now known to occur regularly on the North Carolina coast north of Cape Hatteras.   From inquiries made by the writer, it appears that for a number of years fishermen from New York and New Jersey, setting large-meshed nets in the ocean off Roanoke Island, have caught numbers of cod in fall, winter, and spring, some of the fish weighing 30 pounds.   One fall 30 cod were taken at one lift of a blue-fish net off Nags Head.   In April, 1904, when the writer was at Roanoke Island, numbers of cod were being caught, mostly in sturgeon nets, 1 fish being brought into Manteo on April 6.   It is reported that cod are sometimes found on the Hatteras beaches after storms.   According to Dr. Coker, there is a circumstantial account of the occasional capture of a cod in the lower part of Neuse River.   Professor Goode (1884) states that "stragglers have been observed about Ocracoke Inlet".

It is possible that a winter cod fishery of some importance might be established on the northern part of the coast of the state, either with lines or gill nets. The fish will be found in greatest abundance on the offshore shoals.

Genus UROPHYCIS Gill.   Hakes; Codlings.

Form elongate, slightly compressed; head conical; mouth large, with broad bands of sharp teeth on jaws and vomer; maxillary extending beyond pupil; a small barbel on chin; gill-membranes partly connected, and partly joined to isthmus; scales small; dorsal fins 2, the anterior sometimes with a few rays filamentous, the posterior long and low; anal fin single, similar to second dorsal; caudal fin small, the peduncle slender; ventral fins well separated, filamentous, bifid, composed of 2 slender rays.   Seven species on east coast of America, some of them ranging further south (Gulf of Mexico) than any other American gadids; several attaining large size and caught in immense numbers by New England fishermen. Two species known from the shores of North Carolina. It is possible that the white hake or squirrel hake (*Urophycis tenuis*) and the common hake (*Urophycis chuss*) may also occur on the northern part of the coast of the state; the former is said (Jordan & Evermann, 1898) to range as far as Cape Hatteras and the latter is found as far south as Virginia, but no examples of either have as yet been obtained in this state.

i. Dorsal rays about 8+43; anal rays about 45; pectorals extending to anal origin; scales in lateral series about 90 ....*regius.*
ii. Dorsal rays about 10+62; anal rays about 53; pectorals not extending to vent; scales in lateral series about 155..*earlli.*

(*Urophycis*, tail *Phycis*, the last being an ancient Greek name for some fish living among the rockweed, Fucus.)

330. UROPHYCIS REGIUS (Walbaum).

Codling; Hake.

Blennius regius Walbaum, Artedi Genera Piscium, iii, 186, 1792; after Schöpf.
Urophycis regius, Yarrow, 1877, 206; Beaufort. Jordan & Evermann, 1898, 2553, pl. ccclxiv, fig. 898; "south to Cape Fear".
Phycis regius, Jordan & Gilbert, 1879, 371; Beaufort. Jordan, 1886, 29; Beaufort. Jenkins, 1887, 92; Beaufort.

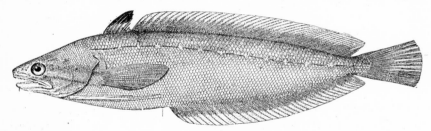

Fig. 176. CODLING. *Urophycis regius.*

DIAGNOSIS.—Form elongate, slightly compressed, depth .2 length; head a little less than .25 length; mouth large, posterior end of maxillary extending well beyond eye, lower jaw the shorter, sharp teeth on jaws and vomer; eye small, contained 4.5 times in length of head, less snout and equal to interorbital width; about 15 gill-rakers on first arch; scales in lateral series about 90; dorsal fin low, beginning over base of pectorals, anterior part with 8 rays, posterior part with 43 rays; anal fin arising nearer snout than base of caudal, the rays 40; caudal fin slightly convex behind; pectorals extending to origin of anal; ventrals inserted half-way between pectorals and anterior margin of eye, reaching as far as vent. Color (living specimens 6 inches long, Beaufort, April 11, 1904): Body gray, mottled with brown, belly glistening white; lateral line with 14 to 16 elongate spots connected by a thin black line; top of head with a pale diamond-shaped area; a dark band across nape and another behind each eye; first dorsal jet black, entirely surrounded by a narrow pure white margin except for a short space at base of black spot anteriorly, a pale yellow edge on anterior border of fin; second dorsal gray, with round dark spots; anal dusky; caudal dusky gray, with dark edge; pectorals dusky with white margin; ventrals glistening white; a few small black dots on side of head, 4 in a vertical series behind eye and 3 or 4 others irregularly placed. (*regius,* royal.)

Found along our Atlantic coast, in shallow to moderately deep water, reaching its southern limit in South Carolina. It is a species of little economic value, as its maximum length is only a foot, while related species are much larger.

One specimen of codling was taken at Beaufort by Dr. Coues in 1871. None of the subsequent collectors at Beaufort up to 1886 met with the species, and they inserted it in their lists on second-hand information. In 1880 Col. Marshall McDonald collected the species at the mouth of Cape Fear River and in the same year Mr. R. Edward Earll obtained specimens in Middle Sound near Wilmington; these examples are in the National Museum (nos. 25294–5, 30333). In Beaufort Harbor the species is common at times; thus in April, 1904, almost every seine haul yielded specimens 5 to 6 inches long; and the fish is also found at other seasons.

331. UROPHYCIS EARLLI (Bean).

"Dickie"; Tom-cod (S. C.); Hake (S. C.); Earll's Hake.

Phycis earlli Bean, Proceedings U. S. National Museum, iii, 1880, 69; Charleston, S. C.   Kendall & Smith, 1894, 21; Hatteras Inlet. Smith, 1893b, pl. lxxiv.
Urophycis earlli, Jordan & Evermann, 1898, 2554, pl. ccclxv, fig. 900.

DIAGNOSIS.—Depth .2 length; head about .25 length; maxillary long, .5 length of head, reaching to or beyond posterior margin of eye; teeth strong; lower jaw included; eye .17 length of head; gill-rakers short and blunt, about 10 on first arch; scales in lateral series about 155; dorsal fins separated by a rounded notch, the rays 10+60; anal rays 53, caudal rounded; pectorals .5 length of head, not reaching as far as vent; ventrals extending but slightly beyond pectorals. Color: brown, with small light blotches on back and sides; dorsal and anal fins edged with brown, second dorsal with light spots. (Named for Mr. R. Edward Earll, who, when assistant in the U. S. Fish Commission, collected the type specimen.)

Fig. 177.   EARLL'S HAKE; DICKIE.   *Urophycis earlli.*

This hake, known only from the coast of North and South Carolina, is not uncommon in the Beaufort and Cape Lookout regions. It has been caught (in May, 1903) in a trap set at the laboratory wharf, and is also sometimes taken by local fishermen. On the adjacent outer shores the fish is common enough to have received a local name, "dickie", although it has no economic value as yet. On December 13, 1890, a party from the fisheries steamer Fish-Hawk landed at Hatteras Inlet and found in eel grass on the beach a living specimen 18 inches long, which is about the maximum length attained by the species. An example 17 inches long was collected at Cape Lookout in the winter of 1903–4 by Mr. S. G. Worth.

Suborder HETEROSOMATA. The Flat-fishes.

These fishes are remarkable for their bodily asymmetry, one side being much more highly developed than the other. They live almost exclusively on the bottom, and one side, which is applied to the bottom, usually lacks color, is flatter than the other, and has no eye. In their early stages, these fishes are bilaterally symmetrical and swim as other fishes do; but as they grow they swim more and more obliquely, and the eye on one side begins to move to the other side of the head, and before they have attained the length of an inch or two, they have permanently assumed a one-sided position, with both eyes on one side of the head. Two families, the flounders and the soles, may be recognized, distinguished by the following characters:

i. Mouth comparatively large, with teeth; eyes large, well separated; margin of preopercle more or less distinct, not concealed by skin............PLEURONECTIDÆ (flounders).
ii. Mouth very small, twisted, without teeth or with only rudimentary teeth; eyes very small, close together; margin of preopercle concealed by skin...............SOLEIDÆ (soles).

Family PLEURONECTIDÆ. The Flounders.

A numerous family of important fishes, mostly marine, found chiefly on sandy bottom, and feeding on fish, crustacea, and other animals. Some species inhabit very deep water, some very shoal water, and others intermediate depths. All are edible and some of them rank among the most valuable of marine fishes in America, Europe, and Asia, chief among them being the halibut (*Hippoglossus hippoglossus*) of the North Atlantic and North Pacific oceans. The body is much compressed, deep, and elliptical in shape; the head is twisted so as to accommodate both eyes on one side; the premaxillary bones are protractile; the gill-arches are 4 in number, and pseudobranchiæ are present; there is no swim-bladder; the viscera are in the anterior part of the body, and the vent is close to the head; the scales are of various form, and usually small; the lateral line, rarely absent, extends on the caudal fin; the dorsal fin, composed only of soft rays, begins on the head and extends nearly to the caudal fin; the anal fin is similar but shorter; the caudal fin is sometimes continuous with dorsal and anal; the pectorals, rarely absent, are placed rather high on the side, and beneath them are the ventrals, one of which is sometimes lacking. The species are oviparous, the eggs being small and numerous. Of the 40 or more genera represented in American waters, 7 are known from the North Carolina coast or on the adjacent ocean bottom.

The flounders are of considerable economic importance in the state, and their value appears to be increasing. In 1889 only 48,200 pounds, worth $872, were sold by the fishermen; in 1897 the catch had risen to 173,975 pounds, valued at $3,199; while in 1902 (the last year for which statistics are available) there were taken for market 261,760 pounds, which brought the fishermen $5,256. Nearly the entire product comes from Beaufort, Carteret, Dare, Hyde, and Pamlico counties, and it is composed largely of several species of Paralichthys.

Key to the North Carolina genera of flounders.

i. Ventral fins similar in position and shape.
   a. Mouth large, the two sides of the jaws about equally developed, the teeth the same on
     both sides; fishes sinistral (i. e., with eyes and color on left side).
     b. Scales ciliated; a distinct caudal peduncle; mouth large, some of anterior teeth
       canine; gill-rakers long and slender; anterior rays of dorsal fin not produced.
                                               PARALICHTHYS.
     bb. Scales ctenoid; caudal peduncle very short; mouth moderate, teeth small, none canine;
       gill-rakers short and broad; anterior rays of dorsal fin produced..ANCYLOPSETTA.
   aa. Mouth rather small, the two sides of jaws not similar (the bones in the blind side being
     strongly curved, those on the eyed side nearly straight), the teeth mostly on the under
     side; fishes dextral (i. e., with eyes and color on right side.)..PSEUDOPLEURONECTES.
ii. Ventral fins dissimilar in position and shape, the fin on the eyed side being longer and
   extending along the edge of the abdomen; fishes sinistral.
   c. Teeth in upper jaw in 2 series, in lower jaw in 1 series, anterior teeth in upper jaw
     enlarged; interorbital space broad (in male)........................ SYACIUM.
   cc. Teeth in both jaws uniserial; interorbital space very narrow.
     d. Lateral line with a well marked arch in front; anterior dorsal rays produced; teeth
       on vomer; anterior dorsal rays produced; interorbital space broad...LOPHOPSETTA.
     dd. Lateral line without arch in front; anterior dorsal rays not produced; no teeth on
       vomer; interorbital space very narrow.
       e. Mouth moderate, the maxillary more than .33 length of head..CITHARICHTHYS.
       ee. Mouth small, the maxillary less than .33 length of head ....ETROPUS.

Genus PARALICHTHYS Girard.   Summer Flounders; Plaice.

Fishes of moderate or rather large size, found on both coasts of America and
also in Asia.   Mouth large, oblique, with a single row of sharp, slender teeth in
each jaw; gill-rakers slender; lateral line strongly arched anteriorly; scales
ctenoid or ciliated; origin of dorsal fin in advance of eye; middle rays of caudal
fin longest, the margin double concave.   Of the 10 American species, the 3 following are known from North Carolina, and probably 1 other (*Paralichthys
squamilentus*) will eventually be found there:

i. Gill-rakers long and slender, 20 to 25 in number, the longest .66 length of eye; dorsal rays
   about 90; anal rays about 70; body with large, ocellated dark spots...........*dentatus.*
ii. Gill-rakers shorter, 12 or 13 in number; body without ocellated spots.
   a. Dorsal rays about 90; anal rays about 70; color dark olive, mostly uniform.
                                                  lethostigmus.
   aa. Dorsal rays about 75; anal rays about 60; color dark olive, with numerous pale spots.
                                                  albiguttus.

(*Paralichthys*, parallel fish.)

332. PARALICHTHYS DENTATUS (Linnæus).

"Flounder"; "Mud Flounder"; "Sand Flounder''; Summer Flounder; Plaice.

Pleuronectes dentatus Linnæus, Systema Naturæ, ed. xii, 1, 458, 1766.
Chœnopsetta ocellaris, Yarrow, 1877, 206; Beaufort.
Pseudorhombus ocellaris, Jordan & Gilbert, 1879, 370; Beaufort.
Pseudorhombus dentatus, Jordan & Gilbert, 1879, 370; Beaufort.
Paralichthys dentatus, Jordan, 1886, 29; Beaufort. Jordan & Evermann, 1898, 2629, pl. ccclxxiii, fig. 922.
   Linton, 1905, 410; Beaufort.

DIAGNOSIS.—Body ovate, its depth .37 length; length of head contained 3.5 to 4 times in
length; mouth large, oblique, the maxillary extending beyond eye, lower jaw projecting;
anterior teeth in both jaws large, strong, and wide set, lateral teeth small and close set; eyes
small, .15 length of head; interorbital space about width of eye in adult; scales small, cycloid;
lateral line with about 100 tubes, the arch about .25 length of straight part; gill-rakers long and
slender, 20 to 25 in number; fins scaly; dorsal fin low, the rays 85 to 93; anal rays 65 to 73.

Color: above light olive, with many small white spots on body and vertical fins; sides with 12 to 15 large dark spots with white edges. (*dentatus*, toothed.)

The summer flounder is the most valuable of the flat-fishes found along the eastern seaboard of the United States.   Its range extends from Massachusetts to Florida, but it is most abundant northward, and is gradually replaced by *Paralichthys lethostigmus* southward.   The species is often found in shallow water, but is also caught in water as deep as 20 fathoms.   It has the habit of ascending streams, and is often taken far from salt water.   At Beaufort the fish is called "sand flounder" or "mud flounder" according to its color, although the fishermen do not believe there is any real difference.   Summer flounder and plaice are names employed to the northward; in the eighteenth century "plaice" was used in North and South Carolina, and is probably the best designation for the species.

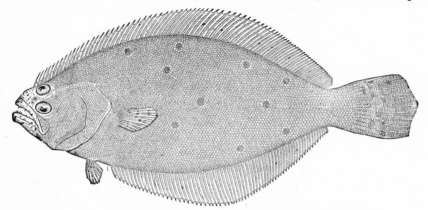

Fig. 178. SUMMER FLOUNDER; PLAICE. *Paralichthys dentatus.*

Excepting the halibut, this is the largest of all our east coast flat-fishes. The maximum weight reaches, and may possibly exceed, 30 pounds, but the average is only 3 pounds, although fish weighing 7 to 10 pounds are not rare. The food comprises small fish, squid, crabs, shrimp, mollusks, sand-dollars, and other animals.   While the fish usually takes its food on or near the bottom, it not infrequently pursues schools of small fish at the surface.

At Beaufort this fish is found throughout the summer, but not abundantly, and is also occasionally taken in winter; it is most numerous and is taken in largest numbers in fall, when it is sometimes observed in schools.   Some of the local fishermen say the flounders then "school up to go away".   Dr. Coker contributes the following account of the flounder fishery at Beaufort:

"Flounder-lighting" or "floundering" is much practiced on calm dark nights in summer and early fall.   In the place of a mast in the skiff used for this purpose, there is a post, bearing an iron arm which may be rotated.   The end of the arm bears a wire firebasket, in which a bright blaze is kindled, from "lightwood" or pine-kots, etc.   The "flounderer" stands in the bow, and, as he or a companion poles the boat along the shores or around the marshes or shoals, takes the flounders with a gig or spear.   A flounderer of long experience tells me that these fish are usually found lying on the surface of the sand or mud, on the side of a "bed" which they make as a shallow basin on the bottom. Sometimes they are buried, but their position can be detected from the smooth area on the bottom with the outline of the flounder; the exposed eyes and head will then be seen. When the tide is falling, they are keeping off shore in deeper water, and are therefore less easy to find; but on the "young flood" they follow the water up on the shore, and are then most easy to see. On moonlight nights (still according to his account), flounders are very difficult to get, as they run away from the boat. By the same method, less the light, flounders are sometimes taken by day. Flounders taken in summer are chiefly retailed on the streets or in the markets. Most of the flounders shipped are taken in seines in fall.

333. PARALICHTHYS LETHOSTIGMUS Jordan & Gilbert.

"Flounder"; Southern Flounder.

Paralichthys lethostigmus Jordan & Gilbert, Proceedings U. S. National Museum, 1884, 237; Jacksonville, Fla. Jordan, 1886, 29; Beaufort. Smith, 1893*a*, 196, 200; Edenton Bay, Roanoke River. Jordan & Evermann, 1898, 2630.
Pseudorhombus dentatus, Jordan & Gilbert, 1879, 370; Beaufort (in part).
Pseudorhombus ocellaris, Jordan & Gilbert, 1879, 370; Beaufort (in part).

DIAGNOSIS.—Similar to *Paralichthys dentatus*, but with fewer gill-rakers (12 on first arch), with bend in lateral line .33 length of straight part, and of different color. Upper side dark olive, often without markings but usually with a few darker mottlings or spots. (*lethostigmus*, with forgotten spots.)

This species is quite similar to *Paralichthys dentatus*, and has been confused with it in the earlier lists of North Carolina fishes. It ranges as far north as New York, but is most common from Chesapeake Bay to the Gulf coast. It is similar in size and habits to the summer flounder. Besides being common in the coastal salt waters of North Carolina, it regularly resorts to fresh waters, and is the only local flounder with that habit. The National Museum contains a specimen collected at Avoça, on Albemarle Sound, in 1878, by J. W. Milner. The present writer, in April, 1891, found the species not uncommon in the western end of Albemarle Sound, where it was often caught in pound nets and seines with shad and alewives; it was also found to ascend the muddy Roanoke River some distance above Plymouth, where 1 example 2 feet long and another 8 inches long were collected.

334. PARALICHTHYS ALBIGUTTUS Jordan & Gilbert.

"Flounder".

Paralichthys albiguttus Jordan & Gilbert, Proceedings U. S. National Museum, 1878, 370; Pensacola. Jordan, 1886, 29; Beaufort. Jordan & Evermann, 1898, 2631. Linton, 1905, 411; Beaufort.
Pseudorhombus ocellaris, Jordan & Gilbert, 1879, 370; Beaufort (in part).
Pseudorhombus dentatus, Jordan & Gilbert, 1879, 370; Beaufort (in part).

DIAGNOSIS.—Body elliptical, its depth contained 2.33 times in length; head contained 3.75 times in total length; mouth large, maxillary extending beyond eye; about 7 large teeth on side of lower jaw and 4 or 5 in front of upper jaw, side teeth minute; eyes small, .14 or .17 length of head; gill-rakers broad, toothed behind, 13 in number, the longest .4 as long as eye; arch of lateral line .33 length of straight part; scales cycloid, covered with skin bearing small flaps on many scales; fins low; dorsal rays 72 to 80; anal rays about 60; pectorals rather less than .5 length of head; ventrals .33 length of head; caudal margin double-concave. Color:

above dark olive mottled with numerous pale spots; 3 dark spots edged with white sometimes present on posterior part of lateral line, and 2 others on either side of anterior end of straight part of lateral line. (*albiguttus*, white-spotted.)

This fish, which at Beaufort shares with other species of Paralichthys the name of "flounder", is common on the South Atlantic and Gulf coasts.   It reaches a length of 1.5 feet or more, and is used for food, but no definite information about its economic value is at hand, as it is not distinguished from the related species.   The fish is common at Beaufort, and numbers have been taken in summer in the laboratory seines at Bird Shoal and Cape Lookout. Specimens examined by Professor Linton in July and August had been feeding on fish, shrimp and other small crustaceans, mollusks, and worms.   On April 23, 1904, the writer collected numerous 2-inch specimens on the beach at Fort Macon.

Genus ANCYLOPSETTA Gill.   Four-spotted Flounders.

This genus is characterized by having a very broad, sinistral body, both sides of which are covered with strongly ctenoid scales; very oblique mouth with uniserial jaw teeth; a very short caudal peduncle; short, broad gill-rakers, with rough teeth; an elongated left ventral fin; and dorsal fin with anterior rays produced and directed forward.   One species.   (*Ancylopsetta*, hooked turbot.)

335. ANCYLOPSETTA QUADROCELLATA Gill.

Four-spotted Flounder; Fluke.

Ancylopsetta quadrocellata Gill, Proceedings Academy of Natural Sciences of Philadelphia, 1864, 224; Pensacola. Jordan, 1886, 29; Beaufort. Jenkins, 1887, 93; Beaufort. Jordan & Evermann, 1898, 2634, pl. ccclxxv, fig. 925.
Pseudorhombus quadrocellatus, Jordan & Gilbert, 1879, 370; Beaufort.
Chænopsetta oblonga, Yarrow, 1877, 206; Beaufort.

DIAGNOSIS.—Body much compressed, very broad, ovoid, the depth .6 length; head .25 length; mouth small, maxillary extending to middle of orbit; teeth small, about 14 on each side of lower jaw; eye equal to snout and .2 head; gill-rakers very short, thick, 8 or 9 in number; curve of lateral line strongly marked, about half length of straight part; scales in lateral series 70; dorsal rays 69 to 76, the fin arising in front of pupil, anterior rays long; anal rays 54 to 58; caudal short and rounded; ventral fin of left side as long as pectoral, .5 length of head.   Color: brownish above, with 4 very large ocellated spots, consisting of a dark central mass, a narrow white margin, and a dark area externally; the dark spots often have small white centers; vertical fins reddish-brown, with a few small, round dark and white spots. (*quadrocellata*, four-spotted.)

The four-spotted flounder occurs from North Carolina southward.   In North Carolina waters it is apparently not common.   Jordan & Gilbert collected 2 specimens in Beaufort Harbor, and Jenkins reported it as uncommon there. The laboratory contains a large specimen collected by Mr. S. G. Worth at Cape Lookout, March 12, 1904; it is 11.25 inches long over all or 9.25 inches to base of tail, and is the one on which the foregoing diagnosis is based.   In smaller examples (4 to 5 inches long), of which numbers have been collected in June and July in Beaufort Harbor and Bogue Sound, there are on the side many small ocelli, smaller than the eye, and numerous small black spots on head; the fins are mottled with black, and the first dorsal lobe may be quite black.   The small markings on the body disappear with age. There is in the National Museum one specimen collected by Mr. R. E. Earll in Middle Sound near Wilmington in 1880.

Genus PSEUDOPLEURONECTES Bleeker. Winter Flounders.

This genus, which contains 1 American species, is distinguished by firm, regularly placed, ctenoid scales on the eyed side; a single row of incisor teeth on under (right) side of each jaw; lateral line without arch; and scaly fin-rays. (*Pseudopleuronectes*, false *Pleuronectes*.)

336. PSEUDOPLEURONECTES AMERICANUS (Walbaum).

Winter Flounder; Common Flat-fish.

Pleuronectes americanus Walbaum, Artedi Genera Piscium, 113, 1792; New York.
Pseudopleuronectes americanus, Yarrow, 1877, 205: Beaufort. Jordan & Gilbert, 1879, 368; Beaufort (after Yarrow). Smith & Kendall, 1897, 173; Neuse River. Jordan & Evermann, 1898, 2647, pl. ccclxxix, fig. 933.

DIAGNOSIS.—Form elliptical, the depth contained 2.25 times in length; head .25 length; upper (right) side thickly covered with ctenoid scales, under side nearly naked; jaws unsymmetrical, only the left side of each toothed; teeth close together and forming a continuous cutting edge; interorbital space .5 width of eye, convex, scaly; scales in lateral series about 83; dorsal rays 65, the longest shorter than pectoral fins; anal rays 48. Color: above dull brown, sometimes obscurely spotted or mottled, sometimes nearly uniform; white below.

The common flat-fish or winter flounder ranges from Labrador to Virginia, and occurs as a straggler in North Carolina and Georgia. It is very abundant in southern New England, and is an important food fish from Chesapeake Bay northward, being caught with lines and nets. The maximum weight is under 5 pounds, and the average under 2 pounds. Yarrow reported the fish as rare at Beaufort; later collectors do not appear to have met with it. Some years ago the United States Bureau of Fisheries received from New Bern a specimen a foot in length that had been taken in Neuse River near that place.

Genus SYACIUM Ranzani.

In this genus the body is elliptical and sinistral, the mouth is moderate with curved gape, the interorbital space is very broad in the male and narrower in the female, the vomer has no teeth, the gill-rakers are short and thick, the lateral line is straight, the scales are ciliate, both pectoral fins are present, the dorsal fin is low and has no elevated anterior rays, and the caudal is short. Four American species, the range of 2 of which extends to the South Atlantic coast. (*Syacium*, a little pulse; a name of no obvious application.)

337. SYACIUM PAPILLOSUM (Linnæus).

Pleuronectes papillosus Linnæus, Systema Naturæ, ed. x, 271, 1758: Brazil.
Syacium papillosum, Jordan & Evermann, 1898, 2671, pl. ccclxxxiii, fig. 941.

DIAGNOSIS.—Depth contained 2.33 times in length; head contained 3.66 times in length; mouth rather large, the maxillary extending to middle of eye; eye large, .25 length of head, lower eye in advance of upper; gill-rakers about 10, 8 below angle, the longest equal to pupil; scales 50 to 60; dorsal rays 80, fin beginning in advance of lower eye, the first rays arising on blind side; anal rays 60 to 70, the fin arising slightly in advance of pectorals; caudal bitruncate; pectoral of eyed side with upper rays greatly elongated (in male); ventral of blind side slightly in advance of other, which is inserted on ridge of abdomen. Color: nearly uniform brown, with more or less obscure darker mottlings; blind side dusky; fins mottled, the pectoral of left side barred. (*papillosum*, full of papillæ.)

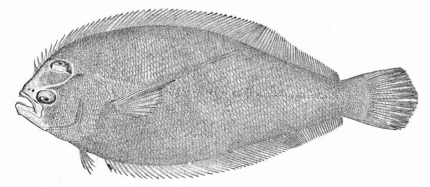

Fig. 179. *Syacium papillosum.*

This species has been recorded from various places on the coast from Charleston to Rio Janeiro, but has not heretofore been reported from North Carolina. In the summer of 1902, the Fish-Hawk collected 1 specimen 3.5 inches long at Beaufort. The maximum length is a foot, but the average is much less.

Genus LOPHOPSETTA Gill. Window-pane Flounders; Sand Flounders.

Body broad, sinistral, much compressed, translucent, covered with small cycloid scales; mouth large; maxillary extending to pupil; gill-rakers long and numerous; lateral line with a marked arch anteriorly; dorsal fin beginning in front of eye, the anterior rays produced and branched; ventral fin of left side inserted on ridge of abdomen by a broad base. One species. (*Lophopsetta*, tufted turbot.)

338. LOPHOPSETTA MACULATA (Mitchill).

"Flounder"; Sand Flounder; Spotted Sand Flounder; Window-pane Flounder.

Pleuronectes maculatus Mitchill, Report Fishes of New York, 9, 1814; New York.
Lophopsetta maculata, Yarrow, 1877, 205; Beaufort. Jordan & Gilbert, 1879, 371; Beaufort. Jordan & Evermann, 1898, 2660, pl. ccclxxxii, fig. 938. Linton, 1905, 414; Beaufort.
Bothus maculatus, Jordan, 1886, 29; Beaufort. Jenkins, 1887, 92; Beaufort.

DIAGNOSIS.—Form rhomboidal, compressed, the greatest depth .66 length; head .28 length; mouth large, a bony tubercle on anterior end of maxillary of upper side, lower jaw with a knob at chin, teeth in each jaw in a single series laterally and in a band in front; eye .25 length of head; gill-rakers about 33; body and head scaly; maxillary, mandible, and snout naked; scales in lateral series about 85; dorsal rays 65, those of anterior third of fin branched at tips and produced, those at beginning of posterior third longest; anal rays 52; caudal fin rather slender, rounded. Color: light brown above, mottled with paler and with numerous small black spots; dorsal, caudal, and anal fins with dark brown spots. (*maculata*, spotted.)

This flounder is found coastwise from Maine to South Carolina.   The names
window-pane and daylight, by which it is sometimes known, have reference to
the thinness of its body, so that light is transmitted through it.   Although its
flesh is well flavored, the fish has so little substance that it has no economic value.
It is common in Beaufort Harbor on sand bars.   Yarrow makes it the object of a
torch fishery with spears, but his remarks apply to the flounders of the genus

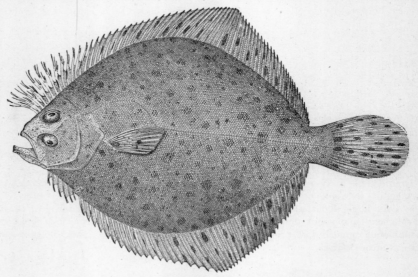

Fig. 180.   SAND FLOUNDER.   *Lophopsetta maculata.*

Paralichthys, which are the only species of economic importance at Beaufort.
Numerous specimens examined at Beaufort by Prof. Linton contained fish,
crabs, and shrimp.

Genus CITHARICHTHYS Bleeker.   Whiffs.

Body oblong, sinistral, covered with thin, deciduous, ctenoid or cycloid
scales; mouth with single series of teeth in each jaw; lateral line straight; dorsal
fin beginning on or near snout, without produced anterior rays.   Rather small
flounders, chiefly found on sandy shores of tropical America; the 3 following
species known from the North Carolina coast, 1 of them from offshore:

i. Eye large, .25 head.
    a. Depth of body about .4 length; mouth very small, maxillary .28 head; color plain; deep-
        water species...*arctifrons.*
    aa. Depth of body about .5 length; mouth larger, maxillary .4 head; side and fins dark-
        spotted; shoal-water species...*macrops.*
ii. Eye small, .16 head...*spilopterus.*

(*Citharichthys*, a fish that lies on its side.)

339. CITHARICHTHYS ARCTIFRONS Goode.
Whiff

Cithartichhys arctifrons Goode, Proceedings U. S. National Museum 1880, 341; Gulf Stream off New England. Jordan & Evermann, 1898, 2683.

DIAGNOSIS.—Body rather elongate, depth contained 2.66 to 2.5 times in length; head .25 length of body; mouth small, teeth small; eye .25 length of head; scales in lateral series 40, in transverse series 16; dorsal rays 68; anal rays 67; pectoral fin on eyed side twice length of other. Color: dirty light brown. Length, 6 inches. (*arctifrons*, contracted forehead.)

This flounder is known from depths of 19 to 373 fathoms off the east coast of the United States. Three specimens were taken off Cape Lookout, by the Fish-Hawk (at stations 7323 and 7331) on August 26 and 27, 1902, at depths of 141 and 154 fathoms.

340. CITHARICHTHYS MACROPS Dresel.
Whiff.

Citharichthys macrops Dresel, Proceedings U. S. National Museum 1884, 539; Pensacola. Jenkins, 1885, 11; Beaufort. Jordan, 1886, 29; Beaufort. Jenkins, 1887, 92; Beaufort. Jordan & Evermann, 1898, 2684, pl. ccclxxxv, fig. 944.

DIAGNOSIS.—Body oval, depth .5 length; head .25 length; mouth oblique, curved, maxillary extending to middle of eye; teeth minute; eye .25 length of head; gill-rakers 19, .5 length of eye; scales large, about 40 in lateral series and 30 in transverse series; dorsal fin arising on blind side near tip of snout, dorsal rays 80; anal rays 56; caudal rounded. Color: light brown, with numerous rounded dark brown spots on body; dorsal, anal and caudal fins also spotted. Length, 5 inches. (*macrops*, large-eyed.)

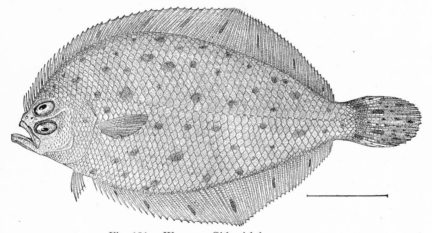

Fig. 181. WHIFF. *Citharichthys macrops.*

This species of whiff is rather common on the South Atlantic and Gulf coasts. It was first taken in North Carolina in 1885 by Dr. Jenkins, who obtained a few specimens in Beaufort Harbor. It is a small species, having no food value.

341. CITHARICHTHYS SPILOPTERUS Günther.

Whiff.

Citharichthys spilopterus Günther, Catalogue of Fishes in British Museum, iv, 421, 1862; New Orleans, San Domingo, and Jamaica. Jordan & Evermann, 1898, 2685.

DIAGNOSIS.—Depth of body a little less than .5 length; head .28 length; mouth large, jaws strongly curved, lower jaw slightly included, maxillary .4 length of head and extending to posterior border of lower eye; teeth small; snout short; eye small, about .16 length of head gill-rakers short and slender, one-third diameter of eye, the number on 2 arms of first arch; 4+12; scales cycloid, the number in lateral series 45 to 48; dorsal rays 75 to 80, the fin arising over anterior margin of eye, the longest rays .5 head; anal rays about 60, the fin arising a a little posterior to base of pectorals; pectorals about .5 length of head, the fin on blind side only slightly shorter than other. Color: translucent greenish-brown, with dark spots; a few dark blotches along bases of dorsal and anal fins. (*spilopterus*, spotted fin.)

Ranges along the Atlantic coast from Brazil to New Jersey and is common southward, but has not heretofore been recorded from North Carolina. Numerous specimens, the largest 4.5 inches long, were caught with a trawl net, at a depth of 9 fathoms, 2 miles east of Beaufort Inlet, on Sept. 1, 1899. The maximum length of the species is about 6 inches.

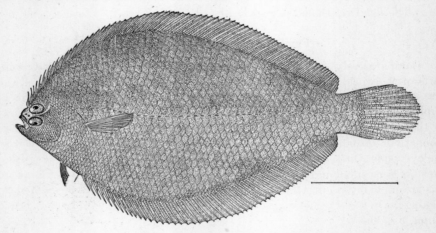

Fig. 182. ETROPE. *Etropus crossotus.*

Genus ETROPUS Jordan & Gilbert. Etropes.

Small sinistral species with deep, ovoid body, covered with thin, deciduous, ctenoid scales above, naked below; mouth very small, with slender, sharp, close-set jaw teeth; no vomerine teeth; dorsal fin beginning over eye, ventral fins not joined to anal, the left ventral inserted on edge of abdomen; lateral line straight. Of the 3 species known from the Atlantic coast of the United States, the following is recorded from North Carolina. (*Etropus*, abdomen foot, in allusion to position of ventral fins.)

342. ETROPUS CROSSOTUS Jordan & Gilbert.

Etrope.

Etropus crossotus Jordan & Gilbert, Proceedings U. S. National Museum 1881, 364; Mazatlan. Jenkins, 1885, 11; Beaufort. Jordan, 1886, 29; Beaufort. Jenkins, 1887, 92; Beaufort. Jordan & Evermann, 1898, 2689, pl. ccclxxxvi. fig. 946. Linton, 1905, 415; Beaufort.
?Etropus microstomus, Jenkins, 1885; Beaufort. Jordan, 1886, 29; Beaufort.
?Citharichthys microstomus, Jenkins, 1887, 92; Beaufort.

DIAGNOSIS.—Dorsal and ventral outlines strongly arched anteriorly, depth contained 1.75 to 2 times in length; head small, contained 4.8 times in length; cleft of mouth less than diameter of eye; teeth in upper jaw on blind side, in lower jaw on both sides; eyes large, separated by a narrow ridge; opercle on under side edged with a row of white cilia; scales in lateral series about 45; dorsal rays 76 to 85, the middle rays longest, none produced; anal rays 56 to 67; caudal fin double truncate; left pectoral fin the longer, .75 length of head; ventral fin on right side the longer, .5 length of head. Color: olive brown with dark blotches; vertical fins mottled with black and gray; pectoral and ventral of left side spotted. (*crossotus*, fringed.)

This species inhabits both coasts of tropical America, and on the eastern side ranges as far north as North Carolina, where, however, it is not common. Several examples were obtained in Beaufort Harbor by Dr. Jenkins in 1885. In 1902, 3 specimens were obtained for the laboratory in a trawl net at Cape Lookout. The length attained is 6 inches.

Family SOLEIDÆ. The Soles.

Comparatively small flat-fishes, found in warm and temperate waters in all parts of the world, some of them inhabiting deep water and others shoal water. The American species are of little economic value, but the European are very important, one of them, the English sole (*Solea solea*), being by many regarded as the most delicious salt-water fish. The body is either dextral or sinistral, elongate or rotund, scaly or naked; the mouth is very small, and twisted toward the eyed side; the teeth, in villiform bands, are either obsolete or very small; the eyes are very small and close together; the gill-openings are narrow; the pectoral fins are small or absent; the ventrals are small and one or both of them may be lacking. Of the 4 American genera, 2 are represented in the North Carolina fauna, as follows:

i. Eyes on right side, separated by a bony ridge; body ovate; right ventral fin with a long base confluent with anal fin; scales on blind side of head fringed; lateral line present.
ACHIRUS.
ii. Eyes on left side, not separated by a bony ridge; body elongate; left ventral not connected with anal; scales on head not fringed; lateral line absent..............SYMPHURUS.

Genus ACHIRUS Lacépède. Hog-chokers; American Soles.

A numerous genus of small soles, chiefly American, with dextral, very much compressed and oval body, both sides covered with rough, ctenoid scales extending on the fins; scales of nape and chin enlarged, those on blind side of head with their teeth elongated, forming cirri; straight lateral line; nostrils with flaps, the under nostril fringed; teeth only on blind side of jaws; dorsal fin beginning on snout, caudal peduncle short, pectoral fin of left side lacking, that of right side small or rudimentary, ventral fin of right side joined to anal by a membrane. Of the dozen American species, only 1 is found in North Carolina waters. (*Achirus*, without hands, that is, pectoral fins.)

343. ACHIRUS FASCIATUS Lacépède.

"Flounder"; "Hog-choker"; Sole.

Achirus fasciatus Lacépède, Histoire Naturelle des Poissons, iv, 659, 662, 1803; Charleston. Smith 1893a, 196; Edenton Bay. Evermann & Cox, 1896, 305; Neuse River near Raleigh. Jordan & Evermann, 1898, 2700, pl. ccclxxxvii, fig. 948; Neuse River, Beaufort, etc. Smith, 1901, 134; Lake Mattamuskeet.
Achirus lineatus, Yarrow, 1877, 205; Beaufort. Jordan & Gilbert, 1879, 368; Beaufort, and Neuse River at Goldsboro.
Achirus achirus mollis, Jordan, 1886, 30; Beaufort. Jenkins, 1887, 93; Beaufort.

DIAGNOSIS.—Body broad, the anterior and posterior curves similar, depth contained 1.75 times in length; head .28 length; mouth extending beyond front of lower eye, right lower lip fringed; upper eye anterior to lower, eye .14 length of head; nostril expanded into a wide tube; gill opening short; head and body covered with ctenoid scales; 66 to 75 in lateral series; lateral line straight; dorsal rays 50 to 55, the fin arising by short rays at tip of snout, rays of posterior third of fin longest; anal rays 37 to 46; caudal rounded; ventral rays 3 or 4. Color: above mottled dusky olive, with 7 or 8 dark, narrow, vertical stripes; every second or third membrane of vertical fins blackish; blind side usually white with numerous round, dark spots, sometimes without markings. (*fasciatus*, banded.)

Fig. 183. HOG-CHOKER. *Achirus fasciatus.*

The hog-choker is found from Massachusetts to Texas, and is the best known of the American soles. It has the interesting habit of ascending streams, and in places is found permanently in fresh water. As it rarely exceeds 6 inches in length, it is of practically no food value.

At Beaufort it is apparently rare, but in the lower courses of the North Carolina rivers it is common. It is a regular but uncommon inhabitant of Neuse River as high up as Raleigh, is abundant in the western end of Albemarle Sound, and occurs in Lake Mattamuskeet. Mr. W. P. Seal reports that in small tidal ditches near the Cape Fear River in the vicinity of Wilmington young hog-chokers are quite abundant in spring.

The curious name of "hollybut" (local spelling, evidently a corruption of halibut) is applied to this fish in the vicinity of Swansboro and Bogue Inlet. The usual names used by the fishermen of the state are "hog-choker" and "flounder".

A specimen 5 inches long taken at Bird Shoal, Beaufort, July 23, 1904, is marked by 6 groups of narrow, vertical, dark lines, 2 or 3 lines in each group at the dorsal and ventral margins but only 1 line going entirely across body; under surface profusely marked with round dark brown spots of various sizes.

Genus SYMPHURUS Rafinesque. Tongue-fishes.

Elongated soles, with sinistral body rounded anteriorly and pointed posteriorly, covered with ctenoid scales, small eyes almost touching, small mouth twisted toward blind side, narrow gill-slits, gill-membranes joined above to shoulder girdle and united below, lateral line absent, pectoral fins lacking in adults, vertical fins confluent around tail, ventral fin of left side present and separate from anal. The species usually inhabit considerable depths, are of small size, and nearly all are American. Only 1 inhabits the shore waters of the Atlantic coast. (*Symphurus*, grown to the tail, in allusion to the union of dorsal and anal fins with the caudal.)

344. SYMPHURUS PLAGIUSA (Linnæus).

"Sole"; Tongue-fish.

Pleuronectes plagiusa Linnæus, Systema Naturæ, ed. xii, 455, 1766; probably Charleston, S. C.
Plagiusa plagiusa, Yarrow, 1877, 205; Beaufort.
Aphoristia plagiusa, Jordan & Gilbert, 1879, 368; Beaufort.
Aphoristia fasciata, Jordan, 1886, 30; Beaufort.
Aphorista plagiusa, Jenkins, 1887, 93; Beaufort.
Symphurus plagiusa, Jordan & Evermann, 1898, 2710, pl. ccclxxxviii, fig. 950; Beaufort, etc. Linton, 1905,
    415; Beaufort.

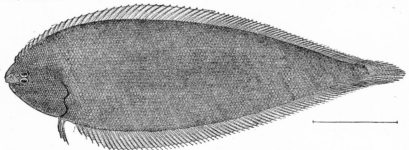

Fig. 184. TONGUE-FISH. *Symphurus plagiusa.*

DIAGNOSIS.—Body moderately elongate, dorsal and ventral outlines similar, depth .33 length; head .2 length; scales in lateral series 80; dorsal rays 86, anal rays 71, the longest rays .33 length of head; tail rounded. Color: gray or light brown; in some specimens about 10 broken broad black cross-bars on head and body, in others 6 to 8 complete cross-bars, and in others no bars but a series of well-separated black spots collected into bands; below creamy white, with pale yellow margin; fins obscurely but profusely mottled with black. (*plagiusa*, oblique.)

Ranges from Cape Hatteras to Pensacola, and is common on sandy shores. In Beaufort Harbor it is abundant on shoals, and has been taken by all collectors, beginning with Professor Gill in 1860, whose specimen is in the National Museum. Yarrow's statement, that this species will take the hook freely but is generally captured by spearing at night and is esteemed a valuable food fish, does not apply and was doubtless intended for *Paralichthys*. The foregoing diagnosis is based on specimens 5 inches long from the Beaufort region.

Order PEDICULATI. The Pediculate Fishes.

The position of these fishes is at the bottom of the class of fishes. A prominent feature, on which the ordinal name is based, is the excessive development of the carpal (wrist) bones, resulting in an elongation of the pectoral fins, which are used to support the body when the fish is resting on the bottom; this is well shown in the accompanying figures of the pediculate fishes. All the species are marine, and frequent the bottom. Of the 4 American families 3 are represented in North Carolina, each by a single species.

Family LOPHIIDÆ. The Anglers.

In these fishes the depressed body is relatively small and abruptly diminishes in size from the shoulders backward, while the head is greatly developed, very wide, depressed, with an enormous mouth; jaws with bands of sharp teeth of unequal size, similar teeth on vomer and palatines; gills 3, gill-opening large and in the lower axil of the pectorals, gill-rakers absent; pseudobranchiæ present; air-bladder and pyloric cœca present; skin scaleless, head and sides with conspicuous flaps; dorsal fins 2, widely separated, the spinous part consisting of 3 separated tentacle-like spines on head and 3 smaller ones connected by a membrane; soft rays connected to form a single ordinary fin; anal similar to second dorsal; pectorals very large and fleshy; ventrals jugular, widely separated, the rays 1,5.

Genus LOPHIUS Linnæus. Anglers.

Size very large; mouth exceedingly wide and directed upward; lower jaw projecting; upper jaw protractile; dorsal spines overhanging the mouth and serving as lures for the prey; gill-openings below and behind the pectorals; vertebræ 27 to 32. (*Lophius*, the ancient name for the fish in Europe.)

345. LOPHIUS PISCATORIUS Linnæus.*
"All-mouth"; Angler; Goose-fish.

Lophius piscatorius Linnæus, Systema Naturæ, ed. x, i, 236, 1758; seas of Europe. Jordan & Gilbert, 1879, 365; Cape Lookout. Jenkins, 1887, 93; Cape Lookout. Jordan & Evermann, 1898, 2713, pl. ccclxxxviii, fig. 952; "southward along the shore to Cape Hatteras".

*A very interesting account of this fish has recently been published by Dr. Theodore Gill, under the title, "The Life History of the Angler", in Smithsonian Miscellaneous Collections, vol. 47, 1905.

DIAGNOSIS.—Head as wide as long, and longer than body; eyes small, separated by a space about equal to snout; head very spinous in young, becoming less so with age; skin smooth; the head surrounded by a fringe of short dermal flaps, similar flaps on sides of body; a 3-pointed humeral spine; dorsal rays III+III+10, the anterior spine with an expanded tip; anal rays 9; caudal margin straight; pectorals rounded, their bases constricted. Color: above mottled brown, below white; caudal and pectorals black edged. (*piscatorius*, relating to an angler; in allusion to the bait-like dorsal spines.)

The angler is found on both sides of the Atlantic, in rather shoal water. While passing most of its life on the bottom, it sometimes comes to surface and basks there. It attains a length of 4 feet. On the North Carolina coast it is well known to the fishermen under the expressive name of "all-mouth". It is very common at Cape Lookout, and is regarded as a great nuisance in the net fishing, for as many as 20 large specimens are sometimes found in a sink-net at one lift. No use is made of the fish here or elsewhere in the United States,.

The angler is noted for its repulsive appearance and extreme voracity. By means of its moving dorsal filaments it decoys small fish into the vicinity of its huge mouth. It also feeds on coots, ducks, and other sea birds, and one of its vernacular American names, "goose-fish", has allusion to its food. Crabs and other invertebrates are eaten also.

The eggs of the "all-mouth" are laid in summer and float near the surface, the batch from each fish being enclosed in a gelatinous substance, the mass forming a sheet or veil sometimes more than 30 feet long and 2 to 5 feet wide. The eggs are .08 inch in diameter, and more than 1,000,000 may be deposited by 1 fish. When the eggs hatch the young emerge from the mass of jelly, and pass a number of weeks at the surface of the sea.

Family ANTENNARIIDÆ. The Frog-fishes.

Small pelagic fishes of striking form and colors, usually living among floating seaweeds and becoming widely dispersed by winds and currents. Body and head compressed; mouth large, vertical or very oblique; premaxillaries protractile, lower jaw projecting, jaw teeth in cardiform bands; gill-arches 2.5 or 3; gill-openings very small, near the lower axil of pectorals; pseudobranchiæ absent; pyloric cœca wanting; spinous dorsal fin represented by 1 to 3 detached, tentacular spines; soft dorsal long and high; the anal similar but smaller; pectorals large; ventrals jugular, close together. Numerous species occur in all tropical parts of the world; 15 to 20 American species belonging in 2 genera; several species besides the following occur as far north as Florida and may eventually be found in North Carolina.

Genus PTEROPHRYNE Gill. Sargassum-fishes; Mouse-fishes.

Exceedingly curious fishes of highly variegated coloration, found chiefly in the West Indies but distributed by the Gulf Stream and other currents on the coast of the United States, and accidentally to Africa and Europe. Body somewhat compressed, abdomen protuberant; head large; mouth oblique, small but distensible; teeth on palate; gill-openings pore-like, in the lower part of axil;

skin and dorsal fins with flaps or appendages; 3 detached dorsal spines; pectoral base slender; ventrals long and expanded. Two known species. (*Pterophyrne*, wing toad.)

346. PTEROPHRYNE HISTRIO (Linnæus).

Mouse-fish; Sargassum-fish.

Lophius histrio Linnæus, Systema Naturæ, ed. x, 237, 1758.
Pterophryne histrio, Jordan & Evermann, 1898, 2716, Gudger, 1905c, 841–843; Beaufort.

DIAGNOSIS.—Depth more than .5 total length; head about .5 length; eye small, .5 snout; dermal flaps numerous on abdomen and dorsal spines, but also on head and sides; dorsal formula III + 14, the spines large, the anterior spine bifurcate at tip; anal rays 7; caudal rounded; pectoral rays 10; ventrals about .5 head, longer than pectorals. Color: yellow, with large irregular light and dark brown mottlings and small white spots; vertical fins barred with brown. (*histrio*, a harlequin.)

When masses of gulf-weed, or Sargassum, are blown ashore from the Gulf Stream, this species is often found under them, its colors in wonderful harmony with the seaweed. Numbers of specimens have thus been noted in Beaufort Harbor. The original habitat of the fish is the tropical Atlantic, but it has been involuntarily distributed along our east coast as far north as Woods Hole, Mass., where it is at times common in summer. The length of the adult fish is 3.5 to 6 inches.

The habits of the species are known chiefly from its behavior in aquaria. The fish are cannibalistic, denuding their fellows of their fleshy appendages and fins and sometimes swallowing their smaller companions whole.

Our knowledge of the spawning habits and eggs of the species depends almost entirely on observations at the government laboratories at Woods Hole and Beaufort. The spawning season is from July to October, and a number of captive specimens have laid their curious egg-rafts while in aquaria. The eggs are deposited in a band- or ribbon-like mass from 1.5 to more than 3 feet long, about 3 inches wide, and .25 inch thick; they are only one-fortieth of an inch in diameter, and very numerous, and are held together by a transparent jelly which is buoyant. Nothing is known about the embryology, as the eggs have not been fertilized. On July 25, 1903, a fish 3.5 inches long which had been at the Beaufort laboratory for 7 weeks laid a mass of eggs three times as large as the fish. This specimen and its eggs were studied and reported on by Prof. E. W. Gudger, of the State Normal College at Greensboro, North Carolina.

Family OGCOCEPHALIDÆ. The Bat-fishes.

In this family of pediculate fishes, the flattening of the head is carried even further than in the anglers (Lophiidæ); the trunk is relatively small and slender; the snout is more or less elevated; the teeth are in bands, and either villiform or cardiform; the gill-openings are minute slits above the base of the pectorals; the branchiostegals number 5, and no pseudobranchiæ are present; the skin is covered with small bony spines or tubercles; the spinous dorsal fin is represented by a tentacle under the elongated forehead; the soft dorsal and anal are very small; the caudal and ventrals are well developed, the latter well separated; the pectorals are large and have a strong, elongated base. The species are rather numerous, and fall into about 8 genera; some are found in very deep water, others, mostly American, occur coastwise.

Genus OGCOCEPHALUS Fisher. Bat-fishes.

Very curiously shaped fishes, with broad, much flattened head and relatively small, tapering body; forehead elongated into a process which overhangs the small mouth; eyes large, lateral; bands of fine teeth on jaws, vomer, and palatines; skin covered with small, bony tubercles; number of gill-arches 2.5; air-bladder and pyloric cœca absent; dorsal and anal fins minute; pectorals large, horizontal, surmounting posterior angles of head; ventrals widely separated. Small, shoal-water fishes, inhabiting the West Indies, 2 species ranging as far north as our South Atlantic coast. (*Ogcocephalus*, hook-head.)

347. OGCOCEPHALUS VESPERTILIO (Linnæus).

Bat-fish.

Lphius ve spertilio Linnæus, Systema Naturæ, ed. x, i, 236, 1758; American Seas.
Ogcocephalus vespertilio, Jordan & Evermann, 1898, 2737, pl. cccxcii, figs. 958, 958*a*, 958*b*.

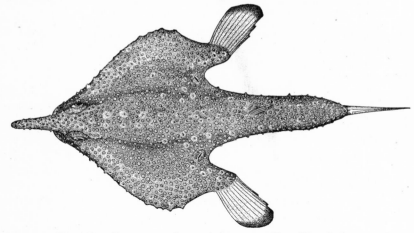

Fig. 185. Bat-fish. *Ogcocephalus vespertilio*. Dorsal view.

DIAGNOSIS.—Body much flattened, rather stout, the greatest depth .2 total length; head much wider than long, the length .5 total length; rostral process very long but of variable length; averaging .12 of head; mouth small, the maxillary extending beyond pupil; teeth in villiform bands; gill-slits very short, about diameter of pupil; skin thickly beset with bony tubercles; dorsal rays 4, the fin inserted nearer to gill-openings than to base of caudal; anal rays 4; pectorals directed outward and backward, their posterior margin extending beyond dorsal fin; ventrals long, horizontal. Color: above grayish brown with black spots, below coppery; dorsal plain; anal with dusky margin; caudal and pectorals white with a broad black margin; ventrals white. (*vespertilio*, a bat.)

This is a West Indian fish, not heretofore reported north of the Florida keys. An example 5.25 inches long now in the Beaufort laboratory was collected by the Fish-Hawk off Beaufort in 1902; in it the rostral process is very long, being contained 5.5 times in length of head; the eye is .4 length of this process; the length of dorsal fin equals diameter of eye; and the anal fin is twice length of dorsal, its origin being midway between origin of dorsal and base of caudal. The species reaches a length of 12 inches.

Fig. 186. BAT-FISH. *Ogcocephalus vespertilio.* Front view.

GLOSSARY OF TERMS USED IN DESCRIBING FISHES.

Abdomen. The belly; that part of a fish between the pectoral and anal fins; the cavity containing the digestive and reproductive organs.

Actinosts. Small bones at base of pectoral fins, corresponding to wrist bones in man.

Adipose. Fatty; a name applied to the small fin without rays on the back of trout, catfish, and various other fishes.

Adnate. Grown together; said of a fin which is attached to the body by one side as well as at the base.

Air-bladder. A membranous sac filled with gases (oxygen, nitrogen, carbon dioxide) lying along the backbone in or posterior to the abdominal cavity, corresponding to the lungs of higher animals and serving the purpose of lungs in some fishes; called also swimbladder and sound.

Anadromous. Running up; said of salt-water fishes which run up streams to spawn, as the shad, the alewives, the striped bass, etc.

Anal. Pertaining to the anus or vent; the unpaired or vertical fin on the median line behind the vent.

Antrorse. Turned or bent forward; the opposite of retrorse.

Anus. The posterior extremity of the intestine; the vent.

Articulate. Jointed; said of the soft fin rays.

Barbels. Slender fleshy projections about the mouth, as in the black drum and catfishes, containing nerves for touch and taste.

Branchiæ. The gills.

Branchial. Pertaining to the gills.

Branchiostegals. Slender bony rays forming part of the lower posterior covering for the gills and supporting the branchiostegal membrane.

Caducous. Falling off early or easily; said of teeth, scales, etc.

Canine. Long conical teeth in the jaws of fishes.

Cardiform. Coarse, sharp teeth in jaws of fishes.

Carpus. The bones at the base of the pectoral fin, corresponding to the wrist in man.

Catadromous. Running down; said of fishes which descend to the sea to spawn, as the common eel.

Caudal. Pertaining to the tail; the fin at the posterior extremity of the body in fishes.

Caudal peduncle. That part of the body of a fish between the dorsal (or anal) and caudal fins, usually the slenderest part of a fish.

Cephalic. Pertaining to the head.

Ciliated. Provided with hairs or hair-like projections.

Cirri. Minute projections forming a fringe.

Claspers. Organs attached to the ventral fins of male skates and sharks.

Cœcal. Pertaining to the cœcum.

Cœcum. A blind tube or sac connected with the pylorus—the posterior part of the stomach.

Compressed. Flattened from side to side.

Ctenoid. Said of scales whose posterior edge is spinous or like the teeth of a comb.

Cranial. Pertaining to the skull.

Cranium. The skull.

Cycloid. Said of scales which show concentric lines or striations.

Deciduous. Falling off or out; said of teeth and scales that are shed or easily lost.

Decurved. Curved downward.

Dentate. Toothed; having tooth-like processes.

Depressed. Flattened vertically.

Depth. The vertical diameter.

Distal. Farthest away from base or point of attachment.

Dorsal. Relating to the back; the fin on the back.

Emarginate. Slightly notched at the end, as the tail of a fish.

Fauna. The totality of the animals of a given region.

Filament. A thread-like projection.

Filiform. Having a thread-like form.

Fontanelle. An opening between the bones of the skull.

Foramen. An opening or hole.

Furcate. Forked.

Fusiform. Spindle-shaped.

Ganoid. A group of fishes characterized by having body more or less completely covered with bony plate-like scales; also said of the peculiar scales of such fishes.

Gape. The opening of the mouth.

Gills. The respiratory organs of fishes, performing the functions of the lungs of higher animals; there are 2 to 4 on each side in ordinary fishes.

Gill-arches. The bones supporting the gills and gill-rakers; usually consisting of a short upper arm and a long lower arm.

Gill-membranes. The membranes covering the branchiostegal rays; the membranes of the two sides may be joined together across the isthmus (q. v.) or inserted on the isthmus.

Gill-opening. The slit-like aperture leading to the gill-cavity.

Gill-rakers. Bony processes of various shapes and sizes attached to the inner margin of the gill-arches, used in straining food from the water.

Gonads. Sexual glands.

Height. Vertical diameter.

Hemal. The term applied (1) to the lowermost spine of the caudal vertebræ in fishes; (2) to the arch for the passage of a blood vessel at the base of such a spine.

Heterocercal. Term applied to the tails of fishes when vertically unequal, the backbone being deflected upward, as in the sharks.

Homocercal. Term applied to the tails of fishes when equal, the backbone extending to the middle of caudal base, as in most of the common fishes.

Imbricate. Overlapping; said of scales that overlap like shingles.

Incisors. Cutting teeth, usually in front of jaws.

Interorbital. Space between the orbits or eyes.

Isthmus. The region between the lower part of the gill-openings.

Jugular. Pertaining to the throat; said of ventral fins when attached to the throat, in advance of the pectorals.

Keeled. Ridged; having a ridge or elevation, like the keel of a boat.

Lamella. A thin plate or layer.

Larva. The immature stage of certain fishes.

Lateral. Pertaining to the side.

Lateral line. A series of tubes or pores along the sides of fishes, secreting mucus and containing organs for the perception of shocks.

Lunate. Shaped like a (new) moon; said of a fish's tail with a broadly concave margin.

Mandible. The lower jaw.

Maxilla, or maxillary. The upper jaw.

Maxillaries. The outermost and most conspicuous of the bones of the upper jaw.

Molar. A grinding tooth.

Nape. The back of the neck.

Neural arch. The arch in a vertebra through which the spinal cord passes.

Neural canal The series of neural arches.

Neural spine. The uppermost spine of a vertebra; the prolongation of the two bony plates which unite to form a neural arch.

Nuchal. Pertaining to the nape.

Obsolete. Faint; imperfectly developed.

Obtuse. Blunt.

Occipital. Relating to the occiput.

Occiput. The back of the head.

Ocellus (plural ocelli). An eye-like spot; usually a dark spot with a lighter border.

Ocellated. Having an ocellus or ocelli.

Opercle or operculum. The flat bone on the side of the head which protects the gills; the gill-cover.

Opercular flap. The ear-like flap of skin projecting from the posterior edge of the opercle, especially marked in the sun-fishes.

Orbit. The bony cavity in which the eye lies.

Orbicular. Nearly circular in outline.

Oval. Egg-shaped; said of the outline of a fish.

Oviparous. Reproducing by means of eggs which are fertilized and developed outside the body.

Ovoviviparous. Reproducing by means of eggs which are hatched or partly hatched within the body of the parent, as some of the sharks and skates.

Ovum (plural ova). Egg.

Palatines. Two bones in the roof of the mouth, one on each side of the vomer, often provided with teeth.

Papilla. A small fleshy projection.

Papillose. Covered with papillæ.

Pectinate. Toothed like a comb.

Pectoral. Relating to the breast.

Pectoral fins. The uppermost of the paired fins on fishes, usually attached to the side of the breast; corresponding to the anterior limbs or arms of higher animals.

Peduncle. See caudal peduncle.

Pelagic. Relating to the sea; said of fishes that inhabit the high seas, such as the mackerels and dolphins.

Peritoneum. The delicate membrane lining the abdominal cavity and covering the intestines and other viscera.

Pharyngeal bones. Bones at the entrance to the esophagus, usually having 1 or 2 rows of teeth.

Pharynx. The throat.

Plicate. Folded.

Premaxillaries. Two bones, one on each side, forming the anterior part of the upper jaw in fishes; some of the teeth are usually inserted on them.

Preopercle. A flat bone anterior to the opercle.

Preorbital. A flat bone anterior to the eye.

Procumbent. Lying or directed forward.

Procurrent. Extending forward; said of a fin whose lower or anterior rays are inserted beyond the regular base of the fin.

Protractile. Capable of being extended or drawn forward.

Proximal. Nearest to the base.

Pseudobranchiæ. Small gills, usually mere rudiments, on the under side of the opercle.

Punctate. Finely spotted.

Pyloric cœca. Blind sacs connected with the pylorus or lower end of the stomach.

Ray. One of the cartilaginous supports of a fin. Rays are either spiny or soft, and the latter are simple or branched.

Recurved. Turned or curved backward.

Reticular or **reticulate.** Formed like a net-work.

Retrorse. Turned or bent backward.

Rudimentary. Undeveloped.

Rugose. Wrinkled; rough.

Scute. A bony or horny plate, such as exists on the sides of the crevallés.

Septum. A thin partition.

Serrate. Like the edge of a saw.

Setaceous. Provided with bristles.

Setiform. Having the form of a bristle.

Shoulder girdle. The bony girdle, posterior to the head, to which the anterior limbs are attached.

Snout. The region between the anterior end of the head and the eyes.

Spiracles. Respiratory opening in the sharks and rays, corresponding to the nostrils in ordinary fishes.

Subopercle. The bone below the opercle.

Suborbital. Beneath the eye.

Supplementary maxillary. A small bone placed superficially on the upper part of the maxillary in many fishes.

Supraorbital. Over or above the eye.

Symphysis. Line of union of two bones, as the tip of the lower jaw (chin).

Synonym. One of the technical names applied to a given species or genus of fish.

Synonymy. The series of technical names applied to a given genus or species.

Tail. In popular language, usually the caudal fin; in ichthyology either the part of the body posterior to the vent or the part posterior to the anal fin.

Terete. Cylindrical with tapering ends.

Thoracic. Pertaining to the thorax or chest; said of ventral fins attached beneath the pectorals.

Truncate. With a square or straight margin or profile; said of the caudal fin, snout, etc.

Tubercle. A small projection.

Type. The specimen on which the original description of a species is based.

Vent. The posterior opening of the alimentary canal.

Ventral. Relating to the abdomen; said of the paired fins below or behind the pectoral fins, and corresponding to the posterior limbs in higher animals.

Vertebra. One of the bones composing the spinal column.

Vertical. Said of the fins attached on the median line of the body; these are the dorsal, caudal, and anal.

Villiform. Slender, minute teeth arranged in compact bands or patches.

Viviparous. Bringing forth the young alive, as for example some sharks and cyprinodonts.

Vomer. A bone in the center of the roof of the mouth, just behind the premaxillaries; it is often beset with teeth.

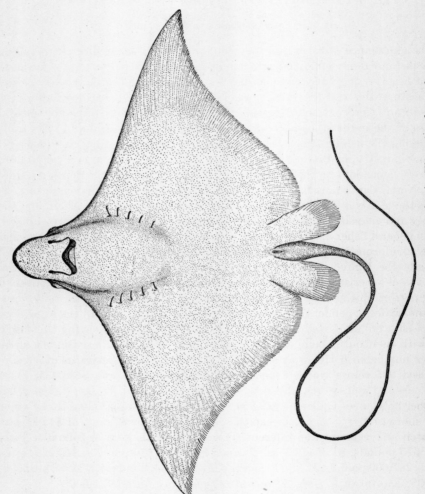

Fig. 187. SPOTTED STING RAY. *Aetobatus narinari.* View of under surface.

THE FISHERIES OF NORTH CAROLINA.

GENERAL IMPORTANCE AND EXTENT.

The abundance of fishes and the peculiarly favorable conditions prevailing in the coastal regions, combined with a mild climate, have permitted the development of fisheries of great variety and extent. At a comparatively early period in the history of the state certain branches of the fisheries became important, and in recent years attained greater extent than elsewhere; while the general progress of the industry has been such as to place North Carolina in the front rank among the fishing states. In the coastwise sections fishing has long been a leading industry, and in few other states has there been so large a population so entirely dependent on the water for a livelihood. Among the South Atlantic States, North Carolina is far in advance in all phases of the fisheries; in fact, as regards the number of persons engaged, the amount of capital invested, and the quantity and value of the annual yield, this state exceeds all the others combined.

No general fishery statistics have been gathered for a number of years, and the latest information pertains to 1902. In that year, according to the official returns of the United States Bureau of Fisheries, 1,100 persons were engaged in the vessel fisheries, 433 persons in the transportation of the catch to market, 10,059 persons in the boat and other fisheries, and 3,163 persons in the various shore industries dependent on the fisheries, a total of 14,755. In the same year 188 vessels were employed in fishing and 199 others in transporting the catch, these with their outfit being valued at $361,000. The boats used in the shore fisheries numbered 6,470, with a value of $222,150. The apparatus of capture comprised 965 seines worth $85,460, 107,190 gill nets worth $236,255, 2,980 pound nets and weirs worth $228,610, and minor nets, lines, dredges, tongs, rakes and other appliances valued at $22,850. The foregoing sums added to the value of the shore property and cash capital, gave a total investment of $1,973,440. The catch and value of the different classes of animals were as follows: Fish, 58,900,675 pounds, $1,354,073; turtles and frogs, 48,570 pounds, $12,229; crustaceans, 287,600 pounds, $17,353; mollusks, 8,347,885 pounds (1,171,880 bushels), $356,005; a total of 67,584,735 pounds, which sold for $1,739,660.

THE PRINCIPAL FISHES.

In the foregoing systematic catalogue, the economic importance of each species of fish has been referred to. Of the 347 species therein listed, about 90 are of present commercial value and figure to a greater or less extent in the markets; but the fishes which give to North Carolina its prominent position as a fishing state are comparatively few in number. Conspicuous among the salt-water fishes are the mullets, squeteagues, croaker, spot, spanish mackerel, and menhaden. The most important of the migratory river fishes are the shad, alewives, hickory shad, striped bass, white perch, eel, and sturgeon. The leading fresh-water species is the large-mouth black bass.

Fishes that are taken in larger quantities in North Carolina than in other states are the spotted squeteague, pig-fish, hickory shad, and black bass; while the local catch of alewives is exceeded only in Maryland and Virginia, of striped bass only in California, of spanish mackerel only in Florida and Virginia, of mullet only in Florida, and of spot only in Virginia.

It is not necessary to refer again in detail to the fisheries for the individual species, but a few special notes on several of the most important fisheries may be supplied as a supplement to the information already given. Of the leading salt-water fish and the peculiar methods adopted for its capture, Dr. Robert E. Coker contributes the following account, which applies more particularly to the Beaufort region:

The common mullet, or "jumping mullet", is the most important food-fish of the Beaufort waters. The mass of the fish consumers of North Carolina and neighboring States demand a cheap fish, and for them the mullet, being of good quality and very abundant, is the chief food fish. The mullet fishery is the largest industry in the State derived from salt-water fishes. The importance of the mullet to the fishermen is increased by the fact that it is taken during the summer when most other fish are scarce. On the whole, the loss of no other fish could so embarass the fisherman as a failure of mullets, and it seems a very unwise policy to use the small-mesh seines, taking the very small, almost finger-sized mullets, which are next to valueless on the market.

Mullets are taken chiefly with "drag nets", or "hauling nets", worked from sail skiffs, singly or in groups of two to four or more in coöperation. The fish are commonly landed on an exposed shoal or beach, or are "pounded". The method known as "footing" is not economical in the case of mullets, as a considerable number escape by jumping over the cork line, and this plan is followed only when other methods are impracticable. A "drag net", or "hauling net", is a seine 150 to 200 or more yards in length and 40 to 80 or more meshes in depth, with mesh of 1-inch to 1½-inch bar. In mullet fishing in early summer a long shallow net with small mesh is desired, later in the season the deeper nets with larger mesh are used. The size of mesh and length and depth of seine to be used are determined according to the size of fish to be taken, and according to whether they are expected to be found scattered over the shoals or in schools and in deeper water.

In "pounding" mullets on the shoals, if the catch is light, it is customary to break the necks as they are meshed to prevent their escape, but if a heavy catch is made it is not economical to do this. The Portsmouth (North Carolina) mullets have quite a reputation in some of the State markets as a result of the method of taking them and preparing them for market, and this method has grown out of the peculiar conditions prevailing about Portsmouth (on Pamlico Sound), near which place there are a great many shoals where the water is a foot or more in depth. The fishermen, working in groups of 2 to 10 skiffs, surround the mullets ("pound" them) on such a shoal with their seines used in combination, then frighten the fish into the nets, and in order that as few as possible may escape, go about breaking the necks as fast as the mullets are meshed. The fish are left in the nets or in the enclosed area until all have been killed. Then they are collected and taken into the boats. The appearance of their fish has become a matter of pride to Portsmouth fishermen, and great care is taken in preparing them for market; the backbone is removed, the intestinal cavity thoroughly washed and the dark lining of the cavity rubbed off with bagging. When carried to market Ports-

A CAMP OF MULLET FISHERMEN ON SHACKLEFORD BANKS.

DRAG-SEINE FISHING ON A NORTH CAROLINA SHOAL.

mouth mullets offer, therefore, a clean and attractive appearance, and are said to be of better flavor; they are eargerly sought in the markets of Washington, N. C., New Bern, and Greenville.

While mullets are not fished with purse seines, occasionally when a large school of mullets is seen while looking for menhaden, a good haul is made in such a seine.

At the stationary fisheries, such as the Mullet Pond fishery on Shackleford Banks, a seine similar to the drag net is used. When the lookout reports a school of fish within their grounds, the boat bearing the seine is put off, the staff on one end of the net is left near the beach, and the boat is rowed around the school with the net paying off over the stern (operation called "shooting the net"). The fish are then hauled on the beach. They may be cleaned and salted at the fishery before being sold. While there used to be a number of these fisheries on the banks and islands north of Beaufort, the Mullet Pond fishery is the only one that does now so well as ten or fifteen years ago. This is due, not, perhaps, to diminution in the number of the fish, but to the scattering of them by the more extensive fishing of recent years. A smaller number is now taken from any given area. South of Beaufort there is still a considerable number of these fisheries.

The limit of the length of hauling nets imposed by law (225 yards) is evaded by working in groups. A large area is in fact more readily surrounded by several short seines than by a single long one. Four seines may be used to enclose a diamond-shaped pound, as follows: Two skiffs take positions together on one side of the area to be enclosed, and the other two at the ends respectively. From each boat one man gets overboard, keeping one end of the seine belonging to his boat. The two skiffs that were together are then rowed apart and toward the initial positions of the other two skiffs, each traversing thus one side of the diamond and "shooting the net" as it goes. Meantime the two skiffs at the ends have been rowed to meet each other at an angle. When these latter skiffs have met (at the fourth angle of the diamond) and the former skiffs have reached the initial positions of the latter, the diamond is complete and each seine occupies one side of it. The fish within the enclosed area may now be frightened into the nets, or, if there is a good current, the staffs, two at each angle, are advanced toward the center and the seines drift with the tide to form gradually flattening loops swinging away from the eight staffs grouped together. Where possible, mullets are landed instead of pounded, and the seines would then be used to form two sides of a larger half-diamond or the circumference of a semi-circle, with the shore as diagonal or diameter.

Mullets are shipped chiefly to the markets of North Carolina, Virginia, and the eastern shore of Maryland. Norfolk is a distributing point for neighboring regions of these three states. While large quantities of mullets are shipped fresh, doubtless more are salted. The leading salt mullet shipper estimates that 20,000 barrels are shipped annually from Beaufort and Morehead City. The process of preparing the salt mullets is simple. The fish are split along the back, cleaned, salted, and placed in a large barrel for 24 hours or more. They are then taken out, allowed to drain, and repacked in a fish barrel; brine is poured over them and a quart of Turks Island salt placed on top. When closed the barrel is ready for shipment. Mullet roe, obtained in the fall (October) is much valued locally, and is shipped to some extent. Charleston, S. C., offers a good market. Some years ago an attempt was made at Beaufort to can the very small mullets. The fish did not sell, probably partly because it was an innovation, partly because of the method of canning. While it may be that with proper method a good canned product could be made, it does not seem expedient to can the young of such an important fish, unless a very good selling product is made.

Along with the jumping mullet occurs the "silverside mullet", but it is not relatively abundant. The local "fork-tail mullet", or "maiden mullet", is probably not a distinct species but a name applied to the medium-sized mullets taken later in the season. The little mullets appearing in October in large schools are supposed to come from Virginia and are sometimes called the "Virginia fleet".

The mullet is valued next to shrimp as bait in hook-and-line fishing, and its indirect value as a food and bait in nature for other fish must be counted; it is preyed upon by trout, blue-fish, and mackerel, and therefore attracts these less abundant and higher-priced fish.

The most abundant of the migratory food fishes of the state are the ale-wives, or river herrings. The extent to which these entered into the fisheries of the counties in 1904 is shown in the following detailed table in which the number, weight, and value of the fish sold fresh and salted are separately given:

YIELD OF ALEWIVES IN NORTH CAROLINA, 1904.

COUNTIES.	FRESH.			SALTED.		
	Number.	Pounds.	Value.	Number.	Pounds.	Value.
Beaufort	436,660	218,330	$3,579			
Bertie	72,500	36,250	590			
Camden	26,000	13,000	190	40,000	13,333	$236
Carteret	18,000	9,000	120			
Chowan	3,991,700	1,995,850	13,156	9,852,300	3,284,101	33,893
Craven	182,614	91,307	1,605			
Currituck	91,000	45,500	1,053	190,000	63,334	950
Dare	815,000	407,500	12,619	4,884,500	1,628,166	24,373
Duplin	900	450	14			
Gates	34,600	17,300	346			
Greene	3,950	1,975	40			
Hertford	146,000	73,000	1,438	23,000	7,666	94
Hyde	16,500	8,250	165			
Lenoir	1,700	850	17			
Martin	103,000	51,500	1,030	280,000	93,333	1,120
New Hanover	4,780	2,390	52			
Pamlico	72,500	36,250	590			
Pasquotank	202,200	101,100	1,702	88,000	29,334	515
Pender	4,000	2,000	50			
Perquimans	743,000	371,500	3,715	360,000	120,000	1,260
Pitt	11,240	5,620	112			
Sampson	17,620	8,810	174			
Tyrrell	382,000	141,000	1,988	454,000	151,334	2,094
Washington	428,000	231,000	1,861	3,695,000	1,231,667	13,667
Total	7,839,464	3,869,732	46,206	19,866,800	6,622,268	78,202

The blue-fish is taken in largest quantities in Dare and Carteret counties. Its economic value in the latter county and the peculiar methods of capture there adopted are thus described by Dr. Coker:

The blue-fish is one of the most important fish of these waters. Its value varies according to size. Large and medium sell best, and as a rule are sent to the northern markets, while the small snappers bring little more than half the price of the other, per pound, and are used chiefly in the state trade.

Formerly quite abundant, blue-fish had become quite scarce, until within the past few years, when they again became plentiful. In 1903 they were taken in unprecedented quantities. Out of several hundred thousand pounds of fish shipped from these points during October 12 to 17, inclusive (one dealer shipped 197,000 pounds and is considered to have handled half the product for that week), more than three-fourths were blue-fish. The shipment of fish during that week was the greatest ever made from these points.

Blue-fish are taken by "drifting" for them in the inlet, by "set nets" on the outside, and, in less degree, by "footing them up" with drag nets and in purse seines. The "drifting" is employed chiefly in fishing for blue-fish and, less often, gray trout. The hauling net is put over and boat and net drift with the tide until the fish strike and are meshed. The shoals in Beaufort Inlet offer a favorable place for this plan of fishing. A variation of this is the "drop-net" method; the net is dropped overboard when fish are detected and the fish are then frightened into it. Seines of different mesh may be in readiness to be used according to the size of the fish expected. Two nets may be used in "setting," one running out perpendicularly to the beach, the other making a loop or sort of pound at the other end. The fish swimming parallel to the beach strike the "leader", where some are meshed, while others turn out, going into the "pound", where most of them are meshed. "Footing them up" is the method commonly used inside with all fish except mullet, where it is not practicable to land them. The school or scattered fish are first surrounded with the seine (drag net), one man overboard holding the staff at one end of the seine while the other rows the skiff, "shooting the net" around the region to be dragged; when the circle is complete one staff is stuck into the ground, and the other placed in the skiff; the seine is then gradually pulled in and, if the haul seems to be light, arranged on the stern; but if there is a good catch, the seine is put in over the side of the boat and is afterwards cleared and placed on the stern ready for a new haul. In pulling in the seine one man handles the cork line, the other, standing opposite, the lead line, pulling it under the ball of his foot, which he uses to hold the line to the bottom and, if it comes hard, to paw, or "foot", the line to him.

A purse seine may be 700 or 800 meshes deep and 100 or more fathoms long, with mesh of .75 to 1 inch bar. A purse line passes through rings at the bottom. Such a seine is usually worked by two "purse boats", each with a crew of 6 to 10 men, the whole pertaining to a two-mast schooner or schooner-rigged sharpie. The purse boats are heavy double-ended row boats 25 feet long or longer, and 7 or more feet in width.

OTHER ECONOMIC WATER ANIMALS.

Besides the fishes, the only water animals of noteworthy importance are oysters and quahogs, or round clams. The value of the oysters exceeds that of any fish except the shad, and within a comparatively few years oysters may become the leading fishery product as a result of cultivation and conservative methods. Oystering is conducted in 12 counties, but is of greatest extent in Beaufort, Carteret, Dare, Hyde and Onslow counties. The output in 1902 was 1,022,813 bushels, which sold for $268,363. Quahogs are taken for market in 7 counties, the largest quantities being obtained in Brunswick and Carteret. In 1902 the total yield was nearly 147,000 bushels, which brought $86,662. The increase in the output of this species in the past 15 years has been marked. The only other mollusks now taken for sale are scallops; small quantities are gathered in Carteret County, the product in 1902 being valued at $980.

Among crustaceans the common blue crab is the only species of importance. It is taken chiefly in Carteret County, and almost the entire catch is sold in the soft-shell stage. The value of this fishery in 1902 was $14,653, a sum that could be largely increased if the fishery were more actively prosecuted. Limited quantities of shrimp are caught in New Hanover and Pender counties, the yield being 84,160 pounds, valued at $2,700.

The reptilian resources of North Carolina comprise alligators, green and other sea turtles, diamond-back and other terrapins, and frogs. At the present time alligators do not exist in sufficient numbers to be regularly sought, and they have ceased to figure in the commercial fisheries. The diamond-back terrapin is taken mostly about Roanoke Island, but the catch of it and of other terrapins and turtles is comparatively small, being valued at only $11,630 in 1902.   Frogs are hunted to a limited extent in Pasquotank and Camden counties, where about 1,000 dozen, worth $600, were obtained in 1902.

FUTURE OF THE INDUSTRY.

The recent trend of the North Carolina fisheries has not been altogether satisfactory, and the condition of the industry demands the thoughtful consideration of fishermen and lawmakers.   The state has shown itself ready to enact restrictive legislation, even when it has been apparent that some hardship would result to fishermen of certain localities; and there is every reason to believe that additional legislation will be provided when its necessity has been fully appreciated.   Protective measures addressed to diminishing fishes must be radical if they are to accomplish any real benefit, and must necessarily be modified from time to time as their effects and defects become apparent.

An acquaintance with the fisheries of North Carolina extending over more than 20 years justifies the author in expressing the following outline views regarding the future of the industry:

1.   The fisheries may be expected to deteriorate—

(a) Through failure of the state to provide prompt and adequate protection to those fishes which begin to show a decrease in abundance.   The history of the sturgeon is an unmistakable indication of what will eventually happen to the shad, alewives, striped bass, and other species unless ample provision is made for the survival of a sufficient percentage of the annual run until spawning has ensued.

(b) Because of unnecessarily wasteful methods, such as the capture of larger quantities of food fishes than can be utilized or disposed of to advantage and the useless destruction of large numbers of fishes of no present market value but of prospective importance.

(c) Owing to careless methods of packing and preserving the catch, and to failure to keep abreast of the progress of the times in matters affecting the shipment and sale of fish.

2.   The fisheries are not only capable of maintenance for an indefinite period but are undoubtedly susceptible of great improvement—

(a) Through recognition and avoidance of the foregoing causes of decline.

(b) Through the utilization of resources now only imperfectly made use of or entirely neglected.

(c) Through the development of new fishing grounds or more thorough exploitation of old grounds.   This applies particularly to the offshore line and net fisheries, on the submerged banks and in the surface waters.

(d) Through increased shipping facilities along the shores, and through the increased use of motor vessels in the inshore and offshore fisheries.

(e) Through the increase in the abundance of fish and other economic creatures as a result of cultivation on the part of the government, the state and private individuals.

CULTIVATION AND ACCLIMATIZATION OF FISHES IN NORTH CAROLINA.*

IMPORTANCE OF SUCH WORK.

In many states the artificial propagation of food and game fishes is regarded as a coördinate, if not as potent, a factor in the maintenance of the supply as restrictive legislation; and cultivation and protection are therefore often jointly carried on. The number of states in which no fish-cultural operations are conducted is rapidly becoming smaller, and it is only a matter of a few years when every state and territory will have its own fish hatcheries for the replenishing of purely local waters, leaving the general government to devote its energies chiefly to the cultivation of the migratory and coastal fishes. In general, there are no public expenditures that will insure more certain and more immediate returns than those devoted to intelligent and systematic fish-culture; while the private owners of ponds, lakes, and small streams will find that aquiculture is as profitable as agriculture and at the same time yields such a variety in diet and such opportunity for recreation that every one who has the facilities should engage in it.

The supply of food and game fishes of many states has been greatly increased by the introduction of nonindigenous species by the federal government, the state authorities, and private persons; but in North Carolina only a limited amount of such work has been attempted. The demand and the necessity for introducing foreign fishes in this state are comparatively slight, and efforts to improve the fish supply have been and can continue to be directed into more important channels.

Although North Carolina was one of the first states to take up the artificial propagation of fishes, it soon abandoned all work of the kind; and for many years the demands for fish culture in the state have been met as far as practicable by the federal government. It would appear to be incumbent on the state to establish and maintain a number of small and comparatively inexpensive hatcheries, in the most favorable situations, for the special purpose (1) of providing brood stocks of fish for private ponds and streams, so that the cultivation of food and game fishes by individuals may be encouraged and facilitated, and (2) of keeping public waters replenished with various desirable fishes, including those which may serve to attract anglers from outside the state. Among the species that might advantageously be cultivated are brook trout, rainbow trout,

---

* For much of the historical and other matter in this chapter, the author is indebted to Mr. S. G. Worth.

small-mouth black bass, and spotted cat-fish for the mountainous regions, and large mouth black bass, strawberry bass, and various sun-fishes for the lowland waters.

EARLY FISH-CULTURAL WORK.

Prior to the inception of fish culture under state auspices the federal government has conducted some interesting initial and experimental work in local waters, and had employed therein several prominent fish culturists.   Thus in 1873, under the direction of U. S. Fish Commissioner Baird, about 45,000 shad were hatched at New Bern, and 100,000 striped bass at Weldon, and these were planted in local waters.   In 1875 shad hatching was attempted at New Bern by Mr. J. W. Milner on behalf of the general government, but no noteworthy results were obtained.

In 1877 the state began fish-cultural operations on its own account, in compliance with an act of the legislature requiring the board of agriculture " at once to provide for stocking all available waters of the state with the most approved breeds of fishes."   In May of that year, Mr. Frank N. Clark, of Northville, Michigan, was engaged through Professor Baird to superintend shad hatching on the Neuse, and the work was conducted at several points above New Bern, but with little success owing to unfavorable seasonal conditions.   The most important feature of these operations was the employment of a number of local volunteer assistants who were desirous of learning the methods and principles of fish culture; among these was Mr. S. G. Worth, who a few years later became the first superintendent of fisheries.   In the fall of the same year a trout and salmon hatchery was constructed at Swannanoa Gap by Mr. W. F. Page, assisted by Mr. Worth, who later enlarged and improved the hatchery; and the incubation of brook trout eggs and California salmon eggs was begun shortly thereafter.

The shad hatching in 1878 was noteworthy because conducted jointly by Mr. Milner representing the U. S. Fish Commission, Colonel Marshall McDonald representing Virginia, Major T. B. Ferguson representing Maryland, and Colonel L. L. Polk, commissioner of agriculture for North Carolina.   The site of the operations was Salmon Creek at the head of Albemarle Sound, and the season was the most successful up to that time, a number of million fry being produced.   In 1879 a second hatchery was built by the state at Morganton, and during the next three years salmon, trout, and carp were hatched and distributed, the station being abandoned in 1882.

Shad hatching was continued by the United States government in 1879 at the mouth of Chowan River, the steamer Lookout being employed in the work.   In 1880 the state constructed a shad hatchery at Avoca and utilized the eggs furnished by the Capehart seine fisheries at Sutton Beach and Scotch Hall, the operations proving quite successful.   It was in 1881 that the steamer Fish-Hawk was first detailed for the same work, with headquarters at Avoca, and from that time down to a comparatively recent date that vessel was engaged in shad hatching in Albemarle Sound nearly every season.   The state con-

SHAD HATCHERY OF THE U. S. BUREAU OF FISHERIES ON PEMBROKE CREEK NEAR EDENTON.

INTERIOR OF SHAD HATCHERY, SHOWING AUTOMATIC HATCHING JARS.

tinued to operate the hatchery at Avoca until 1884, and in 1882 adopted the McDonald hatching jar, being the first state to employ this most important device.

From 1879 to 1884 the state superintendent of fisheries, Mr. Worth, carried on experimental work in the hatching of the striped bass on Roanoke River near Weldon, and in the last year named, being financially aided by the United States Commissioner of Fisheries, took over 4 million eggs. Thus was laid the foundation for the striped bass work taken up later by Mr. Worth as a superintendent of the Bureau of Fisheries.

In 1885 the state discontinued all fish-cultural work, and since that time the responsibility for maintaining the local fish supply by artificial propagation has devolved on the general government.

INTRODUCTION OF NONINDIGENOUS FISHES.

The carp supplied to North Carolina applicants by the U. S. Bureau of Fisheries in 1879 met with such a cordial reception that there was developed an extraordinary demand for this species, and in 1882 the state fishery authorities were obliged to construct ponds near Raleigh in which to conduct breeding operations. The general government continued to send carp to the state, and in 1883 the product of the local hatching ponds began to be available. In 1885 it was reported that at least 2,000 special carp ponds had been built in North Carolina, and that 92 out of the 96 counties in the state had received carp. Through the overflowing or breaking of the banks of ponds, the carp escaped and gradually became firmly established in the rivers and other open waters, and has now taken its place as one of the best known and most widely distributed of the food fishes of the state.

The history of carp culture in North Carolina has been quite similar to that in various other states. The fish was planted in unsuitable waters or received improper attention; and more was expected of it than was ever claimed by those who advocated its introduction into American waters. The natural result was disappointment, loss of interest, and gradual abandonment of the enterprise by individuals. The carp, however, is suitable to-day, just as it was when its planting was first undertaken, for the stocking of warm, shallow waters of limited area in which no other fish or no better fish will survive or flourish.

The introduction of the rainbow or California trout (*Salmo irideus*) was begun in 1880 and has been continued until the present time, the plants of young fish by the federal government now numbering many thousands each year. The fish has become widely distributed and firmly established, and is one of the most attractive species in the mountainous sections of the state.

The introduction of a number of other fishes into the waters of North Carolina has been attempted from time to time, among these being various kinds of salmon. The early attempts to establish salmons were perhaps justifiable in view of the lack of knowledge of the requirements of those fishes, but they are now known to have been entirely useless expenditures of time and money. Beginning in 1877 and continuing for four years, the federal fishery bureau donated eggs of the quinnat salmon (*Oncorhynchus tschawytscha*) to the state authorities. The eggs were incubated at the Swannanoa and Morganton hatcheries, and 748,000 young were planted in the headwaters of the French Broad, Catawba, and Yadkin rivers. In 1883 it was reported that no apparent results had attended this work, and further efforts in this line were abandoned.

In 1881 the state received from the federal government 20,000 eggs of the Atlantic salmon (*Salmo salar*), which were hatched at Morganton with an approximate loss of 25 per cent, and the resulting fry were deposited in the mountain streams the same year. As the natural habitat of this salmon includes no streams south of New York, the waters of North Carolina were manifestly unsuited for the species and the attempt was almost necessarily a failure, not so much because the mountain streams are not congenial as because of the high

Fig. 188.   RAINBOW TROUT.   *Salmo irideus*.

temperature and muddy character of the rivers in the Piedmont and coastal plain regions through which the salmon would have to pass while going to and from their spawning grounds

A salmon from the planting of which results were much more likely is the landlocked salmon (*Salmo sebago*) of Maine, which inhabits lakes and streams, and has lost the migratory instinct. Two lots of eggs were donated to North Carolina by Professor Baird, and the fry hatched therefrom, to the number of 28,300, were planted in 1878 and 1881 in the Dan, Linville, Mayo and Johns rivers, in various creeks in McDowell and Burke counties, and in numerous ponds near Charlotte, Greensboro, Morganton, Salisbury, and other places. No results from these plants were ever noted. Probably the only waters in North Carolina in which it is reasonable to expect a satisfactory outcome from the planting of landlocked salmon are the artificial lakes on the property of the Toxaway Company in Transylvania County; and the U. S. Bureau of Fisheries has recently planted fry in one of these lakes.

RECENT FISH-CULTURAL WORK.

The U. S. Bureau of Fisheries, in pursuance of its policy of aiding the states in maintaining their fish supply, has devoted much attention to North Carolina. Large numbers of native fishes from outside hatcheries have been planted in the state, among these being the brook trout, the large-mouth and small-mouth black basses, the strawberry bass, various sun-fishes, and several kinds of cat-fishes. The most important work of the general government, however, has been addressed to the shad and the striped bass, and has been conducted in local hatcheries.

For many years the steamer Fish-Hawk was sent to the state each spring for the purpose of hatching shad, the site of the vessel's operations being the western end of Albemarle Sound. This vessel is in reality a floating hatchery, and the main deck can be so arranged as to accommodate a large number of shad eggs. Many millions of young fish, hatched from eggs that would otherwise have been sent to market, were thus deposited in local waters; and the work of the Fish-Hawk must be regarded as one of the most beneficent agencies that have been employed in the interest of the North Carolina fisheries.

Necessity for further operations by the Fish-Hawk was largely reduced by the construction in 1900 of a permanent government shad hatchery at the head of Albemarle Sound, on Pembroke Creek, near Edenton. This modern plant, located in the vicinity of the principal spawning grounds in the state, should be able to liberate each spring such an immense number of young shad that the perpetuity of the run would be insured; but its operations have been greatly restricted by the scarcity of spawning fish, and the full measure of its usefulness has never been accomplished. The serious menace to the shad fishery that this condition indicates has been pointed out to the state, and it is hoped that the restrictive legislation shown to be necessary will accomplish the desired end without resort to more radical measures.

The favorable opportunity for cultivating the striped bass afforded by the large run of this fish in the Roanoke has induced the U. S. Bureau of Fisheries to establish temporary hatching stations near Weldon. The work has been conducted for several years under the direction of Superintendent S. G. Worth, and several million of young fish have been hatched and released in the river each season.

Further work that may be undertaken by the government is the artificial propagation of the sea mullet, spotted squeteague, and other valuable salt-water species. Inquiries extending over a number of seasons have failed to disclose the exact spawning grounds of the mullet, and the artificial hatching of this fish has not yet been accomplished, although it is believed that this and other fish-cultural problems will be experimentally solved at the Beaufort laboratory.

BIBLIOGRAPHY.

Following is a list of the principal published articles relating to the fishes and fisheries of North Carolina. The arrangement is primarily by authors and secondarily by date of publication. Many of the ichthyological papers have been cited in abbreviated reference (author and date) in the synonymy of the various species of fish ("Systematic Catalogue", pages 25 to 402).

ASH, THOMAS.
    1682.   Carolina; or a description of the present state of that country [etc.].   Published
            by T. A., gent. London, 1682.
                Among the fishes mentioned are sturgeon, mullets, salmon, trouts, bass, drum,
            cat-fish, plaice, and eels.
BEAN, BARTON A.
    1903.   Notice of a collection of fishes made by H. H. Brimley in Cane River and Bollings
            Creek, North Carolina, with a description of a new species of Notropis (*N. brimleyi*).
            Proceedings U. S. National Museum, vol. xxvi, p. 913–914.
BEAN, TARLETON H.
    1885.   On the occurrence of *Hadropterus aurantiacus* (Cope) in the French Broad River,
            N. C.   Proceedings U. S. National Museum, vol. viii, 1885, p. 160–166.
    1880.   Description of a new hake (*Phycis earllii*) from South Carolina, and a note on the
            occurrence of *Phycis regius* in North Carolina.   Proceedings U. S. National Museum,
            vol. iii, 1880, p. 69.
BRICKELL, JOHN.
    1737.   The natural history of North Carolina.   With an account of the trade, manners,
            and customs of the Christian and Indian inhabitants.   Illustrated with copper
            plates, whereon are curiously engraved the map of the country, several strange
            beasts, insects, trees, and plants, etc.   Dublin, 1737.
                The work contains numerous references to fishes, and many plates, but has
            little merit, the best portions being freely plagiarized from Lawson's volume pub-
            lished 28 years before.
COBB, JOHN N.
    1906.   Investigations relative to the shad fisheries of North Carolina.   Economic Paper
            no. 12, North Carolina Geological Survey, 39 p., 11 maps.   Raleigh.
                A very valuable paper, showing condition of the shad fishery in each water in
            1906 and location of apparatus used in catching shad.
COPE, EDWARD DRINKER.
    1868.   On the distribution of freshwater fishes in the Allegheny region of southwestern
            Virginia.   Journal of the Academy of Natural Sciences of Philadelphia, vol. vi,
            2d ser., art. v, p. 207–247.
    1869.   Synopsis of the Cyprinidæ of Pennsylvania.   Transactions of the American Philo-
            sophical Society, Philadelphia, vol. xiii, n. s., art. xiii, p. 351–399, pl. x–xiii.   (Read
            Oct. 19, 1866.)
    1870a. On some etheostomine perch from Tennessee and North Carolina.   Proceedings
            American Philosophical Society, vol. xi, 1870, p. 261–270.
                Describes as new from North Carolina the darters *Etheostoma nevisense*, *Pœcilich-
            thys vitreus*, *P. vulneratus*, *P. rufilineatus*, and *Boleosoma maculaticeps*.
    1870b. A partial synopsis of the fishes of the fresh waters of North Carolina.   Proceed-
            ings American Philosophical Society, vol. xi, 1870, p. 448–495.
                This is the most important contribution to the literature of the fresh-water fishes
            of North Carolina.   It is based chiefly on collections made by Cope in 1869 in the
            Tennessee, Cumberland, Catawba, Yadkin, and Neuse basins, and contains descrip-
            tions of many new species.   A second edition, with special cover, preface, and
            addendum, was privately printed from the same plates in March, 1877.

COXE, FRANK.
    1884. Opening the Broad and other rivers of North Carolina to shad, bass, etc. Bulletin U. S. Fish Commission, vol. iv, 1884, p. 232.
EARLL, R. EDWARD.
    1887. North Carolina and its fisheries, in The Fisheries and Fishery Industries of the United States, section ii, A geographical review of the fishing industries and fishing communities for the year 1880, p. 475–497.
EVERMANN, BARTON WARREN, AND COX, ULYSSES O.
    1896. The fishes of the Neuse River basin. Bulletin U. S. Fish Commission, vol. xv, 1895, p. 303–310.
        An annotated list of all the fishes recorded from the Neuse, with a review of the papers on the fishes of this stream. The basis of the report was a collection from the vicinity of Raleigh made by Messrs. Brimley.
GILL, THEODORE.
    1903. The devilfish and some other fishes in North Carolina. Forest and Stream, vol. ix, May 30, 1903, p. 431.
        Refers to Elliott's "Sports of the Carolinas" and Brickell's "The Natural History of North Carolina", and notes the names "sea tench", "Welshman", and "Irishman" applied to fishes in the latter work.
    1905. Note on the habits of an ophidiid (cuskeel). Science, n. s., vol. xxii, Sept. 15, 1905, p. 342.
        An introduction to Gudger's article on the same subject.
GIRARD, CHARLES.
    1856. Researches upon the cyprinoid fishes inhabiting the fresh waters of the United States of America west of the Mississippi Valley, from specimens in the Museum of the Smithsonian Institution. Proceedings of the Academy of Natural Sciences of Philadelphia, vol. viii, 1856, p. 165–213.
GOODE, GEORGE BROWN, and associates.
    1884. Natural history of useful aquatic animals. The Fisheries and Fishery Industries of the United States, section i; vol. i, text, p. 1–895, vol. ii, plates. Washington.
GUDGER, EUGENE WILLIS.
    1905a. The breeding habits and segmentation of the egg of the pipefish, Siphostoma floridæ. Proceedings U. S. National Museum, vol. xxix, p. 447–500, pl. v–xi.
        Based on studies made and material collected at Beaufort, N. C., in 1902, 1903, and 1904.
    1905b. A note on the habits of Rissola marginata. Science, n. s., vol. xxii, Sept. 15, 1905, p. 342–343.
    1905c. A note on the eggs and egg-laying of Pterophryne histrio, the gulfweed fish. Science, n. s., vol. xxii, Dec. 22, 1905, p. 841–843.
        Observations on spawning of the sargassum-fish in Beaufort laboratory in 1903.
HOLBROOK, JOHN EDWARDS.
    1855. Ichthyology of South Carolina. Second edition 1860, 205 p., 28 pl. Charleston, S. C.
JENKINS, OLIVER P.
    1885. Notes on the fishes of Beaufort Harbor, North Carolina. Johns Hopkins University Circular, October, 1885, p. 11.
        Lists 20 species "that do not occur in either of the lists referred to" (i. e., Yarrow's and Jordan & Gilbert's; but as a matter of fact several of them had already been recorded.
    1887. A list of the fishes of Beaufort Harbor, North Carolina. Studies from the Biological Laboratory, Johns Hopkins University, vol. iv, p. 83–94, 1887.
JORDAN, DAVID STARR.
    1878. A synopsis of the family Catostomidæ. Bulletin U. S. National Museum, no. 12, p. 97–237.
    1886. Notes on fishes collected at Beaufort, North Carolina, with a revised list of the species known from that locality. Proceedings U. S. National Museum, vol. ix, 1886, p. 25–30.
    1889a. Description of fourteen species of fresh-water fishes collected by the U. S. Fish Commission in the summer of 1888. Proceedings U. S. National Museum, vol. xi, 1888, p. 351–362, 3 pl.
    1889b. Report of explorations made during 1888 in the Allegheny region of Virginia, North Carolina, and Tennessee, and in western Indiana, with an account of the fishes found in each of the river basins of those regions. Bulletin U. S. Fish Commission, vol. viii, 1888, p. 97–173, 3 pl., 17 fig.

JORDAN, DAVID STARR, AND BRAYTON, ALEMBERT W.
   1878.   On the distribution of the fishes of the Allegheny region of South Carolina, Georgia,
            and Tennessee, with descriptions of new or little known species.   Bulletin U. S.
            National Museum, vol. xii, 1878, p. 1–95.
JORDAN, DAVID STARR, AND EVERMANN, BARTON WARREN.
            The fishes of North and Middle America.   Bulletin no. 47, U. S. National Mu-
            seum, 4 vol., 3313 pages, 392 pl.
   1896, text, part i.
   1898, text, parts ii and iii.
   1900, text and plates, part iv.
JORDAN, DAVID STARR, AND GILBERT, CHARLES H.
   1879.   Notes on fishes of Beaufort Harbor, North Carolina.   Proceedings U. S. National
            Museum, vol. i, 1878, p. 365–388.
KENDALL, WILLIAM CONVERSE.
   1902.   Notes on the silversides of the genus *Menidia* of the east coast of the United States,
            with descriptions of two new subspecies.   Report U. S. Fish Commission 1901,
            p. 241–267.
KENDALL, WILLIAM CONVERSE, AND SMITH, HUGH M.
   1894.   Extension of the recorded range of certain marine and fresh-water fishes of the
            Atlantic coast of the United States.   Bulletin U. S. Fish Commission, vol. xiv,
            1894, p. 15–24.
            Records Earll's hake from Hatteras Inlet, the first instance of its occurrence
            in North Carolina.
LAWSON, JOHN.
   1709.   A new voyage to Carolina; containing the exact description and natural history
            of that country [etc.].   London.
            The publication of this history was apparently begun in 1708, but some copies
            bear date of 1710 and a copy belonging to the State of North Carolina is dated 1714,
            with title page reading "The history of Carolina; containing the exact description
            and natural history of that country; together with the present state thereof.   And a
            journal of a thousand miles, travel'd thro' several nations of Indians.   Giving a
            particular account of their customs, manners, etc.   By John Lawson, Gent. Sur-
            veyor-General of North Carolina."   Reprint from this copy, 171 p., Charlotte, N. C.,
            1903.
            The book contains a very interesting account of the fishes of the state, devoting
            about 9 pages to the subject and giving lists of the fresh-water and salt-water
            species, with notes on many of them.   About 60 species are named.
LINTON, EDWIN.
   1905.   Parasites of fishes of Beaufort, North Carolina.   Bulletin of the Bureau of Fisheries,
            vol. xxiv, 1904, p. 321–428, pl. i–xxxiv.   Issued Oct. 19, 1905.
            Deals primarily with the internal parasites of the fishes of the Beaufort region,
            but contains also very useful data on the food of the fishes as determined by an
            examination of their stomach contents.   Several species of fishes not previously
            known from the state are incidentally mentioned.   The paper is a contribution
            from the Beaufort laboratory.
MCDONALD, MARSHALL.
   1884.   California trout planted in Roanoke River in July, 1883, retaken in June, 1884.
            Bulletin U. S. Fish Commission, vol. iv, 1884, p. 286.
   1887.   Fisheries of the rivers and sounds of North Carolina, in The Fisheries and Fishery
            Industries of the United States, section v, History and methods of the fisheries,
            vol. i, p. 625–637.
MILNER, J. W.
   1882.   Summary of fishing records for shad and alewives kept at Willow Branch fishery,
            North Carolina, from 1835 to 1874.   Bulletin U. S. Fish Commission, vol. i, 1881,
            p. 396–400.
NORTH CAROLINA BOARD OF AGRICULTURE.
   1881.   Biennial report of the board of agriculture to the general assembly of North Car-
            olina, 1879 and 1880, 71 p.   Raleigh.
            Fish propagation (p. 7–8).
   1883.   Handbook of the State of North Carolina, exhibiting its resources and industries.
            Raleigh.
            Fisheries and artificial propagation of fish are referred to briefly (p. 128–131).

NORTH CAROLINA BUREAU OF LABOR STATISTICS.

  1894. Eighth annual report of the Bureau of Labor Statistics of the State of North Car-
         olina for the year 1894. The fishery industry of North Carolina, p. 248–256.
            Text and tables quoted from Smith, 1893b.

  1895. Ninth annual report of the Bureau of Labor Statistics of the State of North Caro-
         lina for the year 1895. Fishing industry, p. 371–385.
            Copies text and tables from previous report, and quotes letter from Dr. W. R.
         Capehart giving information regarding fisheries of Albemarle Sound.

POLK, L. L.

  1879. Report of L. L. Polk, commissioner of agriculture, for 1877 and 1878. Public
         document no. 8, session 1879. Raleigh.
            Fish propagation is discussed at some length (p. 7–15).

PRATT, JOSEPH HYDE (Compiler).

  1906. Report of committee appointed by Governor R. B. Glenn to investigate the fishing
         industries in North Carolina. Economic Paper no. 13, North Carolina Geological
         Survey, 75 p. Raleigh.
            Considers the condition of the fisheries, and makes comprehensive recommenda-
         tions for a revised fish code.

RAVENEL, W. DE C.

  1888. Information bearing on the propagation of mullet. Bulletin U. S. Fish Commis-
         sion, vol. vii, 1887, p. 197–202.

SMITH, HUGH M.

  1893a. Report on a collection of fishes from the Albemarle region of North Carolina.
          Bulletin U. S. Fish Commission, vol. xi, 1891, p. 185–200.
             Based on a collection made by the writer in April, 1892, in Albemarle Sound and
          tributaries.

  1893b. Fisheries of North Carolina, in Report on the fisheries of the South Atlantic States.
          Bulletin U. S. Fish Commission, vol. xi, 1891, p. 282–306, 31 pl.
             Discusses the fisheries, fishing grounds, and fishery resources of the State; gives
          detailed statistics of the industry for 1889 and 1890; and shows illustrations of 80
          of the principal fishes of the region, with their local names.

  1901. [Fishes of Lake Mattamuskeet, North Carolina.] Report U. S. Fish Commission
         1900, p. 133, 134.
            A brief account of the fish life of this interesting lake.

  1905. Note on a rare flying-fish (Cypselurus lutkeni). Science, n. s., vol. xxi, May 12,
         1905, p. 746.
            Mentions capture of a specimen at Beaufort, N. C., and states that the type, the
         only other known specimen, probably came from the same place.

SMITH, HUGH M., and KENDALL, WILLIAM CONVERSE.

  1897. Notes on the extension of the recorded range of certain fishes of the United States
         coast. Report U. S. Fish Commission 1896, p. 169–176.
            Mentions the capture of a winter flounder at New Bern, N. C.

STEVENSON, CHARLES H.

  1899. The shad fisheries of the Atlantic coast of the United States. Report U. S.
         Fish Commission 1898, p. 101–269.
            The history, methods, and results of the North Carolina shad fishery are con-
         sidered (p. 155–176).

WALKE, E. H.

  1883. Spawning of Esox (pike or pickerel) in North Carolina. Bulletin U. S. Fish Com-
         mission, vol. iii, 1883, p. 295.

WILSON, H. V.

  1900. Marine biology at Beaufort. American Naturalist, vol. xxxiv, May, 1900, p. 339–
         360.

WORTH, S. G.

  1879. Fish culture in North Carolina. [Report to the North Carolina Commissioner of
         Agriculture], 26 p. appended to Report of L. L. Polk, commissioner of agriculture,
         1877–1878, Public Document no. 8, session 1879.

  1881. Report of superintendent of fish and fisheries for the years of 1879–'80. Report
         of the board of agriculture to the general assembly of North Carolina, 1879 and
         1880, p. 25–51.
            Refers (p. 40) to planting of rainbow trout (4,300 in number) in streams and
         ponds in western counties in March, 1880.

  1882a. The artificial propagation of the striped bass (Roccus lineatus) on Albemarle
          Sound. Bulletin U. S. Fish Commission, vol. i, 1881, p. 174–177.

1882b. A poor season for shad hatching in North Carolina. Bulletin U. S. Fish Commission, vol. ii, 1882, p. 54.

1883a. Fish culture in North Carolina. Monthly Bulletin North Carolina Board of Agriculture, August, 1883, p. 3–8.

1883b. Second biennial report of S. G. Worth, superintendent of fish and fisheries of North Carolina (for 1881–'2). Report of the board of agriculture, document no. 18, 1883 session of the North Carolina legislature, p. 62–81.

1884a. The fishing industry of North Carolina. Monthly Bulletin of North Carolina Department of Agriculture, March, 1884, p. 8–9.
    Refers to a single seine haul of 400,000 herring.

1884b. Report upon the propagation of striped bass at Weldon, N. C., in the spring of 1884. Bulletin U. S. Fish Commission, vol. iv, 1884, p. 225–230, pl. i.

1885. Third biennial report of the superintendent of fish and fisheries, of the state of North Carolina, for the years 1883–'84, 35 p. Raleigh.

1903. Striped bass hatching in North Carolina. Transactions American Fisheries Society 1903, p. 98–102.
    Refers to recent fish-cultural work of the Bureau of Fisheries on Roanoke River.

YARROW, H. C.
1874. Notes on the shad as observed at Beaufort Harbor, North Carolina, and vicinity. Report of Commissioner of Fish and Fisheries 1872–3, p. 452–456.

1877. Notes on the natural history of Fort Macon, North Carolina, and vicinity. No. 3—Fishes. Proceedings Academy of Natural Sciences of Philadelphia, vol. xxix, 1877, p. 203–218.

INDEX OF COMMON NAMES OF FISHES.

No

INDEX OF SCIENTIFIC NAMES.

[This index contains the scientific names of the orders, families, genera, and species of fishes represented in the North Carolina fauna. In the case of specific names, synonyms also are given.]

GENERAL INDEX.

[For common names of fishes and scientific names of orders, families, genera, and species of fishes, see the preceding special indexes.]

PUBLICATIONS

of the

NORTH CAROLINA GEOLOGICAL AND ECONOMIC SURVEY.

BULLETINS.

1.   Iron Ores of North Carolina, by Henry B. C. Nitze, 1893.   8°, 239 pp., 20 pl., and map.   *Postage 10 cents.*

2.   Building Stone in North Carolina, by T. L. Watson and F. B. Laney in collaboration with George P. Merrill, 1906.   8°, 283 pp., 32 pl., 2 figs.   *Postage 25 cents.   Cloth-bound copy 50 cents extra.*

3.   Gold Deposits in North Carolina, by Henry B. C. Nitze and George B. Hanna, 1896.   8°, 196 pp., 14 pl., and map.   *Out of print.*

4.   Road Material and Road Construction in North Carolina, by J. A. Holmes and William Cain, 1893.   8°, 88 pp.   *Out of print.*

5.   The Forests, Forest Lands and Forest Products of Eastern North Carolina, by W. W. Ashe, 1894.   8°, 128 pp., 5 pl.   *Postage 5 cents.*

6.   The Timber Trees of North Carolina, by Gifford Pinchot and W. W. Ashe, 1897.   8°, 227 pp., 22 pl.   *Postage 10 cents.*

7.   Forest Fires: Their Destructive Work, Causes and Prevention, by W. W. Ashe, 1895.   8°, 66 pp., 1 pl.   *Postage 5 cents.*

8.   Water-powers in North Carolina, by George F. Swain, Joseph A. Holmes and E. W. Myers, 1899.   8°, 362 pp., 16 pl.   *Postage 16 cents.*

9.   Monazite and Monazite Deposits in North Carolina, by Henry B. C. Nitze, 1895.   8°, 47 pp., 5 pl.   *Postage 4 cents.*

10.   Gold Mining in North Carolina and other Appalachian States, by Henry B. C. Nitze and A. J. Wilkins, 1897.   8°, 164 pp., 10 pl.   *Postage 10 cents.*

11.   Corundum and the Basic Magnesian Rocks of Western North Carolina, by J. Volney Lewis, 1895.   8°, 107 pp. , 6 pl.   *Postage 4 cents.*

12.   Drinking-water Supplies in North Carolina, by Joseph A. Holmes.   *In preparation.*

13.   Clay Deposits and Clay Industries in North Carolina, by Heinrich Reis, 1897.   8°, 157 pp., 12 pl.   *Postage 10 cents.*

14.   The Cultivation of the Diamond-back Terrapin, by R. E. Coker, 1906.   8°, 67 pp., 23 pl., 2 figs.   *Postage 6 cents.*

15.   Mineral Waters of North Carolina, by F. P. Venable.   *In press.*

16.   A List of Elevations in North Carolina, by J. A. Holmes and E. W. Myers.   *In preparation.*

17.   Historical Sketch of North Carolina Scientific and Economic Surveys; and Bibliography of North Carolina Geology, Mineralogy and Natural History, by J. A. Holmes and L. C. Glenn.   *In preparation.*

18.   Road Materials and Construction, by Joseph A. Holmes and William Cain.   *In preparation.*

19.   The Tin Deposits of the Carolinas, by Joseph Hyde Pratt and Douglass B. Sterrett, 1905.   8°, 64 pp., 8 figs.   *Postage 4 cents.*

20.   The Loblolly Pine in Eastern North Carolina, by W. W. Ashe.   *In preparation.*

ECONOMIC PAPERS.

1. The Maple-Sugar Industry in Western North Carolina, by W. W. Ashe, 1897. 8°, 34 pp. *Postage 2 cents.*

2. Recent Road Legislation in North Carolina, by J. A. Holmes. *Out of print.*

3. Talc and Pyrophyllite Deposits in North Carolina, by Joseph Hyde Pratt, 1900. 8°, 29 pp., 2 maps. *Postage 2 cents.*

4. The Mining Industry in North Carolina During 1900, by Joseph Hyde Pratt, 1901. 8°, 36 pp., and map. *Postage 2 cents.*

5. Road Laws of North Carolina, by J. A. Holmes. *Out of print.*

6. The Mining Industry in North Carolina During 1901, by Joseph Hyde Pratt, 1902. 8°, 102 pp. *Postage 4 cents.*

7. Mining Industry in North Carolina During 1902, by Joseph Hyde Pratt, 1903. 8°, 27 pp. *Postage 2 cents.*

8. The Mining Industry in North Carolina During 1903, by Joseph Hyde Pratt, 1904. 8°, 74 pp. *Postage 4 cents.*

9. The Mining Industry in North Carolina During 1904, by Joseph Hyde Pratt, 1905. 8°, 95 pp. *Postage 4 cents.*

10. Oyster Culture in North Carolina, by Robert E. Coker, 1905. 8°, 39 pp. *Postage 2 cents.*

11. The Mining Industry in North Carolina During 1905, by Joseph Hyde Pratt, 1906.

12. Investigations Relative to the Shad Fisheries of North Carolina, by John N. Cobb, 1906. 8°, 74 pp., 8 maps. *Postage 6 cents.*

13. Report of Committee on Fisheries in North Carolina. Compiled by Joseph Hyde Pratt, 1906. 8°, 78 pp. *Postage 4 cents.*

REPORTS ON RESOURCES.

Vol. I. Corundum and the Basic Magnesian Rocks in Western North Carolina, by Joseph Hyde Pratt and J. Volney Lewis, 1905. 8°, 464 pp., 44 pl., 35 figs. *Postage 32 cents. Cloth-bound copy 50 cents extra.*

Vol. II. The Fishes of North Carolina, by Hugh M. Smith, 1907. 8°, xii + 456 pp., 21 pl., 188 figs. *Postage 32 cents. Cloth-bound copy 50 cents extra.*

Vol. III. Miscellaneous Mineral Resources in North Carolina, by Joseph Hyde Pratt. *In preparation.*

These publications are mailed to libraries and to individuals who may desire information on any of the special subjects named, free of charge, except that in each case applicants for the reports should forward the amount of *postage* needed, as indicated above, for mailing the bulletins desired, to the *State Geologist, Chapel Hill, N. C.*

NG EM